List of Common Elements

Name	Symbol	Approximate Atomic Weight	Name	Symbol	Approximate Atomic Weight
Aluminum.....	Al	27	Magnesium....	Mg	24
Antimony.....	Sb	122	Manganese....	Mn	55
Arsenic........	As	75	Mercury.......	Hg	200.6
Barium........	Ba	137	Nickel........	Ni	58.7
Bismuth.......	Bi	209	Nitrogen......	N	14
Bromine.......	Br	80	Oxygen.......	O	16
Calcium......	Ca	40	Phosphorus....	P	31
Carbon........	C	12	Platinum......	Pt	195
Chlorine.......	Cl	35.5	Potassium.....	K	39
Chromium.....	Cr	52	Silicon........	Si	28
Cobalt........	Co	59	Silver........	Ag	108
Copper........	Cu	63.5	Sodium........	Na	23
Fluorine.......	F	19	Strontium.....	Sr	87.6
Gold..........	Au	197	Sulfur........	S	32
Hydrogen......	H	1	Tin...........	Sn	118.7
Iodine.........	I	127	Titanium......	Ti	48
Iron..........	Fe	56	Tungsten......	W	184
Lead..........	Pb	207	Zinc.........	Zn	65

Valences Shown by Common Elements and Radicals

Name	Symbol	Valence	Name	Symbol	Valence
Aluminum.....	Al	+3	Hydrogen.....	H	+1
Ammonium....	NH$_4$	+1	Lead..........	Pb	+2
Barium........	Ba	+2	Magnesium....	Mg	+2
Calcium.......	Ca	+2	Mercuric......	Hg	+2
Chromic.......	Cr	+3	Mercurous.....	Hg	+1
Cobalt........	Co	+2	Nickel........	Ni	+2
Cupric........	Cu	+2	Potassium.....	K	+1
Cuprous.......	Cu	+1	Silver........	Ag	+1
Ferric.........	Fe	+3	Sodium........	Na	+1
Ferrous........	Fe	+2	Zinc..........	Zn	+2
Acetate........	C$_2$H$_3$O$_2$	−1	Hypochlorite...	ClO	−1
Bicarbonate....	HCO$_3$	−1	Iodide........	I	−1
Bisulfate.......	HSO$_4$	−1	Nitrate........	NO$_3$	−1
Bromide.......	Br	−1	Nitrite........	NO$_2$	−1
Carbonate.....	CO$_3$	−2	Oxide.........	O	−2
Chlorate.......	ClO$_3$	−1	Permanganate .	MnO$_4$	−1
Chloride.......	Cl	−1	Peroxide.......	O$_2$	−2
Chromate......	CrO$_4$	−2	Phosphate.....	PO$_4$	−3
Ferricyanide...	Fe(CN)$_6$	−3	Sulfate........	SO$_4$	−2
Ferrocyanide...	Fe(CN)$_6$	−4	Sulfide........	S	−2
Fluoride.......	F	−1	Sulfite........	SO$_3$	−2
Hydroxide.....	OH	−1	Tartrate.......	C$_4$H$_4$O$_6$	−2

30

MODERN CHEMISTRY

THE HOLT SCIENCE PROGRAM

SCIENCE 1, *Observation and Experiment, by Davis, Burnett, and Gross*
SCIENCE 2, *Experiment and Discovery, by Davis, Burnett, and Gross*
SCIENCE 3, *Discovery and Progress, by Davis, Burnett, and Gross*

MODERN BIOLOGY, *by Moon, Mann, and Otto*
● MODERN CHEMISTRY, *by Dull, Metcalfe, and Williams*
MODERN PHYSICS, *by Dull, Metcalfe, and Brooks*

LIVING THINGS, *by Fitzpatrick and Bain*
MODERN PHYSICAL SCIENCE, *by Brooks and Tracy*
MODERN HEALTH, *by Otto, Julian, and Tether*

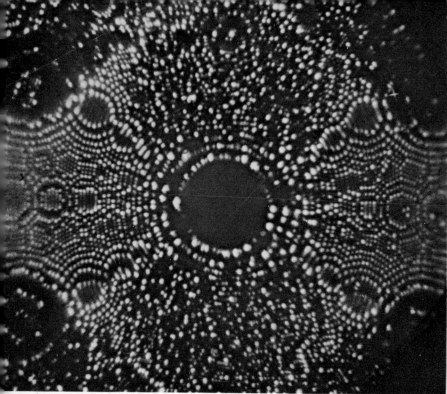

Photograph of the Atoms of a Metal Surface by E. W. Müller, Pennsylvania State University

MODERN

The above photograph shows the atomic lattice structure of a tungsten metal surface magnified over a million times. This photograph was taken using a field ion microscope. A field ion microscope is a vacuum tube in which helium ions, repelled from the atoms of a metal surface, move through an electrical field toward a fluorescent screen and form a magnified image of the surface. The photograph shows the atoms at the end of a spherical tungsten needle tip, 6.5 millionths of a centimeter in radius.

This color photograph was made by superimposing a red and a green copy of two subsequent photographs of the same surface. Small alterations in the surface, due to the evaporation and condensation of a few tungsten atoms are shown by this technique. Newly deposited atoms appear green, while those that were removed during the experiment appear red. The unchanged atoms appear yellow.

In some parts of the photograph the arrangement of atoms is less perfect than in others. Such important effects as the strength of a metal, crystal growth, adsorption, surface reactions, and catalysis depend to a large extent on imperfections in the crystal lattice. You will learn about many of these effects during your study of chemistry. The field ion microscope is a useful research tool for investigating such effects.

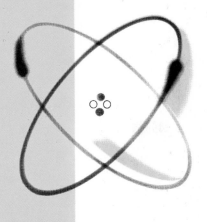

CHEMISTRY

CHARLES E. DULL

H. CLARK METCALFE

JOHN E. WILLIAMS

HENRY HOLT AND COMPANY...NEW YORK

The Authors of MODERN CHEMISTRY

QD33
D8
1958

H. CLARK METCALFE is Head of the Science Department in Wilkinsburg Senior High School, Wilkinsburg, Pennsylvania.

JOHN E. WILLIAMS is Head of the Science Department, Broad Ripple High School, Indianapolis, Indiana.

CHARLES E. DULL was Head of the Science Department in West Side High School and Supervisor of Science for the Junior and Senior High Schools, Newark, New Jersey.

The Artists of MODERN CHEMISTRY

DESIGN, FORMAT, AND COVER . . . Celeste Whitney
UNIT AND CHAPTER HEADS . . . Evelyn Urbanowich
SCIENTIFIC LINE DRAWINGS . . . Felix Cooper
COVER ILLUSTRATOR . . . Robert Pious

58P8

Copyright © 1958 by
HENRY HOLT AND COMPANY, INCORPORATED
Library of Congress Catalogue Number 58–5001
Printed in the United States of America
11951–7318

PREFACE

MODERN CHEMISTRY is an all-purpose textbook designed to meet the varying needs of the standard high school course in chemistry. Classroom developed from its first edition, this revision carries forward the sound idea of classroom testing.

To present the study of chemistry in the light of modern theory and to keep the subject matter abreast of the latest developments in the field, this edition has been completely revised and rewritten. After an introduction to some fundamental terms and concepts of physical science, the authors develop the topics of atomic structure, the Periodic Table, and chemical bonding. The remainder of the theoretical and descriptive material of the course is then based on the relationship between the structure of materials and the properties these materials exhibit.

Teachers will find ample material in MODERN CHEMISTRY for an outstanding college-preparatory course. For those students who do not plan to go to college, there is sufficient elementary theory and interest-arousing descriptive material for a complete and thorough course. It has been the authors' purpose to include more material than can be covered in one school year, thus permitting a wide choice of topics and allowing for selectivity according to student, school, and community differences. Teachers should feel free to choose those topics which best meet their local needs. As a guide in the selection of material, some whole chapters, paragraphs in other chapters, and certain questions and problems have been marked with a red, green, blue or brown star (★). These starred sections are intended only for the better students. The needs of the average student are amply provided for in the unstarred material which constitutes the major portion of the text.

Careful attention has been given to teaching and learning aids. The inductive approach, so helpful to teachers and students alike, has been used wherever possible. The language of chemistry has been made clear and meaningful by the use of monosyllabic words and short sentences, except for certain strictly scientific words. Chemical words and terms are defined and pronounced in a short glossary at the beginning of each chapter and again, when the word or term appears in the text, it is printed in *boldface italics* and defined. These words and terms are also listed at the end of each chapter in the material entitled *Test Yourself on These Terms*. In addition, an extensive *Glossary* appears at the back of the book and includes definitions of all words and terms presented in the text. The complete *Appendix,* also in the back of the book, contains tables of useful data.

The material for each chapter concludes with *Questions* on the text proper, graded according to difficulty in *Groups A* and *B*. There are many more *Problems* than in previous editions of this book and these are also graded into *Group A* and *Group B*. The average student should master all the *Group A* questions and problems; the better students will be able to do both. Special activities appear under the title *Some Things for You to Do*.

At the end of each unit there appear two sets of more difficult exercises: *Check Your Progress in Chemistry* and *Challenging Your Knowledge*. The former contains an abundance of drill material in chemical equations and in all types of problems as a cumulative review, while the latter consists of questions and problems which will really challenge even the best students.

Because of their great learning value, line diagrams are used extensively. The text is also illustrated with many fine photographs, chosen with great care for their teaching value.

Many teachers from all parts of the country have helped the authors in preparing this edition of MODERN CHEMISTRY. Appreciation is especially due to the following teachers who have analyzed the previous edition of the book and have offered many excellent suggestions which have been incorporated in the final manuscript: Walter D. Brubaker, Redondo High School, Redondo Beach, California; John O. Peterson, San Diego High School, San Diego 2, California; Carl Wampole, Central High School, Fort Wayne, Indiana; Mrs. Frank L. Boyden, Deerfield Academy, Deerfield, Massachusetts; E. Harold Coburn, Buckley High School, Hartford, Connecticut; Franklin D. Kizer, State Supervisor of Science and Mathematics, State Department of Education, Richmond, Virginia; Harold G. Meyers, Bloomfield Public Schools, Bloomfield, New Jersey; C. M. Caldwell, Springfield High School, Springfield, Ohio; Guy B. Homman, Instructor of Chemistry, Senior High School, Manhattan, Kansas; and Joseph F. Becker, Union High School, Union, New Jersey.

In addition, the following teachers have been kind enough to read either special parts of, or the entire manuscript, and have offered invaluable assistance by their helpful criticisms: John O. Peterson, San Diego High School, San Diego, California; Walter Brubaker, Redondo High School, Redondo Beach, California; Franklin D. Kizer, State Supervisor of Science and Mathematics, State Department of Education, Richmond, Virginia; Alden W. Smith, Greenwich High School, Greenwich, Connecticut; Paul Hirni, Head, Chemistry Department, Baldwin High School, Baldwin, New York; Jacob Dewitt, Sturgis High School, Sturgis, Michigan; Feliks Wiatrowski, Head, Science Department, Riley Junior and Senior High School, South Bend, Indiana; Professor Julian Miller, Department of Chemistry, Columbia University, New York, N.Y.; Louis Weiss, Chairman of the Chemistry Department, Brooklyn Technical High School, Brooklyn, N.Y.; Joseph F. Castka, Chairman of the Science Department, Martin Van Buren High School, Queens Village, N.Y.; and Owens Hand Browne, Head of the Department of Chemistry, Saint Marys Junior College, Raleigh, North Carolina. To all of these the authors extend their gratitude.

The previous edition of MODERN CHEMISTRY was written by the late William O. Brooks of Technical High School, Springfield, Massachusetts, with the co-authorship of H. Clark Metcalfe. This edition has been prepared by Mr. Metcalfe, with the collaboration of John E. Williams.

CONTENTS

CHEMISTRY IN A MODERN WORLD

In the picture above you see a chemist working in a modern research laboratory. He has an abiding curiosity, an extensive knowledge of his subject, and precise, up-to-date laboratory equipment. No wonder he has earned a distinguished position in modern industry.

Perhaps without knowing it, you see chemical changes all around you. Every day you use chemical products without realizing that they resulted from careful study and experimentation in a laboratory before being made available to the public. As you will see, chemistry influences every part of your daily life.

Three chapters are included in this introductory unit: *Chemistry, a Science of Matter and Energy; The Composition of Matter;* and *Matter and Its Changes.* Each is important to your understanding and mastery of Unit 1.

Chapter 1

CHEMISTRY:

A SCIENCE OF

MATTER AND ENERGY

1. INTRODUCING YOU TO CHEMISTRY

1. Chemistry is a physical science. Through the ages, man has learned many things about himself and his environment. However, it was not until he started to write down his discoveries and observations that modern science, as such, began. Early scientists soon started to organize and classify their discoveries and observations. This organized knowledge has developed into the fundamental sciences with which we are familiar today. They are expanding at an ever-increasing rate.

All the sciences may be grouped into two large divisions: *1.* the *biological sciences,* which deal with living things, their structure, life processes, and environment; and *2.* the *physical sciences,* which are concerned with the physical relationships about us. The sciences help us to recognize and appreciate the orderliness in nature.

Chemistry is the science dealing with the composition of materials and the changes in composition which these materials undergo.

Physics is concerned primarily with changes in materials which do *not* involve a change in composition.

Mathematics is the science of our number system. It gives us a means of expressing the relationships we observe in nature and of performing useful and necessary computations. Mathematics

VOCABULARY

Active material. One which reacts readily with other materials.

Density. The weight of a material per unit volume.

Energy. The capacity for doing work.

Inactive material. One which reacts, but not very readily, with other materials.

Inert material. One which does not react with other materials under the ordinary conditions of chemical reactions.

Inertia. Resistance of matter to change of position or motion.

Law. A statement of scientific fact concerning natural phenomena.

Mass. The measure of inertia of a body.

Matter. Anything which occupies space and has weight.

Phenomenon. An observed condition or situation in nature.

has been called the *language of the sciences.*

2. What is the method of science? In some instances, important scientific discoveries have come about quite by accident. However, most of our scientific knowledge is the result of carefully planned investigations carried on by trained scientists. Their method, known as the **scientific method,** *is simply a logical approach to the solution of any problem which lends itself to investigation.* It is a method which requires strict honesty, the ability to withhold a decision until all the evidence is in, and the desire for truth.

The application of this method may be illustrated by the following: *1.* the scientist describes an observed situation or **phenomenon;** *2.* he looks up all the available information about the phenomenon; *3.* he then proposes a *hypothesis,* or possible explanation, which is based on logic and the previously recorded information; *4.* he next plans and conducts laboratory experiments in order to obtain as much additional data as possible on the subject; *5.* these new data are compared with all previously recorded data and are then carefully analyzed. If all this evidence tends to support the original hypothesis, the scientist works out a *theory,* or probable explanation supported by abundant data; and *6.* when enough conclusive data become available to prove that the theory is true, it may be restated as a **law.**

Laws of science tell us how materials *do* behave, but they do not tell us how materials *must* behave. When a law is finally established, it seldom completely confirms one particular theory. It may result from many theories which have undergone successive changes due to the contributions of many scientists over a span of several generations.

The term *theory* is often used in chemistry in a different and much broader sense. Chemists may include all the laws and experimental evidence making up a body of related knowledge

Fig. 1–1. Curiosity is the beginning of discovery.

into a general theory concerning the behavior of matter. Some examples of chemical theories which you will soon study are the *kinetic theory*, the *atomic theory*, and the *theory of ionization*.

3. Why study chemistry? You will find that chemistry plays a very important part in your life. Let us see some of the ways in which it affects you.

1. It answers many of your questions. Why does coal burn? Why does iron rust? What happens when milk turns sour? These all deal with the composition and changes in composition of materials. Chemistry furnishes the answers to these questions.

2. You will need it in your vocation or profession. Whatever vocation or profession you follow, you will find that chemistry enters the picture. A nurse handles chemicals constantly. A pharmacist must know the chemistry of the medicines he dispenses. The chemistry of fertilizers is important to the farmer. A salesman can speak more intelligently when he knows the composition of the products he sells. Chemistry helps the housewife buy materials for the home wisely. Lawyers can-

not argue a case in court without knowing the nature and composition of the materials in dispute. Of course, physicians, dentists, biologists, and engineers make constant use of chemistry in their professions.

3. Industry depends on chemistry. What would the world be like without iron and steel, rubber, aluminum, plastics, glass, paints, gasoline, and motor oils? Each of these basic industrial materials is a product of the application of chemistry. The fertilizers which enrich our soil, the insecticides we spray on plants, the new textile fibers that clothe us—these are all applications of chemistry. New synthetic drugs, enamels, lacquers, and alloys have come from the chemical laboratory. And the end is not yet in sight, by any means.

4. Chemists create new and better products. Almost every day you read in the newspapers of some new product of chemical research. A few years ago you may have played with a dough-like toy known as bouncing putty. It was an early member of a new chemical family known as *silicones*. Today many silicones have been developed which pos-

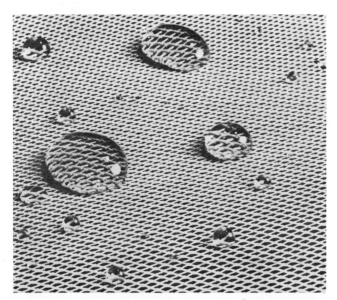

Fig. 1-2. Air readily passes through this water-repellent, silicone-treated material.

sess remarkable properties of durability over unusual temperature ranges. Special silicones have made possible longer lasting paints and polishes, better lubricants, improved heat and electrical insulators, water-repellent fabrics which "breathe," abhesives—or releasing agents, and defoamers. Even bouncing putty, once considered to be a chemical curiosity, is being used as the core of golf balls.

The fight against disease moves ahead with the development of each new drug and antibiotic. *Psychochemicals* (*sy*-ko-kem-ih-kals) are substances used in treating mental illness. *Reserpine* (re-*ser*-pin) and *Frenquel* are examples of psychochemicals which are bringing about a revolution in the treatment of mental illness. We know of the success of the Salk vaccine in the fight against polio. *Cytillin* (sy-*tih*-lin)

shows great promise in the treatment of diseases of the circulatory system. More potent relatives of *cortisone* (*kor*-tih-zone), such as *prednisone* (*pred*-nih-zone) and *prednisolone* (pred-*nih*-zoh-lone), are being used in the fight against arthritis.

The metal known as *zirconium* has a very high melting point and is used in nuclear reactors of some atomic energy installations. *Titanium* (ty-*tay*-nee-um) is becoming more important in the production of jet and rocket engines. A new type of color film has been developed which has enabled amateur photographers to produce high quality color prints and enlargements in their own darkrooms. And what of the new synthetic fiber paper, the improved liquid fertilizers, better fungicides and pesticides? All these result from the patient research of trained chemists.

Fig. 1–3. Air is an example of matter in the gaseous state. When moving at high velocities it can cause great destruction. This photograph shows hurricane damage in Rhode Island.

2. MATTER AND ENERGY

4. What is matter? All materials about us consist of matter. With our senses—sight, touch, taste, and smell—we recognize various kinds of matter. This book, your desk, the air you breathe, the water you drink are examples of matter. Some kinds of matter are easily observed. A stone or a piece of wood may be seen and held in the hand. Other kinds of matter are recognized less readily, such as the air or even water in a quiet pool. However, we ride on compressed air in automobile tires. We know of the tremendous damage which can be caused by rapidly moving air (see Fig. 1-3).

We say that **matter** *is anything which occupies space and has weight.* Matter possesses **inertia,** *which is a resistance to change of position or motion.* It may be acted on by *forces* which may set it in motion, or change its motion. While all these statements are descriptive of matter, they do not provide us with a completely satisfactory definition. Scientists, with their great knowledge of the properties and behavior of matter, are not yet able to define it precisely. Nature still holds many secrets to challenge the minds of men.

★ **5. Mass and weight.** *The quantity of matter which a body possesses is known as its **mass.*** If we try to move something we notice that it resists our effort. Its mass is the measure of this resistance. Thus *mass is the measure of the inertia of the body* and is responsible for it.

Mass is also responsible for the weight of the body. **Weight** *is the measure of the earth's attraction for a body.* If we were to attach an object to a spring balance we would find that it weighs less as we take it away from the center of the earth. The mass, or quantity of matter, on the other hand remains unchanged. *The mass of a body is constant.*

Mass is usually measured by comparison with known masses. If the masses of two bodies are the same they will have equal weights while in the same location. Thus the mass of a body, when determined by *weighing* it on a chemical balance, is commonly referred to as its weight. This practice is general throughout chemistry and should not be confusing if you understand the meaning of the terms mass and weight.

6. The density of matter varies. Matter occupies space and therefore has volume. From our everyday experiences we recognize that materials have different weights. We say that lead is heavy and that cork is light. This has little meaning unless we have in mind equal volumes of lead and cork. *The weight of a unit volume of a material is called its **density.*** By comparing the weights of equal volumes of materials we are

Fig. 1–4. Equal volumes of different substances do not have the same weight.

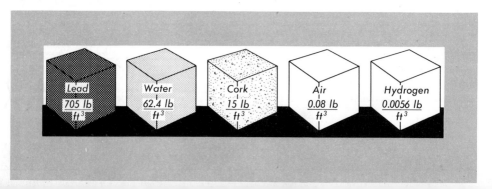

Lead	Water	Cork	Air	Hydrogen
705 lb	62.4 lb	15 lb	0.08 lb	0.0056 lb
ft³	ft³	ft³	ft³	ft³

able to see that the density of different kinds of matter varies. Thus lead, weighing 705 pounds per cubic foot, is 47 times denser than cork weighing 15 pounds per cubic foot (see Fig. 1-4).

7. There are three states of matter. We call a block of ice a solid. It may melt and form a liquid. As it evaporates, liquid water changes into a vapor or gas. Iron, too, is a solid but it may be melted and converted into a liquid. When iron is boiled, it forms iron vapor. Materials exist either in the *solid,* or the *liquid,* or the *gaseous* state. We can usually change matter from one state into another by changing its temperature.

A block of wood placed on a table keeps its shape and its volume. To change its shape or its volume you would have to use considerable pressure on the block from the outside. A solid does not need lateral (side) support to prevent it from losing its shape. *Solids have both a definite volume and a definite shape.*

Suppose we pour a quart of water out on the top of a table. The water is not rigid but spreads out in all directions. A liquid must have lateral (side) support to retain its shape. For that reason a liquid takes the shape of its container. We find, however, that a liquid has a definite volume if we try to put a quart of milk into a pint bottle. Therefore we conclude that *liquids have a definite volume, and that they take the shape of their containers.*

If we inflate an automobile tire, we find that the air takes the shape of the tire, which is its container. The tire is really full of air, but if a blow-out occurs, the escaping air expands in volume. A pint of liquid does not expand and form a quart if it is put into a quart bottle. But a pint of air would expand and occupy all that space if it were placed in a really empty quart bottle. *Gases have neither a definite shape nor a definite volume.* This fact makes it difficult to measure the volume of gases. If they are warmed, they expand decidedly, but their volume is reduced when the pressure on them is increased. In measuring gas volumes, we must specify *both the temperature and the pressure* to which they are subjected.

Both liquids and gases are known as fluids. These are materials which flow readily and require vessels to contain them. We think of solids as being rigid yet none is perfectly rigid. Butter, for example, may not be very solid on a warm summer day. Similarly, there are no perfectly fluid materials. Molasses, water, and carbon dioxide may be observed to flow, but certainly at different rates.

Liquids, having definite volume, have a free surface. Water may be contained in an open vessel. Matter in the gaseous state must be bounded on all sides by the container. Gases are fluids which do not have a free surface.

Fluids which cannot exist as liquids having a free surface at ordinary conditions of temperature and pressure are correctly termed *gases*. *Vapor* is the term used to denote the gaseous state of fluids which exist as liquids under normal conditions. Thus we speak of water *vapor* and oxygen *gas*.

8. The properties of matter. We are able to identify matter and determine its usefulness by studying its properties. We may organize the specific properties of materials under two general headings: *1. physical;* and *2. chemical.*

Physical properties include *color,*

odor, solubility, density, hardness, melting and *boiling points,* and *crystalline* or *amorphous forms.* These physical properties do not apply equally to all states of matter. For example, hardness and crystalline form are not properties of fluids. Similarly, odor is of little value in describing many solids. *Physical properties are those which can be determined without causing a change in the identity of a material.*

Under chemical properties we include *chemical activity,* or behavior with other materials. Some materials are **active,** reacting readily with others. Some other materials are **inactive.** These inactive materials do react, but not very readily, with others. Still other materials are **inert.** These do not react at all under ordinary conditions. In our study of chemical properties, we shall be interested to know whether a material burns. We shall also inquire how it reacts with air, with water, with acids, and with alkalies. *Chemical properties are those which pertain to the behavior of a material in changes in which its identity is altered.*

9. What is energy? We find much the same difficulty in defining energy as we did in defining matter. Scientists know a great deal about energy and how it may be used but they cannot define it precisely. *Energy is usually defined as the capacity for doing work.* Energy is associated with matter but it is not a form of matter. We have no knowledge of matter which does not possess energy.

10. There are several forms of energy. Our most common forms of energy are *mechanical energy* and *heat energy.* Mechanical energy may be of two types: *1. **potential energy** or the energy of position;* and *2. **kinetic energy** or the energy of motion.* Thus water at the brink of a waterfall has potential energy due to its elevated position. As the water descends it acquires kinetic energy due to its motion. Heat energy is released whenever fuels are burned. Practically all our industrial power is provided by heat energy from burning fuel and from the kinetic energy of falling water.

Other forms of energy are *electrical energy, chemical energy, light energy,* and *nuclear energy.* Chemical energy is a basic concern of the chemical industry. Nuclear energy is being developed as a source of industrial power.

We may convert or *transform* one form of energy into another. As an example, suppose we burn coal to produce energy. Some of the chemical energy of the coal and the oxygen of the air is released as heat during the burning action. The heat energy may be transferred to water and convert it to steam. The steam can then drive a turbine to produce kinetic energy. A dynamo may be turned to generate electrical energy. This may then be transformed into heat in an electric iron or in an electric toaster. Or it may be transformed into light energy in an incandescent lamp or carbon arc. Or it may also be transformed into mechanical energy in an electric motor which runs a clock or a locomotive.

11. The conservation of matter and energy. About 50 years ago Albert Einstein (1879–1955) suggested that matter and energy are related. This relationship is shown by his now famous equation $E = mc^2$. E represents the amount of energy, m the amount of matter, and c is a constant equal to the velocity of light. A great number of experiments during the last 25 years have estab-

Fig. 1–5. The Law of Conservation of Matter and Energy was demonstrated when the A bomb was first used against Japan in World War II.

lished the truth of this relationship.

Matter can be converted to energy and energy to matter. The conversion factor, c^2, is involved in both transformations. Indeed, the amount of matter is changed if the amount of energy is changed. Thus matter and energy are not two different physical quantities, which we can define independently. Instead, *they may be considered to be two different forms of the same physical quantity.* The facts are formulated into a law of science known as the **Law of Conservation of Matter and Energy.** This law may be stated formally as follows: *matter and energy are interchangeable; and the total matter and energy in the universe is constant.*

Energy is either given up or absorbed whenever a material enters into a reaction. Only in nuclear reactions involving a tremendous quantity of energy, such as the explosion of a hydrogen bomb, does the amount of matter transformed into energy become significant. Ordinary chemical reactions which occur in the laboratory involve such small matter changes that there is no method of detecting them. For all ordinary purposes such changes of matter into energy may be ignored. We may then recognize the following useful generalization: *in an ordinary chemical change, the total mass (weight) of the reacting materials is equal to the total mass (weight) of the products.*

3. MEASUREMENTS IN CHEMISTRY

12. The Centigrade temperature scale. Scientific measurements of temperature are generally made on the *Centigrade scale.* This temperature scale was devised by a Swedish astronomer, Anders Celsius (1701–1744). It is often referred to as the Celsius scale. Two *fixed points,* the freezing and boiling points of water, are used to graduate the scale. On the Centigrade scale the two fixed points are called *0 degrees* (0° C) and *100 degrees* (100° C). The intervening space is divided into 100 equal intervals or 100 Centigrade degrees (100 C°).

13. The metric system is used in science. The study of science could not be precise without a suitable system of measurement. The English system, which we use in our daily activities, presents many disadvantages in scientific measurements. It is a system which, in a sense, just grew up. Its chief disadvantage is that there are no simple numerical relationships between the different units.

The *metric system,* with which you may already be familiar, was developed in France near the end of the eighteenth century. It is used in scientific work throughout the world and is in general use in practically all countries except the United States and Great Britain. *It is a decimal system that has*

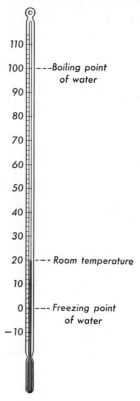

Fig. 1–6. The Centigrade thermometer is widely used in scientific work. Compare the temperatures shown here with those on the common Fahrenheit thermometer.

Fig. 1–7. The centimeter is nearly 0.4 of an inch in length. One inch equals 2.54 centimeters.

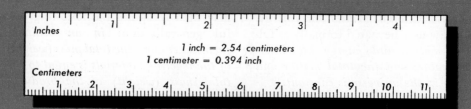

Inches

1 inch = 2.54 centimeters
1 centimeter = 0.394 inch

Centimeters

LENGTH:	10 millimeters (mm)	= 1 centimeter (cm)
	100 centimeters	= 1 meter (m)
	1000 meters	= 1 kilometer (km)
VOLUME:	1000 milliliters (ml)	= 1 liter (l)
	1000 liters	= 1 kiloliter (kl)
WEIGHT:	1000 milligrams (mg)	= 1 gram (g)
	1000 grams	= 1 kilogram (kg)

BRIEF TABLE OF METRIC EQUIVALENTS

simple numerical relationships between units. The disadvantage in its every-day usage lies in the fact that the basic units do not have the practical sizes of those of the English system. They do not lend themselves to the convenient custom of reducing by halves and quarters.

14. What are the units of the metric system? The metric system includes measures of *length, volume* (capacity), and *weight*. The unit of length is the *meter* (m), of volume is the *liter* (l), and of weight is the *gram* (g). Prefixes are used with these units to complete the system. Latin prefixes are employed to identify descending values. These are *deci-* (0.1), *centi-* (0.01), and *milli-* (0.001). Greek prefixes are used to identify ascending values; *deka-* (10),

hecto- (100), and *kilo-* (1000). The prefixes shown in the table above with the three metric units will be used throughout your study of chemistry. It will be helpful to memorize them.

As originally conceived, the metric system was to be based on natural standards with the meter as the fundamental unit. The meter was intended to be one ten-millionth of the distance from the earth's equator to either pole. However, the original calculations were found to contain slight errors. The ***standard meter** is now defined as the distance between two parallel lines engraved on a platinum-iridium bar*

Fig. 1–8. These drawings show comparisons between the English and the metric systems of measuring weight and volume. Note that the liter is slightly larger than the U.S. liquid quart, and that the kilogram is more than twice as heavy as the avoirdupois pound.

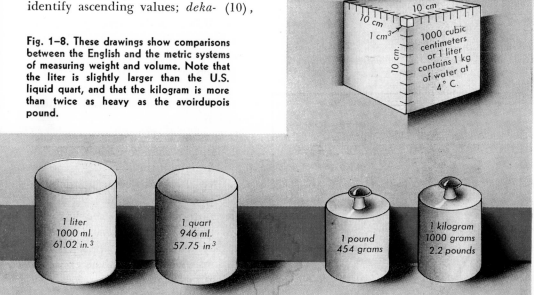

10 cm
10 cm
1 cm³
10 cm
1000 cubic centimeters or 1 liter contains 1 kg of water at 4° C.

1 liter
1000 ml.
61.02 in.³

1 quart
946 ml.
57.75 in³

1 pound
454 grams

1 kilogram
1000 grams
2.2 pounds

TABLE OF METRIC VOLUME–WEIGHT RELATIONS

> 1 cm³ of water has 1 ml volume and weighs 1 g
> 1000 cm³ of water has 1 l volume and weighs 1 kg

which is preserved at the International Bureau of Weights and Measures near Paris. The meter is slightly longer than the English yard, being equal to 39.37 inches. One inch is 2.54 centimeters.

The gram was intended to be the mass of 1 cubic centimeter (cm³) of water at 4° C, the temperature at which it is most dense. The **gram** *is now defined as one thousandth of the mass of the standard kilogram resting in the International Bureau of Weights and Measures.* The gram is an exceedingly small unit equal to 0.035 ounce. One pound is equal to approximately 454 grams. One kilogram is approximately 2.2 pounds.

The **liter** *is defined as the volume of one kilogram of water at 4° C.* Because of another slight error 1 kilogram of water having a volume of 1 liter does not measure precisely 1000 cm³. The error is so slight that, except for purposes of definition, it can be neglected. Since water is a universal standard, the

Fig. 1–9. A modern platform balance is used for ordinary weighing in the laboratory. It may have a sensitivity of 0.1 gram.

remarkable simplicity of the metric system can be seen in the above table.

The liter is slightly larger than the U. S. liquid quart. It is equal to 1.06 quarts. A liter, or 1000 cm³, equals 61 in³.

★ **15. The scientific notation of numbers.** In science we often meet numbers which are extremely large or extremely small. The speed of light is 30,000,000,000 centimeters per second. The mass of the earth is about 6,000,000,000,000,000,000,000,000,000 grams. The mass of an electron is approximately 0.00000000000000000000000000091 gram. The wave length of yellow light is about 0.000059 cm. These numbers have little meaning in the ordinary sense. In *scientific notation* we may write them conveniently and economically. In this system a number has the form

$$M \times 10^n$$

where M is a number between 1 and 10 and n is a positive or negative integer.

We may now write the unusual quantities already given in our new form as shown in the table on page 13.

To change a number into scientific notation form:

1. Determine M by moving the decimal point so that you leave only one nonzero digit to the left of it.

2. Determine n by counting the number of places you have moved the decimal point; if moved to the left, n is positive; if to the right, n is negative. The laws of exponents apply in computations involving numbers expressed in scientific notation.

$$30,000,000,000 = 3 \times 10^{10}$$
$$6,000,000,000,000,000,000,000,000,000 = 6 \times 10^{27}$$
$$0.0000000000000000000000000091 = 9.1 \times 10^{-28}$$
$$0.000059 = 5.9 \times 10^{-5}$$

NUMBERS IN SCIENTIFIC NOTATION FORM

★ **16. Accuracy of measurements.** Your work in chemistry will involve many different kinds of measurements. In some instances these will be rather precise, in others rather crude. Chemistry students generally tend to imply more accuracy in their measurements than the instruments they use justify. The degree of accuracy of any measurement you make will depend on two factors: *1.* your ability to use the measuring device properly; and *2.* the precision of the device. Where measurements are used in computing results, *your final result is no more accurate than the least accurate measurement used.*

Laboratory measurements usually require that you estimate the fraction beyond the smallest division on the instrument. Since this estimated figure is a *guess* it is of doubtful accuracy. It is customary to retain *one* doubtful figure in the result.

Suppose you wish to determine the volume of a metal block. Your measuring instrument is a meter stick having 1 mm divisions. You find the sides to be 3.54 cm, 4.85 cm, and 5.42 cm, estimating the last figure in each case. Each measurement thus consists of two *significant figures* and one *doubtful figure.*

The area of one surface is

$$3.54 \text{ cm} \times 4.85 \text{ cm} = 17.1690 \text{ cm}^2$$

Remembering that the product of anything multiplied by a doubtful figure is also doubtful, and that only one such figure may be carried, the result is rounded to 17.2 cm². The volume of the block then becomes

$$17.2 \text{ cm}^2 \times 5.42 \text{ cm} = 93.224 \text{ cm}^3$$

Again the result is properly expressed as 93.2 cm³, the volume of the metal block. Had all of the doubtful figures been retained throughout the computation, the volume would be 93.*055980* cm³. You can easily see that this degree of accuracy, millionths of a cubic centimeter, cannot be obtained with a meter stick graduated in tenths of a centimeter.

There is a limit of accuracy inherent in any experimental setup. It depends on the precision of the measuring devices used. It is the aim of the chemist, and of the chemistry student as well, to perform the various operations and measurements with such skill that the experimental accuracy will be limited only by the apparatus used.

Fig. 1–10. The analytical balance may have a sensitivity of 0.0001 gram.

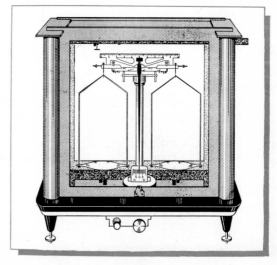

Summary

Chemistry is the science dealing with materials, their composition, and the changes which they undergo. The scientific method is a logical approach to the solution of any problem which lends itself to investigation.

Matter is anything which occupies space and has weight. Matter possesses inertia. The measure of inertia of an object is called its mass. Weight is the measure of the earth's attraction for an object. Mass is determined indirectly by weighing and is usually referred to in chemistry as weight.

There are three states of matter: solid, liquid, and gaseous. The state of any substance depends largely upon its temperature. Some substances exist as gases, others as liquids, and still others as solids, at ordinary temperatures. The properties of matter are classified as either physical or chemical.

Energy is the capacity for doing work. The Law of Conservation of Matter and Energy tells us that matter and energy are interchangeable and the sum total in the universe is constant.

The Centigrade (Celsius) temperature scale is used almost entirely in chemistry. The two fixed points are 0° C and 100° C.

The metric system is used in chemistry. The unit of length is the meter, of volume is the liter, and of weight is the gram. Metric prefixes common in chemistry are milli- (0.001), centi- (0.01), and kilo- (1000).

The scientific notation form is convenient for expressing large and small numbers. Such numbers are in the general form $M \times 10^n$.

There is a limit of accuracy inherent in any measuring device. The significant figures derived from any measurement should be known in order that computations may be carried out economically and results may show the extent of accuracy.

Test yourself on these terms

active material	inactive material	metric system
amorphous	inert material	milli-
centi-	inertia	phenomenon
Centigrade scale	kilo-	physical property
chemical property	kinetic energy	physical sciences
chemistry	law	potential energy
crystalline	Law of Conservation	scientific method
density	of Matter and Energy	scientific notation
energy	liquid	solid
fluid	liter	theory
gas	mass	vapor
gram	matter	volume
hypothesis	meter	weight

Questions

Group A

1. Why is chemistry considered to be a fundamental science?
2. What distinguishes (*a*) a solid from a liquid? (*b*) a liquid from a gas?
3. What properties of materials are classed as physical properties?
4. What properties of materials are classed as chemical?
5. What are the three basic units of the metric system?
6. Name the six prefixes used in the metric system and indicate what each one means.
7. Why is the study of chemistry concerned with energy?
8. In scientific work what advantage does the metric system of measure offer over the English system?

Group B

9. Prepare a list of new chemical products which you have read about in newspapers and magazines.
10. (*a*) List five common materials used in the kitchen in your home. (*b*) What properties does each have which makes it suitable for its particular use?
11. Why are both liquids and gases considered to be fluids?
12. What determines whether a certain property of a material is classed as physical or chemical?
13. Why does our sense of touch give us the most direct evidence of the existence of matter?
★ 14. A weighing was made on a trip balance which was graduated in 0.1 g units. The weight was recorded as 73.14 g. (*a*) Which digits would be considered to be significant figures? (*b*) Which digit would be called a doubtful figure?

Problems

(See Table 1, Appendix)

Group A

1. How many millimeters are there (*a*) in 1 centimeter? (*b*) in 1 meter? (*c*) in 1 kilometer?
2. How many centimeters are there (*a*) in 1 foot? (*b*) in 2 meters? (*c*) How many inches are there in 1 meter?
3. How many milliliters are there in (*a*) 2 liters? (*b*) 10 liters? (*c*) How many liters are there in 1 m³?
4. Calculate the number of milligrams (*a*) in 0.4 kilogram; (*b*) in 1 pound. (*c*) How many grams are there in 2 kilograms?
5. (*a*) What is your height in meters? (*b*) What is your weight in kilograms?
6. A Florence flask has a volume of 250 ml. (*a*) What part of a liter is this? (*b*) How many grams of water will the flask hold?
★ 7. The distance to the sun is approximately 93,000,000 miles. Express this distance in scientific notation form.
★ 8. The thickness of an oil film on water is about 0.0000005 cm. Express this thickness in scientific notation form.

Group B

9. A cubic box contains 1000 g of water. (*a*) What is the volume of the box in milliliters? (*b*) in cubic centimeters? (*c*) What is the length of one side in centimeters? (*d*) in meters?

10. A test tube in the laboratory is 125 mm long and 25 mm in diameter. (*a*) What is its volume in milliliters? (*b*) How many grams of water will it hold?

11. Each member of a class of 24 students needs 10 g of sodium chloride for an experiment. The instructor sets out a one-pound jar of the salt. How many grams should he have left to return to the stock room at the end of the laboratory period?

12. A 1-liter graduated cylinder has an inside diameter of 8 cm. There is a 52 mm ungraduated portion at the top. What is the total height of the cylinder in centimeters?

Some things for you to do

1. Make a collection of clippings from your daily newspaper which deal with chemical research, chemical industries, or new chemical products.

2. Prepare a list of reasons favoring the introduction of the metric system into the United States for general use. State the objections to its introduction.

3. See how many energy transformations you can list pertaining to the operation of an automobile on the highway.

Chapter 2 THE COMPOSITION OF MATTER

1. All matter is divided into three general classes. We are familiar with many different kinds of materials. To study materials without first organizing them into similar groups would be difficult and would require much effort and time. Chemists have found that all forms of matter may be divided into three general groups on the basis of their properties. These three general classes of matter are: *1. elements; 2. compounds;* and *3. mixtures.*

2. What is a mixture? If we examine a piece of granite closely with a hand lens, we can see three different crystal-line materials: quartz, feldspar, and mica. The properties of each differ greatly. *A material which has parts with different properties is said to be* **heterogeneous** (het-er-oh-*jee*-nee-us).

The properties of quartz are the same regardless of its source. One part of a piece of quartz has the same properties as every other part. This is also true of feldspar and mica. *A material which has similar properties throughout is said to be* **homogeneous** (hoh-moh-*jee*-nee-us). Heterogeneous materials are *mixtures* of homogeneous materials.

VOCABULARY

Atom. The smallest part of an element that can enter into combination with other elements.

Compound. A substance which can be decomposed into two or more simpler substances by ordinary chemical means.

Element. A substance which cannot be further decomposed by ordinary chemical means.

Heterogeneous (het-er-oh-*jee*-nee-us) **material.** One which has parts possessing different properties.

Homogeneous (hoh-muh-*jee*-nee-us) **material.** One which has similar properties throughout.

Mixture. A material composed of two or more substances each of which retains its own characteristic properties.

Substance. A homogeneous material consisting of one particular kind of matter.

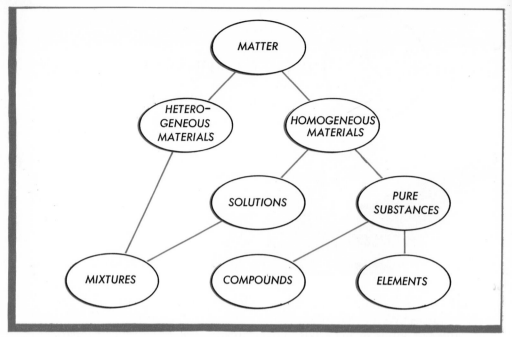

Fig. 2–1. All matter is divided into three general classes: elements, compounds, and mixtures.

All mixtures are not, however, heterogeneous. When sugar is dissolved in water, the solution which is formed has similar properties throughout. Thus the solution is homogeneous. We may increase the amount of sugar or water. But we still have a homogeneous mixture of the two materials. The solution has the sweet taste of the sugar it contains. The water may be removed by evaporation and the sugar recovered in its original form. Solutions are therefore homogeneous mixtures. Air is a gaseous solution. Alloys are usually solid solutions. *A **mixture** is a material consisting of two or more kinds of matter each of which retains its own characteristic properties.*

3. Substances include compounds and elements. We have already learned that materials with similar properties throughout are homogeneous. In chemistry, *a **substance** is a homogeneous material consisting of one particular kind of matter.* Both the sugar and the water of our sugar-water solution are sub-stances. Unlike the granite which has the different properties of quartz, feldspar, and mica, the properties of sugar cannot be attributed to anything but the sugar itself and are due to its particular composition. Furthermore, *a substance has a definite chemical composition.*

Let us place a small quantity of sugar in a test tube and heat it over a low flame. The substance readily melts and changes color. Finally we produce a charred black mass in the bottom of the test tube, and drops of clear colorless liquid appear around the cooler open end. The black substance is carbon and the liquid is water. The properties of the sugar no longer exist. Instead we observe the properties of two different substances. Sugar may be recognized as a complex substance or *compound. A **compound** is a substance which may be decomposed into two or more simpler substances by ordinary chemical means.*

Chemists are able to decompose wa-

OXYGEN	49.5%	SODIUM	2.6%
SILICON	25.8%	POTASSIUM	2.4%
ALUMINUM	7.5%	MAGNESIUM	1.9%
IRON	4.7%	HYDROGEN	0.9%
CALCIUM	3.4%	TITANIUM	0.6%
	ALL OTHER ELEMENTS	0.7%	

**THE MOST
ABUNDANT
ELEMENTS**

ter into two simpler substances, hydrogen and oxygen. Thus water is a compound. Chemists have not succeeded, however, in decomposing carbon, hydrogen, or oxygen into any simpler substances. We conclude that these are elementary substances or *elements*. *Elements are substances which cannot be further decomposed by ordinary chemical means.* Elementary substances cannot be further broken down or simplified by the usual methods of carrying out chemical reactions—by application of heat, light, or electrical energy.

4. There are relatively few elements in nature. One of the most fascinating facts of science is that all matter is composed of about 100 elements. Probably 90 different elements occur in a free or combined state in the earth's crust. The atmosphere consists almost entirely of the two elements, nitrogen and oxygen. Water, which covers such a great portion of the surface of the earth, is a combination of hydrogen and oxygen. It is true, however, that natural water contains many dissolved substances.

Only about 30 elements are well known. The relative distribution of the 10 most abundant elements in the atmosphere, lakes, rivers, and oceans, and

the earth's crust is given in the accompanying table.

A few elementary substances such as gold, silver, copper, and sulfur, have been known since ancient times. During the Middle Ages and the Renaissance which followed, more elements were discovered. Through the years, scientists have added even more elements to the list as a result of improved research techniques.

There are now 102 known elements. There is good reason to believe that this number will soon be increased to 104. The theoretical possibility of eventually extending the number to 118 has been suggested. However, present

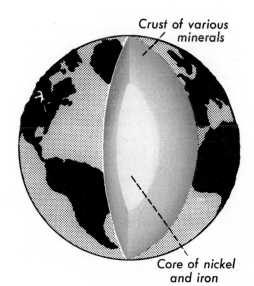

Crust of various
minerals

Core of nickel
and iron

Fig. 2-2. The central core of the earth is believed to be composed of nickel and iron.

Fig. 2–3. Professor Glenn T. Seaborg, University of California, produced the new elements americium, curium, berkelium, californium, einsteinium, and fermium.

evidence indicates that the number probably will not exceed 110.

The 92 elements ranging from hydrogen to uranium are traditionally known as *natural elements*. They constitute the pre-Atomic Age list of elements. Atomic bomb research during World War II led to the *synthesis* of *neptunium* named for the planet Neptune, and *plutonium* named for Pluto. These were followed by *americium* (am-er-*ih*-see-um) named for America, *curium* (*ku*-ree-um) named in honor of Madame Curie, *berkelium* (*berk*-lee-um) for Berkeley (the site of the University of California), and *californium* for the university and the state. More recently *einsteinium* named for Albert Einstein, *fermium* named for Enrico Fermi, *mendelevium* (men-del-*ev*-ee-um) named for Dmitri Mendeleyev (men-deh-*lay*-eff), and *nobelium*, named for Alfred Nobel have made the total 102.

5. There are two general classes of elements. Elements differ enough in their properties so that chemists recognize two classes: *1. metals;* and *2. nonmetals.*

1. Metals. Some elements have a luster similar to that of steel or silver. They reflect heat and light readily. They conduct heat and electricity remarkably well. Some are ductile and can be drawn into wire, or malleable and can be hammered into thin sheets. Elements which have such properties are known as **metals.** Some examples of metals are: gold, silver, copper, iron, zinc, tin, lead, magnesium, calcium, and aluminum. Mercury is a liquid metal.

2. Nonmetals. These are usually poor conductors of heat and electricity. They cannot be hammered into sheets or drawn into wire because they are usually too brittle. Sulfur is an example of such a nonmetal. Some nonmetals such as iodine, carbon, and phosphorus are solid at room temperatures. Bromine is a liquid nonmetal. Others are gaseous, as oxygen, nitrogen, and chlorine.

You will also find some borderline cases among the elements. Some have certain properties characteristic of metals and at the same time other properties characteristic of nonmetals. Arsenic and antimony are two examples of this type. They are sometimes called **metalloids.**

6. What do we mean by a chemical symbol? Jöns Jakob Berzelius (1779–1848), a Swedish chemist, was the first to use letters as symbols for the elements. These replaced the crude picture system used by the alchemists in the Middle Ages. Berzelius used the first letter of the name of an element as its symbol. For example, the letter **O** represents oxygen, and the letter **H** represents hydrogen.

Since there are over 100 elements known, and there are only twenty-six letters in our alphabet, the names of several elements must begin with the same letter. Berzelius suggested using the second letter of the name of the element with the first letter in such cases. Or, the first letter with some other letter whose sound is conspicuous when the name of the element is pronounced might be added. For example, the symbol for carbon is **C**; for calcium, **Ca**; for chlorine, **Cl**; for chromium, **Cr**; and for cobalt, **Co.** The first letter of a symbol is *always* a capital, but the second letter of a symbol is *never* capitalized. For example, **Co** is the symbol for cobalt, but **CO** is the formula for the compound known as *carbon monoxide*.

In several cases, the symbol for an element is derived from the Latin name of the element. For example, the symbol for iron is **Fe**, from the Latin *ferrum*. **Pb,** the symbol for lead, comes from the Latin word *plumbum*. The symbols for silver, **Ag,** and sodium, **Na,** come from the Latin words, *argentum* and *natrium*.

7. What is the significance of a symbol? A symbol as used in chemistry is more than an abbreviation. When we use the symbol **O**, it first of all means oxygen. More than that, it means *one atom* of oxygen. *The **atom** is the smallest particle of an element that can enter into combination with other elements.* Just as a mason uses different kinds of bricks to build houses, so the chemist uses different kinds of atoms to build chemical compounds.

8. Compounds differ from mixtures. When matter is made up of two or more elements, they may be mixed mechanically, or they may be combined chemically. The material will be either a *mixture* or a *compound* depending on what happened to the elements. If it is a mixture, the properties of each of the elements present will be recognized. On the other hand, if the elements are chemically combined, a complex substance with its own characteristic properties will be observed.

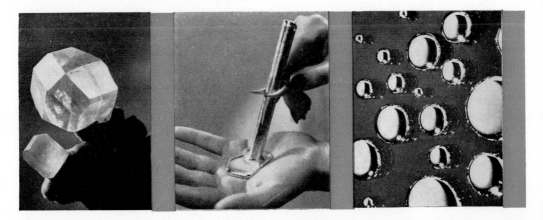

Fig. 2–4. Sulfur (left) is nonmetallic and usually occurs as yellow crystals. Gallium (center) is a metallic element that will melt in your hand. Its boiling point is about 2000° C. Mercury (right) is the only metallic element that is liquid at room temperature.

Suppose we add powdered sulfur to some iron powder on a sheet of paper and stir the two substances together. There is no evidence of chemical action. No light is produced and no heat is given off. We find that the two substances may be mixed in any proportion. It is possible to use a large amount of iron and a small amount of sulfur or a large portion of sulfur and a small portion of iron.

Now let us lift the paper containing our mixture and move it back and forth over a strong magnet. We observe that the iron particles may be separated from the sulfur. Next we place a small portion of the mixture in hydrochloric acid. The iron reacts with the acid and disappears from view leaving the sulfur unaffected. Now we place another portion of the mixture in carbon disulfide. The sulfur dissolves in this liquid leaving the iron powder behind.

In each of the tests performed we have seen that the properties of the iron and those of the sulfur persist. This behavior is typical of that of a mixture. The components do not lose their identity. They may be mixed in any proportion without evidence of chemical activity.

Perhaps we can establish the conditions which will enable the iron and the sulfur to unite chemically to form a compound. Let us mix 7 g of iron powder with 4 g of sulfur and pour enough of the mixture into a test tube to fill it one third full. Then we heat the mixture until it begins to glow. Even after we remove the tube from the flame, the action continues, and the whole mass soon becomes red hot. *Both heat and light are produced during the chemical action which causes the sul-*

fur to unite chemically with the iron to form a compound.

When the reaction ceases and the tube cools, we will break the tube and examine the product. It does not resemble either the iron or the sulfur. Each element has lost its characteristic properties. The iron cannot be removed by a magnet. The sulfur cannot be dissolved out of the product with carbon disulfide. Hydrochloric acid acts on the mixture of iron and sulfur to produce hydrogen. It acts on this new product to produce hydrogen sulfide. *A new substance with a new set of properties has been formed.*

If we took this new product to a chemist to have it analyzed, he would find that it is made up of seven parts by weight of iron to four parts by weight of sulfur. *A compound is always made up of the same elements in a definite proportion by weight.* For example, the new compound, which chemists call *iron sulfide,* is composed of 63.5% iron and 36.5% sulfur. That does not mean that we could not make iron sulfide by starting with eight parts of iron and four parts of sulfur. But it does mean that in such a case, one part by weight of iron would remain as an unused surplus after the seven parts of iron had combined with four parts of sulfur.

The several differences between a mixture and a compound are summarized in the table on page 23.

9. The Law of Definite Proportions. Louis Proust (1755–1826), a French chemist, was one of the first to observe that elements always combine with one another in a definite ratio by weight. About fifty years later, Jean Servais Stas, a Belgian chemist, performed a series of precise experiments which

DIFFERENCES BETWEEN A MIXTURE AND A COMPOUND

MIXTURE	COMPOUND
1. In a mixture, the components may be present in any proportion.	1. A compound always has a definite composition by weight.
2. In the preparation of a mixture, there is no evidence of any chemical action taking place.	2. In the preparation of a compound, some evidence of chemical action is usually apparent (light, heat, etc.).
3. In a mixture, the components do not lose their identity. The components of a mixture may be separated by mechanical means.	3. In a compound, the constituents lose their identity. The constituents of a compound can be separated by chemical means only.

confirmed the observations of Proust. We now recognize the work of Proust as the *Law of Definite Proportions: every compound has a definite composition by weight.*

Because the Law of Definite Proportions is true, a manufacturer of chemical compounds can find out just how much of each constituent to use in making each compound.

10. Some common examples of mixtures and compounds. Air is a mixture. Its composition varies somewhat in different localities. Other familiar examples of mixtures include such well-known substances as baking powders, concrete, and various kinds of soil. There is practically no limit to the number of possible mixtures. They may be made up of two or more elements, of two or more compounds, or of both elements and compounds.

Some of our large dictionaries define almost a half-million words, all formed from the 26 letters of our alphabet. Try to imagine the number of compounds it would be possible to make from 100 or more elements. But some letters do not combine well with others to form words. In the same way, some elements do not unite readily with others to form compounds. Half a dozen are known which almost never form compounds. There are enough elements that do combine, however, to form the *several hundred thousand* compounds known to chemists. Water, table salt, sugar, marble, alcohol, baking soda, ether, glycerol, turpentine, starch, nitric and sulfuric acids are examples of some compounds used by chemists.

The simplest compounds are made up of two different elements. We know that iron sulfide is such a compound. Carbon dioxide is composed only of carbon and oxygen. Table salt consists of the element sodium combined with the element chlorine. Sodium is an active metallic element which must be protected from contact with air and water. Chlorine is a poisonous gas. But when combined chemically, the two form common table salt.

Many compounds are composed of no more than three different elements. Carbon, hydrogen, and oxygen are the components of sugar. These same three elements, combined in different proportions, form many other compounds having decidedly different properties.

Summary

Matter is classed either as a mixture or a pure substance. Pure substances are either compounds or elements. Compounds are substances which may be decomposed into two or more simpler substances by ordinary chemical means. Elements are substances which may not be further decomposed by ordinary chemical means. Mixtures are materials composed of two or more substances each of which retains its own characteristic properties.

While over 100 elements are known, no more than 90 exist outside of the scientist's laboratories. These make up all of the world that we know. Only about 30 elements are well known. Ten elements form about 99% of the earth's crust. Oxygen is the most abundant element, silicon ranks second in abundance. Elements may be classed as metals and nonmetals; however, some are called metalloids.

Symbols are used to represent elements. The symbol of an element stands for one atom of that element. The atom is the smallest particle of an element that can enter into combination with other elements.

The Law of Definite Proportions states that every compound has a definite composition by weight.

Test yourself on these terms

atom	heterogeneous	metalloid
chemical symbol	homogeneous	mixture
compound	Law of Definite Proportions	nonmetal
element	metal	substance

Questions

Group A

1. What are the three general classes of matter?
2. Distinguish between matter and a substance.
3. Distinguish between a complex substance and an elementary substance.
4. (*a*) What are the two general classes of elements? (*b*) Do all elements fit definitely into one of these classes?
5. Distinguish between a compound and a mixture.
6. What are the five most abundant elements?
7. (*a*) What are the properties of metals? (*b*) of nonmetals?
8. (*a*) How many elements are known? (*b*) How many were known prior to the atomic-bomb research of World War II?
9. What is the meaning of the chemical symbol?
10. (*a*) List five familiar substances which you recognize to be elements. (*b*) List five which are compounds. (*c*) List five familiar mixtures.

Group B

11. What difference in the properties of white sand and sugar would enable a mixture of the two substances to be separated?
12. How would you carry out the separation of the sand-sugar mixture of Question 11?
13. Why is a solution recognized as a mixture?
14. What is the meaning of the phrase "definite proportion by weight"?
15. Why is the Law of Definite Proportions very important to chemists?
16. Consult the complete list of known elements appearing on the inside of the back cover of this book and compile a list of those about which you already have some knowledge. Give the name, symbol, and the pertinent bit of knowledge in column form.

Some things for you to do

1. New uses are being found for some of the less common elements. Ask your teacher to let you borrow a recent advanced chemistry text to find the uses which are now being made of selenium, titanium, zirconium, iridium, gallium, and indium.
2. Look up the words from which the symbols for antimony, copper, gold, mercury, potassium, tin, and tungsten are taken or derived.

Chapter 3 MATTER AND ITS CHANGES

1. THE NATURE OF MATTER

1. Of what particles is matter composed? When you crush a lump of sugar you can see that it is made up of many small particles of sugar. You may go further and grind these particles into the finest of powders, but each tiny piece will still be sugar. Now suppose you dissolve the sugar in water. The tiny particles disappear completely. Even a microscopic examination of the solution will not reveal their presence. However, your sense of taste tells you that sugar is present in the water solution. Similarly, the odor of gas escaping from an open gas valve tells you of its presence. You cannot see gas particles in the air of the room, even if you use the most powerful microscope. These and many similar experiments have led scientists to believe that the *ultimate particles* of matter must be exceedingly small.

Greek philosophers, as early as 400 B.C., believed that matter was indestructible. They also thought that it could be subdivided into ultimate particles. Democritus (deh-*mock*-rih-tus) (460–370 B.C.) referred to such particles as *atoms,* from a Greek word meaning indivisible. This ancient philosopher

VOCABULARY

Catalyst. An agent which affects a chemical action without itself being permanently altered.

Diatomic. Consisting of two atoms.

Endothermic. Pertaining to a reaction which occurs with the absorption of heat.

Exothermic. Pertaining to a reaction which occurs with the evolution of heat.

Kinetic theory. The theory that minute particles of substances are in motion.

Molecule. The smallest portion of an element or a compound that can exist free and still exhibit all of the properties of the substance.

Monatomic. Consisting of one atom.

Precipitate. A substance, usually a solid, which separates from a solution as a result of some physical or chemical change.

derived his fundamental knowledge almost entirely from his own thinking. The modern scientific method is to call on nature to reveal fundamental truths. Thus the ideas the early philosophers had about matter have very little resemblance to our present knowledge of the nature of matter.

The English chemist John Dalton (1766–1844) spoke of ultimate particles of matter and referred to them as *atoms*. He sometimes tried to distinguish between elementary and complex substances by using the term *complex atom*. Count Amadeo Avogadro (1776–1856), an Italian chemist and physicist, used the term *molecules* for the ultimate particles.

Today we recognize that pure substances exist either as compounds or elements. We have seen that compounds consist of different elements which are chemically combined. In Chapter 2 we defined the smallest particle of an element that can enter into combination with other elements as an atom. Chemical elements are made up of such minute particles. *All atoms of a particular element are essentially alike but are different from those of all other elements.*

Each part of a compound is similar in composition to every other part. A particular compound is always composed of the same elements in the same proportion by weight (Law of Definite Proportions). The simplest kind of compound is made up of particles consisting of no less than two atoms, one from each of two elements. The smallest part of a compound is called a *molecule* and consists of a group of atoms chemically joined together. In the modern sense, *the **molecule** is the smallest particle of any substance which has the properties of that substance.* Thus we see that the molecule denotes the particles of gases and the corresponding particles of liquids and solids.

2. How large are molecules? Molecules vary greatly in size. It has been estimated that if a drop of water could be magnified until it became as large as the earth, its molecules would be about one meter in diameter. The simple molecules of gases, consisting of one, two, or three atoms, have diameters of approximately 3×10^{-8} cm. Some virus protein molecules, consisting of approximately 750,000 atoms and having diameters of about 2.30×10^{-6} cm have been photographed with an electron microscope. Today we use a more suit-

Fig. 3–1. The electron microscope is capable of magnifications to 200,000 diameters.

able scale for atoms and molecules, the *Angström scale,* this range of molecular diameters is from 3 Å to 230 Å. (1 Å = 1 × 10⁻⁸ cm).

The forces that hold the atoms of different elements together to form molecules of compounds may also cause atoms of a single element to combine. Free and isolated atoms are rarely found in nature. Instead, atoms of most elements are combined with one another at ordinary temperatures to form larger structural particles. Notable exceptions are the inert elements: helium, argon, neon, krypton, xenon (*zee*-non), and radon. The atoms of these rare gases do not combine with each other to form larger particles. There is no distinction, therefore, between the atoms and molecules of these gases. We may say that a molecule of helium consists of a single atom.

The molecules of the ordinary gaseous elements, oxygen, nitrogen, hydrogen, fluorine, and chlorine are made up of two atoms. The molecules of compounds may range from a minimum of two atoms to extremely large numbers of atoms.

3. Are all substances composed of molecules? The atoms which make up molecules are bound by strong forces. These forces are electrical in nature and will be discussed in Chapter 6. The attracting forces between molecules are much weaker. In gases they are practically negligible because gas molecules are relatively far apart from one another. Gas molecules are therefore essentially independent particles and fill whatever space is available to them. But what of the structure of liquids and solids?

Many liquids are known to have molecular structures similar to that of their gaseous state. Iodine vapor has molecules composed of two atoms. Liquid iodine likewise has **diatomic** (two-atomed) **molecules.** They are much closer together, however, than those in gaseous iodine. Such liquid molecules are subject to attracting forces strong enough to form a free surface (definite volume) but too weak to hold them in any fixed order (no definite shape).

Solids may be separated into two general groups: *1. crystalline solids;* and *2. amorphous solids.* **Crystalline solids** have a regular arrangement of particles. **Amorphous solids** are those which have a completely random particle arrangement and are, in a literal sense, *shapeless.* Many solids which scientists once thought were amorphous have been found to have a minute crystalline structure.

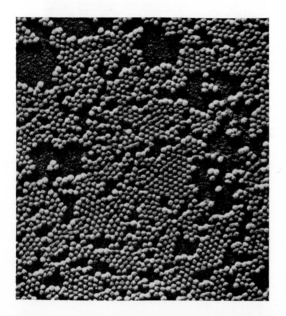

Fig. 3–2. Very large molecules, like these polio virus molecules, can be seen with the aid of the electron microscope.

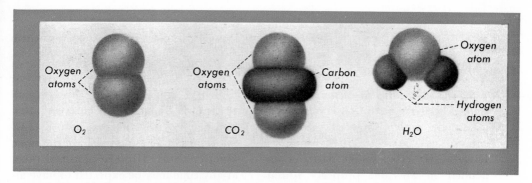

Fig. 3–3. The oxygen molecule is diatomic. The carbon dioxide molecule is composed of one carbon atom and two oxygen atoms. The two hydrogen atoms of the water molecule are on the same side of the oxygen atom, the angle H–O–H being 105°.

Some solids are made up of simple molecules. Solid iodine consists of diatomic molecules arranged in systematic order forming *molecular crystals*. Other solids show no molecular structure at all. Sodium chloride crystals are of this sort. Molecules of sodium chloride do not exist as such except at very high temperatures.

4. The formulas of compounds. We have learned that a chemical symbol stands for one atom of a particular element. We can therefore represent the *monatomic* (single-atomed) *molecules* of the inert elements fully by using just their symbols. If a molecule is more complex, we can show the number of atoms in the molecule by means of a numerical subscript following the symbol. Thus we represent diatomic molecules of the ordinary elementary gases by H_2, O_2, N_2, F_2, and Cl_2. *It is customary to represent the elements other than those known to have diatomic molecules as monatomic.*

Chemists use chemical symbols and numerical subscripts in a shorthand method of representing the composition of compounds. Such shorthand notations are called *formulas.* The formula for water is H_2O. It represents *one molecule* of water and indicates that the water molecule consists of *two*

atoms of hydrogen and *one atom* of oxygen. The formula of water is read *H-two-O.* The expression 2 H_2O represents *two molecules* of water, each containing two atoms of hydrogen and one atom of oxygen. Similarly, 5 H_2O signifies *five molecules* of water. When no other coefficient is used ahead of a formula, 1 as a coefficient is understood.

If the molecular structure of a substance has been determined experimentally, the formula may truly represent a molecule of that substance. Thus hydrogen peroxide has the formula H_2O_2 rather than HO since it is known that the molecule contains two atoms of hydrogen and two atoms of oxygen. Whenever a formula is written with subscripts not in the simplest whole number ratio we may safely assume that it is a *molecular formula.*

Many compounds do not have simple molecular structures or, as in the case of sodium chloride, do not contain molecules at all. Formulas for such substances cannot stand for molecules. They do, however, express the constituent elements and the relative number of atoms of each. Such formulas are usually expressed in the simplest whole number ratio and are known as *empirical formulas.* The formula for sodium chloride, $NaCl$, is empirical.

2. THE KINETIC THEORY

5. The molecules of gases have motion. There are many observations we may make which show us that molecules of gases are constantly in motion. If we observe tiny smoke particles suspended in air and properly illuminated under a microscope, we see them buffeted about in a kind of vibratory fashion. This continuous motion is produced by the numerous collisions with moving gas molecules.

If we remove the stopper from a container of ammonia, its irritating properties soon become evident throughout the room. When the chemistry class makes the foul-odored hydrogen sulfide gas in the laboratory, objections from other students and teachers come from all parts of the building. The gases are said to *diffuse* (or scatter) throughout the laboratory or throughout the building.

6. Moving molecules have kinetic energy. A gas under normal conditions will occupy roughly 1000 times the volume of its liquid or solid state. The molecules of a gas are, therefore, widely separated. Each moving molecule will continue in a given direction until it collides either with another molecule or with the wall of the container. It has been estimated that some molecules move in random directions at speeds of the order of 5×10^5 mm/sec and travel average distances of 1×10^{-4} mm between collisions with other molecules or the walls of the container. We may expect such molecules to experience 5×10^9, or 5 billion collisions per second. The collisions with the vessel walls are responsible for the *pressure* of gases.

As you already know, objects in motion have kinetic energy. This is equally true of molecules of gases or automobiles moving along a highway. All molecules of a gas do not have the same kinetic energy. However, most of them at any time may be expected to have an energy value near the average kinetic energy of all the molecules. *An increase in the temperature increases the rate at which the molecules move.* Thus the temperature of a gas provides an indication of the average kinetic energy of the molecules.

A container of gas may stand indefinitely under constant conditions without change of temperature or pressure. This would indicate that the gas molecules do not give up any portion of their kinetic energy when they collide. Instead, they rebound, taking all their energy with them. Molecules of gases are said to be *perfectly elastic* and their motions are entirely random.

7. The diffusion of gases. Recognizing these characteristics of gas molecules, let us now consider the way in which gases diffuse. If the air is pumped out of a container and a gas is then allowed to enter it, we observe that the container is instantly filled with the gas. We would expect this to occur because of the great speed of the molecules and the lack of collisions.

Molecules of a gas escaping into a room already occupied by other gases will, of course, experience frequent collisions, perhaps as many as 5 billion per second. The random directions of motion resulting will delay the scattering of the molecules of the new gas throughout the other gases. Eventually, we may expect that the random motion of all of the gas molecules will result

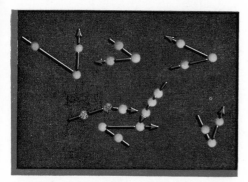

Fig. 3-4. This enlarged diagram shows the movement of particles of paint as they are bombarded by invisible molecules of the liquid in which they are suspended.

in their uniform distribution throughout the room. *This process of spreading out spontaneously to fill a space uniformly is characteristic of all gases and is known as* **diffusion.** Gaseous diffusion is slowed down, but not prevented, by the presence of other gases.

★ **8. All gases do not diffuse at the same rate.** All gases existing at the same temperature have the same average kinetic energy. Should we then expect their molecules to have the same average velocities? The kinetic energy of a particle is dependent on both its mass and velocity. Thus molecules of different gases having the same kinetic energy will move at different rates if their masses are different. The lighter molecules will move more rapidly, the heavier molecules more slowly. The rates of diffusion of such gases will be in proportion to their molecular velocities. Indeed, hydrogen, which is the least dense of all gases, diffuses more rapidly than other gases under similar conditions. At room temperature the velocity of hydrogen molecules is about one mile per second. This is four times the velocity of oxygen molecules under similar conditions.

★ **9. Motion in liquids and solids.** There is abundant evidence that the atoms and molecules of liquids and solids are in motion. Under a microscope you can see very finely divided particles, suspended in water or other liquids, move about in a helter-skelter manner. The motion is increased by using lighter or smaller particles and by higher temperatures. This is in agreement with the **Kinetic Theory** and we may conclude that the observed random motion is caused by collisions with molecules of the liquid.

Water and other liquids, such as perfume, *evaporate* because molecules continually escape from the surface. The odors of solids like camphor and naphthalene (moth balls) give evidence of the motion of molecules of these substances. The vapor molecules of solids or liquids in closed containers exert pressure as do all confined gases. This *vapor pressure* reaches some maximum value depending on the temperature of the substance. We may conclude that an *equilibrium* is attained between molecules evaporating from the surface and vapor molecules re-entering the surface. All solid and liquid substances have characteristic *equilibrium vapor pressures* which increase with temperature.

Fig. 3-5. Water molecules escape at the surface of the liquid. Some rebound into the surface after colliding with molecules of gases in the air or with water vapor molecules.

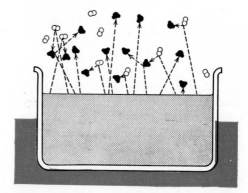

The molecules of the vapors of liquids and solids have properties similar to those which we have attributed to gases. As stated previously, there is no distinction between a vapor and a gas other than the temperatures at which they normally exist. On cooling, gases may become liquids, and with further cooling, may become solids.

The molecules of gases, being relatively far apart and having high kinetic energy, are practically independent of each other. The particles of liquids and solids are close together and the forces between them are therefore much stronger. In liquids the kinetic energy of the molecules is still sufficient to par-

tially overcome these forces. Motion is random, but greatly restricted. The particles of solids are still further restricted in their motion. The forces are sufficient to cause the unit particles to occupy fixed positions in the crystal structure. Random motion occurs only about these fixed positions. In contrast to gases, liquids and solids form free surfaces, and solids have rigid structures.

X-ray photographs of crystals become less distinct as the crystal temperature is increased. The fixed positions of the particles within the crystal structure become less certain as their kinetic energy rises.

3. CHANGES IN MATTER

10. What are physical changes? Ice melts, water boils, liquids freeze, glass breaks, and sugar dissolves in water. We may heat a piece of platinum wire until it glows. In all these cases matter undergoes some change. Its form may be different or it may have experienced a change of state or energy level. However, in no case has the matter lost its identity. Sometimes by a reversal of the action which caused the change, the material will be restored to its original form and the same identifying properties will again be readily recognized.

These are examples of *physical changes*. In such changes only alterations in physical properties are apparent; the composition of the material is not changed. *Physical changes are those in which the identifying properties of substances remain unchanged.*

Modern ideas concerning solutions suggest that some types of physical changes may involve intermediate processes which are not physical in nature. These ideas will be treated in Chap-

ter 19, Solution and Crystallization.

11. What are chemical changes? You know that wood burns, iron rusts, silver tarnishes, milk sours, plants decay, and acids react with metals. In each of these actions the identifying properties of the original substance are altered. New substances with different properties are recognized. Changes occur which alter the composition of matter. *Chemical changes are those in which new substances with new properties are formed.*

Chemical action may involve the combining of atoms of elementary substances to form compounds. Complex substances may be broken down into simpler compounds or into the elements which compose them. Compounds may react with other compounds or elements to form new and different compounds. *The science of chemistry is concerned specifically with the chemical changes of substances and with methods of controlling the speed and direction of these changes.*

12. Chemical changes involve energy. Chemical changes are always accompanied by energy changes. Substances possess energy because of their composition and structure. This is a kind of potential energy which chemists generally refer to as *chemical energy*. The products of chemical changes are different in composition and structure from the original substances and thus will have larger or smaller amounts of chemical energy. If the amount is smaller, energy will be *liberated* during the change, usually in the form of *heat* and sometimes *light* or *electricity*. If the amount of chemical energy is larger, energy will be *absorbed* during the change.

Calcium carbide is produced in the intense heat of the electric furnace. Carbon disulfide is formed when hot sulfur vapor is passed over white-hot carbon in an electric furnace. Heat energy is absorbed all the time that such chemical actions are taking place. *Any chemical change which absorbs heat energy as it progresses is said to be endothermic.*

Some chemical changes are of importance because of their products. Others are carried out because of the energy which is released. In the burning of fuels, large amounts of heat energy are released rapidly. Many similar changes occur in nature, but take place so slowly that the evolution of heat is not noticed. *Any chemical change which liberates heat energy as it proceeds is said to be exothermic.* The majority of chemical changes which occur in nature are exothermic.

In the burning of fuels, light energy usually accompanies the release of heat. A photoflash lamp is designed to release a maximum amount of energy as light. The final proof of a chemical change rests with the analysis of the products. However, the evolution of heat and light offers evidence that chemical action is taking place.

The explosion of dynamite or gunpowder produces *mechanical energy*. Similarly, the explosion of gasoline vapor mixed with air in the cylinder of an automobile engine is an example of chemical action.

Fig. 3–6. X-ray diffraction photograph of ice. Chemists use X-ray diffraction in their study of crystal structure.

In the flashlight cell the zinc cylinder is acted on chemically when the cell is in use. *Electrical energy* is produced by this action and indicates that the chemical change is taking place.

The *evolution of a gas* is often used as evidence that chemical action is taking place. We must be careful, however, to avoid mistaking the boiling of a liquid or the escaping of a dissolved gas from solution for chemical action. In many cases an insoluble solid is formed by adding one solution to another. The *formation of an insoluble solid, called a* **precipitate**, shows that a chemical change is taking place.

13. How are chemical changes brought about? Chemists use several agents to bring about chemical changes or to control those which have already started. Some type of energy is often used.

1. Heat energy. We kindle a match by rubbing it over a rough surface to warm it by friction. By holding the lighted match to a piece of paper we may start the paper burning. The heat from the burning match is used to start this chemical change. It is, however, an exothermic action and we do not need to continue furnishing heat in order to keep the paper burning. Many chemical actions which occur in the preparation of foods are endothermic. Heat is supplied to keep these reactions going. As a rule, increasing the temperature hastens the speed of chemical changes. *Each increase in temperature of 10 C° approximately doubles the speed of chemical action.*

2. Light energy. The process of photosynthesis by which green plants manufacture simple sugar from carbon dioxide and water takes place *only* in sunlight. When we open the shutter of a camera for only a fraction of a second, light falls on the sensitive film. This starts a chemical change in the film which enables us to develop a picture.

3. Electrical energy. If we pass an electric current through water which

Fig. 3–7. The energy set free by chemical reactions is utilized to propel rockets to great heights.

contains a little acid, the water will be decomposed by the electric current into hydrogen and oxygen. We use this method of bringing about a chemical change when we charge a storage battery. Electricity is also used commercially to produce changes, as in the electric furnace. Electrical energy is used in the plating of one metal on another, in the extraction of aluminum and other metals from their ores, and in the purifying of some metals.

4. Solution in water. Baking powder is a mixture of two or more compounds. No chemical action occurs as long as the powder is kept *dry*. But when we add baking powder to water, chemical action begins immediately and a gas bubbles off. Many chemicals which do not react in the *dry* state begin to react as soon as they are dissolved in water.

5. Catalysis (kuh-*tal*-uh-sis). Some chemical changes may be brought about by *catalysts* (*kat*-uh-lists). These are specific agents which enable changes to occur that would otherwise be difficult or impractical to carry out. You will soon be preparing oxygen in the laboratory by heating a mixture of potassium chlorate and manganese dioxide. Without the manganese dioxide the experiment would have to be carried out at a higher temperature. Also, the gas would be produced more slowly. The manganese dioxide aids the action by its presence. It may be recovered in its original form at the conclusion of the experiment. We can define *a **catalyst** as an agent which affects a chemical action without itself being permanently altered.* Many chemical processes, such as the production of vegetable shortening, the manufacture of synthetic rubber, and the preparation of high-octane gasoline, depend on catalysis for their successful operation.

14. What are nuclear changes? New substances are produced during a chemical change by the rearrangement of the atoms of the original substances. In a *nuclear change* new substances with new properties are also produced. *However, in a **nuclear change,** the new substances are formed by changes in the identity of the atoms themselves.*

In nature some nuclear changes take place spontaneously. Radium atoms disintegrate in successive stages, finally becoming lead. Scientists are able to bring about many important nuclear changes. The synthetic elements named in Chapter 2 are products of nuclear changes. Nuclear reactions will be discussed at greater length in Unit 13.

Summary

Molecules are the smallest particles of substances which normally exist in nature. Gases consist of simple molecules. Some liquids and solids are known to be made up of simple molecules. Some crystalline solids do not have molecular structure. Molecules of elements are made up of one or more like atoms. Molecules of compounds are made up of two or more unlike atoms.

A formula is used by chemists to represent the composition of a substance. A molecular formula shows what atoms are present in each molecule, and the number of each. An empirical formula expresses the constituent elements in the compound and the relative number of atoms of each.

The particles of matter have motion and thus possess kinetic energy. Many indirect observations of molecular motion led to the formulation of the Kinetic Theory of Matter. Temperature is an indication of the average kinetic energy of the particles of matter. The molecules of gases are relatively far apart and are practically independent of each other. Particles of liquids are much more restricted but do experience random motion. Particles of solids are still more restricted in their motion and vibrate about fixed positions.

Changes in matter are of three kinds: 1. physical; 2. chemical; and 3. nuclear. Physical changes do not alter the composition of matter. Chemical changes result in the formation of new substances with new properties. In nuclear changes new substances result from changes in the identity of atoms. If heat energy is released during a chemical change it is said to be exothermic. If heat energy is absorbed it is endothermic. The energy involved in chemical changes is usually in the form of heat, light, or electricity.

Heat, light, electricity, solution in water, and catalysts are agents which aid in producing and controlling chemical changes.

Test yourself on these terms

amorphous solid	empirical formula	molecule
Ångström scale	endothermic	monatomic molecule
catalyst	evaporation	nuclear change
chemical change	exothermic	physical change
crystalline solid	formula	precipitate
diatomic molecule	kinetic theory	symbol
diffusion	molecular formula	vapor pressure

Questions

Group A

1. Distinguish between an atom and a molecule.
2. What is the difference between a symbol and a formula?
3. (a) What gaseous elements have diatomic molecules? (b) How is each represented?
4. (a) What gaseous elements have monatomic molecules? (b) How is each represented?
5. How many atoms of each element are there in the following formulas: sugar, $C_{12}H_{22}O_{11}$; sand, SiO_2; salt, $NaCl$; hydrogen peroxide, H_2O_2; soap, $C_{17}H_{35}COONa$?
6. What is the difference between a physical change and a chemical change?
7. What is the meaning of (a) molecular formula? (b) empirical formula?
8. How can a chemist usually increase the speed of a chemical change?
9. What information is given by the following: HCl, 2 H_2SO_4, 4 CCl_4, CO, Co, and 3 H_2O?

Group B

★ 10. Explain the following: (a) solids have definite shape and definite volume; (b) liquids have definite volume but no definite shape; (c) gases have neither definite volume nor definite shape.

11. (a) How may we account for the pressure of a gas in a closed vessel? (b) Why does this pressure remain constant indefinitely under constant conditions?

12. Which of the following changes are physical and which are chemical? (a) burning coal; (b) tarnishing silver; (c) magnetizing steel; (d) exploding gunpowder; (e) boiling water; (f) melting shortening.

13. Which of the chemical changes listed in Question 12 are also exothermic?

★ 14. Ammonia (density 0.77 g/l) and chlorine (density 3.21 g/l) have distinct but different odors. If equal quantities of the two gases are released in the laboratory under exactly similar conditions, which gas will first be detected by students on the far side of the laboratory? Explain.

15. Show by example how each of the following produces chemical changes: (a) heat energy; (b) light energy; (c) electrical energy.

16. What evidence usually indicates chemical action?

Some things for you to do

1. Blow up a toy balloon until it is about half its maximum size. Hold it over a hot steam radiator or an electric hot plate. Explain the increase in size.

2. Look up the melting points of several substances which are known to be molecular as solids, and of several substances which are known to have no simple molecular structure as solids. What can you infer concerning the structure of the solid state of substances which exist as liquids or gases at ordinary temperatures?

3. Drop a small crystal of potassium permanganate into a tall cylinder full of water. Set the cylinder aside where it will not be disturbed. Examine daily for a week. Explain.

4. Pour some perfume into an evaporating dish placed at the rear of your classroom. How much time elapses before its odor can be detected in the front of the room? A perfume molecule may travel approximately 100 feet per second. How do you explain the delay?

Check your progress in chemistry

1. Name several substances that exist in all three states of matter.

2. Make a list of common physical properties and also a list of common chemical properties.

3. What do you understand by the term *law* in science?

4. Give two uses of the term *theory* which are common in chemistry.

5. Give some examples of kinetic and potential energy.

6. Why is it so easy to change from one unit to another in the metric system?

7. What prefixes are commonly used for units in the metric system and what does each represent?

8. What metric unit would you use to represent each of the following: (*a*) the area of the cover of this book; (*b*) a family's daily milk supply; (*c*) your own weight; (*d*) the length of the eye of a darning needle; (*e*) the speed of a moving automobile?

9. What disadvantage would we encounter in the everyday use of the metric system in place of our English system of weights and measures?

10. Where is the metric system commonly used?

11. How many chemical elements are there?

12. Name the 10 most abundant elements in the earth's crust.

13. What two things does a chemical symbol represent?

14. If two or more elements have symbols beginning with the same letter, how do we distinguish them?

15. If a symbol has two letters, (*a*) what is always true of the first letter? (*b*) what is always true of the second letter?

16. State the Law of Definite Proportions.

17. What is the significance of a molecule of sugar?

18. How do you account for the gradual disappearance of water from a saucer?

19. The formula for sulfuric acid is H_2SO_4. What information does it convey?

20. Give (*a*) two examples of gases which have monatomic molecules, (*b*) three examples of gases which have diatomic molecules.

21. Give examples of (*a*) familiar physical changes. (*b*) chemical changes.

22. Give three ways in which energy may bring about a chemical change.

23. Define (*a*) an exothermic reaction. (*b*) an endothermic reaction.

24. (*a*) What is a precipitate? (*b*) How are precipitates commonly produced?

25. What is the difference between a chemical change and a nuclear change?

Challenging your knowledge

1. Give one reason why the metric system is not established by law for general use in this country.

2. (*a*) How many of the elements are metals? (*b*) How many are nonmetals? (Consult the Periodic Table in Chapter 5.)

3. What do you think is the reason why iron and sulfur unite in definite proportions to form iron sulfide?

4. How do you decide whether a certain change is physical or chemical?

5. Carbon dioxide has simple molecular structure in all three states. Make three drawings representing your idea of solid carbon dioxide (Dry Ice), liquid carbon dioxide, and gaseous carbon dioxide.

THE ORGANIZATION OF CHEMISTRY

The energy of the explosion pictured above was produced by the splitting of atoms. You have already learned that atoms are the smallest parts of the chemical elements. In this unit you will learn much more about the structure of atoms, how this structure determines the properties of atoms, and how atoms combine.

Because of his knowledge of the structure and behavior of atoms, the scientist has been able to produce atomic bombs and hydrogen bombs with their tremendous capacity for destruction. But he has also been able to develop many wonderful products which make your life healthier, happier, and safer.

Three chapters are included in this unit: *Atomic Theory and Atomic Structure, The Periodic Law,* and *Molecules and Valence.* Each is fundamental to your understanding of the part atoms play in chemical processes.

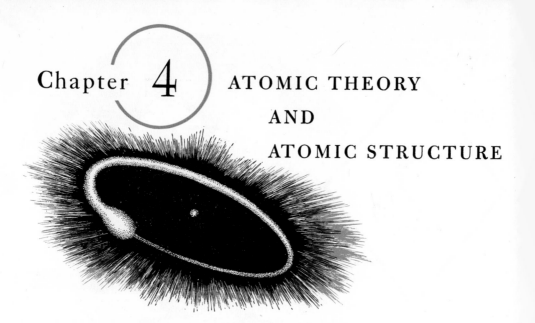

Chapter 4 ATOMIC THEORY AND ATOMIC STRUCTURE

1. Dalton proposed the atomic theory. We have already learned about the ancient idea, first expressed by such Greek philosophers as Democritus, that matter is composed of very small ultimate particles. This concept of ultimate particles, or atoms of matter, was of little value to the development of science until the beginning of the nineteenth century. However, between 1803 and 1808 in England, John Dalton performed many chemical experiments, particularly with gases. He greatly extended the usefulness of man's ideas about atoms. Dalton was the first to realize that *the nature and properties of atoms could be used to explain: 1. the definite composition of all substances; and 2. the way and the proportions in which substances react with one another.* These are the fundamental ideas of Dalton's *atomic the-*

VOCABULARY

Atomic mass. The mass of an atom as expressed in atomic mass units of 1.660×10^{-24} g.

Atomic number. The number of protons in the nucleus of an atom.

Atomic weight. The average relative weight of the atoms of the naturally-occurring mixture of isotopes of an element based on the weight of the atoms of the naturally-occurring mixture of oxygen isotopes as 16.0000.

Electron. A negatively-charged particle found in an atom. It has $\frac{1}{1837}$ of the mass of a hydrogen atom.

Isotope. One of two or more forms of atoms with the same atomic number but with different atomic weights.

Neutron. A neutral particle found in the nucleus of an atom. It has about the same mass as a proton.

Nucleus. The positively-charged, dense central part of an atom.

Proton. A positively-charged particle found in the nucleus of an atom. It has $\frac{1836}{1837}$ of the mass of a hydrogen atom.

Shell. A region about the nucleus of an atom in which electrons move.

ory. Since Dalton's day many discoveries have been made which give us a more detailed picture of how the atomic theory explains the chemical phenomena in the world about us. However, Dalton's two basic ideas remain unchanged.

2. The modern atomic theory. The atomic theory as we understand it today consists of several statements concerning the nature of matter. While no one has ever actually observed atoms, the chemical and physical properties of matter lead scientists to believe that the following statements are true.

1. All matter is made up of very small particles called *atoms.*

2. There are as many *chemically different* kinds of atoms as there are kinds of elements.

3. The atoms of a *given element* have a *definite average mass.*

4. The atoms of *different elements* have *different average masses.*

5. Atoms are not subdivided in *chemical reactions.*

3. The structure of the atom. For almost three quarters of a century scientists have been accumulating evidence about the structure of atoms. Some of this evidence has come from the study of radioactive elements like radium and uranium. The cyclotron, the X-ray tube, and other modern electrical devices for studying the structure of atoms have given additional information. At the present time scientists recognize that atoms are not simple indivisible particles. Instead, they are known to be composed of several different kinds of still smaller particles arranged in a rather complex way.

An atom consists of two main parts. *The positively charged central part is called the* **nucleus.** It is very small and

very dense. Its diameter is about 10^{-13} cm, or 10^{-5} Å. This is about one one-hundred-thousandth of the diameter of the atom itself, since atoms range from 1 Å to 5 Å in diameter. Negatively charged particles, called *electrons*, move about the nucleus in more or less definite regions called **shells** or **energy levels.** About 1913 the Danish scientist Niels Bohr (1885–) pictured the movement of electrons about the nucleus of an atom as similar to the rotation of the planets around the sun. However, we now know that the paths of the electrons are not so definite as the orbits of the planets. Rather, the electrons move about the nucleus of an atom much as a swarm of bees moves about in the area near its hive. Sometimes the electrons are near the nucleus, sometimes they are farther away. By this seemingly haphazard motion the electrons effectively occupy the relatively vast empty space around the nucleus. These electrons form an electronic field about the nucleus which gives the atom its volume and excludes other atoms. Each atom is electrically

Fig. 4–1. John Dalton, an English scientist, developed the first useful atomic theory.

neutral, since the total positive charge of the nucleus is equalled by the total negative charge of the electrons.

4. What are electrons? *Electrons are negatively charged particles with a mass of 9.107 × 10⁻²⁸ g.* This is $\frac{1}{1837}$ of the mass of an atom of hydrogen—the atom of lowest mass. Each electron has one unit of negative electric charge. Electrons were discovered as a result of investigations of the flow of electricity through an evacuated glass tube. These investigations were made by an English scientist, J. J. Thomson (1856–1940), in 1897.

The electron is a very small particle. While its size is not precisely known, its diameter is believed to be about 2×10^{-12} cm or 2×10^{-4} Å. Regardless of the atom of which an electron is a part, all electrons are identical.

5. The nucleus of the atom. The nuclei of atoms of different elements are different. They always have different amounts of positive charge, and have different masses, although the difference in mass between atoms of two different elements is sometimes very slight. A nucleus is made up of two kinds of particles, *protons* and *neutrons*.

Protons are positively charged particles with a mass of 1.672 × 10⁻²⁴ g, which is $\frac{1836}{1837}$ of the mass of an atom of hydrogen. Protons account for most of the mass of a hydrogen atom. This is because the hydrogen atom has a nucleus consisting of a single proton which has a single electron revolving about it. While a proton has much more mass than an electron, it is believed to be somewhat smaller. A proton has one unit of positive electric charge.

Protons were discovered in 1919 by Ernest Rutherford (1871–1937) of Cambridge University, England. He bombarded nitrogen gas with particles given off by the radioactive element, radium. In a particular atom there are an equal number of protons and electrons. Since these particles have equal though opposite electrical charges, each atom is electrically neutral.

Neutrons are neutral particles with a mass of 1.675 × 10⁻²⁴ g, which is about the same mass as a proton. They have no electrical charge. The English scientist, James C. Chadwick (1891–   ), discovered neutrons in 1932.

6. The hydrogen atom is the simplest atom. An atom of hydrogen consists of a nucleus composed of one proton, and one electron moving about it. This electron moves about the nucleus at a most probable distance roughly corresponding to the innermost shell or lowest energy level which an electron can have. This shell or energy level is called the *K shell*. The sizes and distances between the particles of a

Fig. 4–2. A hydrogen atom has a nucleus consisting of one proton. One electron moves about this nucleus in the K shell.

PARTICLES IN AN ATOM

NAME	MASS		CHARGE
ELECTRON	9.107×10^{-28} g	0 a.m.u.	-1
PROTON	1.672×10^{-24} g	1 a.m.u.	$+1$
NEUTRON	1.675×10^{-24} g	1 a.m.u.	0

hydrogen atom may be better understood if we picture the nucleus (a proton) as being the size of a pinhead, 0.1 inch in diameter. Comparatively speaking, the electron, which is somewhat larger, would revolve about the nucleus at an average distance of about 40 feet away. This electron does not follow any definite fixed path about the nucleus. Instead, it moves rapidly about the nucleus in an attempt to completely occupy the surrounding space.

7. The mass of the atom. Chemists find it convenient to use an *atomic mass unit* (*a.m.u.*) of 1.660×10^{-24} g. This is approximately the mass of a proton or a neutron. Accordingly, the mass of a proton or neutron is said to be about 1 atomic mass unit (1 a.m.u.). Because the mass of an electron is so small when compared with that of either a proton or a neutron, its mass is usually considered to be zero atomic mass unit. If we know the structure of an atom, it is easy to determine its approximate atomic mass. The approximate mass of the atom is determined by

adding the number of protons and neutrons together. In the hydrogen atom, for example, the nucleus consists of one proton. This has a mass of approximately 1 a.m.u. There is one electron in the K shell, but its mass is negligible. Therefore, the approximate mass of the hydrogen atom may be expressed as 1 a.m.u.

The exact mass of an atom is rarely a whole number; it is slightly more than or slightly less than the whole number which indicates the number of protons and neutrons in the nucleus. However, for our present work, this difference is not significant, and we shall neglect it.

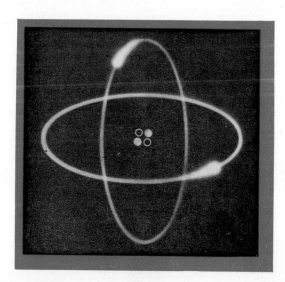

Fig. 4–3. A helium atom has a nucleus consisting of two protons and two neutrons. Two electrons move about this nucleus in the K shell.

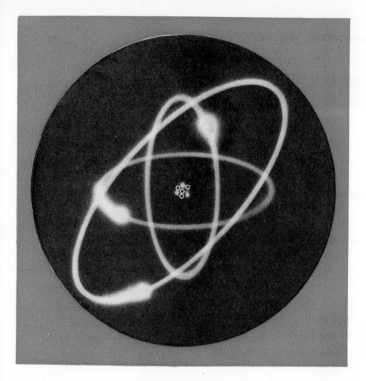

Fig. 4–4. A lithium atom has a nucleus consisting of three protons and four neutrons. Two electrons are in the K shell and one is in the L shell. This is the first element in the second series.

8. The atomic number of an atom.

The **atomic number** of an element is the number of protons in the nucleus of that element. This is one part of the structure of an atom which can be used to definitely identify an element. (The arrangement of electrons about the nucleus of a neutral atom also identifies an element.) We already know that the element hydrogen has one proton in its nucleus. Its atomic number, therefore, is 1. Any nucleus having the atomic number 1 contains one proton, and is a hydrogen nucleus. At the present time there are 102 different elements with atomic numbers ranging from 1 to 102. It is possible to arrange the elements according to the order of increasing atomic number. This simplifies the understanding of atomic structure. If the elements are arranged in this way, the nucleus of one atom differs from the nucleus of the atom preceding it by the addition of one proton.

9. The helium atom.

The second element in order of complexity is the helium atom. Its atomic number is 2. This means that the helium nucleus contains two protons. However, chemists have discovered that the mass of the helium atom is 4 a.m.u. You will probably ask, "How do scientists account for the difference?"

The nucleus of a helium atom contains, besides the protons, two neutrons. These each have unit atomic mass, and with the two protons make up the mass of 4 a.m.u. (Notice that the mass of the electrons is neglected.) *The number of neutrons in the nucleus of any atom may be determined by subtracting the atomic number from the atomic mass* (for helium, $4 - 2 = 2$). Revolving about the helium nucleus are two electrons, both in the K shell, or K energy level. These two electrons are all that can occupy this shell. Thus hydrogen and helium constitute a first series of elements. In this first series the K shell is being filled with two electrons.

10. The lithium atom. Lithium is the element with atomic number 3. Its atoms have a mass of 7 a.m.u. With an atomic number of 3 there will be three protons in its nucleus. These will provide 3 a.m.u. But the total mass of the atom is 7 a.m.u. Therefore, there must be four neutrons in the nucleus to make up the total atomic mass ($7 - 3 = 4$). Surrounding the nucleus there must be three electrons, since the number of protons and the number of electrons in any uncharged atom is the same. Two of these three electrons move in the K shell, or K energy level. The third electron moves about the nucleus at a greater distance and with higher energy than the other two. It moves in the next higher energy level, or next larger shell, which is called the **L shell,** or **L energy level.** The K shell

can contain only two electrons. When it reaches this maximum of two electrons, additional electrons must enter and move in other shells at greater distances from the nucleus.

11. Other atoms of the second series. The element with atomic number 4 is beryllium. It has a mass of 9 a.m.u. Its nucleus is composed of four protons and five neutrons. The four electrons are distributed with two in the K shell and two in the L shell. Next in order of atomic structure are the elements boron, carbon, nitrogen, oxygen, fluorine, and neon. Each successive element has one additional proton and may have one or two additional neutrons in its nucleus. Each has one additional electron in the L shell. The element neon has a total of eight electrons in the L shell. Since eight is the maximum number of electrons which the L shell can contain, this element completes the second series.

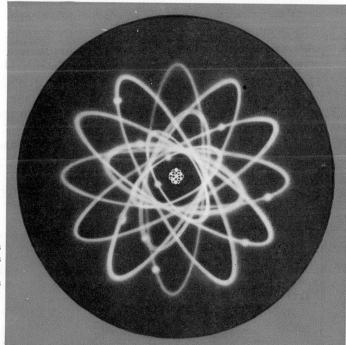

Fig. 4–5. A neon atom has a nucleus consisting of ten protons and ten neutrons. Two electrons are in the K shell and eight are in the L shell. This element completes the second series.

The table at the bottom of the page gives us information about the structure of the atoms in the second series.

Sometimes scientists illustrate the structure of atoms by using electron-dot symbols. Such symbols usually show only the electrons in the outermost shell of an atom. We may write such symbols for the atoms of the first and second series as follows:

$$H \cdot \qquad He \colon$$

$$Li \cdot \qquad Be \cdot \qquad \cdot \dot{B} \cdot \qquad \cdot \dot{C} \cdot$$

$$\cdot \dot{N} \colon \qquad \cdot \dot{O} \colon \qquad \colon \dot{F} \colon \qquad \colon \dot{Ne} \colon$$

Unlike the K shell which has only one general region, or orbit, in which the two electrons move, the L shell has four possible different electron orbits. These possible electron orbits are called *orbitals.* Each orbital may be unoccupied, may be occupied by one electron, or may be occupied by two electrons. An orbital is never occupied by more than two electrons. Two electrons which occupy the same orbital are called an *electron pair.* Neon has an outer shell of four electron pairs. This is an *octet of electrons.*

12. The atoms of the third series. The elements in the third series are sodium, magnesium, aluminum, silicon, phosphorus, sulfur, chlorine, and ar-gon. Each of these elements has a complete K shell of two electrons and a complete L shell of eight electrons. Electron-dot symbols show the entry of successive electrons into the first *four* orbitals of the next higher energy level, the *M shell* or *M energy level.* There is, however, a total of *nine* orbitals in the M shell. Five M-shell orbitals of still higher energy thus remain unoccupied in the elements of the third series. Notice that argon, which completes the series, has an octet of electrons.

$$Na \cdot \qquad Mg \cdot \qquad \cdot Al \cdot \qquad \cdot Si \cdot$$

$$\cdot \dot{P} \colon \qquad \cdot \dot{S} \colon \qquad \colon \dot{Cl} \colon \qquad \colon \dot{A} \colon$$

★ **13. The atoms of the fourth series.** The first two elements in the fourth series, potassium and calcium, have the same electron configuration or arrangement in the K, L, and M energy levels as argon does. Electron-dot symbols for these elements appear as follows:

$$K \cdot \qquad \dot{Ca} \cdot$$

They show the entry of electrons into two orbitals of the *N shell* or *N energy level.* In the next ten elements of this fourth series, successive electrons usually enter one of the five yet-unfilled orbitals of the M shell. These five orbitals of the M shell have higher energies than the lowest orbitals of the N

NAME	SYMBOL	ATOMIC NUMBER	ATOMIC MASS	NUMBER OF PRO-TONS	NUMBER OF NEU-TRONS	NUMBER OF K ELEC-TRONS	NUMBER OF L ELEC-TRONS
LITHIUM	Li	3	7	3	4	2	1
BERYLLIUM	Be	4	9	4	5	2	2
BORON	B	5	11	5	6	2	3
CARBON	C	6	12	6	6	2	4
NITROGEN	N	7	14	7	7	2	5
OXYGEN	O	8	16	8	8	2	6
FLUORINE	F	9	19	9	10	2	7
NEON	Ne	10	20	10	10	2	8

shell. The distribution of M- and N-shell electrons in the most stable form of these atoms is given in the table below. Irregularities are caused by the slightly lower energy of the form actually most stable as compared with the form predicted by theory.

With the element zinc, the M shell is completely filled, and there are two electrons in the N shell. The remaining six elements in the fourth series, gallium, germanium, arsenic, selenium, bromine, and krypton, have completely filled K, L, and M shells. The N-energy level electrons are shown in these electron-dot symbols:

$$\cdot \overset{\cdot}{Ga} \cdot \qquad \cdot \overset{\cdot}{Ge} \cdot \qquad \cdot \overset{\cdot}{As} :$$

$$\cdot \overset{\cdot \cdot}{\underset{\cdot}{Se}} : \qquad : \overset{\cdot \cdot}{\underset{\cdot}{Br}} : \qquad : \overset{\cdot \cdot}{\underset{\cdot}{Kr}} :$$

Krypton, the last member of the fourth series, has an octet of electrons in its N energy level. The N energy level, however, has a maximum of 16 orbitals, 12 of which are unoccupied in the elements of the fourth series.

★ **14. The atoms of the fifth series.** The fifth series of elements, like the fourth, consists of eighteen elements. The first two of these, rubidium and strontium, have inner shells like krypton and successive electrons in the lowest energy orbitals of the **O shell** or

O energy level. Their K, L, M, and N shell electron configuration is the same as that of krypton.

$$Rb \cdot \qquad \overset{\cdot}{Sr} \cdot$$

The next ten elements have successive electrons usually entering the next five orbitals of the N energy level, since this is the group of orbitals with the next higher energy. In atoms of the fifth series, there are still several unoccupied orbitals of the N energy level (see the table at the top of next page).

The element cadmium has completely filled K, L, and M shells, 18 electrons in the N shell, and 2 electrons in the O shell. The remaining six elements of the fifth series, indium, tin, antimony, tellurium, iodine, and xenon, have K, L, M, and N shells like cadmium, but successive electrons enter the orbitals of the O shell with the next higher energy.

$$\cdot \overset{\cdot}{In} \cdot \qquad \cdot \overset{\cdot}{Sn} \cdot \qquad \cdot \overset{\cdot}{Sb} :$$

$$\cdot \overset{\cdot \cdot}{\underset{\cdot}{Te}} : \qquad : \overset{\cdot \cdot}{\underset{\cdot}{I}} : \qquad : \overset{\cdot \cdot}{\underset{\cdot}{Xe}} :$$

Thus the entry of electrons into orbitals of two different shells proceeds in the fifth series of atoms in a manner similar to that of the fourth series. Xenon, the last member of the series,

NAME	SYMBOL	ATOMIC NUMBER	NUMBER OF M ELECTRONS	NUMBER OF N ELECTRONS
SCANDIUM	Sc	21	9	2
TITANIUM	Ti	22	10	2
VANADIUM	V	23	11	2
CHROMIUM	Cr	24	13	1
MANGANESE	Mn	25	13	2
IRON	Fe	26	14	2
COBALT	Co	27	15	2
NICKEL	Ni	28	16	2
COPPER	Cu	29	18	1
ZINC	Zn	30	18	2

NAME	SYMBOL	ATOMIC NUMBER	NUMBER OF N ELECTRONS	NUMBER OF O ELECTRONS
YTTRIUM	Y	39	9	2
ZIRCONIUM	Zr	40	10	2
NIOBIUM	Nb	41	12	1
MOLYBDENUM	Mo	42	13	1
TECHNETIUM	Tc	43	14	1
RUTHENIUM	Ru	44	15	1
RHODIUM	Rh	45	16	1
PALLADIUM	Pd	46	18	0
SILVER	Ag	47	18	1
CADMIUM	Cd	48	18	2

has an octet of electrons in its O energy level, and 9 of the 16 orbitals of the N energy level filled.

★ **15. The atoms of the sixth series.** The sixth series of atoms is much longer than the others. It consists of thirty-two elements. The first two, cesium and barium, have inner shells like xenon and successive electrons in the lowest orbitals of the P energy level.

Cs·   Ba·

In the next fourteen elements of the sixth series, successive electrons usually enter the highest energy group of seven orbitals of the N energy level (see the table at the bottom of this page). In the element ytterbium, the N shell has all of its 16 orbitals filled with 32 electrons.

The next ten elements of the sixth series have successive electrons entering the group of 5 orbitals in the O shell with next higher energy (see the table at top of next page).

The remaining six elements of this series, thallium, lead, bismuth, polonium, astatine, and radon, have 2 electrons in the K shell, 8 in the L shell, 18 in the M shell, 32 in the N shell, and 18 in the O shell. The *P-shell* or *P-energy level* electrons are shown in these electron-dot symbols:

NAME	SYMBOL	ATOMIC NUMBER	NUMBER OF N ELECTRONS	NUMBER OF O ELECTRONS	NUMBER OF P ELECTRONS
LANTHANUM	La	57	18	9	2
CERIUM	Ce	58	20	8	2
PRASEODYMIUM	Pr	59	21	8	2
NEODYMIUM	Nd	60	22	8	2
PROMETHIUM	Pm	61	23	8	2
SAMARIUM	Sm	62	24	8	2
EUROPIUM	Eu	63	25	8	2
GADOLINIUM	Gd	64	25	9	2
TERBIUM	Tb	65	27	8	2
DYSPROSIUM	Dy	66	28	8	2
HOLMIUM	Ho	67	29	8	2
ERBIUM	Er	68	30	8	2
THULIUM	Tm	69	31	8	2
YTTERBIUM	Yb	70	32	8	2

NAME	SYMBOL	ATOMIC NUMBER	NUMBER OF O ELECTRONS	NUMBER OF P ELECTRONS
LUTETIUM	Lu	71	9	2
HAFNIUM	Hf	72	10	2
TANTALUM	Ta	73	11	2
TUNGSTEN	W	74	12	2
RHENIUM	Re	75	13	2
OSMIUM	Os	76	14	2
IRIDIUM	Ir	77	17	0
PLATINUM	Pt	78	17	1
GOLD	Au	79	18	1
MERCURY	Hg	80	18	2

$\cdot \overset{\cdot}{Tl} \cdot$ $\cdot \overset{\cdot}{Pb} \cdot$ $\cdot \overset{\cdot \cdot}{Bi} :$

$\cdot \overset{\cdot \cdot}{Po} :$ $: \overset{\cdot \cdot}{At} :$ $: \overset{\cdot \cdot}{Rn} :$

Radon, the last member of the sixth series, has an octet of electrons in its P energy level, and nine orbitals of the O energy level filled.

★ **16. The elements of the seventh series.** The seventh series of elements is an incomplete series of which only 16 elements are known. The arrangement of their electrons in the O, P, and Q energy levels is believed to be as shown in the table below:

From this study of the configuration of electrons in the atoms of the chemical elements, it is apparent that the electron shells of large diameter are complex, consisting of three or four groups of orbitals of varying energy. Furthermore, the lowest energy orbitals of the large shells have a lower energy than the highest energy orbitals of the next smaller shell. This produces the overlapping of shells and determines the order of entry of successive electrons into these shells. A complete tabulation showing the electron con-

NAME	SYMBOL	ATOMIC NUMBER	NUMBER OF O ELECTRONS	NUMBER OF P ELECTRONS	NUMBER OF Q ELECTRONS
FRANCIUM	Fr	87	18	8	1
RADIUM	Ra	88	18	8	2
ACTINIUM	Ac	89	18	9	2
THORIUM	Th	90	18	10	2
PROTACTINIUM	Pa	91	20	9	2
URANIUM	U	92	21	9	2
NEPTUNIUM	Np	93	23	8	2
PLUTONIUM	Pu	94	24	8	2
AMERICIUM	Am	95	25	8	2
CURIUM	Cm	96	25	9	2
BERKELIUM	Bk	97	27	8	2
CALIFORNIUM	Cf	98	28	8	2
EINSTEINIUM	E	99	29	8	2
FERMIUM	Fm	100	30	8	2
MENDELEVIUM	Mv	101	31	8	2
NOBELIUM	No	102	32	8	2

figurations in the atoms of the elements is in Appendix, Table 4, Electronic Arrangement of the Elements.

17. What are isotopes? In our statement of the modern atomic theory we said that the atoms of a given element have a definite *average* mass. Why do we need that word "average"? Dalton assumed that all the atoms of a definite element were identical in all respects—in mass, in size, and in chemical properties. About 1916 two chemists, T. W. Richards (1868–1928) and Frederick Soddy (1877–   ), working independently, were investigating samples of the element lead from radioactive materials. They found that the atomic mass of these samples did not correspond to the atomic mass of lead taken from mines. They concluded, after careful analysis, that *not all atoms of a single element have the same mass.*

All elements exist in several forms having different masses. They may be of natural occurrence or may be artificially prepared. *These forms of the atoms of a single element do not differ in chemical properties, but do differ slightly in atomic mass.* Such forms of an element are called **isotopes.** Isotopes of a particular element have the same number of protons and electrons, but their nuclei differ in mass because they contain different numbers of neutrons.

There are three known isotopes of hydrogen. The commonest isotope is the hydrogen atom which consists of one proton and one electron. A second isotope is present in naturally occurring hydrogen to the extent of one part in 6900. It consists of one proton and one neutron in the nucleus, with one electron in the K shell. This isotope, you see, still has an *atomic number* of 1, because there is only one proton in its nucleus. But it has an *atomic mass* of 2, because the proton and the neutron each contribute one atomic mass unit toward the total atomic mass. This isotope of hydrogen is called *deuterium* (dyoo-*teer*-ee-um). The third isotope of hydogen is called *tritium.* This isotope has a nucleus containing one proton and two neutrons. The single electron is in the K shell. Tritium has an atomic number of 1, characteristic of hydrogen, but it has an atomic mass of 3.

18. Atomic weights are relative average weights. So far, we have been indicating the masses of individual atoms on an arbitrary scale of atomic mass units. We set up this scale using the mass of a proton or a neutron as one atomic mass unit. On this scale,

Fig. 4–6. The three isotopes, hydrogen, deuterium and tritium. Notice that the only structural difference between them is the number of neutrons in the nucleus.

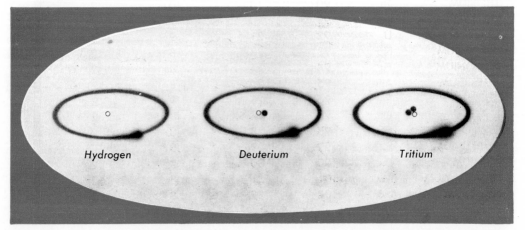

Hydrogen   Deuterium   Tritium

hydogen atoms have a mass of 1 a.m.u. Deuterium atoms have a mass of 2 a.m.u. One isotope of oxygen has a mass of 16 a.m.u. Other examples we might give are one isotope of sulfur, 32 a.m.u., and an isotope of zinc, 64 a.m.u. Note that these values are not the actual masses of these atoms, but they do give us the *relationship* between the masses of these atoms. They are *relative masses*. We observe from these relative masses that certain oxygen atoms have 16 times as much mass as hydrogen atoms. Some sulfur atoms have twice as much mass as oxygen atoms. Certain zinc atoms have 64 times as much mass as hydrogen atoms and 4 times as much mass as oxygen atoms.

The relationship between the weights of different elements which react with one another is of extreme importance to the chemist. It enables him to predict the quantities of materials which will be involved in chemical reactions. However, the actual weights of atoms are very small. The lightest oxygen isotope, for example, weighs 2.65×10^{-23} g. The actual weight of a hydrogen atom is 1.67×10^{-24} g, about one sixteenth as much. It would be difficult for a scientist to have to use such inconveniently small numbers in his calculations!

Long before chemists were able to calculate the actual weight of an atom, or even set up a scale of atomic mass units based on the structure of the atoms, they had worked out a system of *relative weights* for the atoms, based solely on the results of chemical reactions. This system is much simpler than using the actual weights. And for most of the chemist's work it is sufficient. Oxygen combines with most of the other elements, and was selected

as the standard on which the atomic weight scale was to be based. In order that hydrogen atoms, which have the lowest average weight, would not have an atomic weight less than 1, the *atomic weight* of oxygen was set at 16. Then the relative average weight of hydrogen atoms, which actually is about $\frac{1}{16}$ as much as that of oxygen atoms, will be 1. Sulfur atoms, whose average weight is twice as much as oxygen atoms, will have an atomic weight of 16×2, or 32. Atoms of bromine, which chemists found had an average weight 5 times as great as that of an oxygen atom, will have an atomic weight of 5×16, or 80. In the same way, the average weights of the atoms of the other elements were compared with the average weight of oxygen atoms, and relative weight values determined. A complete system of relative weights was thus established.

The chemist's atomic weight values agree approximately with the atomic mass scale. However, there are certain differences which must be pointed out. Natural oxygen, which the chemist defines as having an atomic weight of 16, is actually a mixture of isotopes of oxygen having masses of 16, 17, and 18. This throws the entire atomic weight scale off slightly from the atomic mass scale (the atomic masses must be multiplied by 1.00027 to give the corresponding atomic weights).

The existence of isotopes explains why so many atomic weights of the elements are nearly, but not exactly, whole numbers. The atomic weight of hydrogen is 1.0080. This weight is the average of one deuterium atom (atomic mass, 2.0143) to every 6900 hydrogen atoms (atomic mass, 1.0078). Similarly, there are two isotopes of chlorine.

One has an atomic mass of 35, the other an atomic mass of 37. They are mixed, however, in such proportion that the atomic weight is 35.457. In naturally occurring compounds the percentage of each isotope of a given element is nearly always the same. (Sulfur is an important exception.) Only through this fortunate circumstance is the average weight of the isotopic forms (which is the chemist's atomic weight) a constant quantity.

19. The determination of atomic weights. For many years chemists carried out very precise analyses of carefully prepared chemical compounds to determine the relative weights of elements which combined in order to establish the table of atomic weights. At the present time, the values given in the Table of Atomic Weights, on the inside of the back cover of this book, are about the most precise which chemical analysis can yield. As a result, very little of this type of research is now being conducted. A newer, more accurate method of determining and verifying atomic weights has been developed by nuclear research. This method consists of adding the weights of the individual particles which make up the isotopes of the atom whose weight is being calculated. This gives the mass of each isotope. Since the relative percentage of the various isotopes in the naturally occurring elements is known, an atomic weight may be calculated. A correction is made in the mass of the fundamental atomic particles because of their particular arrangement in each isotope. Such calculated atomic weights are in many cases more accurate than can be determined by the best chemical analysis. This method is now being used to verify the accuracy of chemical atomic weight determinations.

The Table of Atomic Weights on the inside of the back cover of this book includes the most recent accurate figures. They are still revised occasionally. You should not memorize them. The approximate atomic weights given on the inside of the front cover are sufficiently accurate for use in solving problems in high school chemistry. Your instructor may wish you to memorize some or all of these approximate values. For accurate chemical analysis, the exact atomic weights must always be used.

Summary

The modern atomic theory states that: _1._ all matter is made up of very small particles called atoms; _2._ there are as many chemically different kinds of atoms as there are kinds of elements; _3._ the atoms of a given element have a definite average mass; _4._ the atoms of different elements have different average masses; _5._ atoms are not subdivided in chemical reactions.

Atoms are composed of positively charged particles—protons; negatively charged particles—electrons; and neutral particles—neutrons. Protons and neutrons are found in the central nucleus of an atom. Electrons move about this nucleus in regions called shells or energy levels.

If the structure of an atom is known, its atomic mass may be approximated by adding the number of protons and neutrons together. The atomic number of an atom is the number of protons in its nucleus.

The atoms of all the elements may be classified according to the order in which the shells or energy levels become filled with electrons. Isotopes are forms of the same element, with the same chemical properties, but with atoms which differ slightly in mass.

The atomic weight of an element is the average relative weight of the atoms of the naturally occurring mixture of isotopes of the element based on the weight of the atoms of the naturally-occurring mixture of oxygen isotopes as 16.0000.

Test yourself on these terms

atom	electron	nucleus
atomic mass	electron configuration	octet
atomic mass unit	electron-dot symbol	orbital
atomic number	electron pair	proton
atomic theory	energy level	shell
atomic weight	isotope	tritium
deuterium	neutron	ultimate particles

Questions

Group A

1. What is the modern atomic theory?
2. (a) What are the main parts of an atom? (b) What particles are found in each part? (c) Describe each type of particle.
3. How does the size of the nucleus of an atom compare with the size of an atom?
4. What is a shell or energy level?
5. Describe the probable movement of electrons about the nucleus of an atom.
6. Describe a hydrogen atom.
7. (a) What is an atomic mass unit? (b) If you know the number and kinds of particles in an atom, how can you calculate its atomic mass?
8. What is the atomic number of an atom?
9. How do you calculate the number of neutrons in the nucleus of an atom?
10. An atomic nucleus contains 6 protons and 6 neutrons. About the nucleus move 6 electrons, 2 in the K shell and 4 in the L shell. (a) What is the atomic number of this atom? (b) What is its atomic mass? (c) What is the name of the atom?
11. How are shells or energy levels designated?
12. (a) What is an orbital? (b) How many electrons may occupy an orbital? (c) What is an electron pair?
13. What are isotopes?
14. What is the atomic weight of an element?
15. Why was oxygen selected as the standard on which the atomic weight scale is based?
16. From the Table of Atomic Weights given inside the back cover of this

book, find the atomic numbers and atomic weights of: (*a*) silver; (*b*) gold; (*c*) copper; (*d*) sulfur; (*e*) uranium.

Group B

17. What did Dalton believe could be explained by knowledge of the nature and properties of atoms?
18. If you arrange the elements in order of increasing atomic number, how do successive elements differ in: (*a*) number of protons? (*b*) number of electrons? (*c*) number of neutrons?
19. How many shells are partially or fully occupied in the mendelevium atom?
20. Describe the electron configurations of the elements in the second series.
21. Draw electron-dot symbols for the elements in the third series.
22. Why do the fourth and fifth series of elements contain 18 elements, rather than 8 as in the second and third series?
23. The element bromine exists as two isotopes, Br-79 and Br-81. Its atomic weight is 80. What must be the proportion of these two isotopes to give this average weight?
24. By means of diagrams show the difference between the third isotope of hydrogen, tritium, and an isotope of helium with an atomic mass of 3.
25. What is the atomic weight of an element whose atoms are approximately 9 times as heavy as those of oxygen? Consult the Table of Atomic Weights inside the back cover of your book to find which element this is.
26. Why is the word "average" used in the statement: The atoms of a given element have a definite average mass?
27. In what two ways may atomic weights be determined?
28. Why does the chemist use a system of relative atomic weights rather than the actual atomic weights?
★ 29. How many orbitals are there in: (*a*) the K shell? (*b*) the L shell? (*c*) the M shell? (*d*) the N shell? (*e*) the O shell?
★ 30. How many M-shell orbitals are filled: (*a*) in the element argon? (*b*) in the element krypton?
★ 31. How many N-shell orbitals are filled: (*a*) in the element krypton? (*b*) in the element xenon? (*c*) in the element radon?
★ 32. How many O-shell orbitals are filled: (*a*) in the element xenon? (*b*) in the element radon?

Some things for you to do

1. Look up the accounts of the discovery of protons, electrons, and neutrons, and describe the experiments which resulted in these discoveries to the class.
2. From a table of isotopes in a Handbook, find the number and mass of the naturally-occurring stable isotopes of: (*a*) carbon; (*b*) sulfur; (*c*) iron; (*d*) copper; (*e*) silver.
3. Make a model of an oxygen atom using different colored beads for protons, neutrons, and electrons. Use stiff wire, such as from coat hangers, to represent orbitals and support the electrons.

Chapter 5   THE PERIODIC LAW

```
[H]                                                          [He]
Li Be                                        B  C  N  O  F  Ne
Na Mg                                        Al Si P  S  Cl A
K  Ca Sc Ti V  Cr Mn Fe Co Ni Cu Zn Ga Ge As Se Br Kr
Rb Sr Y  Zr Nb Mo Tc Ru Rh Pd Ag Cd In Sn Sb Te I  Xe
Cs Ba La-Lu Hf Ta W  Re Os Ir Pt Au Hg Tl Pb Bi Po At Rn
Fr Ra Ac-
```

1. Classification makes the study of chemical elements easier. If you had to study the properties of each of the 102 chemical elements to have even an elementary knowledge of chemistry, the task would be great. However, if some elements had similar properties, and if they could be grouped together, it would not be too hard to remember the distinguishing properties of the group. It might even be possible to remember some of the variations in properties among the members of the group, if the variations were in a fairly regular fashion.

During the late eighteenth and early nineteenth centuries, chemists began to identify certain substances as chemical elements. They also recognized that there were similarities in the properties of some of these elements. They discovered that sodium and potassium were soft, silvery metals. They found that calcium, barium, and strontium could be prepared as elements by similar chemical changes; that sulfur, selenium, and tellurium formed similar chemical compounds; and that chlorine, bromine, and iodine were colored nonmetallic elements. But such isolated

VOCABULARY

Group. A vertical column of elements in the Periodic Table.

Period. A horizontal row of elements in the Periodic Table.

Periodic Table. A tabular arrangement of the chemical elements based on their atomic structure.

Rare earth element. An element which differs in electronic configuration from that of next lower or higher atomic number only in the number of electrons in the second-from-outside shell.

Transition element. An element which differs in electronic configuration from that of next lower or higher atomic number only in the number of electrons in the next-to-the-outside shell.

cases did not seem to help very much. They did not offer much promise of classifying all the known chemical elements into any unifying system.

2. Some early attempts were made to classify elements. About 1800, certain chemists began to determine the atomic weights of some elements with fair accuracy. Attempts were soon made to classify the elements on this basis. As early as 1817, Johann Wolfgang Döbereiner (doh-ber-eye-ner) (1780–1849), made an interesting observation. He noticed that the atomic weight of bromine was almost equal to the average of the atomic weights of iodine and chlorine.

$$(127 + 35.5) \div 2 = 81.25, \text{ the average}$$

(The atomic weight of bromine is 79.9.) He also observed that the atomic weight of strontium, 87.6, was close to the average of the atomic weights of calcium and barium.

$$(40 + 137) \div 2 = 88.5$$

In a like way he found that the atomic weight of selenium, 79.2, was not too different from the average of the atomic weights of sulfur and tellurium.

$$(32 + 127.5) \div 2 = 79.75$$

Such groups of elements were called *triads.*

In 1864 John A. Newlands (1838–1898) grouped all the known elements in the order of their atomic weights. He then divided them into groups of seven elements each. He made this division because the eighth element was found to have chemical properties similar to the first element of the preceding series. Hence, he made that element the first one in a second series. He talked incessantly to the chemists of his time about his *law of octaves,* but they merely laughed at his ideas. They made so much fun of him that he lost interest and stopped his efforts to classify elements.

Lothar Meyer (1830–1895) in Germany plotted a graph showing an attempt to group elements according to atomic weights.

3. Mendeleyev made an important contribution. Dmitri Mendeleyev (men-deh-*lay*-eff) (1834–1907) —the name is spelled in a variety of ways—worked out a *Periodic Table of the Elements.* In this table the different elements are arranged in the order of their atomic weights. In Mendeleyev's system of classification, the first two series or periods contained *seven elements* each. The next three periods contained *seventeen elements* each. The Periodic Tables we use today are largely based on the pioneer work done by Mendeleyev.

Fig. 5–1. Dmitri Mendeleyev, a Russian chemist, worked out the first Periodic Table of the Chemical Elements.

When Mendeleyev first prepared his Periodic Table, he realized that all the elements were probably not yet discovered. For example, scandium, gallium, and germanium were unknown in Mendeleyev's day. Mendeleyev carefully studied the properties of those elements he knew. From this study he learned where to leave gaps in his table for those to be discovered later, and predicted that new elements would be discovered to fit these gaps. He also predicted the properties of these new elements. His predictions were later found to be quite accurate when compared with the actual properties of the elements.

Mendeleyev noticed, just as Newlands had, that the chemical properties of the elements recur at definite intervals. Therefore, he concluded that the chemical properties of elements are periodic functions of their atomic weights.

In Mendeleyev's table, the first two periods, or series, had seven elements before there was a recurrence of properties. In the third period, Mendeleyev found there were seventeen elements before there was recurrence of properties. Periods 4 and 5 were long series,

too. The discovery of the inert gases, neon, argon, krypton, and xenon, by Sir William Ramsay (1852–1916) during the 1890's, together with the earlier discovered element, helium, added an additional element to each period in Mendeleyev's table.

4. How are atomic numbers determined? About 45 years after Mendeleyev's work on the Periodic Table, another important discovery was made. This gave further aid to the problem of classifying the elements. We learned in Chapter 4 that the atomic number of an element indicates the number of protons in its nucleus. Henry Gwyn-Jeffreys Moseley (1887–1915), one of the most brilliant of young English scientists, used X rays to determine the atomic numbers of the elements.

X rays are radiations similar to light or radio waves but which have a high frequency and a short wave length. X rays are produced when high-speed electrons strike the metal target in an evacuated tube (see Fig. 5-3). Moseley found that the wave lengths of the X rays produced in such tubes depend on the kind of metal used as a target. Therefore, he used as targets various metals ranging in atomic weight from

Fig. 5–2. Right, Henry Gwyn-Jeffreys Moseley, an English physicist, used X rays to determine the atomic numbers of the elements.

Fig. 5–3. Moseley used an X-ray tube in determining the atomic numbers of the elements.

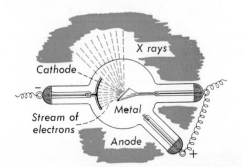

1.0080	1
H	
1	

LIGHT METALS

alkali line *+2* *alkaline earths*

HEAVY METAL·

I A		II A		III B		IV B		V B		VI B		VII B		VIII B					

6.940 **Li** 3	2 1	9.013 **Be** 4	2 2														
22.991 **Na** 11	2 8 1	24.32 **Mg** 12	2 8 2														
39.100 **K** 19	2 8 8 1	40.08 **Ca** 20	2 8 8 2	44.96 **Sc** 21	2 8 9 2	47.90 **Ti** 22	2 8 10 2	50.95 **V** 23	2 8 11 2	52.01 **Cr** 24	2 8 13 1	54.94 **Mn** 25	2 8 13 2	55.85 **Fe** 26	2 8 14 2	58.94 **Co** 27
85.48 **Rb** 37	2 8 18 8 1	87.63 **Sr** 38	2 8 18 8 2	88.92 **Y** 39	2 8 18 9 2	91.22 **Zr** 40	2 8 18 10 2	92.91 **Nb** 41	2 8 18 12 1	95.95 **Mo** 42	2 8 18 13 1	[99] **Tc** 43	2 8 18 14 1	101.1 **Ru** 44	2 8 18 15 1	102.91 **Rh** 45
132.91 **Cs** 55	2 8 18 18 1	137.36 **Ba** 56	2 8 18 8 2	57 to 71 Lanthanide Series Rare Earth Elements	2 8 18 18 8 2	178.58 **Hf** 72	2 8 18 32 10 2	180.95 **Ta** 73	2 8 18 32 11 2	183.86 **W** 74	2 8 18 32 12 2	186.22 **Re** 75	2 8 18 32 13 2	190.2 **Os** 76	2 8 18 32 14 2	192.2 **Ir** 77
[223] **Fr** 87	2 8 18 32 18 8 1	226.05 **Ra** 88	2 8 18 32 18 8 2	89 to 102 Actinide Series Rare Earth Elements												

Lanthanide Series	138.92 **La** 57	2 8 18 18 9 2	140.13 **Ce** 58	2 8 18 20 8 2	140.92 **Pr** 59	2 8 18 21 8 2	144.27 **Nd** 60	2 8 18 22 8 2	[145] **Pm** 61	2 8 18 23 8 2	150.35 **Sm** 62	2 8 18 24 8 2	152.0 **Eu** 63	2 8 18 25 8 2	157.26 **Gd** 64	2 8 18 25 9 2

Actinide Series	227 **Ac** 89	2 8 18 32 18 9 2	232.05 **Th** 90	2 8 18 32 18 10 2	231 **Pa** 91	2 8 18 32 20 9 2	238.07 **U** 92	2 8 18 32 21 9 2	[237] **Np** 93	2 8 18 32 23 8 2	[242] **Pu** 94	2 8 18 32 24 8 2	[243] **Am** 95	2 8 18 32 25 8 2	[245] **Cm** 96	2 8 18 32 25 9 2

OF THE ELEMENTS

NONMETALS

		III A	IV A	V A	VI A	VII A	VIII A
							4.003 He 2
		10.82 B 5 (2 3)	12.011 C 6 (2 4)	14.008 N 7 (2 5)	16.0000 O 8 (2 6)	19.00 F 9 (2 7)	20.183 Ne 10 (2 8)
I B	II B	26.98 Al 13 (2 8 3)	28.09 Si 14 (2 8 4)	30.975 P 15 (2 8 5)	32.066 S 16 (2 8 6)	35.457 Cl 17 (2 8 7)	39.944 A 18 (2 8 8)
58.71 Ni 28 (2 8 16 2)	63.54 Cu 29 (2 8 18 1)	65.38 Zn 30 (2 8 18 2)	69.72 Ga 31 (2 8 18 3)	72.60 Ge 32 (2 8 18 4)	74.91 As 33 (2 8 18 5)	78.96 Se 34 (2 8 18 6)	79.916 Br 35 (2 8 18 7)	83.8 Kr 36 (2 8 18 8)
106.7 Pd 46 (2 8 18 18 0)	107.880 Ag 47 (2 8 18 18 1)	112.41 Cd 48 (2 8 18 18 2)	114.82 In 49 (2 8 18 18 3)	118.70 Sn 50 (2 8 18 18 4)	121.76 Sb 51 (2 8 18 18 5)	127.61 Te 52 (2 8 18 18 6)	126.91 I 53 (2 8 18 18 7)	131.30 Xe 54 (2 8 18 18 8)
195.09 Pt 78 (2 8 18 32 17 1)	197.0 Au 79 (2 8 18 32 18 1)	200.61 Hg 80 (2 8 18 32 18 2)	204.39 Tl 81 (2 8 18 32 18 3)	207.21 Pb 82 (2 8 18 32 18 4)	209.00 Bi 83 (2 8 18 32 18 5)	210 Po 84 (2 8 18 32 18 6)	[211] At 85 (2 8 18 32 18 7)	222 Rn 86 (2 8 18 32 18 8)

RARE EARTH ELEMENTS

158.93 Tb 65 (2 8 18 27 8 2)	162.51 Dy 66 (2 8 18 28 8 2)	164.94 Ho 67 (2 8 18 29 8 2)	167.27 Er 68 (2 8 18 30 8 2)	168.94 Tm 69 (2 8 18 31 8 2)	173.04 Yb 70 (2 8 18 32 8 2)	174.99 Lu 71 (2 8 18 32 9 2)

[245] Bk 97 (2 8 18 32 27 8 2)	[248] Cf 98 (2 8 18 32 28 8 2)	[255] E 99 (2 8 18 32 29 8 2)	[252] Fm 100 (2 8 18 32 30 8 2)	[256] Mv 101 (2 8 18 32 31 8 2)	No 102 (2 8 18 32 32 8 2)	

A value given in brackets denotes the mass number of the isotope of longest known half-life.

aluminum to gold. He found that the wave lengths of X rays became shorter as he used elements which have more of what we now recognize as protons in their nuclei. The higher the atomic number of an element, the shorter the wave length of X rays will be when that element is used as a target within the X-ray tube.

Moseley found in some cases an unusual variation in the wave lengths of X rays between two successive elements. The variation was twice as great as his calculations justified. He concluded that in such cases an element was missing from the Periodic Table. Several elements have since been discovered which fill the gaps that Moseley had indicated.

5. The discovery of atomic numbers changed the Periodic Law. Let us arrange the elements in a Periodic Table in the order of their atomic numbers instead of in the order of their atomic weights. When arranged this way, some of the problems of arrangement disappear. Arranged according to increasing atomic weights, potassium precedes argon. Yet, when arranged according to properties in the table, potassium follows argon. This is in agreement with the atomic numbers, argon 18, and potassium 19. A similar case is that of tellurium (atomic number 52) and iodine (atomic number 53).

Because of Moseley's discovery of atomic numbers, the **Periodic Law** was changed to its present form: *the chemical properties of elements are periodic functions of their atomic numbers.* In other words, the chemical properties of elements recur after certain intervals, provided the elements are arranged in a table in the order of their atomic numbers.

6. How is the modern Periodic Table arranged? The modern Periodic Table is shown on pages 58–59. It will help you to understand the Periodic Table and its importance in chemistry if you will continually refer to the table as you study this section. This is how it works.

Each element is assigned a separate block in the table. In the center of the block is the chemical symbol for the element. Below the symbol is the atomic number of the element. Above the symbol is the atomic weight. To the right of each symbol are the numbers which indicate the distribution of electrons in the shells of the atoms of this element. A horizontal row of blocks on the table is called a *period.* A vertical column is called a *group* or *family.*

Hydrogen, atomic number 1, because of its many unique properties is placed at the top of the table by itself. It is placed in the first column at the left of the table because it has 1 electron in its outermost shell. Helium, atomic number 2, is placed at the top of the extreme right-hand column as the simplest member of the group of elements known as the *inert gases.* Note that helium has 2 electrons in its K shell, and that with these 2 electrons, the K shell is complete. Hydrogen and helium comprise the first period of elements.

The second period consists of eight elements: *lithium,* a soft, silvery, active metal, whose atoms have 1 electron in their outer shell, the L shell; *beryllium,* a silvery metal, less active than lithium, whose atoms have 2 electrons in their L shell; *boron,* a black solid with few metallic properties, whose atoms have 3 electrons in their L shell; *carbon,* a solid element with very distinctive chemical properties intermediate between those of metals and nonmetals, 4 electrons in the L shell; *nitrogen,* a colorless gas, nonmetallic properties, 5 electrons in its L shell; *oxygen,* a colorless gas, strong nonmetallic properties, 6 electrons in the L shell; *fluorine,* a pale-yellow gas, very strong nonmetallic properties, 7 electrons in its L shell; and *neon,* a colorless, inert gas, 8 electrons in its L shell. From this brief description of the properties of these elements, we see that they range from an active metallic element to an active nonmetallic element, with the last element in the period being inert. This variation in properties from metallic to nonmetallic is accompanied by an increase in the number of L-shell electrons from 1 to 7. The inert element neon has 8 electrons, an octet of electrons, in the L shell.

The third period also consists of eight elements: *sodium,* a soft, silvery, active metal similar to lithium, 1 electron in its outermost shell, the M shell; *magnesium,* a silvery metal similar in properties to beryllium, 2 electrons in its M shell; *aluminum,* a silvery metal with some nonmetallic properties, 3 electrons in the M shell; *silicon,* a dark-colored nonmetallic element with some properties resembling carbon, 4 electrons in the M shell; *phosphorus,* a nonmetallic solid element which forms compounds similar to those of nitrogen, 5 electrons in its M shell; *sulfur,* a yellow nonmetallic solid element, 6 electrons in its M shell; *chlorine,* a yellow-green gas with strong nonmetallic properties resembling those of fluorine, 7 electrons in the M shell; and *argon,* a colorless, inert gas, 8 electrons in its M shell. Again, the elements range from strong metallic to strong nonmetallic properties as the number of

electrons in the outer shell varies from 1 to 7. The element with an octet of electrons in its outer shell is an inert gas.

We now notice that elements with similar properties have a similar number of electrons in their outer shell. They fall into the same group or family in the Periodic Table.

In Group IA in the Periodic Table, we find the Sodium Family, a group of six similar, very active, metallic elements. Their atoms all have only 1 electron in their outermost shell. *Francium* is the most complex member of the Sodium Family. Its position in the Periodic Table indicates that it is probably the most active metal. Group IIA consists of six active metals whose chemical properties are very much alike. They each have 2 electrons in their outer shell. This is the Calcium Family. The most active member of this family is *radium.*

The elements in Group IIIA vary from nonmetallic to metallic properties as the atoms become more complex. The atoms of this group have 3 electrons in their outer shell. The elements of Group IVA vary in a similar fashion; they have 4 electrons in their outer shell. Elements of both of these groups have complete or very stable inner shells.

Group VA is the Nitrogen Family. *Nitrogen* and *phosphorus,* the elements in this family at the top of the table, are nonmetallic. The element *bismuth* at the bottom of the table is metallic. *Arsenic* and *antimony* exhibit both metallic and nonmetallic properties. Each of these atoms has 5 electrons in the outer shell, and has complete or very stable inner shells.

Group VIA is the Oxygen Family.

The properties of the elements of this family vary from active nonmetallic to metallic as the atoms become more complex. Each element has 6 electrons in its outer shell with complete or very stable inner shells. The elements in Group VIIA, the Halogen Family, are very active nonmetals. They each have 7 electrons in their outer shell, and have complete or very stable inner shells. The most active member of the Halogen Family is its simplest element, *fluorine.* Thus we see that the activity of the elements ranges from the most active metal at the lower left corner of the Periodic Table to the most active nonmetal at the upper right corner.

Group VIIIA is the Inert Gas Family. With the exception of *helium,* which has a pair of electrons as its outer shell, these atoms have an octet of electrons as their outer shell. Each has the greatest number of electrons in its outer shell which it is possible for an outer shell to contain. They are chemically inert.

The fourth period of elements is the first long period. In addition to the eight elements in Groups IA to VIIIA, there are also ten elements in Groups IIIB to VIIIB and IB and IIB as shown in the Periodic Table. Note that Group VIIIB has three elements in each period. These ten elements are called **transition elements.** They all are metallic elements with 1 or 2 electrons in their outer shell. Successive electrons enter the group of 5 orbitals of the M energy level in most cases.

The fifth period of elements also includes ten transition elements, in which successive electrons enter the group of 5 orbitals of the N energy level. These elements are all metals.

The sixth period consists of thirty-two elements. In addition to the ten transition elements, there is a group of fourteen *rare earth elements.* These elements have almost identical chemical properties. They are called the *Lanthanide Series.* The *two* outer shells of these atoms are almost the same. Successive electrons enter the group of 7 orbitals of the N energy level, as the number of electrons in this energy level increases from 18 to 32.

The seventh period of elements is at present an incomplete period. It is assumed to be similar to the sixth period. The rare earth elements in this period are called the *Actinide Series.* At present, only fourteen members of this series are known.

In the Periodic Table on pages 58–59, the elements are roughly divided into light metals, heavy metals, nonmetals, and inert gases. The line separating the heavy metals from the nonmetals is a zigzag line running diagonally down and to the right near the right end of the table. The elements which border this zigzag line are the *metalloids.* These elements show both metallic and nonmetallic properties under different conditions.

7. The value of the Periodic Table. We have already learned how in former years the Periodic Table served as a check on atomic weight determinations and for the prediction of new elements. These uses are now outdated. For the present, however, the Periodic Table serves us as a useful systematic, though not perfect, classification of elements according to their properties. This helps us to know the types of compounds which they form, and makes the study of chemistry easier.

You will notice from the Periodic Table that only one more element must be produced to complete the Actinide Series. Scientists are working on the production of this element at the present time. Their interest in making it is partly to learn its properties so as to discover whether it fits in with the theory of atomic structure on which the Periodic Table is based. If element 104, when it is produced, has properties similar to those of element 72, below which it would be placed in the table, it will indeed be a significant verification of the correctness of our theories of atomic structure.

Summary

After early attempts by other scientists to classify elements as triads, or in octaves, Mendeleyev arranged the elements in the order of their atomic weights. He concluded that the chemical properties of elements are periodic functions of their atomic weights.

Moseley found that X rays could be used to determine the atomic number of an element. An increase in the number of protons in the nucleus of a metal used as the target in an X-ray tube decreases the wave length of the X rays it produces. When elements are arranged in the order of their atomic numbers, some discrepancies in Mendeleyev's arrangement disappear. As a result of this discovery, the Periodic Law is now stated: the chemical properties of elements are periodic functions of their atomic numbers.

In the modern Periodic Table the families of elements with similar properties, or groups, are in vertical columns. Each element in a family has a similar number of electrons in its outer shell. At the left of the table the most active elements are at the bottom. At the right of the table, they are at the top. A row of elements is called a period. In a given period, the properties of the elements gradually pass from strong metallic to strong nonmetallic nature, with the last member of a period being an inert gaseous element.

Test yourself on these terms

Actinide Series	law of octaves	Periodic Table
Calcium Family	Mendeleyev	rare earth element
family	metalloid	series
group	Nitrogen Family	Sodium Family
Halogen Family	Oxygen Family	transition element
Inert Gas Family	period	triad
Lanthanide Series	Periodic Law	X rays

Questions

Group A

1. (a) On what basis did Mendeleyev arrange the elements in his Periodic Table? (b) On what basis are they arranged today?
2. What use did Mendeleyev make of his Periodic Table?

3. How are X rays used to determine the atomic number of an element?
4. What is the Periodic Law?
5. (*a*) What information is given in each block of the Periodic Table? (*b*) How are these data arranged in each block?
6. (*a*) What is a group or family of elements? (*b*) What position does one occupy in the Periodic Table?
7. (*a*) What is a series or period of elements? (*b*) What position does one occupy in the Periodic Table?
8. (*a*) Name the elements in the second period. (*b*) How does the number of electrons in the outer shell vary in these elements? (*c*) How do their properties compare?
9. What is similar about the electron configurations of elements with similar properties?
10. How do the elements at the left of the Periodic Table vary in activity?
11. How do the elements in Group VIIA vary in activity?
12. What name is given to the elements which border the line dividing the heavy metals from the nonmetals?

Group B

13. How are the elements in Döbereiner's triads related?
14. What was the basis for Newlands' *law of octaves?*
15. What family of elements was missing from Mendeleyev's Periodic Table?
16. (*a*) What are X rays? (*b*) How are they produced?
17. (*a*) How did Mendeleyev know where to leave gaps for undiscovered elements in his Periodic Table? (*b*) How did Moseley know where to leave gaps for undiscovered elements?
18. (*a*) Why is hydrogen placed separately in the Periodic Table? (*b*) Why is it placed above Group IA?
19. (*a*) What are transition elements? (*b*) In which periods of elements do they appear?
20. (*a*) What are rare earth elements? (*b*) In which periods of elements do they appear?
21. What is the present value of the Periodic Table?
22. What is the probable electron configuration that element 106 would have?
23. What determines the number of elements in each period of the Periodic Table?
24. How many O-shell orbitals would be filled theoretically in element 118?

Some things for you to do

1. Look up in a history of chemistry or a college textbook of chemistry the predictions that Mendeleyev made for "ekaboron," "ekaluminum," and "ekasilicon," and compare them with the properties of scandium, gallium, and germanium, respectively.
2. Make a spiral model of the Periodic Table. Use a large size can for the cylinder. Cut white paper the proper size to encircle the can. Lay out the table on this paper, remembering to make the periods slant so that helium and lithium, neon and sodium, argon and potassium, etc., follow one another in a spiral.

Chapter 6 MOLECULES AND VALENCE

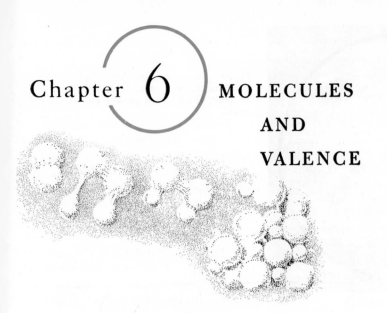

1. VALENCE

1. Atoms combine to form molecules. In Chapter 3 we learned that atoms of elements *could* combine during a chemical change to form molecules of compounds. Now that we know the structure of the atoms of the elements, we are ready to learn *how* atoms combine with one another to form molecules.

2. Atoms of different elements have different combining capacity. The following series of formulas shows that different numbers of hydrogen and chlorine atoms can combine with single atoms of other elements.

HCl	NaCl
H_2O	$CaCl_2$
NH_3	$AlCl_3$
CH_4	CCl_4

We see that one atom of hydrogen combines with one atom of chlorine. One atom of sodium also combines with one atom of chlorine. But to form a molecule of a compound of hydrogen and oxygen, two atoms of hydrogen are needed for each oxygen atom. Likewise, two chlorine atoms are required for each calcium atom when a compound of calcium and chlorine is formed. One

VOCABULARY

Binary compound. A compound consisting of only two elements.

Chemical bond. The linkage between atoms produced by transfer or sharing of electrons.

Covalent bonding. Bonding in which atoms share a pair of electrons.

Ion. An atom or group of atoms with an unbalanced electrostatic charge.

Ionic bonding. Bonding in which one or more electrons are transferred from one atom to another.

Radical. A group of atoms which usually behaves as if it were a single atom.

Valence. The number of electrons gained, lost, or shared by an atom in bonding with one or more atoms.

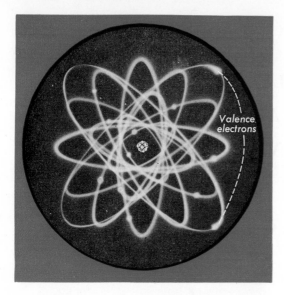
Valence electrons

Fig. 6–1. The magnesium atom has two electrons in its outer, incomplete M shell. These are its valence electrons.

atom of nitrogen combines with three hydrogen atoms, while one atom of aluminum combines with three chlorine atoms. One atom of carbon combines with either four hydrogen atoms or four chlorine atoms. Why do we find this difference in the number of hydrogen and chlorine atoms which will combine with a single atom of another element? Is there any relation between the structure of an atom and the number of other atoms with which it will combine?

3. What is valence? It would be rather awkward for chemists to talk about the "combining capacity" of an element. Instead, they have coined a special, shorter word which means "combining capacity." That word is *valence*. In Section 6 of this chapter we will give a more accurate definition of valence, but for the present, let us realize that *valence means the combining capacity of an element.*

4. What causes valence? The electrons in the outermost shell of an atom play a very active part in the formation of compounds. For this reason the electrons in an *incomplete* outer shell are called the **valence electrons.** The re-

mainder of the atom, excluding the valence electrons, is called the **kernel** of the atom. In the formation of chemical compounds from the elements, the *valence electrons are either transferred from the outer shell of one atom to the outer shell of another atom, or shared among the outer shells of the combining atoms.* This produces **chemical bonds.** When an atom of one element enters into chemical combination with an atom of another element, both atoms usually attain a stable outer shell consisting of an octet of electrons. (Hydrogen either loses its single electron or attains a stable outer shell of two electrons. Lithium loses its single L-shell electron to attain a stable outer shell of two electrons.) *This particular kind of electronic structure, resembling that of the inert gases, has chemical stability.*

Energy changes are always involved in the process of electron transfer or electron sharing. In *most* cases when compounds are formed from the elements, energy is liberated—the process of electron transfer is always exothermic and that of electron sharing is usually exothermic. In *a few* cases of compound formation by electron sharing, energy is absorbed—the process of electron sharing may sometimes be endothermic.

5. The types of chemical bonding. The types of chemical bonding generally recognized are **ionic bonding** (electrovalence) and **covalent bonding** (covalence).

1. Ionic bonding. In the formation of a compound by ionic bonding, elec-

	SODIUM ATOM	SODIUM ION	CHLORINE ATOM	CHLORIDE ION
NUMBER OF PROTONS	11	11	17	17
NUMBER OF ELECTRONS	11	10	17	18
NET CHARGE	0	+1	0	−1
SYMBOL	Na^0	Na^+	Cl^0	Cl^-

trons are actually transferred from the outer shell of one atom to the outer shell of a second atom. By this process both atoms attain outer shells containing eight electrons. For example, when sodium reacts with chlorine to form sodium chloride, the single electron in the M shell of the sodium atom is transferred to the M shell of the chlorine atom. The sodium atom, now deficient in one electron, has the stable electronic configuration of neon. The chlorine atom, now with one excess electron, has the stable electronic configuration of argon. Since only 1 atom of each element is required for the electron transfer which produces these stable electronic configurations, the formula of the resulting compound is NaCl. The particles which are produced by this transfer of an electron are no longer electrically neutral atoms of sodium and chlorine. They are an electrostatically-charged *sodium ion* with a single excess positive charge and an electrostatically-charged *chloride ion* with a single excess negative charge. *An* **ion** *is an atom or a group of atoms with an unbalanced electrostatic charge.* The table at the top of the page shows the number of protons and electrons in these atoms and ions, their resultant electrostatic charges, and their electrovalent symbols. Also see Fig. 6-2.

Using only the M-shell electrons, the electron-dot symbol for an atom of sodium is

$$Na \cdot$$

while that for an atom of chlorine is

$$\cdot \ddot{\underset{\cdot\cdot}{Cl}} :$$

Fig. 6–2. This diagram shows the arrangement of the sodium and chloride ions in sodium chloride.

Fig. 6–3. This diagram shows the arrangement of the magnesium and bromide ions in magnesium bromide.

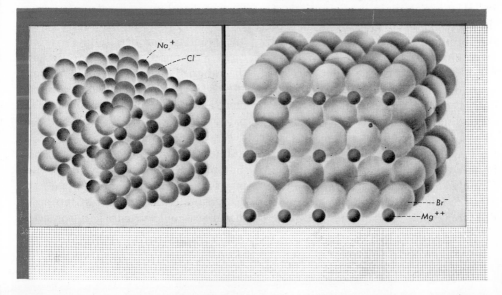

	MAGNESIUM ATOM	MAGNESIUM ION	BROMINE ATOM	BROMIDE ION
NUMBER OF PROTONS	12	12	35	35
NUMBER OF ELECTRONS	12	10	35	36
NET CHARGE	0	+2	0	−1
SYMBOL	Mg^0	Mg^{++}	Br^0	Br^-

After reaction, the formula for sodium chloride may be represented by an electron-dot formula as

$$Na^+ \; :\overset{\cdot\cdot}{\underset{\cdot\cdot}{Cl}}:^-$$

or by a simpler ionic formula as Na^+Cl^-. (The symbols for electrons, ● and ·, which are used here and in other electron-dot formulas in this chapter, are only to show you the origin of the electrons in the completed shells. They *do not mean* that electrons from different atoms are different from each other. All electrons, regardless of the atom of which they were originally a part, are identical.)

In another example, the formation of magnesium bromide, the 2 outer M-shell electrons of the magnesium are transferred. *Both* M-shell electrons must be transferred in order for the magnesium atom to acquire the stability of the electronic configuration of the inert gas, neon. But the N shell of the bromine atom already contains seven electrons, and eight is the number needed for a stable octet of electrons. So 1 bromine atom has place for only 1 of the 2 electrons which the magnesium atom transfers. This means that 2 bromine atoms are needed to react with 1 magnesium atom. Each bromine atom gains 1 electron. The formula for magnesium bromide is $MgBr_2$. The particles which compose this compound are magnesium ions,

each with two excess positive charges, and bromide ions, each with a single excess negative charge. These particles are found in crystals of magnesium bromide in the ratio of 2 bromide ions to 1 magnesium ion (see the table at the top of this page and also Fig. 6-3).

The electron-dot symbol for an atom of magnesium is

$$Mg\,\overset{\cdot}{}$$

while that for an atom of bromine is

$$\cdot\overset{\cdot\cdot}{Br}:$$

The electron-dot formula for magnesium bromide will then be

$$:\overset{\cdot\cdot}{\underset{\cdot\cdot}{Br}}:^- \; Mg^{++} \; :\overset{\cdot\cdot}{\underset{\cdot\cdot}{Br}}:^-$$

and the ionic formula will be $Mg^{++}Br_2^-$.

2. Covalent bonding. The second type of bonding is covalent bonding. Here electrons are not transferred from one atom to another, but two atoms each share one of their electrons with the other. These two shared electrons effectively fill an orbital in each element and thus form a covalent electron pair. This constitutes the bond between these two atoms.

The atoms of the common gases form diatomic molecules by covalent bonding. For instance, in the diatomic hydrogen molecule, each hydrogen atom shares its single valence electron with

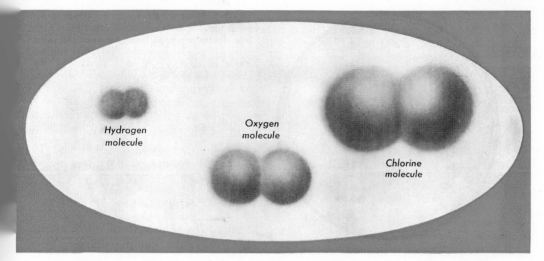

Fig. 6–4. The molecules of the common gases, such as those of hydrogen, oxygen, and chlorine represented here, consist of two atoms joined by covalent bonding.

the other. These electrons revolve about both nuclei, so that each atom has two electrons revolving about it. Each atom, in effect, has the single orbital of its K energy level filled. This means that each hydrogen atom has, in effect, the stable K-shell configuration of a helium atom. The electron-dot formula for a molecule of hydrogen is

$$H:H$$

Diatomic chlorine molecules are formed in the same way. Each atom shares one electron with the other, filling, in effect, an incomplete orbital in the M level of each. This gives both the stable electron arrangement of the inert gas argon, with an octet of electrons in the M shell. The electron-dot formula for a molecule of chlorine is

$$: \overset{..}{Cl} : \overset{..}{Cl} :$$

Oxygen also exists as diatomic molecules. But an atom of oxygen is represented as

$$\cdot \overset{..}{O} :$$

so a molecule of oxygen has the electron-dot formula

$$: \overset{..}{O} : \overset{..}{O} :$$

Unlike atoms also combine by covalent bonding. Several simple compounds formed by covalent bonding are hydrogen chloride, water, ammonia, and methane. Their electron-dot structures are shown in the table at the bottom of page 70. Notice that a pair of shared electrons constitutes the bond between two atoms, and that each atom acquires a stable outer shell of two or eight electrons.

There are some covalent molecules in which both electrons which form the covalent bond between two atoms have come from only one of the atoms. Sulfur trioxide molecules include two bonds of this type. The third bond is a double covalent bond formed by the sharing of four electrons, two from an oxygen atom, and two from the sulfur atom. In the electron-dot formula for sulfur trioxide, shown on the next page, the colored dots represent electrons

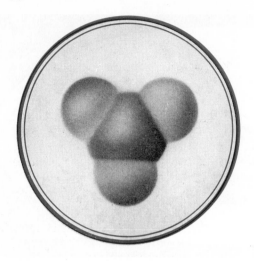

Fig. 6–5. There are three covalent bonds in the sulfur trioxide molecule represented here. One is a double covalent bond between the sulfur atom and one oxygen atom. The other two are single covalent bonds, each formed by the sharing of a pair of the sulfur atom's electrons by an oxygen atom.

Frequently chemists indicate a shared pair of electrons—a covalent bond—by a dash (—) instead of by two dots (:). Thus the formula for hydrogen chloride may be written

$$H:\ddot{\underset{..}{Cl}}: \quad \text{or} \quad H—\ddot{\underset{..}{Cl}}:$$

or omitting the electrons which are not involved in the bonding, simply

$$H—Cl$$

Similarly, the formula for methane,

$$\begin{matrix} & H & \\ H & :\overset{..}{C}: & H \\ & H & \end{matrix}$$

becomes

$$\begin{matrix} & H & \\ & | & \\ H & —C— & H \\ & | & \\ & H & \end{matrix}$$

from the sulfur atom and the black dots represent the electrons from the oxygen atoms. Note how the two types of bonds in this molecule are represented.

$$\begin{matrix} & :\overset{..}{O}: & \\ \ddot{O}::S & \rangle & —— \\ \uparrow & :\overset{..}{O}: & \end{matrix}$$

A double covalent bond

Both electrons in these bonds come from the sulfur atom

	HYDROGEN CHLORIDE	WATER	AMMONIA	METHANE
INDIVIDUAL ATOMS	$H\cdot, \quad \cdot\ddot{\underset{..}{Cl}}:$	$H\cdot, H\cdot, \cdot\ddot{O}:$	$H\cdot, H\cdot, H\cdot, \cdot\ddot{N}:$	$H\cdot, H\cdot, H\cdot, H\cdot, \cdot\dot{C}$
MOLECULES	$H:\ddot{\underset{..}{Cl}}:$	$H:\overset{..}{\underset{H}{O}}:$	$H:\overset{H}{\underset{H}{N}}:$	$H:\overset{H}{\underset{H}{C}}:H$
DRAWING OF MOLECULE				

Or the formula for sulfur trioxide,

becomes

with a double dash ($=$) representing the double covalent bond.

6. What is the chemical definition of valence? Now that we have seen how compounds are formed by these two types of chemical bonding, we are ready for a more complete definition of the term valence. *Valence is the number of electrons which an atom gains, loses, or shares in bonding with one or more atoms.* Valence is shown by atoms only when they are combined. It is not shown by uncombined atoms. That is why the valence of a single atom of an element is said to be 0. An atom of the element sodium has 0 valence. Sodium in sodium chloride has a valence of $+1$, since the sodium atom has lost 1 electron and the resulting sodium ion has an excess of 1 positive charge. An atom of the element chlorine has 0 valence. But in sodium chloride, the chlorine has a valence of -1, since the chlorine atom gained 1 electron and the resulting chloride ion has 1 excess negative charge.

The valence of atoms in covalent compounds is an absolute number, since there is only electron sharing. In hydrogen chloride, the valence of both the hydrogen and the chlorine is 1, since they each share 1 of their electrons. In water, the valence of hydro-gen is again 1, but the valence of oxygen is 2. Each hydrogen atom shares 1 of its electrons with the oxygen, but the oxygen atom shares 2 of its electrons—1 with each hydrogen. In sulfur trioxide, the valence of sulfur is 6, while the valence of each oxygen atom is 2. The sulfur atom shares all 6 of its electrons with the oxygen atoms, while each oxygen atom either shares 2 of its electrons with the sulfur or completes its octet of electrons with 2 electrons from the sulfur atom.

It is also important to note that while atoms transfer or share electrons to form chemical bonds, there are still an equal number of protons and electrons in the group of atoms forming a molecule or forming the relative proportions indicated by an empirical formula. Consequently, molecules or the relative proportions of atoms indicated by an empirical formula have the same electrical balance or electrical neutrality found in single uncombined atoms.

The table on the next page summarizes structural and valence data for some of the simple elements of Groups IA, IIA, VIA, VIIA, and VIIIA of the Periodic Table.

★ **7. Atomic structure and chemical bonding.** Since the metallic elements are those which generally have only 1, 2, or 3 electrons in their outer shell, and these electrons are bound rather loosely to the nucleus, metals usually form ionic bonds when combining with nonmetallic elements. Likewise the distinctly nonmetallic elements, such as oxygen, sulfur, and the members of the Halogen Family, have outer shells which are nearly like those of the inert gases. The addition of 1 or 2 electrons to their shells gives them this stable configuration. Consequently, when they

ELEMENT		HYDRO-GEN	HELIUM	OXY-GEN	NEON	SO-DIUM	MAGNE-SIUM	CHLO-RINE
ATOMIC STRUC-TURE	Nuclear charge	+1	+2	+8	+10	+11	+12	+17
	Number of electrons	1	2	2,6	2,8	2,8,1	2,8,2	2,8,7
KERNEL STRUC-TURE	Nuclear charge	+1	+2	+8	+10	+11	+12	+17
	Number of electrons	0	2	2	2,8	2,8	2,8	2,8
VALENCE STRUC-TURE	Number of electrons	1	0	6	0	1	2	7
VALENCE NOTA-TION	Electro-valence	H^+	He^0	$O^=$	Ne^0	Na^+	Mg^{++}	Cl^-
	Covalence	H·	He:	·Ö:	:Ṅe:	Na·	Mg·	:Cl:

combine with metallic elements, the bond is usually ionic. Sodium chloride, NaCl, calcium bromide, $CaBr_2$, and barium oxide, BaO, are examples of compounds with ionic bonds.

When nonmetallic elements combine with each other (and by far the greater number of compounds are formed in this manner), the bonding is predominantly covalent. The nonmetallic elements combine by the sharing of electrons to form molecules of covalent compounds. Water, H_2O, ammonia, NH_3, and carbon tetrachloride, CCl_4, are examples of compounds with covalent bonds.

While we have classed chemical bonds as ionic bonds or covalent bonds, these are not clear, distinct classifications. On the Periodic Table, the type of bonding gradually changes from purely ionic, as is the case between the active metals of Groups IA and IIA and oxygen or the halogens, to covalent bonding in the metalloids and between nonmetals. The Inert Gases have electronic configurations which are chemically very stable. They do not form chemical compounds of the usual types. Under certain very unusual conditions, unstable "compounds" which are neither ionic nor covalent have been prepared from some of these inert elements.

★ **8. The structure of crystalline solids.** Crystalline solids may be *molecular, macromolecular,* or *ionic.*

Some solids are made up of simple molecules. Solid iodine consists of diatomic molecules arranged in systematic order forming *molecular crystals.* The melting points of such solids are usually low. Other solids have unit structures which are somewhat more complex than the simplest molecular form would provide. They may be composed of specific molecular groups or aggregates of these groups regularly arranged throughout the solid. Such molecular groups or aggregates are called **macromolecules.** They may be very complex and quite large when compared to simple molecules. A diamond is such a crystalline solid. A cut and polished diamond is a macromolecule. Still other solids show no molecular structure at all. The *ions* composing such substances are arranged in a characteristic pattern which is repeated in each dimension to the faces of the crystal. Sodium chloride crystals are of this sort. Macromolecular and ionic solids have high melting points. Molecules of sodium chloride do not exist as such except at very high temperatures.

9. Elements may show several valences. Many elements exhibit more than one valence. Some differences in the valence shown by an element depend on the kind of bond which it forms with other elements. However, another factor is important. Some heavy-metal elements, with four or five electronic subshells, can transfer the electrons in the outermost subshell and sometimes transfer one or two electrons from the next-to-outermost subshell. The electrons in excess of an octet in the next-to-outermost subshell are those available for transfer. Iron is such a heavy-metal element. In forming compounds, it can transfer two electrons from the N shell, and sometimes, in more energetic reactions, an additional electron can be transferred from the outer subshell of the M shell. Thus its valence can be $+2$, or $+3$. This accounts for the variable valence shown by many of the heavy metals.

10. What are radicals? Some groups of elements act like single atoms in forming compounds. These groups of elements are called *radicals.* Some of the common radicals are the sulfate ion, $SO_4^=$, the nitrate ion, NO_3^-, and the phosphate ion, $PO_4^\equiv$. The bonds within these radicals are predominantly covalent, but the groups of atoms have an excess of electrons when combined, and thus are negative ions. There is only one common positive radical, the ammonium ion NH_4^+,

Fig. 6–7. Solid iodine (left) forms molecular crystals. Compare its molecular structure with that of the diamond (right) which forms molecular groups called macromolecules.

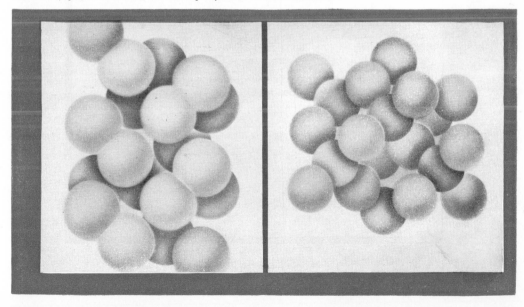

produced when a molecule of ammonia, NH_3, acquires a proton. Electron-dot representations of these radicals are:

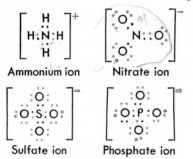

Ammonium ion   Nitrate ion

Sulfate ion   Phosphate ion

In the ammonium radical there are 11 protons (7 in the nitrogen nucleus and 1 in each of four hydrogen nuclei)

and 10 electrons (2 in the K shell of the nitrogen atom, and the 8 valence electrons shown). With 11 protons and only 10 electrons, the radical has a net charge, or valence, of +1. The valences of the other radicals may be worked out in similar fashion. The electrons represented by small circles are acquired by the radical from other elements through electron transfer.

11. The Table of Valences of Elements and Radicals. A knowledge of the ionic valences of common elements and radicals is very important in chemistry. They are given in the following table. Before proceeding further, *this table must be thoroughly memorized.*

VALENCES SHOWN BY COMMON ELEMENTS AND RADICALS		
+1	**+2**	**+3**
Ammonium, NH_4^+	Barium, Ba^{++}	Aluminum, Al^{+++}
Cuprous, Cu^+	Calcium, Ca^{++}	Chromic, Cr^{+++}
Hydrogen, H^+	Cupric, Cu^{++}	Ferric, Fe^{+++}
Mercurous, Hg^+	Ferrous, Fe^{++}	
Potassium, K^+	Lead, Pb^{++}	
Silver, Ag^+	Magnesium, Mg^{++}	
Sodium, Na^+	Mercuric, Hg^{++}	
	Nickel, Ni^{++}	
	Zinc, Zn^{++}	
−1	**−2**	**−3**
Acetate, $C_2H_3O_2^-$	Carbonate, $CO_3^=$	Phosphate, $PO_4^\equiv$
Bicarbonate, HCO_3^-	Chromate, $CrO_4^=$	
Bisulfate, HSO_4^-	Oxide, $O^=$	
Bromide, Br^-	Peroxide, $O_2^=$	
Chlorate, ClO_3^-	Sulfate, $SO_4^=$	
Chloride, Cl^-	Sulfide, $S^=$	
Fluoride, F^-	Sulfite, $SO_3^=$	
Hydroxide, OH^-		
Iodide, I^-		
Nitrate, NO_3^-		
Nitrite, NO_2^-		

2. FORMULA WRITING

12. How are valences used in writing formulas? The valence of an element tells us how many electrons it gains, loses, or shares in forming compounds. We can easily derive the formulas for many compounds by means of the table of valences without having to become involved with the details of atomic structure and chemical bonding. First let's try sodium chloride. Sodium has a valence of +1, while chlorine as the chloride ion has a valence of −1. When we write the formulas for compounds, the total valence of the first, or positive, part of the compound must be equal but opposite in charge to the total valence of the second, or negative part of the compound. The total valence of an element is found by multiplying the valence of the element by the number of atoms of that element taken. Since the valence of 1 atom of sodium is equal but opposite in charge to the valence of 1 atom of chlorine, the formula for sodium chloride indicates 1 atom of each element. The formula is NaCl.

Next we shall try calcium chloride. Calcium has a valence of +2. Chlorine as the chloride ion has a valence of −1. In order that the total valence of the positive part of the compound be equal but opposite in charge to that of the negative part of the compound, we shall need 2 chlorine atoms. One calcium atom has a valence of +2, while the total valence of 2 chlorine atoms is −2. The formula is $CaCl_2$. The subscript $_2$ indicates that 2 atoms of chlorine combine with 1 atom of calcium in forming calcium chloride.

What will be the formula for aluminum bromide? Aluminum has a valence of +3. Bromine as the bromide ion has a valence of −1. To make the total valence of each part of the compound equal but opposite in charge to the other, we will need 3 bromide ions. They will have a total valence of −3, which will match the +3 of the aluminum. The formula is $AlBr_3$.

13. Writing the formulas for other compounds. In the case of lead sulfate, our work is easy. Lead has a valence of +2. Sulfate radical has a valence of −2. Since the valences are already equal but opposite in charge, we need only 1 lead atom and 1 sulfate radical to form the compound. The formula is $PbSO_4$.

In writing the formula for magnesium hydroxide, we must use a radical more than one time in a formula. The symbol for magnesium with a valence of +2 is Mg^{++}. Hydroxide with a valence of −1 is written OH^-. We shall need 2 hydroxide radicals in order to have a negative valence which is equal but opposite in charge to the positive valence of magnesium. In writing this formula we use parentheses to enclose the hydroxide radical, (OH). Then, the subscript $_2$ is written outside the parentheses, $(OH)_2$. This shows that it is the *entire* OH radical which is taken twice. The complete formula for magnesium hydroxide is $Mg(OH)_2$. We must *not* write this formula $MgOH_2$. If the formula were so written, it would indicate that there are 2 hydrogen atoms and 1 oxygen atom, not 2 hydroxide radicals. Chemists put the subscript number outside the parentheses to indicate that the radical inside the parentheses is found that number of times in the formula. Parentheses are not used when a radical is found only once in the formula for a substance.

Let us try another similar formula, that for lead acetate. Lead has the symbol Pb with a valence of $+2$. The acetate radical is $C_2H_3O_2$ with a valence of -1. We shall need one atom of lead and two acetate radicals for the formula. Following the same system that we used for writing the formula for magnesium hydroxide, the formula for lead acetate becomes $Pb(C_2H_3O_2)_2$. Note that in order to show that there are two acetate radicals in the formula, we enclose the $C_2H_3O_2$ in parentheses, and place the subscript $_2$ outside.

Ammonium sulfate has two radicals in its formula. The ammonium radical is NH_4 with a valence of $+1$. The sulfate radical is SO_4 with a valence of -2. In order to make the total valences equal but opposite in charge, we shall need to use 2 ammonium radicals. To represent these in the formula, we shall enclose the NH_4 in parentheses and put the subscript $_2$ outside. The formula is then written $(NH_4)_2SO_4$.

Finally, let us write the formula for ferric carbonate. Iron in its ferric form has a valence of $+3$. The valence of the carbonate radical is -2. In order to make the total valence of the positive part of the formula equal but opposite in charge to the total valence of the negative part of the formula, we must use 2 atoms of iron and 3 carbonate radicals. A total of six electrons is transferred—three from each of two iron atoms to two to each of three carbonate radicals. The formula is $Fe_2(CO_3)_3$.

14. How are compounds named from their formulas? For many types of compounds all that is necessary is to give the name of the first part of the formula and then follow it with the name of the second part. $BaSO_4$ is called barium sulfate (Ba^{++} is the barium ion. $SO_4^=$ is the sulfate radical). $FeCl_3$ is ferric chloride. Here we must notice that there are two possible valence states for iron. One is fer*rous,* with a valence of $+2$. The other is fer*ric,* with a valence of $+3$. Since there are 3 chlorine atoms associated with the iron in this formula, the iron has a valence of $+3$, and the compound is *ferric chloride.* $FeCl_2$ is *ferrous chloride.* You will notice that when an element has two valences, the *-ous* suffix is used with the ion of lower valence and the *-ic* suffix with the ion of higher valence.

Another system is sometimes used to name certain binary compounds. *Binary compounds* are those which consist of only two elements. Some of these are named by the following steps.

1. The first word of the name is made up of: *a.* a prefix to indicate the number of atoms of the first element appearing in the formula, if more than one; and *b.* the name of the first element in the formula.

2. The second word of the name is made up of: *a.* a prefix to indicate the number of atoms of the second element appearing in the formula, if there exists more than one compound of these two elements; *b.* the root of the name of the second element; and *c.* the suffix, *-ide,* which means that *only* the elements named are present.

Carbon monoxide is written CO. Only one atom of the first element appears in the formula, so no prefix is used with the first word; it consists only of the name of the first element, *carbon.* The prefix *mon-* is used in the second word of the name because there is only one atom of oxygen in this formula, but there is more than one compound of carbon and oxygen. *Ox-* is the root of the name of the element oxygen. Then comes the suffix *-ide*.

In like manner, CO_2 is carbon dioxide. The prefix denoting three is *tri-;* for four it is *tetra-;* and for five it is *pent-* or *penta*. These prefixes are used with both the first and second words in the name. As examples, we might give $SbCl_3$, antimony trichloride; CCl_4, carbon tetrachloride; and As_2S_5, diarsenic pentasulfide.

The methods of naming compounds which have just been described have been used for many years by chemists. Recently another system of nomenclature was introduced, but has not yet gained wide acceptance. This system is briefly described in the Appendix, Table 3.

15. What is the significance of a formula? A formula gives an indication of the simplest molecule which may exist between combining elements. This simplest formula may be only an empirical formula. The actual molecule which is formed may be the same as the empirical formula, or it may be a multiple of the unit indicated in the empirical formula. For compounds which do not exist as molecules, a formula is empirical and merely indicates the relative number of atoms of each element present.

As a beginner in chemistry you must be warned against expecting too much from the valence scheme. A formula can give no more information than that required to write it. It is possible to write the formula for a compound and then learn that such a compound just does not exist! There are many formulas, too, for compounds which do exist but which do not follow the rules of ionic valence. You will be unable to

explain the formulas of any of these well-known compounds by the ionic valence scheme: H_2O_2, C_2H_2, CaC_2, C_2H_4, CO, or Fe_3O_4. Some of these apparent discrepancies are explained by covalent chemical bonding in the molecule:

H
:O:O:
H   H:C:::C:H

Ca++
        H H
⁻C:::C⁻   C::C   :C:::O:
        H H

Others are the result of oversimplification of the formula. Fe_3O_4, for instance, is a formula which is oversimplified. It actually should be written $FeO\cdot Fe_2O_3$.

16. Valence explains the Law of Definite Proportions. We are now able to understand the real significance of the Law of Definite Proportions. It is very easily explained by the principles of valence which we have just learned. The fact that atoms share, or transfer, or receive certain numbers of electrons when they combine controls the proportion in which those elements can combine. Only 1 hydrogen atom can combine with 1 chlorine atom. The hydrogen atom can share only 1 electron and the chlorine atom needs only 1 electron to complete its octet of M-shell electrons. The ratio of the two atoms which combine can be only 1 to 1. It cannot be 1 to 2, or 3 to 2, or some other ratio. Consequently, hydrogen chloride is always HCl, 1 atom of hydrogen to 1 atom of chlorine. The reason for other compounds being formed with very definite proportions depends on valence—the combining power of the individual atoms.

Summary

Valence means the combining capacity of an element. Chemical bonds are produced when valence electrons are either transferred from the outer shell of one atom to the outer shell of another atom, or are shared with electrons in the outer shell of another atom. The formation of chemical bonds usually enables an atom to acquire a chemically stable outer shell consisting of an octet of electrons.

There are two types of chemical bonding. *1.* Ionic bonding, in which electrons are actually transferred from the outer shell of one atom to the outer shell of a second atom. The resulting particles are ions—atoms or groups of atoms with an unbalanced electrostatic charge. *2.* Covalent bonding, in which two atoms share a pair of electrons and form molecules. Valence is the number of electrons which an atom gains, loses, or shares in bonding with one or more atoms. Elements may show several valences.

Radicals are groups of atoms which act like single atoms in forming compounds.

When we write formulas for compounds using the Table of Valences, the total valence of the first part of the compound must equal the total valence of the second part of the compound. (The total valence of a part of a compound is found by multiplying the valence of the part by the number of those parts taken.) The number of atoms or radicals taken is adjusted so the total valences are equal, and subscripts are used to indicate the number of atoms or radicals taken. These compounds are named by giving the names of the two parts of the compound.

When we name binary compounds, those containing only two elements: *1.* the first word consists of (*a*) a prefix to indicate the number of atoms of the first element appearing in the formula, if more than one, and (*b*) the name of the first element in the formula; *2.* the second word consists of (*a*) a prefix to indicate the number of atoms of the second element, if there is more than one compound of these two elements, (*b*) the root of the name of the second element, and (*c*) the suffix *-ide.*

A formula indicates the simplest molecule which may exist between combining elements.

Valence explains the Law of Definite Proportions. The number of electrons which can be gained, lost, or shared controls the proportions in which atoms can combine.

Test yourself on these terms

binary compound	electrovalence	macromolecule
chemical bond	formula	molecular crystal
chemical stability	ion	radical
complete shell	ionic bonding	subscript
covalence	ionic crystal	total valence
covalent bonding	kernel	valence
diatomic	Law of Definite Proportions	valence electrons

Questions

Group A

1. What is valence?
2. (a) What part of the atom is involved in the production of a chemical bond? (b) How are such bonds formed?
3. (a) What are the types of chemical bonding? (b) What particles result from each type of bonding?
4. (a) What is an ion? (b) How does it differ from an atom?
5. What is the valence of: (a) sodium; (b) cuprous; (c) ferric; (d) nickel; (e) hydrogen?
6. What are the names of the following radicals: (a) NH_4; (b) SO_4; (c) NO_3; (d) CO_3; (e) $C_2H_3O_2$?
7. What is the valence of: (a) HCO_3; (b) Br; (c) CrO_4; (d) SO_3; (e) PO_4?
8. Write the formulas for the following compounds: (a) barium chloride; (b) calcium oxide; (c) magnesium sulfate; (d) silver bromide; (e) zinc carbonate.
9. What are the names of the following compounds: (a) $NaHCO_3$; (b) H_2O_2; (c) $HgCl_2$; (d) $Fe(OH)_3$; (e) $Ni(C_2H_3O_2)_2$?
10. Write the formulas for the following compounds: (a) ammonium nitrate; (b) aluminum sulfide; (c) cupric hydroxide; (d) lead phosphate; (e) ferric sulfate.
11. Name these compounds: (a) CuCl; (b) CaS; (c) $KHSO_4$; (d) $NaNO_2$; (e) $Al(ClO_3)_3$.
12. Write the formulas for the following compounds: (a) chromic fluoride; (b) nickel chlorate; (c) potassium bicarbonate; (d) calcium chromate; (e) mercuric iodide.
13. What are the names of the following compounds: (a) Na_2O_2; (b) NH_4NO_2; (c) $Mg_3(PO_4)_2$; (d) $FeSO_4$; (e) Ag_2CO_3?
14. Write formulas for: (a) sodium bisulfate; (b) lead chromate; (c) cuprous chloride; (d) mercurous nitrate; (e) ferrous oxide.
15. Name the following: (a) K_2SO_3; (b) $BaCrO_4$; (c) $Cr(OH)_3$; (d) $PbBr_2$; (e) HgI.
16. How does valence explain the Law of Definite Proportions?

Group B

17. (a) What kind of outer electronic shell does an atom usually attain when it combines with other atoms? (b) Why is this electronic structure chemically stable?
18. Describe the types of energy changes which may occur: (a) in electron transfer; and (b) in sharing of electrons.
19. Draw an electron-dot symbol for: (a) a potassium atom; (b) a potassium ion.
20. Draw an electron-dot symbol for (a) a sulfur atom; (b) a sulfide ion.
21. Write the names for these compounds according to the system for naming binary compounds: (a) SO_3; (b) $SiCl_4$; (c) PBr_3; (d) As_2O_5; (e) PbO.

22. Write the formulas for these compounds: (a) sulfur dioxide; (b) bismuth trichloride; (c) manganese dioxide; (d) arsenic pentiodide; (e) carbon tetraiodide.

23. Explain why copper shows valences of +1 and +2.

24. (a) How is a radical similar to a molecule? (b) How does a radical differ from a molecule?

★ 25. Classify the following compounds according to ionic or covalent bonding: (a) potassium bromide; (b) magnesium chloride; (c) carbon monoxide; (d) sodium oxide; (e) sulfur dioxide.

★ 26. Naphthalene crystals melt at 80° C, while sodium bromide crystals melt at 755° C. Which crystals are ionic and which are molecular?

27. Nitrogen atoms are joined in N_2 molecules by a triple covalent bond. Draw the electron-dot formula for a nitrogen molecule.

28. Draw an electron-dot formula to show a possible structure for carbon dioxide.

Check your progress in chemistry

1. What are the six steps in the application of the scientific method?

2. What generalization did Einstein make which has contributed to our understanding of matter and energy?

3. Define the following terms: (a) matter; (b) heterogeneous material; (c) homogeneous material; (d) mixture; (e) element; (f) compound.

4. What is the meaning of the chemical symbol Na?

5. On the basis of the Kinetic Theory, how are the following observations explained: (a) gases are compressible; (b) gases exert pressure; (c) gases have a lower density than solids or liquids; (d) gases will completely fill any container into which they are admitted; (e) gases can be liquefied by compression?

6. What methods may be used to bring about chemical changes?

7. Give five statements to summarize the atomic theory.

8. Nitrogen has an atomic number of 7 and an atomic weight of 14. Explain how a nitrogen atom is made up.

9. What is the significance of the Roman numeral designation of the A groups such as IA, IIA, IIIA, etc., on the Periodic Table?

10. Draw electron-dot symbols for the elements of the second series.

11. What is a probable electron distribution for element 104?

12. Why are the Inert Gases inert?

13. How do you explain the fact that chlorine has an atomic weight of 35.457, yet there are no atoms of chlorine that weigh this amount?

14. When we say that magnesium has an atomic weight of 24, what do we mean?

15. What similarities are there in the elements of Group IA?

16. How do the properties of the elements change as you go across period four of the Periodic Table?

17. Which family of elements on the Periodic Table has 6 electrons in the outermost shell?

18. Why does sodium have a valence of +1 in compounds and sulfide have a valence of −2?

19. How does ionic bonding differ from covalent bonding?
20. What is the formula for: (a) aluminum hydroxide; (b) cuprous oxide; (c) ammonium sulfide; (d) lead acetate; (e) ferric bromide; (f) magnesium bicarbonate; (g) silver sulfide; (h) mercuric iodide; (i) potassium sulfite; (j) nickel phosphate?
21. Give the names of the following compounds: (a) CO; (b) CO_2; (c) SO_2; (d) SO_3; (e) N_2O_3; (f) N_2O_5.
22. Draw an electron-dot formula for (a) barium chloride; (b) sulfur dioxide.

Challenging your knowledge

1. Write formulas for the following compounds: (a) cesium bromide; (b) hydrogen selenide; (c) radium carbonate; (d) indium hydroxide; (e) rubidium chromate.
2. Why is 6 a possible valence for chromium?
3. Make a chart showing the order in which electrons enter the subshells of the various energy levels as the atoms increase in complexity.
4. (a) How was the magnitude of an atomic mass unit decided upon? (b) Why is there a difference between the atomic mass scale and the atomic weight scale?
5. Why are tellurium and iodine in proper position in the Periodic Table according to atomic numbers but not according to atomic weights?
6. Naturally-occurring copper consists of the following percentages of two isotopes: 69.09% Cu-63 and 30.91% Cu-65. Cu-63 has a mass of 62.957 a.m.u., and Cu-65 has a mass of 64.955 a.m.u. What is the calculated atomic weight of copper? How does it compare with the accepted value for the atomic weight of copper?

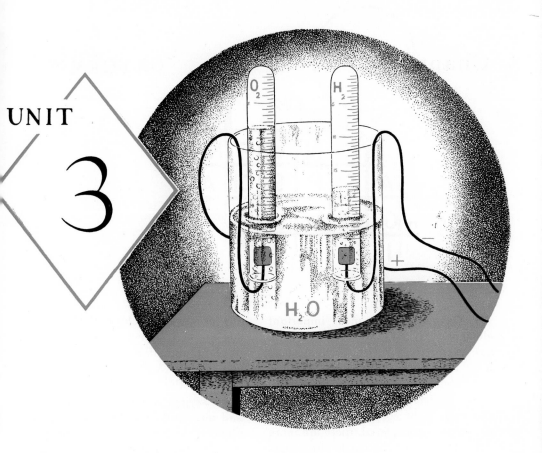

Water and its Elements

The drawing above shows the decomposition of our most common liquid, water, into its constituent elements, hydrogen and oxygen. This decomposition is brought about by means of electricity.

In this unit you will learn much more about this interesting electrochemical process. In addition you will learn about the properties and reactions of the gases, oxygen and hydrogen. You will discover how gas volumes are affected by changes in pressure and temperature. And lastly, you will study the chemical properties and methods of purification of water.

Four chapters are included in this unit: *Oxygen, Hydrogen, The Gas Laws,* and *Water.* You are sure to find many new and interesting things about these common substances during your study of this unit.

Chapter 7

OXYGEN

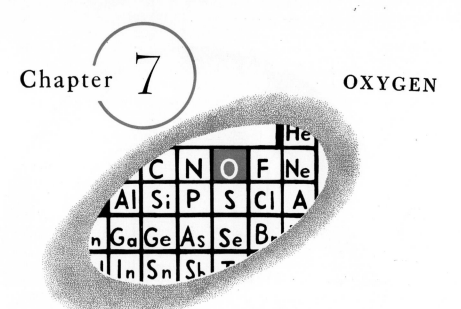

1. OXYGEN

1. Oxygen is our most important element. Oxygen, atomic number 8, has several characteristics which make it the most important element. It is the most abundant element in the earth's crust. In fact, it has been estimated that even if the composition of the entire earth is considered, there are more oxygen atoms in the earth, the waters on the earth, and in the atmosphere surrounding the earth, than atoms of any other single element. Oxygen, as you know, is necessary for the support of plant, animal, and human life. Oxygen combines with more elements than does any other single element.

2. Oxygen is found in the land, sea, and air. About one fifth of the atmosphere is oxygen. Animals living in water get their oxygen from the small amount that is dissolved in water. Oxygen in the air and oxygen that is dis-

VOCABULARY

Allotrope. One of the two or more different forms of an element.

Anode. The positive terminal of an electrolytic cell.

Cathode. The negative terminal of an electrolytic cell.

Combustion. Any chemical action which occurs so rapidly that both noticeable heat and light are produced.

Electrolysis. Separation of a compound into simpler substances by electricity.

Kindling temperature. The lowest temperature at which a substance takes fire and continues to burn.

Oxidation. The process by which oxygen unites with some other substance. (This involves a loss of electrons.)

Oxide. A compound consisting of oxygen and usually one other element.

Resonance. The property of an atom or molecule of shifting its electronic structure between two or more different patterns.

Spontaneous combustion. A combustion started by the accumulation of heat from slow oxidation.

Volatile. Easily vaporized.

solved in water are examples of *free* or *elementary oxygen*. As the free element, oxygen consists of diatomic covalent molecules, O_2. Oxygen that has united with other elements to form compounds is called *combined oxygen*. Combined oxygen is much more plentiful than free oxygen. Water contains almost 89% oxygen by weight in combination with hydrogen. Such minerals as clay, sand, and limestone contain a large percentage of combined oxygen. In fact, oxygen is one of the elements present in most of the rocks and minerals of the earth's crust.

3. Joseph Priestley is credited as the discoverer of oxygen. Priestley (1733–1804) was an English clergyman and scientific experimenter. His greatest discovery came in 1774 when he used a lens to focus the sun's rays on mercuric oxide, a red powder. When mercuric oxide is heated strongly, the bond between the atoms is broken, oxygen comes off as a gas, and mercury remains. The equation for this chemical change is:

$$2\,HgO \rightarrow 2\,Hg + O_2\uparrow$$

A chemist uses an equation like this to show what happens during a chemical reaction. He writes the formulas of the material, or materials, he starts with (in this case mercuric oxide, HgO) on the left. Instead of an equals sign (=), he uses an arrow ($\rightarrow$). When you read the equation, you should read the arrow as "yields." The materials produced in the reaction are placed at the right of the arrow. This reaction produces mercury, Hg, and oxygen, O_2. If the product is a gas, as oxygen is in this case, we place an arrow pointing upward beside its formula to show that it is a gas. A word interpretation

of this equation would be: Two molecules of mercuric oxide, when heated, yield two atoms of mercury and a molecule of oxygen gas. The writing of chemical equations will be discussed in more detail in Chapter 12.

Priestley did not call the gas which he discovered oxygen. He described it as "perfect air" or "very active air." He was delighted to find that a candle would continue to burn in the gas at a lively rate. Priestley inhaled some of the gas and said that he felt peculiarly free and light for some time. The gas was later named *oxygen* by the French chemist Lavoisier (la-*vwah*-see-ay).

It is remarkable that Karl Wilhelm Scheele (*shay*-luh) (1742–1786), a Swedish chemist, also discovered oxygen about the same time. His results were not published until several years after his discovery, and by that time

Fig. 7–1. Joseph Priestley, an English scientific experimenter, was a co-discoverer of oxygen.

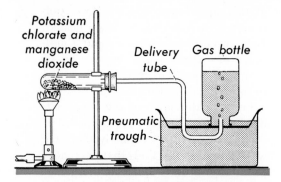

Fig. 7-2. An apparatus of this type may be used for the laboratory preparation of oxygen.

Priestley had been generally acknowledged as the discoverer of oxygen. Undoubtedly Scheele should be given equal credit as its co-discoverer.

4. How is oxygen prepared? There are several ways of preparing this element.

1. By heating potassium chlorate. This is the laboratory method most commonly used. Potassium chlorate is a white, crystalline solid composed of potassium, chlorine, and oxygen. When this compound is heated, it decomposes. Oxygen is given off and potassium chloride is left as a residue. The equation is:

$$2 \; KClO_3 \rightarrow 2 \; KCl + 3 \; O_2\uparrow$$

Manganese dioxide is usually mixed with the potassium chlorate in this laboratory preparation. But the manganese dioxide is a catalyst or catalytic agent. It is not permanently changed in the reaction; therefore we do not include it in the equation (see Chapter 3, Section 13, Subsection 5).

Fig. 7-2 shows us how oxygen is generated and collected in the laboratory. The oxygen gas which is produced in the large test tube passes through the delivery tube into an inverted bottle that has previously been filled with water. As the oxygen rises in the bottle, it displaces, or takes the place of, the water. This method of collecting gases is known as *water displacement*. It is used for gases which are not appreciably soluble in water.

2. By the addition of water to sodium peroxide. Sodium peroxide, Na_2O_2, is a compound which is prepared by burning sodium in air. If

Fig. 7-3. Oxygen may also be prepared in the laboratory by adding water to sodium peroxide.

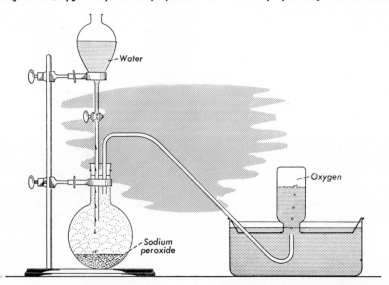

water is allowed to drop onto sodium peroxide in a generator like that shown in Fig. 7-3, oxygen is liberated.

$$2 Na_2O_2 + 2 H_2O \rightarrow 4 NaOH + O_2\uparrow$$

This is a convenient laboratory method for preparing small quantities of oxygen since it does not require heat. But sodium peroxide is a more expensive source of oxygen than potassium chlorate.

3. By the electrolysis of water. Fig. 7-4 represents a laboratory apparatus in which water may be electrolyzed or decomposed by electrical energy. A direct current of electricity is passed through the water. Oxygen gas collects at the positive terminal (anode), and hydrogen gas at the negative terminal (cathode). Sulfuric acid is added to make the water a better conductor of electricity.

$$2 H_2O \rightarrow 2 H_2\uparrow + O_2\uparrow$$

Large quantities of electrical energy are needed to decompose the water. The hydrogen, which is produced simultaneously in the apparatus, may be collected and sold as a by-product.

4. From liquid air. This is the common industrial method for preparing oxygen. Air can be changed to a liquid. We need only to compress it greatly at the same time that it is being cooled to a very low temperature ($-200°$ C). The liquid air which results consists largely of oxygen and nitrogen. Liquid nitrogen ($-195.8°$ C) has a boiling point about thirteen degrees lower than that of liquid oxygen ($-183°$ C). Hence, if we permit liquid air to stand, the nitrogen will soon boil away and leave nearly pure liquid oxygen. The oxygen, which then boils away, is collected, and is pure enough for indus-

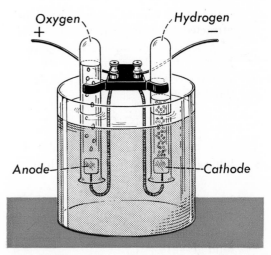

Fig. 7–4. An apparatus of this type may be used to decompose water by electrolysis.

trial purposes. The raw material for this method of preparing oxygen costs nothing, but the machinery used is very expensive. Other gases are obtained from the liquid air and are sold as by-products.

5. The physical properties of oxygen. Pure oxygen is a colorless, odorless, tasteless gas which is slightly denser than air. At standard conditions of temperature ($0°$ C) and pressure (760 mm), one liter of oxygen weighs 1.43 g. Under the same conditions, one liter of air weighs 1.29 g. Oxygen is slightly soluble in water. The colder the water is, the greater is the volume of oxygen that can be dissolved in it. About five liters of oxygen can be dissolved in 100 liters of water at $0°$ C, but the same volume of water at $20°$ C can dissolve only three liters.

Any gas may be converted into a liquid if it is compressed under a high enough pressure, and cooled sufficiently at the same time. Oxygen may be converted into a liquid which is pale-blue in color. Liquid oxygen boils at

−183.0° C. Liquid oxygen is slightly attracted by a magnet. It is this effect of a magnet on liquid oxygen which leads us to believe that there are un-paired electrons in an oxygen molecule. That is why

$$:\overset{..}{\underset{.}{O}}:\overset{..}{\underset{.}{O}}:$$

is a more accurate electron-dot formula for an oxygen molecule than

$$:\overset{..}{O}::\overset{..}{O}:$$

Further cooling of liquid oxygen results in its freezing to a pale-blue crystalline solid at −218.4° C.

6. The chemical properties of oxygen. Oxygen is one of the most active elements. It combines with all of the elements except the inert gases. The most important chemical property of oxygen is its activity. Pure oxygen is much more active than air, which contains one volume of oxygen diluted with about four volumes of nitrogen and other gases. An increase in temperature increases the activity of oxygen greatly. Iron, at room temperature and in the presence of moisture, unites slowly with oxygen. The resulting product is ferric oxide, commonly called *iron rust.*

$$4\ Fe + 3\ O_2 \rightarrow 2\ Fe_2O_3$$

If we heat a strand of steel picture wire or a small bundle of steel wool red hot and plunge it into pure oxygen, the steel burns brilliantly and gives off bright sparks. Molten drops of another oxide of iron, Fe_3O_4, are formed in this reaction.

$$3\ Fe + 2\ O_2 \rightarrow Fe_3O_4$$

Oxygen also unites with some non-metals, such as sulfur and phosphorus.

$$S + O_2 \rightarrow SO_2\uparrow$$
$$4\ P + 5\ O_2 \rightarrow P_4O_{10}$$

Both of these nonmetals burn readily in air, but even more rapidly in pure oxygen. When so burned, they give off a bright light. In each case, the union of oxygen with another element forms a compound known as an oxide. *An oxide is a compound consisting of oxygen and (usually) one other element.*

Oxides are common compounds. Such metals as tin, lead, copper, and zinc unite with oxygen to form oxides, either slowly when cold, or more rapidly when heated. Hydrogen unites with oxygen to form water, H_2O.

$$2\ H_2 + O_2 \rightarrow 2\ H_2O$$

Carbon unites with oxygen to form carbon dioxide, CO_2, when there is an excess of oxygen present, or indirectly to form carbon monoxide, CO, when there is an excess of carbon.

$$C + O_2 \rightarrow CO_2\uparrow$$
$$CO_2 + C \rightarrow 2\ CO\uparrow$$

7. The test for oxygen. A blazing splint continues to burn in air, but it burns more vigorously in pure oxygen. If we lower a glowing splint into a bottle of pure oxygen, the splint will burst into flame immediately. *This is the test to identify oxygen.*

8. The uses of oxygen. *1. Oxygen is the prime essential for life.* Food and water are also essential for life, but we could get along for longer periods if our food and water were cut off than if our supply of oxygen were removed. Without oxygen, living things could exist for only a short while. In the higher animals and in man, oxygen enters the lungs as air is inhaled. It diffuses through thin membranes of the lungs into the blood stream from which it may diffuse into the various cells of the body.

Fish and other animals that live in water get their oxygen from the air that is dissolved in the water.

In the case of plants, all of them—except some of the simplest ones like certain bacteria—require oxygen for their life processes.

2. Oxygen is used in special occupations. It is common for a fireman to enter a smoke-filled, burning building. Miners sometimes enter mines which are filled with poisonous gases. In such cases, an oxygen mask may be worn to give the wearer an independent supply of pure oxygen. Although deep-sea divers are usually supplied with fresh air pumped directly to them from the surface, they are sometimes equipped with a self-contained oxygen apparatus.

Aviators who ascend to high altitudes may suffer from dizziness, or even unconsciousness, because the air is too rare to supply enough oxygen for breathing. On such flights supplementary oxygen is supplied to the aviator through a tube or through an oxygen mask.

Fig. 7–5. Equipped with a pressure suit and oxygen, Captain J. W. Kittinger soared to an altitude of 18 miles in this metal capsule. Below, the balloon that raised the capsule to this record altitude.

Fig. 7–6. Oxygen, under pressure of several hundred pounds per square inch, is stored and shipped in large steel cylinders. Strong valves at the top of the cylinders may be opened to release the oxygen as it is needed.

3. Oxygen tents are used in hospitals. Pure oxygen, or air to which more oxygen has been added, is sometimes given to persons suffering from pneumonia or other diseases. It is also administered to persons who may be too weak to inhale a normal quantity of air, such as persons who have experienced heart attacks. For these purposes the patient is placed in an oxygen tent. An electric motor keeps the tent supplied with air to which oxygen is added in any desired proportion.

In cases of asphyxiation from inhaling smoke or suffocating gases, from apparent drowning, or from electric shock, oxygen may be administered by means of an inhalator.

4. Oxygen aids in the purification of water and sewage. Sunlight and oxygen are excellent agents for destroying harmful bacteria. Rivers containing sewage are purified by flowing considerable distances in contact with the oxygen of the air. The oxygen from the air which dissolves in the water supports the life of organisms which act on and decompose the polluting materials. In the sewage disposal plants of some cities, sewage is sprayed into the air in tiny jets in order to increase the amount of dissolved oxygen and thus hasten the purification process.

Fountains, cascades, and other devices are used to aid in city water purification. By exposing water to contact with air, bacteria are destroyed, and the water also becomes more palatable for drinking.

5. Oxygen is used in torches for welding. The oxyhydrogen torch was invented in 1801 by Robert Hare (1781–1858), an American chemist. Essentially it consists of two concentric tubes. Hydrogen from a storage cylinder passes through the outer tube and is lighted at the tip. The oxygen from a separate cylinder passes through the inner tube. It unites chemically with the hydrogen and produces a very hot flame. The oxyhydrogen torch, which yields a temperature of about 2300° C, is still used for melting platinum and quartz, as well as to fuse aluminum oxide in making artificial rubies. But for many purposes today, the oxyacetylene torch is more popular. As you see in Fig. 7-9, acetylene is used instead of hydrogen as the flammable gas. The flame of this torch has a very high temperature, estimated at about 3400° C to 3700° C. It is used extensively to cut steel rails, to cut apart automobiles locked together in a crash, or to cut iron and steel in wrecking buildings. It is also used for welding metals.

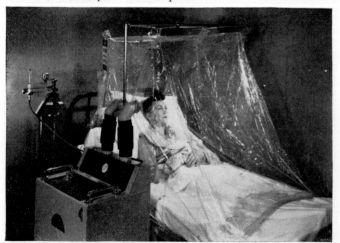

Fig. 7–7. An oxygen tent is used in the treatment of persons who are suffering from respiratory diseases or who are too weak to inhale a normal quantity of air. An electric motor keeps the tent supplied with air to which oxygen in any desired proportion is added.

2. OXIDATION AND COMBUSTION

9. What is oxidation? Suppose we scrape the surface of a piece of sheet lead until it is bright and lustrous. In a few days we find that the surface of the lead has again become dull and tarnished. The oxygen in the air has united slowly with the lead to form this tarnish, which is lead oxide. In a somewhat similar way, the oxygen which we take into our lungs in breathing unites with the carbon and hydrogen in our foods. It *oxidizes* them, or *converts them into oxides.* The carbon and oxygen unite to form carbon dioxide. The hydrogen unites with the oxygen to form water. In each of these cases, heat is evolved, but no light is produced. It is this heat from oxidation which keeps the temperature of a normal, healthy human body at about 98.6° F. The decay of wood and vegetable matter and the rusting of certain metals like iron are examples of slow oxidation. We may define **oxidation,** for the present, as *that process by which oxygen unites with some other substances.* This combination of a substance with oxygen will involve *a loss of electrons of the oxidized material* to the oxygen. This broader definition of oxidation will be more fully utilized in Chapter 23.

In the process of oxidation, the oxygen is usually supplied from the air, which consists of approximately one fifth oxygen by volume. If a more vigorous oxidizing action is needed, pure oxygen gas may be used. If a compound is particularly rich in oxygen, and if it readily gives up some of that oxygen, that compound is a good *oxidizing agent.* Examples of good oxidizing agents are hydrogen peroxide, H_2O_2, nitric acid, HNO_3, and potassium chlorate, $KClO_3$.

10. What do we mean by combustion? If we hold a piece of magnesium ribbon in the flame of a burner, it will ignite and burn with an intense white light. It unites with oxygen so rapidly that both light and noticeable heat are produced. **Combustion** *or* **burning** *is defined as any chemical action which occurs so rapidly that both noticeable heat and light are produced.* When wood burns, the carbon and hydrogen

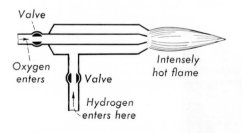

Valve

Oxygen enters

Valve

Intensely hot flame

Hydrogen enters here

Fig. 7-8. (Above) The oxyhydrogen torch produces a flame with a temperature of about 2300° C.

Fig. 7-9. (Right) The oxyacetylene torch is used for cutting and welding metals.

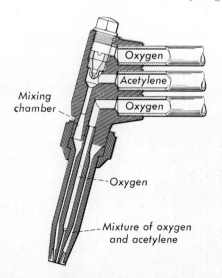

Mixing chamber

Oxygen

Acetylene

Oxygen

Oxygen

Mixture of oxygen and acetylene

of the wood unite chemically with the oxygen of the surrounding air. Ordinary combustion, then, is rapid oxidation in which heat and light are evolved.

Burning, or combustion, is a process involving two materials. We must have both a combustible material and air, or oxygen, for ordinary burning to occur. Materials burn more rapidly in oxygen than they do in air, and some burn in oxygen which do not burn in air at all. Magnesium burns in air, but it burns almost explosively in oxygen. Finely divided iron burns in oxygen, giving off dazzling white sparks.

11. Burning was misunderstood until modern times. In early days, fire and burning were so mysterious that fire worship was not uncommon. Scientists through the ages pondered over this mysterious process and proposed theories to explain it. When substances burned, they seemed to lose something as the flames rose skyward. One theory of burning, which was popular during the 18th century, was the *phlogiston theory* of combustion. According to this theory, a combustible material was rich in a substance called *phlogiston.*

When the material burned, the phlogiston escaped. No one had ever seen phlogiston, of course, but scientists assumed that it was there. Priestley was a firm believer in the phlogiston theory, even to the time of his death. The theory was absurd, but progress in chemistry was delayed until a correct explanation of burning became known. We are indebted to Lavoisier, a French scientist, for the correct explanation of burning and oxidation.

12. Lavoisier's twelve-day experiment. Antoine Laurent Lavoisier (1743–1794), the brilliant French scientist, had been studying the rusting of metals in air when he learned of Priestley's experiments with "perfect air." He came to the conclusion that the "perfect air" was really a part of ordinary air. But he wished to prove his point and therefore devised the following experiment. This is now considered one of the classic experiments of chemistry.

The retort shown in Fig. 7-11 *contained a weighed quantity of mercury,* and the bell jar *contained a measured volume of air* at the beginning of the experiment. The pneumatic trough

Fig. 7-10. Combustion is any chemical action which occurs so rapidly that both noticeable heat and light are produced. The burning of this building in air is an example of combustion.

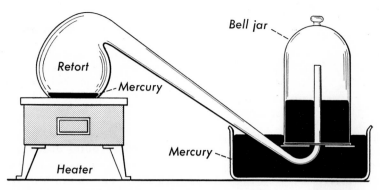

Fig. 7–11. By using apparatus such as this, Lavoisier proved that Priestley's "perfect air" was a part of ordinary air. Lavoisier gave "perfect air" its present name of oxygen.

also contained mercury. When Lavoisier heated the mercury in the retort at a rather low temperature, some of it turned to a red powder. At the same time, the volume of air in the bell jar was reduced. After 12 days no further action took place. *The mercury in the retort had acquired a coating of red powder. The volume of the air in the bell jar had shrunk to four fifths of its former volume.* Thus Lavoisier proved that one fifth of the air is a gas that is capable of uniting with mercury to form a red powder. He named the gas *oxygen.* Today we recognize the red powder as being mercuric oxide, and represent the reaction which took place between the mercury and the oxygen of the air by the following equation:

$$2\,Hg + O_2 \rightarrow 2\,HgO$$

After the first part of the experiment was completed, Lavoisier heated the red powder which had been formed, but more strongly than at first. He found that the gas which was liberated was exactly like Priestley's "perfect air." In fact, this part of Lavoisier's experiment is the same as the reaction by which Priestley discovered oxygen:

$$2\,HgO \rightarrow 2\,Hg + O_2\uparrow$$

13. What do we mean by kindling temperature? Before wood or other combustible material can begin to burn, heat must be applied to warm it to its *kindling temperature. The lowest temperature at which a substance takes fire; and continues to burn, is called its* **kindling temperature.**

Different substances have different kindling temperatures. The warmth of your hand is sufficient to kindle phosphorus, but you must not try it, because phosphorus produces painful burns. The head of a match is made of some material with a low kindling temperature. When the head is scratched, the friction develops enough heat to kindle the matchstick (see Fig. 7-12).

14. Increasing the surface area increases the rate of combustion. Combustion occurs only at the surface of a burning material. Let us support a match head on the tube of a burner as shown in Fig. 7-13. The fact that the match is not kindled shows that the flame is hollow and that burning takes place only at the surface where the gas comes into contact with the air. This may also be shown momentarily by

Fig. 7–12. Why is a match made this way?

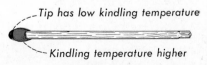

-- *Tip has low kindling temperature*

-- *Kindling temperature higher*

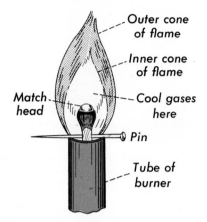

Outer cone of flame

Inner cone of flame

Match head

Cool gases here

Pin

Tube of burner

Fig. 7–13. The unburned match shows that combustion occurs only at the surface where the gases are uniting with oxygen.

thrusting a sheet of paper down on the flame. The charred spot on the paper will be circular, with an uncharred spot in the center.

If we split a block of wood into two pieces, we produce two new surfaces at which combustion can take place. Such pieces will burn faster than a single block. If these pieces are split again, more new surfaces are exposed to the oxygen in the air, and combustion is still more rapid. Excelsior and paper burn rapidly because they have such large surface areas at which combustion can occur.

15. What causes dust explosions? If a powdered substance is loose enough so that oxygen can mix with it readily, it will burn almost instantly. One type of explosion occurs as a practically instantaneous combustion throughout the entire mass. An explosion may be destructive because of the sudden expansion of the heated gases produced by the burning.

Dust scattered through the air of a coal mine, or tiny particles of cork dust in a linoleum factory, or particles of flour in a flour mill may explode with terrific force if they are kindled by an accidental spark. Such an explosion is called a *dust explosion* (see Fig. 7-14).

16. How do we extinguish fires? We must keep in mind that three requirements are needed before combustion can occur: *1.* a supply of combustible material; *2.* a supply of oxygen; *3.* a substance heated to its kindling temperature.

The elimination of any one of these three requirements will extinguish a fire. All the known methods of extinguishing fires make use of at least one of the following principles: *1.* removing the combustible material; *2.* shutting off the supply of oxygen; *3.* cooling the burning substance below its kindling temperature.

Fig. 7-14. A dust explosion started the fire in these grain elevators.

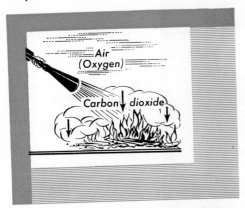

Fig. 7–15. The carbon dioxide "snow" from a CO₂ extinguisher cools the burning material below its kindling temperature. It also forms a heavy gas that blankets the fire.

Some examples of each principle will emphasize each requirement. The scattering of the burning embers of a campfire and turning off the gas on a range are examples of removing the combustible material. Water lowers the temperature of a burning substance, and as the water evaporates, its vapor displaces the supply of oxygen. The effect of lowering the temperature may also be shown by holding a spiral of heavy copper wire in a candle flame. The copper conducts heat away so rapidly that the temperature falls below the kindling point, and the flame is extinguished. Dry sand is often effective for extinguishing oil fires because it cools the burning oil below its kindling temperature, and also displaces the supply of oxygen.

17. What is spontaneous combustion? A *spontaneous combustion* is a fire that seems to start itself. Such fires are due to oxidation in a confined space. We know that oxidation liberates heat. If the heat from oxidation cannot escape easily, it accumulates and increases the temperature of the combustible material. Eventually the kindling point is reached and burning results.

Suppose we place a piece of white phosphorus about as large as a pinhead on an asbestos board. We can assume from the white fumes which rise that oxidation is taking place. Next, let us cover the phosphorus with a little powdered boneblack. The boneblack keeps most of the heat of oxidation from escaping. In a few minutes the phosphorus will take fire.

Many fires start from spontaneous combustion. This often occurs in piles of soft coal, particularly if powdered coal covers a mass of lump coal in the center of the pile. The curing of hay is another process of oxidation. If hay is put into a barn before it is properly dried, oxidation will continue within the confined space and spontaneous combustion may result. Many barns are set on fire in this manner. Paint "dries" because the linseed oil which it contains absorbs oxygen from the air, forming an elastic solid. It is a form of oxidation, and heat is liberated as the paint "dries." For this reason cloths that have been used to wipe spilled

Fig. 7–16. When the copper spiral is lowered into the candle flame, it conducts heat away so rapidly that the flame is cooled below its kindling temperature. As a result, the candle is extinguished.

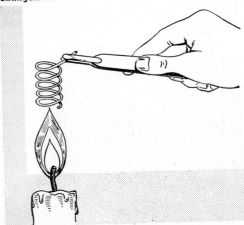

Fig. 7-17. Oily rags, such as those used to wipe up spilled paint, should be put in a metal can as a precaution in preventing fires from starting by spontaneous combustion.

paint are especially dangerous. They should first be hung outdoors where there is a good circulation of air, and then, if they must be kept, stored in a closed metal can as an additional precaution in preventing destructive fires.

18. What are the products of some common oxidations? When you exhale through a clear solution of limewater, a milky, white precipitate is produced. The precipitate is calcium carbonate

Fig. 7-18. A candle is made of compounds containing carbon and hydrogen. When the candle burns, these compounds are oxidized to carbon dioxide and water.

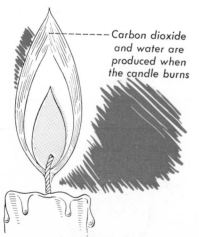

Carbon dioxide and water are produced when the candle burns

and is formed by the reaction between limewater, $Ca(OH)_2$, and the carbon dioxide in your exhaled breath. The carbon dioxide is formed by the slow oxidation of the food you eat.

If you exhale against a cold windowpane, water condenses on the glass. The water is a product of oxidation. It is produced in this case by the oxidation of hydrogen which was present in your food. Slow oxidation of the digested food in your body is a process that produces the same products as the active burning of fuels. The two processes differ principally in the speed and temperature at which they occur.

Fuel gas contains carbon and hydrogen. When it is burned it forms carbon dioxide and water vapor. As you probably know, a wax candle, wood, coal, and such fuels as gasoline and natural gas are composed largely of carbon and hydrogen. When they are burned, carbon dioxide and water vapor are the products.

19. What is a flame? A candle burns with a yellow flame. But before the flame is produced, the wax of the candle must be melted and then changed into a vapor. We will place a glass cylinder over a burning candle so that only a little air enters at the bottom, as shown in Fig. 7-19. We find that it is possible to extinguish the flame and then relight it by bringing a lighted taper just inside the top of the cylinder. The burning taper does not touch the wick, but it ignites the gas which is rising from the wick. This experiment shows that a flame is a burning gas.

*Materials that are easily changed to a gas, or vaporized, are said to be **volatile**.* You know how extremely volatile a liquid gasoline is—how readily it vaporizes. If some gasoline is poured in an open dish, the vapors are easily ignited, and the gasoline burns with much flame. Kerosene is less volatile than gasoline. Hence, the flames from burning kerosene do not rise as high as those from gasoline. Charcoal and coke glow as they burn, but produce little or no flame. They are nearly pure carbon, a solid that does not change to a gas easily. Hard coal does not produce much flame because it contains little volatile matter. Many volatile substances are not combustible. Carbon tetrachloride, often used as a nonflammable cleaning fluid, is an example.

20. How does your laboratory burner operate? To secure better combustion, your burner is designed to mix some air with the gas before it is ignited.

A burner of the type shown in Fig. 7-20 was devised by a German chemist, Robert W. Bunsen (1811–1899). The laboratory burners used today have been somewhat improved over Bunsen's design. In the laboratory burner the gas enters the tube or barrel

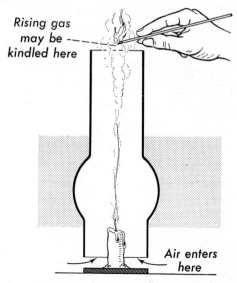

Fig. 7–19. A flame is a burning gas.

through a small opening called the tip or *spud*. The flow of gas through the tip is controlled by the needle valve. Air enters through the holes in the lower end of the barrel or tube. This air mixes with the gas in the tube before it reaches the top of the tube where it is ignited and burns. The tube can be turned to regulate the amount of air that enters. The complete operation of a burner will be explained in the laboratory by your instructor.

Fig. 7–20. A laboratory gas burner, showing the parts of the flame.

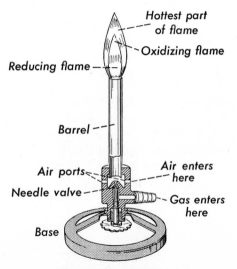

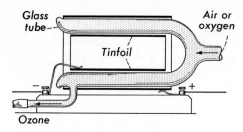

Glass tube

Tinfoil

Air or oxygen

− +

Ozone

Fig. 7–21. Oxygen can be converted to ozone by an electrical discharge in this apparatus.

21. How do the parts of a burner flame differ? An examination of the flame of your burner shows that it consists of two distinct cones (see Fig. 7-20). The outer cone is called the *oxidizing flame*. A piece of copper held in such a flame quickly becomes covered with a black layer of cupric oxide. If we hold the oxide of some metal, cupric oxide for example, in the inner cone of the burner flame, a process occurs that is the opposite of oxidation. The cupric oxide is soon *reduced* to the metallic state in the inner cone. The inner cone is called the *reducing flame*. The flame of the laboratory burner has a temperature of about 1600° C in the hottest part, just above the tip of the inner cone.

22. Some substances do not burn. Some substances burn readily and are said to be *flammable*. Other substances are *nonflammable* and do not burn under ordinary conditions. Nearly all oxides are nonflammable. Water and carbon dioxide make excellent fire extinguishers because they are nonflammable. Similarly, the oxides of calcium, magnesium, and silicon make good materials for lining furnaces because they are incombustible. These substances are already fully oxidized, and therefore are nonflammable.

3. OZONE

23. The occurrence of ozone. A peculiar odor is often noticed where static electricity machines are operating. This odor is due to the presence of ozone, a more active form of oxygen, in the air. Electrical discharges through the air, such as sparks from a static electricity machine or a lightning flash, convert some of the oxygen of the air into a more active form, called ozone. The ultraviolet rays from the sun change some of the oxygen in the upper layers of the atmosphere into ozone.

24. The preparation of ozone. Ozone is produced by passing oxygen through an apparatus like that shown in Fig. 7-21, which consists of glass tubes that are partially covered with layers of tinfoil. The inner layers of tinfoil are connected with one terminal of an induction coil or static machine. The outer layers are connected to the other terminal. The discharge of electricity from one layer to the other provides the energy to convert some of the oxygen into ozone.

25. There is a difference between oxygen and ozone. There are several chemical elements which exist in two or more different forms. Oxygen is one such element. We shall learn later that some other elements, such as carbon, sulfur, and phosphorus, may occur in different forms. In such cases, *the different forms of the element are called allotropes*. Ordinary oxygen and ozone are thus allotropes of oxygen. Allotropes are generally given different names, such as oxygen and ozone, or as in the case of carbon, graphite and diamond are the names of two allotropes.

In converting oxygen to ozone, energy is absorbed. Ozone, therefore, has greater energy than oxygen, and consequently is less stable and more active. Three volumes of oxygen form two volumes of ozone, because oxygen, O_2, has 2 atoms per molecule, while ozone, O_3, has 3 atoms per molecule.

$$3 \ O_2 + \text{energy} \rightarrow 2 \ O_3\uparrow$$

26. The structure of the ozone molecule. Resonance. If we attempt to write an electron-dot formula for the ozone molecule, we discover that there are two possible formulas which provide each oxygen atom with an octet of electrons:

:Ö:
:O: or   :O:
:O: :O:

If ozone actually consisted of these types of molecules, we should find that one of the oxygen-oxygen bonds in the ozone molecule is different from the other. However, the properties of ozone indicate that the two bonds in the molecule are identical. Evidently, then, neither of our electron-dot formulas shows a true picture of the structure of an ozone molecule. The actual molecule shows properties which are an average or *hybrid* of these two types of molecules. The oxygen-oxygen bonds in ozone molecules are intermediate in properties between single and double covalent bonds. The double bond is said to *resonate* between the two positions. *The property of a molecule of shifting its electronic structure between two or more different patterns is called resonance.* It is quite a common property of covalent compounds.

27. The properties of ozone. Ozone is a blue gas with an irritating odor. It is denser than oxygen and considerably more soluble in water. Because ozone molecules have more energy than oxygen molecules, ozone is one of the most vigorous oxidizing agents known. It destroys bacteria, and it causes many colors to fade rapidly.

28. Ozone has several important uses. It has been used to some extent for bleaching wood pulp, textile fibers, oils, and waxes. Attempts have been made to use ozone in ventilating systems of buildings to purify the air. Unfortunately, ozone is too irritating to the nasal passages and cannot be used in sufficient quantity to destroy the bacteria in the air. It is useful, however, for destroying the odors in slaughter houses, cold-storage rooms, and restaurant kitchens, because the oxides of many organic odor-causing substances are odorless gases.

Fig. 7-22. A molecule of oxygen consists of two atoms of oxygen while a molecule of ozone consists of three atoms of oxygen. Oxygen and ozone are allotropes.

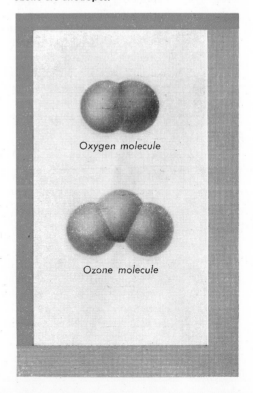

Oxygen molecule

Ozone molecule

Summary

Oxygen, the most abundant element, is found in the air, in water, and in many rocks of the earth's crust. Priestley and Scheele first prepared oxygen by heating mercuric oxide. In the laboratory, it is usually prepared by heating a mixture of potassium chlorate and manganese dioxide. The manganese dioxide acts as a catalyst. Commercially, oxygen is prepared by the electrolysis of water, or from liquid air.

Oxygen is a colorless, odorless, tasteless gas, which is slightly denser than air, and slightly soluble in water. It is a very active element, especially at high temperatures. It combines with other elements to form oxides.

Oxygen is an absolute necessity for life. Firemen, divers, and some aviators use tanks of oxygen in their occupations. Patients who have difficulty in breathing are sometimes administered oxygen. Oxygen aids in the purification of water and sewage. Oxyhydrogen and oxyacetylene torches are used to produce high temperatures and in welding.

Oxidation is that process by which oxygen unites with some other substance. Combustion is rapid oxidation in which noticeable heat and light are produced. Lavoisier was the first to correctly explain the nature of burning. For combustion to occur, we must have a combustible substance; it must be heated to its kindling temperature; and a supply of oxygen must be available. Conversely, to put out a fire, we must remove the combustible material; or we must cool it below its kindling temperature; or we must shut off the supply of oxygen.

A flame is a burning gas. Easily vaporized materials are said to be volatile. Laboratory gas burners are designed to mix some air with the gas before it is burned. Gas flames have an outer cone, called the oxidizing flame, and an inner cone, called the reducing flame.

Ozone is a more active form of oxygen that is produced by an electric discharge. Ordinary oxygen and ozone are allotropic forms of oxygen. The ozone molecule is a resonance hybrid of two types of structure. Resonance is the property of an atom or molecule of shifting its electronic structure between two or more different patterns. Ozone is a vigorous oxidizing agent, destroying bacteria and causing colors to fade.

Test yourself on these terms

allotrope	flammable	oxyacetylene torch
anode	kindling temperature	oxygen tent
burning	Lavoisier	oxyhydrogen torch
catalyst	liquid air	ozone
cathode	meaning of →	phlogiston theory
combined oxygen	meaning of ↑	Priestley
combustion	nonflammable	reducing flame
dust explosion	oxidation	resonance
electrolysis	oxide	volatile
elementary oxygen	oxidizing agent	water displacement
flame	oxidizing flame	method

uestions

Group A

1. Why is oxygen the most important element?
2. Distinguish between: (a) elementary oxygen, and (b) combined oxygen. Give an example of the occurrence of each.
3. Why is manganese dioxide used in the laboratory preparation of oxygen?
4. (a) What method of gas collection is used for oxygen? (b) What property must a gas have so that it may be collected by this method?
5. What are the physical properties of oxygen gas?
6. What type of compound is formed when oxygen combines with another element?
7. How can an old battleship be divided into pieces of steel scrap?
8. Distinguish between oxidation and combustion.
9. (a) What is an oxidizing agent? (b) In ordinary burning, what is the oxidizing agent?
10. Why do we use crumpled paper, sticks of wood, and finally coal, in starting a coal fire?
11. Why does a pile of magazines burn poorly in a rubbish burner?
12. What are the three requirements for combustion to occur?
13. Give three examples of fires that are sometimes started by spontaneous combustion. How may they be prevented?
14. What are the products of oxidation of the carbon and hydrogen compounds in food produced in the body?
15. What are the products of oxidation of the carbon and hydrogen compounds in fuels burned in a furnace?
16. Draw a diagram and explain the operation of a laboratory burner.
17. (a) What is an allotrope? (b) Give two examples of elements which exist in allotropic forms.
18. (a) What advantages does ozone possess for air purification? (b) Why, then, is it not extensively used in air-conditioning systems?

Group B

19. Describe Priestley's discovery of oxygen.
20. What is the word interpretation of the following equation:
    $2 H_2 + O_2 \rightarrow 2 H_2O$?
21. Which has the lower boiling temperature, oxygen or nitrogen?
22. How can you test a colorless, odorless, and tasteless gas to determine whether it is oxygen or not?
23. Why do we drown in water, and yet fishes die in air?
24. (a) Describe Lavoisier's Twelve-Day Experiment. (b) What significance was it to the development of chemistry?
25. Why do dust explosions sometimes occur in flour mills?
26. Give examples of each of the three methods for extinguishing fires.
27. (a) What is the cause of a spontaneous combustion? (b) Give some precautions which will overcome this hazard.
28. What are the similarities and differences in the oxidations described in Questions 14 and 15?

29. By means of electron-dot formulas illustrate resonance in the ozone molecule.
30. Why do we believe that an oxygen molecule contains unpaired electrons?

Problems

Group A

1. Water is 88.89% oxygen. How many grams of oxygen can be obtained by the electrolysis of 100 grams of water?
2. How many liters of oxygen will be produced in Problem 1? One liter of oxygen weighs 1.43 g.
3. Iron rust is 30% oxygen and 70% iron. What weight of iron rust can be formed from 50 lb of iron?

Group B

4. When 12 g of carbon is burned, 44 g of carbon dioxide is produced. How much carbon dioxide goes up the chimney during a season when 10 tons of coal are burned, if the coal contains 80% carbon?
5. Potassium chlorate contains 39% oxygen, and mercuric oxide contains 7% oxygen. How many grams of mercuric oxide would have to be heated to give the same amount of oxygen as that obtained from the heating of 100 g of potassium chlorate?
6. What volume will 100 g of oxygen occupy at 0° C and 760 mm pressure?

Some things for you to do

1. Look up the basic ideas of the phlogiston theory in a history of chemistry or an encyclopedia. Find out how an experiment such as the burning of magnesium ribbon in air would have been explained by this theory. What data would you need concerning this experiment to prove the theory false?
2. Spread a little lycopodium powder on an asbestos square and try to ignite it with a Bunsen burner. Note how difficult it is to get a compact mass to burn. Now spread some of the lycopodium powder on a cardboard. Shake the cardboard about two feet above a Bunsen burner flame in such a way that the lycopodium powder falls as a dust cloud. A flash of flame similar to a dust explosion results.
3. Crumple some paper towels into a loose paper wad, and support the wad on an iron tripod. Dissolve a tiny piece of phosphorus in 10 ml of carbon disulfide, and pour the solution over the paper wad. Spontaneous combustion should occur within a few minutes. CAUTION: *Dispose of all residues in such a way as to avoid accidental fires later.*
4. Visit an automobile repair shop where oxyacetylene welding is done.
5. If you live near or travel during vacation time through Sunbury, Pennsylvania, visit the Priestley Museum in nearby Northumberland. Here you will see some of the actual apparatus used by Priestley, together with many other relics and personal papers preserved from the days after Priestley moved to the United States.

Chapter 8 HYDROGEN

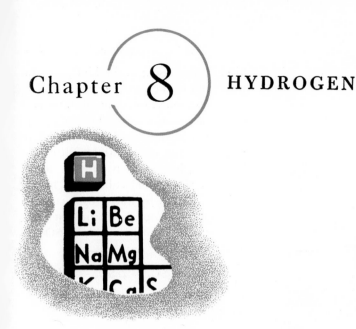

1. The occurrence of hydrogen. Hydrogen, the simplest element, is, like oxygen, a gas at ordinary temperatures. It ranks ninth in abundance by weight among the chemical elements, but it ranks in second or third place if actual numbers of atoms are considered. Hydrogen is usually combined with other elements in a variety of compounds. Free, or elementary hydrogen, which exists as covalent diatomic molecules, H_2, is much less common because of its flammability. Very small traces of hydrogen, probably derived from volcanoes and coal mines, do exist in the air. However, such small amounts are present that we do not list it as one of the important gases of the atmosphere. One ninth of water by weight is hydrogen, and all acids contain this element. Hydrogen is present in nearly all plant and animal tissues. Nearly all fuels—natural gas, wood, coal, and oil—contain hydrogen.

2. The early history of hydrogen. In the sixteenth century it was observed that a combustible gas was produced when sulfuric acid reacted with iron. Henry Cavendish (1731–1810), an English scientist, is usually credited as the discoverer of hydrogen, because in 1766 he first prepared a quantity of the gas and observed its properties. Cavendish observed that hydrogen burns. He called the gas "inflammable air." In 1781, as a result of experiments, he proved that water is the only product of the combustion of hydrogen in air.

VOCABULARY

Absorption. A soaking up of one substance through the entire mass of another.

Adsorption. The accumulation of one substance on the surface of another.

Diffusion. The process by which two or more originally separate kinds of atoms or molecules mix because of their atomic or molecular motion.

Hydrogenation. The addition of hydrogen to a material.

Reduction. The removal of oxygen from a substance. (This involves a gain of electrons.)

Fig. 8–1. Henry Cavendish, an English scientist, first prepared a quantity of hydrogen and studied its properties.

Lavoisier in 1783 suggested the present name *hydrogen,* a word derived from two Greek words meaning "water producer."

3. The preparation of hydrogen. Hydrogen may be prepared from some of its important compounds by several methods.

1. From acids by replacement. This is the usual laboratory method. All acids contain hydrogen, which usually may be set free by reaction with certain metals. Several different acids and several different metals can be used. For example, iron, zinc, or magnesium will react with either hydrochloric acid or sulfuric acid to produce hydrogen. The rate at which hydrogen is evolved in such reactions depends upon several factors. These are *a.* the amount of metal surface exposed to the acid; *b.* the temperature; *c.* the strength and kind of acid used; *d.* the kind of metal used; and *e.* the purity of the metal.

Fig. 8-2 shows one type of apparatus commonly used for the laboratory preparation of hydrogen. Zinc is placed in the bottle and either dilute sulfuric or hydrochloric acid is then added through the funnel tube. The hydrogen is collected by water displacement. The equation to show the chemical change when sulfuric acid, H_2SO_4, is used is:

$$Zn + H_2SO_4 \rightarrow ZnSO_4 + H_2\uparrow$$

With hydrochloric acid, HCl, and zinc, the equation for the reaction is:

$$Zn + 2\ HCl \rightarrow ZnCl_2 + H_2\uparrow$$

We may think when we see this experiment carried out that the zinc dissolves in the acid. But that is not the case. This is a *chemical reaction* in which the metal *reacts* with the acid and forms free hydrogen gas and a zinc compound. The zinc sulfate or zinc chloride is dissolved in the excess water, but either may be recovered as white solids by evaporating the water. We see, then, that new substances with new properties are formed. This is definite evidence of a chemical reaction and not of a mere physical change. If we compare the formulas of the acids with the formulas of the zinc compounds produced, we can easily see that an atom of zinc has taken the place of two atoms of hydrogen.

Fig. 8–2. Hydrogen can be prepared in the laboratory by using an apparatus such as this.

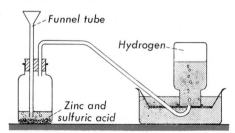

2. *From water by replacement.* Sodium is a silvery metal, soft enough to be easily cut with a knife, and of low enough density to float on water. It is so active chemically, though, that when placed on water, it reacts vigorously with the water and liberates hydrogen gas from it. Each sodium atom replaces one of the hydrogen atoms in a molecule of water. To show this reaction more clearly, let us write the formula for water as HOH, instead of the usual H_2O. Then we have the equation:

$$2 \, Na + 2 \, HOH \rightarrow 2 \, NaOH + H_2\uparrow$$

Each water molecule has had *one* of its hydrogen atoms replaced by a sodium atom. The sodium hydroxide produced may be recovered as a white, crystalline solid if we evaporate the excess water.

Potassium is a metal which is similar to sodium. It is below sodium in the same family in the Periodic Table and is more reactive. When potassium is placed on water, it liberates hydrogen from the water with such vigor that the heat of the reaction is sufficient to ignite the hydrogen. The equation for the reaction of potassium and water is:

$$2 \, K + 2 \, HOH \rightarrow 2 \, KOH + H_2\uparrow$$

Magnesium decomposes *boiling* water slowly. Calcium, in the same family as magnesium, but below it in the Periodic Table, and thus more reactive, will liberate hydrogen slowly from cold water. At a high temperature, iron will liberate hydrogen from steam.

All the methods of preparing hydrogen from water by replacement by metals are laboratory methods.

3. *From water by electrolysis.* When water is decomposed by an electric current, hydrogen as well as oxygen is produced. If oxygen is the main product, then the hydrogen becomes a by-product which can also be sold. This method is used in the United States for producing pure hydrogen in areas where cheap electricity is available. This is also a laboratory method of preparing hydrogen.

4. *From water by hot carbon.* This is a common industrial process for producing hydrogen. When steam is passed over red-hot coal or coke, a mixture of gases called *water gas* is formed. It consists mainly of hydrogen and carbon monoxide. When the mixture is cooled and compressed, the carbon monoxide liquefies, and the remaining hydrogen gas is then compressed into steel cylinders. The equation for the reaction is:

$$C + H_2O \rightarrow CO\uparrow + H_2\uparrow$$

Frequently the carbon monoxide is converted to carbon dioxide by passing the water gas with additional steam over a catalyst, such as iron oxide, at a temperature below 500° C.

$$CO + H_2O \rightarrow CO_2\uparrow + H_2\uparrow$$

Thus additional hydrogen is produced from the steam, and the resulting carbon dioxide is separated by dissolving it in water under moderate pressure.

5. *From hydrocarbons.* Hydrocarbons are compounds composed of hydrogen and carbon which are commonly derived from petroleum or natural gas. If a hydrocarbon, such as propane, C_3H_8, reacts with steam in the presence of a nickel catalyst at a temperature of about 850° C, hydrogen and carbon dioxide are produced.

$$C_3H_8 + 6 \, H_2O \rightarrow 3 \, CO_2\uparrow + 10 \, H_2\uparrow$$

The carbon dioxide may be separated from the hydrogen by dissolving it in water under pressure.

Hydrogen may also be obtained by heating hydrocarbons in the absence of oxygen to decompose them. If methane, CH_4, is so decomposed, the equation for the reaction is:

$$CH_4 \rightarrow C + 2\,H_2\uparrow$$

The carbon produced is in the form of lampblack.

4. The physical properties of hydrogen. Hydrogen gas is colorless, odorless, and tasteless. It is the gas of lowest density. Its density is only one fourteenth that of air. One liter of hydrogen at standard temperature (0° C) and standard pressure (760 mm) weighs only 0.09 gram. It is less soluble in water than oxygen.

In 1898 James Dewar (1842–1923) succeeded in converting hydrogen into a liquid by cooling the gas to a *very low temperature*, and at the same time subjecting it to *very high pressure*. Liquid hydrogen is clear and colorless, and only one fourteenth as dense as water. Thus liquid hydrogen, the liquid of lowest density, weighs only about 70 grams per liter. Under atmospheric pressure, liquid hydrogen boils at −252.7° C. When a part of the liquid is evaporated, the remainder of it freezes to an ice like solid. The melting point of solid hydrogen is −259.1° C. Solid hydrogen is the solid of lowest density, weighing but 88 grams per liter.

An interesting property of hydrogen is its adsorption by certain metals, such as platinum and palladium. *Adsorption is an accumulation of one substance on the surface of another,* whereas **absorption** *is a soaking up of one substance through the entire mass of another,* as in the case of a sponge and water. A piece of platinum *adsorbs,* or

occludes, hydrogen gas, liberating heat in the process. Finely divided platinum offers a larger surface, adsorbing the gas so rapidly that the hydrogen gas may be raised to the kindling temperature. Some gas burners and lighters use this principle for igniting the gas.

Hydrogen diffuses rapidly. This means that hydrogen molecules move about with greater velocity than the heavier molecules of other gases at the same temperature (see Chapter 3, Sections 7 and 8). Let us fill one flask with hydrogen gas and place it above another flask filled with air, as shown in Fig. 8-3. After a few minutes, place the mouth of each flask in the flame of a laboratory burner. The explosions show that the hydrogen molecules moved so that there were some in both flasks.

Even if we separate two gases by a porous barrier, such as a membrane or an unglazed porcelain cup, **diffusion** will take place through the pores. In

Fig. 8–3. Although air is 14 times as dense as hydrogen, the light, fast hydrogen molecules move downward and intermingle with the slower, heavier molecules of the gases in the air in the process called diffusion.

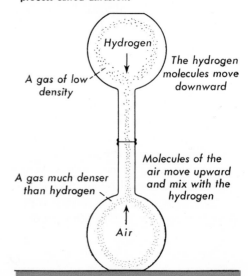

Hydrogen

A gas of low density

The hydrogen molecules move downward

A gas much denser than hydrogen

Molecules of the air move upward and mix with the hydrogen

Air

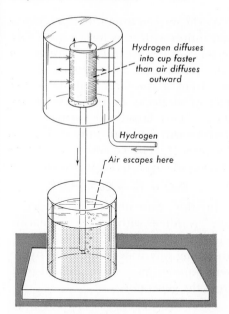

Fig. 8–4. Hydrogen diffuses into the cup faster than air diffuses outward. As a result, some of the air in the cup is forced down the tube and bubbles through the liquid.

Fig. 8-4, an unglazed porcelain cup is closed by a rubber stopper through which a piece of glass tubing has been inserted. When a large beaker filled with hydrogen is placed over the porcelain cup, hydrogen molecules diffuse into the cup faster than the molecules of the gases in air diffuse into the beaker. This creates a pressure in the cup which forces bubbles of gas out the end of the tube.

The rapid diffusion of hydrogen makes it difficult to store in thin-walled containers. Rubber balloons filled with hydrogen will collapse in a short time because the hydrogen will escape through the rubber.

5. The chemical properties of hydrogen. *1. Reaction with oxygen.* Hydrogen burns in air or oxygen with a very hot, pale-blue, nearly invisible flame. Water is the only product of combus-

tion (see Fig. 8-5). The equation follows:

$$2 H_2 + O_2 \rightarrow 2 H_2O$$

We can show by the following experiment that hydrogen does not support combustion. A bottle of hydrogen is held mouth downward while a blazing splint is thrust slowly upward into the bottle (see Fig. 8-6). The hydrogen is ignited and burns at the mouth of the bottle. But the splint does not burn inside the bottle in an atmosphere of hydrogen.

Hydrogen is not a very active element at ordinary temperatures. We know that it combines with oxygen to form water, but a mixture of hydrogen and oxygen must be heated to a temperature of 800° C, or ignited at a lower temperature by an electric spark, to make the gases combine. Then they unite explosively.

2. Reaction with nonmetals. Hydrogen and chlorine do not combine when they are mixed in the dark, but in the presence of direct sunlight they unite explosively, forming hydrogen chloride. A jet of hydrogen will burn in chlorine. The equation for these chemical changes is the same:

$$H_2 + Cl_2 \rightarrow 2 HCl\uparrow$$

Fig. 8–5. When hydrogen is burned in air, water is the only product of combustion.

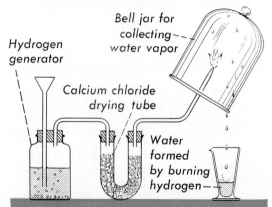

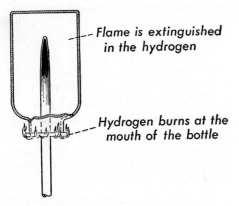

--- Flame is extinguished
in the hydrogen

Hydrogen burns at the
mouth of the bottle

Fig. 8–6. When a blazing splint is thrust upward into a bottle of hydrogen, the hydrogen is ignited and burns at the mouth of the bottle. But the splint does not burn inside the bottle in an atmosphere of hydrogen.

Under suitable conditions, hydrogen may be made to unite with nitrogen to form ammonia, NH_3, a very important compound.

$$3 H_2 + N_2 \rightarrow 2 NH_3\uparrow$$

3. Reaction with metallic oxides. When we heat a piece of sheet copper in the air, the copper is *oxidized,* and a black scale of cupric oxide is formed on the surface. Suppose we put this cupric oxide in a Pyrex glass tube, as shown in Fig. 8-7, and pass a stream of *dry* hydrogen over it while the cupric oxide is being heated. The hydrogen

takes the oxygen from the cupric oxide, and unites with it to form water. *Such removal of oxygen from a compound is called* **reduction.** The removal of oxygen from a substance will involve *a gain of electrons by the reduced substance.* This broader definition of reduction will be more fully utilized in Chapter 23. The equation for the reduction of cupric oxide by hydrogen is:

$$CuO + H_2 \rightarrow Cu + H_2O\uparrow$$

In this experiment the U-shaped tube is filled with calcium chloride, which is used to dry the hydrogen by absorbing any water which the hydrogen bubbles may have carried over from the generator.

From these experiments we see that *oxidation and reduction are opposite processes.* A little study, too, will convince us that neither process can take place without the other. For example, the cupric oxide was *reduced* to metallic copper. But the hydrogen was *oxidized* to water. The cupric oxide acted as an *oxidizing agent* and the hydrogen acted as a *reducing agent.*

6. The test for hydrogen. Suppose you have been given a colorless gas which you wish to prove to be hydrogen. If the gas burns in air and forms water, you know that it contains hy-

Fig. 8–7. When hydrogen is passed over hot cupric oxide, it takes the oxygen from it (reduces it), so that only elementary copper remains.

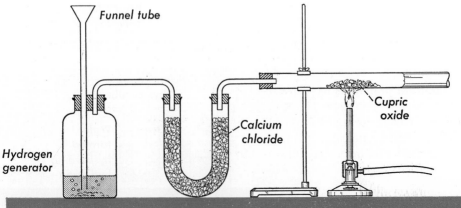

Funnel tube

Cupric
oxide

Calcium
chloride

Hydrogen
generator

drogen. *If a gas burns in air or oxygen with a nearly colorless flame and produces nothing but water as the product,* we have conclusive proof that serves as a test for hydrogen.

7. The uses for hydrogen. Hydrogen is used:

1. For its low density. Because hydrogen is the gas of lowest density, it has been used for filling balloons, both toy balloons for children and large gas bags for airships. What is called the "lifting power" of hydrogen is really the *difference* between the weight of a given volume of air and that of the same volume of hydrogen. Just as a cork rises when released under water, we find that a balloon filled with hydrogen will rise through the air. To lift heavy weights, balloons filled with hydrogen must be large in order that they displace a large amount of air. However, the tendency of hydrogen to leak through tiny openings and its flammability have caused some terrible disasters. Helium, the inert gas with about 93% as much "lifting power" as hydrogen, is much safer. Since it is chemically inert, it is, of course, not flammable. Military balloons of the United States are inflated with helium. The Weather Bureau sends hydrogen-filled balloons aloft to observe air currents and weather conditions in the upper atmosphere.

2. As a reducing agent. Hydrogen can remove oxygen from the oxides of some metals, such as copper, tin, lead, zinc, and iron. Many metals are found in nature as oxides. In order to extract the metals from the oxides, some reducing agent is used. Hydrogen is sometimes used for this purpose, but more often carbon in the form of coke is used because it is cheaper and more convenient.

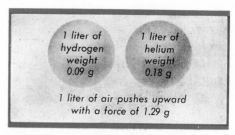

Fig. 8–8. The "lifting power" of 1 liter of hydrogen is 1.29 g − 0.09 g = 1.20 g. That of 1 liter of helium is 1.29 g − 0.18 g = 1.11 g. Thus, helium has 93% as much "lifting power" as hydrogen.

In some cases metals need to be worked in an atmosphere free of oxygen, or in what is called a *reducing atmosphere.* Tungsten, a metal which is used for making the filaments of electric lamps, is worked in a reducing atmosphere. By surrounding the tungsten with hydrogen in a closed furnace, the oxidation of the metal is prevented.

3. As a fuel. Nearly all our fuels contain hydrogen, either free or combined with other elements. Coal gas and oil gas contain hydrogen in quantity. Methane, CH_4, is a major component of natural gas. Hydrogen is used as a fuel for the oxyhydrogen torch. Pure hydrogen makes an excellent fuel. However, it is somewhat more expensive than other available gaseous fuels.

4. For making hydrogen compounds. The greatest use for hydrogen today is in making ammonia, NH_3, by direct union of nitrogen and hydrogen. The ammonia is then used as the starting point for making fertilizers, explosives, and other compounds.

Increased amounts of gasoline are obtained from petroleum by adding hydrogen to some of the higher boiling portions of the oil. High pressures and a catalyst are necessary in this **hydrogenation** of petroleum.

Methanol, or wood alcohol, which is used as an ingredient in antifreeze for automobiles and also as a solvent, is made from hydrogen and carbon monoxide. A catalyst is used to speed up the reaction.

5. *For hardening oils.* Your mother, like many American housewives, probably prefers solid fats to liquid oils for cooking purposes. Accordingly, millions of pounds of cottonseed oil are changed each year from liquid oil to solid fat by hydrogenation. Finely divided nickel is used as a catalyst. Some of the molecules in the liquid oil combine with additional hydrogen atoms in the process, producing a substance that is a solid fat at room temperature, but still a liquid fat at body temperature. Most of the vegetable shortenings you buy at the grocery store are examples of such hydrogenated oil.

Peanut and coconut oil are also hardened by hydrogenation to make margarine or butter substitutes. Some fish oils lose their objectionable odor when they are hydrogenated, and then become suitable for making soap. Lard is sometimes hydrogenated to produce a whiter, firmer product.

6. *In the atomic hydrogen torch.* Molecules of hydrogen are diatomic at ordinary temperatures. Dr. Irving Langmuir (1881–1957), an American

scientist, has shown that it is possible to break up hydrogen molecules into their atoms by passing hydrogen gas through an electric arc. Tungsten electrodes are used, as shown in Fig. 8-9. To produce atomic hydrogen, tremendous energy must be used to overcome the forces binding the atoms into molecules. And the bond between hydrogen atoms in a hydrogen molecule is probably the strongest single covalent bond. The combustion of atomic hydrogen beyond the arc produces heat as water vapor is formed. But also, a much larger amount of heat, equal to the energy expended to break up the hydrogen molecules into atoms, is yielded. Consequently, the atomic hydrogen torch produces the highest sustained temperature which man has been able to produce. (The exploding of an atomic bomb or a hydrogen bomb produces a much higher temperature for very brief intervals.) The temperature produced by the atomic hydrogen torch is estimated at 4000° C. It is used for cutting and welding metals.

7. *In the hydrogen bomb.* The large amount of energy produced by a hydrogen bomb is a result of nuclear reactions taking place between the isotopes of hydrogen, deuterium, and tritium. These reactions will be more fully discussed in Chapter 39.

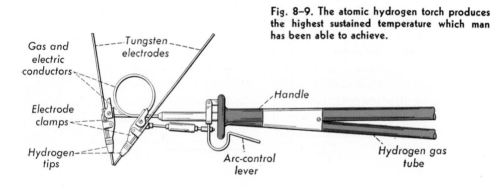

Fig. 8–9. The atomic hydrogen torch produces the highest sustained temperature which man has been able to achieve.

Gas and electric conductors

Tungsten electrodes

Electrode clamps

Hydrogen tips

Handle

Arc-control lever

Hydrogen gas tube

Fig. 8-10. The atomic hydrogen torch is used for welding and cutting metals. The temperature produced is estimated at 4000° C.

Summary

Hydrogen is found in water and in all acids. It was discovered by Cavendish in 1766. In the laboratory it is prepared by reacting an acid with a metal such as zinc, or by adding an active metal such as sodium to water. Commercially, it is prepared from water by electrolysis, by separating the hydrogen from water gas, or from hydrocarbons.

Hydrogen is a colorless, odorless, tasteless gas that has the lowest density of any material known. It is very slightly soluble in water. Platinum and palladium adsorb hydrogen. Hydrogen diffuses readily and can pass through very tiny openings. It burns with a very hot flame that is nearly invisible. Hydrogen is not active at ordinary temperatures. A mixture of hydrogen and oxygen, when ignited, produces an explosion and forms water vapor as the product. Hydrogen and chlorine react to form hydrogen chloride. Hydrogen and nitrogen can be made to unite, forming ammonia.

Reduction may be defined as the removal of oxygen from a compound. Hydrogen is a good reducing agent. Hydrogen readily reduces hot cupric oxide, producing metallic copper and water vapor.

Hydrogen is used for filling balloons because of its low density, but its flammable nature makes such use somewhat dangerous. Hydrogen is sometimes used as a reducing agent in the extraction of metals from oxides. Some gaseous fuels contain elementary hydrogen, while many fuels contain combined hydrogen. Tremendous volumes of hydrogen are used to make ammonia and methanol. The yield of gasoline from petroleum is increased by hydrogenation. Hydrogen is used to convert liquid oils into solid fats for cooking. Hydrogen molecules are split into atoms in the atomic hydrogen torch. The atomic hydrogen torch produces the highest sustained temperature which man has been able to produce, and is used in welding. Hydrogen isotopes are used to produce energy in a hydrogen bomb.

Test yourself on these terms

absorption	hydrocarbon	reducing agent
adsorption	hydrogen	reduction
atomic hydrogen torch	hydrogenation	replacement reaction
Cavendish	lifting power	test for hydrogen
diffusion	occlusion	water gas

Questions

Group A

1. (*a*) What substances are used for the ordinary laboratory preparation of hydrogen? (*b*) What products are formed?
2. Give five physical properties of hydrogen.
3. What happens when a burning splint is thrust into and out of a bottle of hydrogen?
4. (*a*) What product is formed when hydrogen combines with chlorine? (*b*) with nitrogen?
5. Why must all the air be expelled from a hydrogen generator before the gas is lighted at the end of the delivery tube?
6. Why do toy balloons, even when tied tightly, gradually collapse?
7. What happens when sodium is added to water?
8. What solid has the lowest density?
9. Distinguish between *adsorption* and *absorption*.
10. Explain the statement: Oxidation and reduction are opposite processes.
11. Give a use for hydrogen which depends on its: (*a*) low density; (*b*) reducing action; (*c*) combustibility.
12. Describe two commercial methods for preparing hydrogen.
13. In testing bottles of hydrogen gas, should the bottles be held mouth *upward*, or mouth *downward*?
14. How are liquid oils changed to solid fats for cooking purposes?
15. Why do we say that the atomic hydrogen torch produces the highest *sustained* temperature which man has been able to produce?

Group B

16. What reasons can you give for the fact that only very small traces of free hydrogen are present in the atmosphere near the earth's surface?

17. Why is Cavendish credited with the discovery of hydrogen, even though the gas had been known much earlier?

18. What factors determine the rate at which hydrogen is evolved from hydrochloric acid by reaction with coarse iron filings?

19. From its position in the Periodic Table, would you expect cesium to react with water more or less vigorously than potassium?

20. What is the chief operating expense in the production of hydrogen by electrolysis of water?

21. What is a hydrocarbon?

22. In the reaction of steam on hot coke for producing water gas, which substance is: (a) the oxidizing agent; (b) the reducing agent; (c) the substance oxidized; (d) the substance reduced?

23. Describe an experiment to show the diffusion of hydrogen.

24. How may hydrogen be used in the petroleum industry?

25. What happens when a blazing splint is lowered into: (a) a bottle of hydrogen; (b) a bottle of oxygen; (c) a bottle of hydrogen mixed with oxygen; (d) a bottle of hydrogen mixed with air? How do the reactions differ in the two latter cases?

26. Would you use: (a) sand; or (b) water; or (c) either of them for extinguishing the flames from burning potassium? Give a reason for your answer.

27. (a) Is the formation of hydrogen molecules from hydrogen atoms *exothermic* or *endothermic?* (b) What practical use is made of this reaction?

28. Tin oxide reacts with hydrogen to form tin and water vapor. In this reaction, which substance is: (a) the oxidizing agent; (b) the reducing agent; (c) oxidized; (d) reduced?

29. If helium has twice the density of hydrogen, why will helium-filled balloons lift 93% as much as those filled with hydrogen?

30. Suppose the clay cup and inverted beaker of Fig. 8-4 are both filled with hydrogen and the beaker removed: (a) describe the movement of the liquid in the beaker; (b) explain why such movement occurs.

 roblems

Group A

1. Sulfuric acid contains 2.04% hydrogen. How many grams of hydrogen can be prepared from 200 g of sulfuric acid?

2. Water contains 11.11% hydrogen. How many grams of hydrogen can be obtained by the electrolysis of 500 g of water?

3. What will be the volume in liters of the hydrogen produced in Problem 2, if hydrogen weighs 0.09 g/l?

Group B

4. While water contains 11.11% hydrogen, only one-half of it may be replaced when sodium reacts with water. What weight of hydrogen could be obtained from 2 g of water if it is completely reacted with sodium?
5. What volume in milliliters will the gas obtained in Problem 4 occupy?
6. In producing water gas from the reaction of steam on red-hot coke, 12 g of carbon from the coke reacts with 18 g of steam. What volume of hydrogen at 0° C and 760 mm pressure can be obtained from the reaction of 1 metric ton of coke, 90% carbon, by complete reaction with steam? Steam is 11.11% hydrogen.

Some things for you to do

1. Fill a toy rubber balloon with hydrogen from a cylinder of hydrogen gas. Tie the opening securely. If a tank of hydrogen is not available, the laboratory gas supply may be used as a substitute. Leave the balloon in the room for several days, and note how the gas diffuses through the pores of the rubber.
2. Connect a clay pipe by means of rubber tubing with a hydrogen generator. Prepare a bowl of soapy water and add a few drops of glycerol. Now use the stream of hydrogen to blow soap bubbles. Shake the soap bubbles loose, and note how they rise to the ceiling. As they rise, ignite them with a candle attached to a long stick.
3. Prepare some "reduced iron" by heating an iron pipe in which some iron oxide has been placed, and then passing a stream of hydrogen through the pipe. Support the pipe horizontally. Fit a one-hole cork stopper to the end of the pipe nearer the hydrogen generator. Use glass tubing and rubber tubing to connect the generator with the iron pipe.
4. Prepare a biographical sketch of the life of Henry Cavendish and read it to the class.

Chapter 9 THE GAS LAWS

1. PRESSURE CHANGES AFFECT GAS VOLUMES

1. The volume of a gas depends on its temperature and pressure. When you buy a gallon of gasoline or some other liquid, you buy a definite volume of the liquid. It is true that if the liquid is very cold, you receive a slightly greater number of molecules in a gallon than if it is warm. With large volumes of liquid, such as a tank truck of gasoline, expansion and contraction with temperature changes may cause the volume to vary five gallons, or more. But when dealing with smaller volumes of liquids, variations are not particularly noticeable, unless you measure with precision.

With gases, however, we find that the same number of molecules can occupy widely different volumes. The expression "a cubic foot of air" means little unless we also know the temperature and pressure at which it is measured. A cubic foot of the air in your classroom can be compressed to a few cubic inches in volume; it can also expand to fill an empty space as large as your high school auditorium. Steel cylinders of oxygen and hydrogen with an internal volume of two cubic feet are widely used in industry. When such cylinders are returned "empty" they still contain two cubic feet of gas, although when

VOCABULARY

Boyle's Law. The volume of a certain amount of dry gas is inversely proportional to the pressure, provided the temperature remains constant.

Charles' Law. The volume of a certain amount of dry gas varies directly with the Kelvin temperature, provided the pressure remains constant.

Ideal gas. A theoretical gas which conforms exactly to the Gas Laws.

Standard pressure. The pressure exerted by a column of mercury 760 mm high at 0° C.

Standard temperature. 0° Centigrade.

Fig. 9–1. The variation of gas pressure with temperature at constant volume.

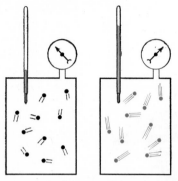

At constant volume, as the temperature of a gas increases, the pressure it exerts increases

they were delivered "full" they may have had 100 times as many molecules of the gas compressed within the cylinder.

In Chapter 3, we learned from the Kinetic Theory that gas molecules are essentially independent particles. They are at relatively great distances from each other, but move rapidly in a random fashion and fill whatever space is available to them. Scientists have computed that if the molecules of the gases in the air that surrounds us could be magnified until they were as big as

Fig. 9–2. The variation of gas volume with temperature at constant pressure.

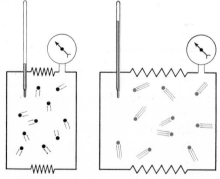

At constant pressure, as the temperature of a gas increases, the volume it occupies increases

baseballs, the average distance between them would be about two feet. This gives us an idea of the relative distance between the tiny molecules that make up all gases. It also explains why we can crowd so many more molecules of a gas into a given space already occupied by gas molecules.

We have already learned that the temperature of a gas is an indication of the average energy of the gas molecules. The higher the temperature of the gas, the more energy the molecules possess, and the more rapidly they move about. As the molecules strike the walls of the container they exert a pressure against it. If the volume which a certain number of gas molecules occupies remains constant, we should expect the pressure exerted by the gas to increase if its temperature is raised. We should also expect the pressure exerted by this same number of gas molecules to decrease if the temperature is lowered (see Fig. 9-1).

Furthermore, if the pressure exerted by this number of gas molecules is to remain the same as the temperature is increased, the volume which the gas occupies must increase. Since the molecules move faster at higher temperatures they strike the walls of the container more frequently and with more force. Only if the area which they strike becomes greater will the force of the molecules striking a unit area remain the same, and the pressure remain the same. The area which they strike can become larger if the volume of the container is larger. In a similar fashion, with pressure remaining constant, and the temperature decreased, the volume which a certain number of gas molecules occupies must become less (see Fig. 9-2).

Finally, if the temperature of these gas molecules remains constant, we should expect the pressure exerted by the gas to be greater if the volume which the gas occupies becomes smaller. And similarly, the pressure exerted by these gas molecules would be less if the volume available to the gas were larger (see Fig. 9-3). As a result of these consequences of the Kinetic Theory, you can readily see that gas volumes are related to the temperature and pressure of the gas. Accordingly, we must consider both temperature and pressure when measuring the volume of a gas.

2. Standard temperature and pressure. Variations in gas volumes make it necessary to select some standard temperature and pressure for use when measuring the volumes, or when comparing them. *Standard temperature is zero degrees Centigrade.* It is the temperature of melting ice, and was selected because it is a convenient and precise temperature. *Standard pressure is the pressure exerted by a column of mercury 760 millimeters high.* We use 760 millimeters of mercury as the standard pressure because that is the average pressure of the atmosphere at sea level. Temperatures are easily measured with an accurate thermometer. The pressure of a gas is measured by means of a barometer. *Standard temperature and pressure is commonly abbreviated as S.T.P.*

3. The mercury barometer is used to measure air pressure. A mercury barometer is used to measure the air pressure. Evangelista Torricelli (toh-ree-*chel*-ee) (1608–1647), an Italian scientist, devised the first mercury barometer in 1643. Torricelli took a glass tube about a meter long, closed it at

Fig. 9–3. The variation of gas pressure with volume at constant temperature.

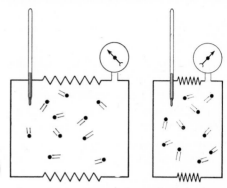

At constant temperature, as the volume of a gas decreases, the pressure it exerts increases

one end, and filled it with mercury. Closing the open end with his thumb, he inverted the tube in a bowl of mercury. When he removed his thumb, a part of the mercury flowed out of the tube. *The air pressure upon the surface of the mercury in the bowl was great enough to support a column of mercury about 760 millimeters high* (see Fig. 9-4). The air pressure varies

Fig. 9–4. The air pressure upon the surface of the mercury in the bowl supports a column of mercury about 760 mm high.

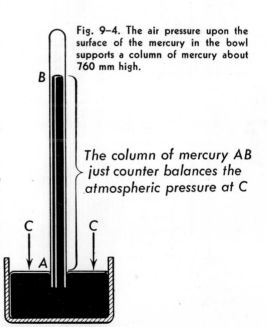

The column of mercury AB just counter balances the atmospheric pressure at C

from day to day, but the average pressure at sea level is just sufficient to support the weight of a column of mercury 760 millimeters high. That is the reason why 760 millimeters of mercury was selected as standard pressure. Such a pressure is called a pressure of *one atmosphere.* The mercury barometer in your laboratory operates on the same principle as the simple barometer Torricelli made. Refinements of construction, however, make it possible to read the laboratory barometer more accurately.

Fig. 9–5. A barometer is used to measure air pressure.

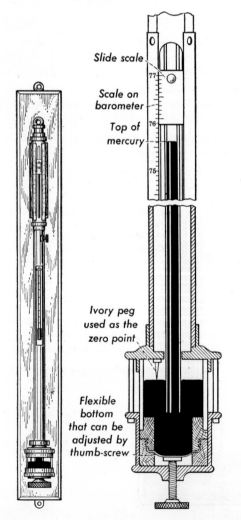

4. Measuring the pressure of a gas collected over mercury. Suppose we deliver some hydrogen into a gas measuring tube called a *eudiometer* (yoo-dih-*om*-eh-ter), which was previously filled with mercury. As hydrogen enters the tube, it bubbles to the top, and pushes the mercury down. Suppose we add enough hydrogen to make the level of the mercury inside the tube just the same as that of the mercury in the bowl (see *1,* Fig. 9-6). *When these two levels are equal, the pressure of the hydrogen is the same as that of the atmosphere.* We can determine this pressure by reading the barometer.

★ Suppose, however, that we did not deliver enough hydrogen into the eudiometer to make the levels equal, and the level inside the tube was above that outside the tube (see *2,* Fig. 9-6). The pressure of the gas inside the tube is less than the pressure of the air outside. Otherwise the enclosed gas would push

Fig. 9–6. In (1) the pressure of the hydrogen is the same as that of the atmosphere. In (2) the pressure of the hydrogen is less than that of the atmosphere. In (3) the pressure of the hydrogen is greater than that of the atmosphere.

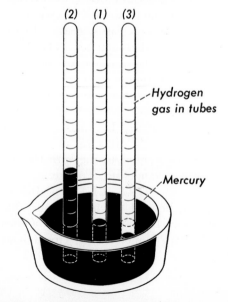

★ SAMPLE PROBLEM

What is the pressure of the gas in a eudiometer tube when the mercury level in the tube is 18 mm higher than that outside? The barometer reads 735 mm.

SOLUTION

Since the mercury level inside is higher than that outside, the pressure on the gas in the eudiometer tube must be less than atmospheric pressure. Accordingly, we subtract the difference in levels from the barometric pressure to obtain the pressure of the gas. 735 mm − 18 mm = 717 mm, the pressure of the gas.

the mercury down to the same level. To determine the pressure of the hydrogen, we must *subtract* the difference between the level of the mercury inside the tube and outside the tube from the barometer reading.

★ If so much hydrogen is delivered into the eudiometer that the mercury level inside the tube drops below that outside, the gas inside the tube will be under a greater pressure than that of the air outside (see *3*, Fig. 9-6). To determine the pressure of the gas in this case, the difference between the level of the mercury inside the tube and outside the tube must be *added* to the barometer reading.

★ Since these corrections are somewhat inconvenient to make, we usually try to adjust the mercury levels inside and outside the tube to be the same by moving the eudiometer up or down in the bowl of mercury. Then the gas pressure inside will be the same as that read on the barometer. But occasionally the bowl of mercury may not be deep enough to make this possible. Then we have to apply the corrections we have just learned. See Sample Problem at the top of the page.

Fig. 9–7. The pressure of the atmosphere supports a column of water 13.6 times higher than the column of mercury it supports.

★ **5. Measuring the pressure of a gas collected over water.** In elementary work, we usually collect gases over water rather than over mercury. Mercury is 13.6 times as dense as water. Thus a given pressure will support a column of water 13.6 times as high as an equivalent column of mercury (Fig. 9-7). When a gas is collected over water, the level of the water inside the eudi-

Fig. 9–8. (Below, right) Even though the liquid levels inside and outside this eudiometer are the same, we must correct for water vapor pressure when determining dry gas pressure because the gas was collected over water.

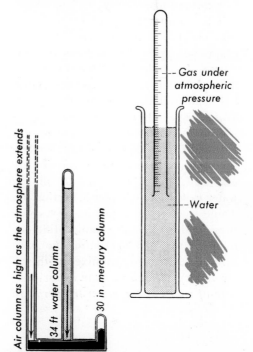

Gas under atmospheric pressure

Water

Air column as high as the atmosphere extends

34 ft water column

30 in mercury column

★ SAMPLE PROBLEM

Oxygen is collected in a eudiometer tube over water. The water level inside the tube is 27.2 mm higher than that outside. The temperature is 20° C. The barometric pressure is 740.0 mm. What is the pressure of the dry oxygen?

SOLUTION

To convert the differences in water levels to an equivalent difference in mercury levels, we divide the difference in water levels by 13.6. 27.2 mm ÷ 13.6 = 2.0 mm, the equivalent difference in mercury levels. Since the level inside the tube is higher than that outside, the difference in levels must be subtracted from the barometric pressure. 740.0 mm − 2.0 mm = 738.0 mm. To correct for the water vapor pressure, we learn from Table 5 in the Appendix that the water vapor pressure at 20° C is 17.5 mm. This must be subtracted from the pressure corrected for difference in levels. 738.0 mm − 17.5 mm = 720.5 mm, the pressure of the dry oxygen.

---

ometer may be above, the same as, or below the water level outside the tube. Pressure corrections similar to those we have just learned about for differences in mercury level must be applied. But since mercury is 13.6 times as dense as water, *a difference in water levels must be divided by 13.6 to convert it to its equivalent length in terms of a column of mercury.*

The advantage of collecting a gas over mercury is that mercury does not evaporate appreciably at room temperatures. But when we bubble a gas through water, the collected gas always has some water vapor mixed with it. Water vapor, like other gases, exerts pressure. Thus the pressure of a gas enclosed in a tube over water is made up of two factors: *1.* the pressure of the gas itself; and *2.* the pressure of the water vapor (see Chapter 3, Section 9). Table 5 in the Appendix gives the pressure due to water vapor at different temperatures. *To determine the pressure of the dry gas* (unmixed with water vapor), *we subtract the vapor pressure of water at the given temperature*

from the total pressure of the gas within the tube. See the Sample Problem at the top of this page.

6. The variation of gas volume with pressure. Boyle's Law. You know that a rubber ball filled with air is very elastic or "springy." If you squeeze the ball, the volume of the gas inside is decreased, but it expands again when you release the pressure. Robert Boyle

Fig. 9–9. Robert Boyle, an English scientist, was the first to make careful measurements to show the relationship between pressures and volumes of gases.

(1627–1691) first made careful measurements to show the relationship between pressures and volumes of gases.

Suppose you have 1000 ml of a confined gas under a pressure of 760 mm of mercury. Boyle found that doubling the pressure on such a volume of gas would reduce the volume to one half its original volume. Boyle formulated the results of his experiments on what he called the "springiness of the air" in a law that bears his name. We may state **Boyle's Law** as follows: *The volume of a certain amount of dry gas is inversely proportional to the pressure, provided the temperature remains constant.*

7. Using Boyle's Law. Suppose we collect over mercury 200 ml of a gas such as hydrogen, on a day when the barometer reads 740 mm. The mercury level inside the tube is adjusted so that it is the same as that outside. The pressure on the confined gas is thus the same as atmospheric pressure, 740 mm. If we permit the tube to stand until the next day, we may find that the temperature of the gas is unchanged, but that the barometer has gone up to 750 mm. When we lower the tube into the bowl of mercury to make the mercury level inside the tube the same as that outside, we find that the volume

of gas has decreased. The new volume of gas is $\frac{740 \text{ mm}}{750 \text{ mm}}$ of its volume on the first day. If we multiply 200 ml by $\frac{740 \text{ mm}}{750 \text{ mm}}$, we obtain 197 ml (approximately), the new volume. It is possible that by the third day the barometer may have dropped to 720 mm. When we adjust the mercury levels so that they are the same inside the tube and out, we find that the volume of the gas has increased to $200 \times \frac{740 \text{ mm}}{720 \text{ mm}}$, or about 205 ml.

In solving problems which involve a change in the volume of a gas because of a change in the pressure on the gas, we follow these three steps in our reasoning:

1. Is this change in the pressure on the gas going to make the volume of the gas become larger or become smaller?

2. If the new volume is to be larger, then we must multiply the original volume by the ratio of the pressures that has a larger numerator than denominator.

3. If the new volume is to be smaller, then we must multiply the original volume by the ratio of the pressures that has a smaller numerator than denominator. See the Sample Problems below and at the top of page 122.

SAMPLE PROBLEM

We collect 500 ml of hydrogen when the pressure is 800 mm of mercury. What volume will the gas occupy when the pressure is 760 mm of mercury?

SOLUTION

Since the pressure is reduced, the volume of the gas will increase. We therefore multiply the original volume by the ratio of the pressures with a larger numerator than denominator. $500 \text{ ml} \times \dfrac{800 \text{ mm}}{760 \text{ mm}} = 526.3 \text{ ml}$, the new volume.

★ SAMPLE PROBLEM

The volume of oxygen in a eudiometer tube is 40.0 ml. The water level inside the tube is 20.4 mm higher inside than outside. The barometer reading is 730.0 mm. The temperature is 22° C. What will be the volume of the dry oxygen at 760.0 mm pressure, if the temperature remains unchanged?

SOLUTION

1. Correction for difference in levels. 730.0 mm − (20.4 mm ÷ 13.6) = 728.5 mm.

2. Correction for water vapor pressure. Water vapor pressure at 22° C is 19.8 mm. 728.5 mm − 19.8 mm = 708.7 mm.

3. Correction for change in pressure. $40.0 \text{ ml} \times \dfrac{708.7 \text{ mm}}{760.0 \text{ mm}} = 37.3$ ml, volume at 760.0 mm and 22° C.

---

2. TEMPERATURE CHANGES AFFECT GAS VOLUMES

8. The variation of gas volume with temperature. Everyone knows that bread dough rises when it is placed in a hot oven. The increase in temperature causes the bubbles of carbon dioxide gas within the dough to expand. The rather large increase in the volume of the dough as it is baked into bread shows that the gas must expand considerably as the temperature is increased. In fact this gas, as well as other gases, expands many times as much per degree rise in temperature as do liquids and solids.

Jacques Charles (1746–1823), a French scientist, first made careful measurements of the changes in volume of gases with changes in temperature. His experiments revealed two things about these changes:

Fig. 9–10. Expansion of the gas bubbles in dough during baking causes an increase in volume as the bread is baked.

1. All gases expand or contract at the same rate with changes in temperature, provided the pressure is unchanged.

2. The change in volume amounts to $\frac{1}{273}$ of the original volume at 0° C for each Centigrade degree the temperature is changed.

We may start with a definite volume of a gas at 0° C and experiment by heating it. Just as the whole of anything may be considered as made up of two halves, $\frac{2}{2}$, or three thirds, $\frac{3}{3}$, so we can consider this volume as $\frac{273}{273}$. If we warm the gas one Centigrade degree, it expands $\frac{1}{273}$ of its original volume. Its new volume will be $\frac{274}{273}$. In the same manner, the gas will expand $\frac{100}{273}$ when it is heated 100 C°. Such expansion, added to the original volume, makes the new volume $\frac{373}{273}$. Any gas warmed 273 Centigrade degrees will expand $\frac{273}{273}$, or its volume will be just doubled, $\frac{546}{273}$.

A gas whose volume is measured at 0° C will contract by $\frac{1}{273}$ of its volume if it is cooled 1 C°. Its new volume will be $\frac{722}{372}$ of its former volume. Cooling

Unbaked dough   Baked bread

Fig. 9–11. The experiments of Jacques Charles, a French scientist, concerning the effect of temperature changes on gas volumes, resulted in Charles' Law.

this gas to −100° C reduces the volume $\frac{100}{273}$. In other words the gas shrinks to $\frac{173}{273}$ of its former volume. At this rate, if we cooled the gas to −273° C, it would lose $\frac{273}{273}$ of its volume, and its volume would become zero. Such a situation cannot occur, however, because all gases become liquids before such a low temperature is reached. This rate of contraction with cooling applies only to gases.

9. The Kelvin temperature scale. Scientists believe that −273.16° C is the lowest possible temperature. At this temperature a body would have lost all the heat that it is possible for it to lose. Scientists have come very close to this lowest possible temperature, but theoretically it is impossible to reach it.

The physicist Sir William Thomson (1824–1907), who is better known by his title, Lord Kelvin, invented the Kelvin temperature scale. In this scale, 0° K (zero degrees Kelvin) is the low-

est possible temperature, −273.16° C. In most calculations this temperature is rounded off to −273° C. A Kelvin degree represents the same temperature change as a Centigrade degree. The following table will help you in comparing the Kelvin and Centigrade temperature scales.

CENTIGRADE	KELVIN
100°	373°
50°	323°
20°	293°
0°	273°
− 100°	173°
− 273°	0°

If you observe the corresponding temperatures on the Centigrade and Kelvin scales, you will note that Kelvin temperatures are just 273 degrees higher than Centigrade temperatures.

Kelvin temperature =
Centigrade temperature + 273°

10. Charles' Law. Thermometers are not graduated to give Kelvin scale readings. But the scale makes it easy to solve problems dealing with the changes in gas volumes as temperatures vary. It eliminates the use of zero and of negative numbers. By the use of the Kelvin temperature scale, we can state *Charles' Law* in a very simple fashion: *The volume of a certain amount of dry gas varies directly with the Kelvin temperature, provided the pressure remains constant.*

11. Use of Charles' Law. In solving problems which involve the change in volume of a gas with changes in temperature, we follow this line of reasoning:

1. Since Charles' Law gives the relationship between gas volumes and

Kelvin temperatures, we must first change the Centigrade temperatures in the problem to Kelvin temperatures. We do this by adding 273° to the Centigrade temperatures.

2. Is this change in temperature going to make the volume of the gas larger or smaller?

3. If the new volume is to be larger, then we must multiply the original volume by the ratio of the Kelvin temperatures that has a larger numerator than denominator.

4. If the new volume is to be smaller, then we must multiply the original volume by the ratio of the Kelvin temperatures that has a smaller numerator than denominator. See Sample Problem below.

12. Combined use of Boyle's and Charles' Laws. The calculation of the new volume of a gas when both temperature and pressure are changed involves no new principles. We merely multiply the original volume first by a ratio of the pressures to determine the new volume corrected for pressure alone. Then we multiply this answer by a ratio of the Kelvin temperatures to calculate the new volume corrected for both pressure and temperature. Usually these two operations are combined in a single mathematical expression before solving, as the Sample Problems on page 125 illustrate. You will find it much easier to solve Gas-Law problems if you use logarithms or a slide rule in making your calculations.

★ **13. The Gas-Law Formula.** So far we have been solving Gas-Law problems by the use of a reasoning method. However, it is possible to reduce the steps of the reasoning method to a formula.

In each problem, we started with the original volume of the gas, which we shall represent as V. We first corrected this original volume for the difference in pressure. If you review the preceding Sample Problems, you will find in each case, regardless of whether the pressure increased or decreased, that the ratio of the pressures was: $\dfrac{\text{original pressure}}{\text{new pressure}}$.

Letting P represent the original pressure and P' represent the new pressure,

---

SAMPLE PROBLEM

We have 500 ml of a gas measured at a temperature of 20° C. If the pressure remains unchanged, what will be the volume of the gas at 0° C?

SOLUTION

First change the Centigrade temperatures to Kelvin temperatures by adding 273° to each. 20° C + 273° = 293° K. 0° C + 273° = 273° K.

Since the temperature is lowered, the volume of the gas at the new temperature will be less than the original volume. We therefore multiply the original volume of the gas by the ratio of the Kelvin temperatures with a smaller numerator than denominator. $500 \text{ ml} \times \dfrac{273° \text{ K}}{293° \text{ K}} = 465.8 \text{ ml}$, the new volume.

SAMPLE PROBLEM

Some gas measures 200 ml at 20° C and 750 mm pressure. What will be the volume of the gas at 15° C and 735 mm pressure?

SOLUTION

20° C = 293° K; 15° C = 288° K.

Since the temperature is to be lowered, the gas volume will decrease from the temperature change. To correct the volume for change in temperature, we multiply the original volume by the ratio of the Kelvin temperatures with a smaller numerator, $\dfrac{288° \text{ K}}{293° \text{ K}}$.

Since the pressure is to be lowered, the gas volume will increase from the pressure change. To correct the volume for change in pressure we multiply the expression already obtained by the ratio of the pressures with a larger numerator, $\dfrac{750 \text{ mm}}{735 \text{ mm}}$.

Combining these steps:

$$200 \text{ ml} \times \frac{288° \text{ K}}{293° \text{ K}} \times \frac{750 \text{ mm}}{735 \text{ mm}} = 200.6 \text{ ml, the new volume.}$$

★ SAMPLE PROBLEM

A gas-measuring tube holds 25.0 ml of air. The air was collected over water when the temperature was 20° C. The water level inside the eudiometer is 68.0 mm higher than that outside. The barometer reading is 740.0 mm. Calculate the volume of dry air at S.T.P.

SOLUTION

1. Correction for difference in levels. 68.0 mm ÷ 13.6 = 5.0 mm. Since the water level inside is higher than that outside, the air is under pressure less than atmospheric, and the correction is subtracted. 740.0 mm − 5.0 mm = 735.0 mm.

2. Correction for water vapor pressure. Table 5 in the Appendix indicates that the water vapor pressure at 20° C is 17.5 mm. This correction is subtracted. 735.0 mm − 17.5 mm = 717.5 mm.

3. Correction for pressure change. Since the pressure on the dry gas increases from 717.5 mm to standard pressure, 760.0 mm, the gas volume will be decreased. We multiply the original volume by $\dfrac{717.5 \text{ mm}}{760.0 \text{ mm}}$.

4. Correction for temperature change. 20° C = 293° K. 0° C (standard temperature) = 273° K. Since the temperature of the gas decreases from 293° K to 273° K, the gas volume will be decreased. We multiply by $\dfrac{273° \text{ K}}{293° \text{ K}}$.

$$25.0 \text{ ml} \times \frac{717.5 \text{ mm}}{760.0 \text{ mm}} \times \frac{273° \text{ K}}{293° \text{ K}} = 22.0 \text{ ml, volume of dry air at S.T.P.}$$

the pressure ratio by which we correct the original volume is $\dfrac{P}{P'}$. Likewise, the ratio by which we correct the original volume for temperature change is: $\dfrac{\text{new Kelvin temperature}}{\text{original Kelvin temperature}}$. Letting T represent the original Kelvin temperature and T' represent the new Kelvin temperature, the temperature correction ratio becomes $\dfrac{T'}{T}$. The product of the original volume and these two ratios gives the corrected gas volume V'. $V \times \dfrac{P}{P'} \times \dfrac{T'}{T} = V'$. Transposing, we obtain another useful version of this formula, $\dfrac{PV}{T} = \dfrac{P'V'}{T'}$.

★ **14. The behavior of real gases.** Boyle's and Charles' Laws describe the behavior of an *ideal* gas. An **ideal gas** would consist of infinitely small molecules which exert no forces on each other.

Real gases within the normal ranges of temperatures and pressures conform very well to the behavior of an ideal gas, even though they consist of molecules of finite size which do exert forces on each other. Under normal temperatures and pressures, the spaces separating the molecules are large enough so that the actual size of the molecules and forces between them have little effect.

Boyle's Law applies to real gases with a fairly high degree of accuracy. But it does not apply to gases under such high pressure that the molecules are close enough together to attract each other. Under this condition the gas is almost at the point at which it condenses into a liquid.

Charles' Law holds for real gases with considerable accuracy, provided the gas is not under such a low temperature condition that the gas molecules will slow down and molecular attraction occurs. At temperature conditions near the point where the gas will condense into a liquid, Charles' Law does not apply.

Summary

If the volume which a certain number of gas molecules occupies remains constant, the pressure exerted by the gas increases if its temperature is raised. If the pressure exerted by this number of gas molecules remains the same as the temperature is increased, the volume the gas occupies increases. If the temperature of these gas molecules remains constant, the pressure exerted by the gas increases if the volume occupied by the gas becomes smaller. Gas volumes are related to the temperature and pressure of the gas.

Standard temperature is zero degrees Centigrade. Standard pressure is the pressure exerted by a column of mercury 760 millimeters high. The temperature of a gas is measured by means of a thermometer, and its pressure is measured with a barometer. When we collect a gas over water, some water vapor becomes mixed with the gas. The amount of pressure due to water vapor varies according to the temperature.

Boyle's Law: The volume of a certain amount of dry gas is inversely proportional to the pressure, provided the temperature remains constant. Jacques

Charles found that all gases expand or contract at the same rate. Gases expand $\frac{1}{273}$ of the volume at 0° C for each Centigrade degree the temperature is raised. The lowest possible temperature is −273° C. The Kelvin temperature scale has its 0° K reading at −273° C. The readings on the Kelvin scale are 273 degrees higher than on the Centigrade scale. Charles' Law: The volume of a certain amount of dry gas varies directly with the Kelvin temperature, provided the pressure remains constant. Boyle's Law and Charles' Law may be combined in the Gas-Law Formula

$$\frac{VP}{T} = \frac{V'P'}{T'}.$$

Test yourself on these terms

barometer	Gas-Law formula	standard temperature
Boyle's Law	Kelvin temperature	S.T.P.
Charles' Law	Kinetic Theory	Torricelli
eudiometer	standard pressure	water vapor pressure

Questions

Group A

1. Why is the term "a cubic foot of air" unsatisfactory?
2. (a) What is standard temperature? (b) What is standard pressure?
★ 3. If some hydrogen gas is enclosed in a eudiometer, what are three possibilities concerning its pressure compared with that of the air in the room?
4. State Boyle's Law.
5. (a) What is the Centigrade temperature corresponding to 0° K? (b) How does any Centigrade temperature compare with the corresponding Kelvin temperature?
6. What is Charles' Law?

Group B

7. How is a gas described by the Kinetic Theory?
8. At constant volume, how is the pressure exerted by a gas related to the temperature?
9. At constant pressure, how is the volume occupied by a gas related to the temperature?
10. At constant temperature, how is the volume occupied by a gas related to its pressure?
★11. (a) What is meant by the vapor pressure of water? (b) What effect does it have on the observed pressure of a gas collected over water? (c) How do we correct the observed pressure to obtain the pressure of the dry gas?
★12. What corrections are applied to the barometer reading: (a) gas measured over mercury, level inside the eudiometer the same as that outside; (b) gas measured over mercury, level inside eudiometer higher than that outside; (c) gas measured over water, level inside eudiometer same as that outside; (d) gas measured over water, level inside eudiometer higher than outside?

roblems

Group A

(Use cancellation whenever possible)

1. Some oxygen occupies 250 ml when the barometer reads 720 mm. What will be the volume the following day when the barometer reads 750 mm?
2. A gas collected when the pressure is 800 mm has a volume of 3040 ml. What volume will the gas occupy at standard pressure?
3. A gas has a volume of 100 ml when the pressure is 735 mm. What volume will the gas occupy at 700 mm pressure?
4. A gas has a volume of 240 ml at 70 cm pressure. What pressure is needed to reduce the volume to 60 ml?
5. Change the following temperatures to Kelvin scale: (*a*) 20° C; (*b*) 85° C; (*c*) −15° C; (*d*) −190° C.
6. Given 90 ml of hydrogen gas collected when the temperature is 27° C. What volume will the hydrogen occupy at 42° C?
7. A gas has a volume of 180 ml when its temperature is 43° C. To what temperature must the gas be lowered to reduce its volume to 135 ml?
8. A gas measures 500 ml at a temperature of −23° C. Find its volume at 23° C.
9. Fifty liters of gas is measured at 27° C. What is the volume of the gas at standard temperature?
10. Reduce to standard conditions: 2280 ml of gas measured at 30° C and 808 mm pressure.
11. Reduce to standard conditions: 1000 ml of gas at −23° C and 700 mm pressure.
12. Reduce to standard conditions: 1520 ml of gas at −33° C and 720 mm pressure.
13. A gas collected when the temperature is 27° C and the pressure is 80 cm measures 500 ml. Find the volume at −3° C and 75 cm.
14. Given 100 ml of gas measured at 17° C and 380 mm pressure. What volume will the gas occupy at 307° C and 500 mm pressure?

Group B

(Use logarithms or a slide rule)

★ 15. In an experiment 35 ml of hydrogen was collected in a eudiometer over mercury. The mercury level inside the eudiometer was 40 mm higher than that outside. The temperature was 25° C and the barometric pressure was 740 mm. Correct the volume of hydrogen to S.T.P.
★ 16. Sixty milliliters of gas is collected over mercury in an inverted graduated cylinder. The mercury level inside the cylinder is 25 mm higher than that outside. Temperature: 20° C; barometer reading: 715 mm. Correct the volume of gas to S.T.P.
★ 17. Hydrogen is collected by water displacement in a eudiometer. Gas volume, 25 ml; liquid levels inside and outside the eudiometer are the same; temperature, 17° C; barometer reading, 720 mm. Correct the volume to that of dry gas at S.T.P.

★ 18. Some nitrogen is collected over water in a gas-measuring tube. Gas volume, 45 ml; liquid levels inside and outside the gas-measuring tube are the same; temperature, 23° C; barometer reading, 732 mm. Correct the volume to that of dry gas at S.T.P.

★ 19. Fifty milliliters of oxygen is collected over water. The water level inside the eudiometer is 65 mm higher than that outside. Temperature, 25° C; barometer reading 727 mm. Correct the volume to that of dry gas at S.T.P.

★ 20. At 18° C and 745 mm pressure, 12 ml of hydrogen is collected over water. The liquid level inside the gas-measuring tube is 95 mm higher than that outside. Correct the volume to that of dry gas at S.T.P.

★ 21. One liter of carbon dioxide at S.T.P. weighs 1.98 g. What is the weight of one liter of the gas, if the pressure increases by 40 mm of mercury?

★ 22. One liter of oxygen at S.T.P. weighs 1.43 g. Find the weight of one liter of oxygen at a temperature of 39° C, if the pressure remains unchanged.

★ 23. One liter of nitrogen weighs 1.26 g at S.T.P. Find the weight of a liter of nitrogen at a temperature of 27° C and 90 cm of mercury pressure.

★ 24. A gas measures 400 ml at a temperature of 25° C, and under a pressure of 800 mm. To what temperature must the gas be cooled if its volume is to be reduced to 350 ml when the pressure falls to 740 mm?

Some things for you to do

1. Show the motion of molecules by adding a few drops of liquid bromine to a large flask. Stopper the flask. CAUTION: *Do not get any bromine on your fingers as it will burn them badly.*

2. Examine the barometer in your chemistry laboratory closely and note the refinements of construction to secure accurate readings. Do not change any of the adjustments on the instrument.

3. Consult recent issues of science news magazines to learn how closely scientists have been able to approach the Absolute zero of temperature.

Chapter 10 WATER

1. THE NATURE OF WATER

1. The abundance of water. Water is both our most abundant and our most useful liquid. The oceans, rivers, and lakes cover about three quarters of the surface of the earth. Besides this visible water, there are large amounts of underground water.

Water vapor is always present in the air, even over deserts. When it rains, part of this water vapor condenses to liquid water and falls to the ground.

Water is found in all living things and is absolutely essential for the continuance of life. Biologists tell us that the body of a man who weighs 140 lb is composed of about 100 lb of water. It is the basic constituent of all body fluids. Fruits and vegetables contain as much as 90% to 95% water. Even meat is about 50% water.

VOCABULARY

Acid anhydride. An oxide of a nonmetal which unites with water to form a solution which contains an acid.

Analysis. A breaking apart to determine the composition, as of a chemical compound.

Anhydrous. Containing no water.

Basic anhydride. An oxide of a metal which unites with water to form a solution which contains a base.

Distillation. The process of evaporation followed by condensation of the vapors in a separate vessel.

Hydrate. A crystallized substance that contains water of hydration.

Hydrogen bond. A weak chemical bond between a hydrogen atom in one polar molecule and the negative atom in a second polar molecule.

Polar molecule. A molecule in which there is a separation of charge caused by a non-uniform electron distribution.

Stable compound. A compound that does not decompose easily.

Synthesis. A combining of simple substances to make a more complex substance.

Unstable compound. A compound that decomposes easily.

2. The physical properties of water.
Pure water is a transparent, odorless, tasteless, and almost colorless liquid. The faint blue or blue-green color of water is apparent only in deep layers.

Any odor or taste in water is due to impurities dissolved in it. These impurities may be dissolved mineral matter, dissolved liquids, or even dissolved gases. The pronounced odor and taste of the water from some mineral springs is due to the presence of such substances in considerable quantity.

Water may exist as a gas, liquid, or solid. Liquid water changes to ice at 0° C, or 32° F, under standard pressure, 760 mm of mercury. As water solidifies, it gives off heat and expands one ninth in volume. Consequently, ice has a density of about 0.9 g/cm³. The density of ice increases slightly as ice is cooled below 0° C.

When water at 0° C is warmed, it contracts until its temperature reaches 4° C. Then water gradually expands as its temperature is raised further. *At its temperature of maximum density, 4° C, one milliliter of water weighs one gram.* This is one of the ways in which water is used as a *scientific standard.* Other ways will be mentioned shortly.

When the pressure on the surface of water is one atmosphere (760 mm of mercury) water will boil at a temperature of 100° C, or 212° F. The steam that is formed by heating water at its boiling temperature occupies a much greater volume than that of the water from which it was formed. When one liter of water evaporates, the steam occupies about 1700 liters at atmospheric pressure.

When water is heated in a closed vessel so that the steam cannot escape, the boiling point of the water is raised above 100° C. Conversely, if the air and water vapor above the liquid in a closed vessel are partially removed by

Fig. 10–1. When we see the vastness of the ocean, we are made more aware of the fact that water covers three quarters of the surface of the earth.

means of a vacuum pump, the water will boil at a lower temperature than 100° C. Pressure cookers are popular for cooking food because the higher temperature of the water cooks the food in a shorter time, thus saving fuel. Vacuum evaporators are used to evaporate milk and to concentrate sugar solutions. Under a vacuum the liquid boils away at a temperature that is low enough so that the sugar is not scorched.

3. The structure and properties of water molecules. Water molecules are composed of two atoms of hydrogen and one atom of oxygen, joined by covalent bonds. Certain properties of water, some of which will be explained presently and others which will be explained in Chapter 20, indicate that these atoms are not joined in a straight line. Rather, they form an angle as indicated by the electron-dot formula

$$H:\overset{..}{\underset{..}{O}}:$$
$$H$$

Since the positive charge of the oxygen nucleus is so much stronger than the positive charges of the hydrogen nuclei, the electrons are not uniformly distributed in the molecule. The electrons, on the average, are clustered nearer to the oxygen nucleus.

This has the effect of making the oxygen part of the molecule somewhat negatively charged, and leaves the hydrogen parts positively charged. Since the two hydrogen atoms are similarly charged, they tend to repel one another. This increases the size of the angle between the bonds in the molecule from the 90° we should expect from the electron-dot formula to about 105°. A water molecule may therefore be more properly represented as

$$O^=$$
$$H^+ \qquad H^+$$

Fig. 10-3. Vacuum evaporators are used to concentrate the dilute sugar juice obtained from sugar cane. Under reduced pressure the water is evaporated from the sugar juice without scorching the sugar.

A molecule, such as a water molecule, *in which there is a separation of charge caused by a nonuniform electron distribution is a **polar molecule.***

The regions of different charge on water molecules enable them to join together, or associate, into groups of molecules. A hydrogen atom of one water molecule may be weakly, but effectively, attracted to the oxygen of a second water molecule. Such a bond is called a **hydrogen bond.** A hydrogen of the second water molecule may be attracted to the oxygen of a third water molecule, and so on. While the number of molecules in a group decreases with an increase in temperature, the number usually ranges from eight to four in liquid water.

Ice consists of water molecules arranged in a definite hexagonal structure. They are held together by hydrogen bonds in a rather open pattern (see Fig. 10-4). As heat is applied to ice, the increased energy of the atoms and molecules causes them to vibrate more vigorously. This stretches the hydrogen

bonds, and the ice expands as it is heated.

When the melting point of ice is reached, the energy of the atoms and molecules is so great that the rigid open lattice structure of the ice crystals breaks down—the ice turns into water. Despite the fact that the hydrogen bonds in water at 0° C are longer than those in ice, they are more flexible and the groups of liquid molecules can crowd together more compactly than those in ice. As a result, H_2O molecules occupy less volume as water than they do as ice. Therefore, the density of ice is less than water.

As water is warmed from 0° C, two phenomena having opposite effects occur: *1.* The breaking down of some hydrogen bonds enables water molecules to crowd more closely together; and

2. the increased energy of the water molecules causes them to spread apart. Up to 4° C, the first effect predominates and water increases in density. Above 4° C, while the first phenomenon continues to occur, the effect of

Fig. 10–4. The crystal structure of ice.

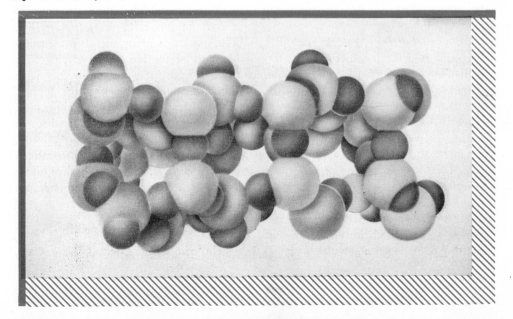

the second is so much greater that the density of water decreases.

It is the presence of groups of molecules in water, which must absorb enough energy to be broken up into single molecules before water boils, that makes the boiling point of water so high, and makes it necessary to use a large amount of heat to vaporize water at its normal boiling point.

4. Water is commonly used as a standard. It is easy to obtain water in *fairly pure* condition. For this reason it is used as a scientific standard in several ways.

1. For defining the relationship between volume and mass in the metric system. We have already mentioned that one milliliter of water at its temperature of maximum density, 4° C, weighs one gram.

2. For establishing a temperature scale and graduating thermometers. The temperature at which water freezes is called 0° C or 32° F and fixes the *ice-point* on the thermometer scale. The boiling point of water under a pressure of 760 mm of mercury is called 100° C or 212° F and determines the *steam-point* on the thermometer scale.

3. For measuring heat. In defining the units used for measuring heat, water is used as a standard. For example, *the **calorie** is defined as the amount of heat that is needed to warm one gram of water one Centigrade degree. The **British thermal unit**,* commonly abbreviated *Btu, is the amount of heat needed to raise one pound of water one Fahrenheit degree.*

4. For a standard of specific gravity. Water is the standard for the specific gravity of solids and liquids. If we find that one cubic centimeter of iron is 7.6

times as heavy as one cubic centimeter of water, we say that the *specific gravity* of iron is 7.6.

5. The chemical behavior of water.
1. The stability of water. Water is a very **stable compound.** By that we mean that it is *a compound which does not break up, or decompose, easily.* We call mercuric oxide a rather **unstable compound** because *it does not require much energy to decompose it into its elements.* But such is not the case with water. In fact, water is so stable that it does not decompose appreciably until its temperature reaches about 2700° C. The stability of water is evidence of the strength of the covalent bonds between the oxygen and hydrogen atoms.

2. Behavior with metals. In our study of hydrogen, we learned that such active metals as sodium and potassium react with cold water, setting free hydrogen and forming basic solutions.

$$2 \, Na + 2 \, HOH \rightarrow 2 \, NaOH + H_2\uparrow$$

Magnesium reacts with boiling water. When heated red hot, iron reacts with steam forming iron oxide and hydrogen. Aluminum and zinc also react with water at high temperatures.

3. Behavior with metallic oxides. The oxides of many metals are insoluble and water has little or no effect upon them. But water does react with the oxides of the very active metals. The oxides of sodium, potassium, and calcium unite with water and form soluble hydroxides. Soluble hydroxides are compounds whose water solutions contain a *base.* Calcium hydroxide is formed when water is added to calcium oxide, CaO.

$$CaO + H_2O \rightarrow Ca(OH)_2$$

The compound calcium oxide, CaO,

is known as an *anhydride*. The word anhydride means "without water." Since it forms a solution containing a base when water is added to it, calcium oxide is called a *basic anhydride*. We may define a **basic anhydride** as the *oxide of a metal which will unite with water to form a solution containing a base.*

4. Behavior with oxides of nonmetals. The oxides of such nonmetals as carbon, sulfur, and phosphorus unite with water to form a solution containing an *acid*. For example, water unites with carbon dioxide to form carbonic acid, H_2CO_3.

$$CO_2 + H_2O \rightarrow H_2CO_3$$

Carbon dioxide is an anhydride, and since it forms a solution containing an acid with water, it is called an *acid anhydride*. In general, *the oxides of the nonmetals unite with water to form solutions which contain an acid, and consequently are known as* **acid anhydrides.**

5. Water of hydration. Many positive ions, and a few negative ions, have a definite number of water molecules around them in crystals formed by evaporating the water from their solutions. This water is called *water of hydration* or *water of crystallization. A crystallized substance that contains water of hydration is a* **hydrate.** For example, blue crystals of cupric sulfate consist of cupric ions, each surrounded by four water molecules, and sulfate ions, each with one water molecule. We write the formula of this substance as $CuSO_4 \cdot 5\,H_2O$. The water molecules are totaled, and their loose attachment to the cupric and sulfate ions (shown empirically as $CuSO_4$) is indicated by the raised dot. If we heat hy-

drates to a temperature slightly above the boiling point of water, the water of hydration is driven off.

$$CuSO_4 \cdot 5\,H_2O \rightarrow CuSO_4 + 5\,H_2O$$

The substance which then remains is called an **anhydrous compound.** Anhydrous cupric sulfate, $CuSO_4$, is a white powder that may be prepared by heating the blue crystals gently in a test tube. The fact that water turns anhydrous cupric sulfate blue may be used as a *test for water.*

6. Water promotes many chemical changes. A good example of one of these changes is baking powder, which is a mixture of dry chemicals. As long as the baking powder is kept perfectly dry, no chemical action occurs. But when we add water to the baking powder, the chemicals in the mixture react immediately, and bubbles of gas are liberated (see Fig. 10-5). Mixtures of many other dry substances do not react until water is added. The role of water in promoting chemical changes will be more fully explained in Unit 6.

6. The composition of water by volume. *1.* By **analysis,** or "taking apart."

Fig. 10–5. Water acts to promote some reactions, as shown when water is added to dry baking powder.

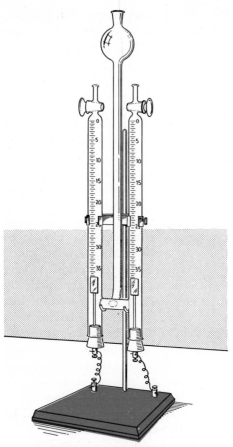

Fig. 10–6. By using an apparatus of this type, we can decompose water and measure the volumes of hydrogen and oxygen that are liberated.

An apparatus of the type shown in Fig. 10-6 can be used to decompose water by the use of an electric current. We may collect the gases and test them to identify each one. If the tubes are graduated, we can tell how many milliliters of each gas are produced. In every case, we find that *when water is subjected to analysis it yields two volumes of hydrogen to one volume of oxygen.*

2. By **synthesis**, or *"putting together."* The apparatus in Fig. 10-7 includes a gas measuring tube, or eudiometer.

It is graduated to enable us to read the volume of any gas, or any mixture of gases, which is introduced into it. Two short platinum wires are sealed into the upper end of the tube so an electric spark can be used to ignite mixtures of gases inside the tube.

As shown in Fig. 10-7A, the tube is first filled with mercury. Suppose we introduce 20 ml of hydrogen and 20 ml of oxygen into the tube, as illustrated in Fig. 10-7B. Then if we pass an electric spark between the wires, the mixture ignites and forms water vapor. As the water vapor condenses, mercury rises in the tube. But there will be 10 ml of gas remaining in the tube. If we withdraw this gas and test it, we find that it is oxygen. Thus 20 ml of hydrogen united with 10 ml of oxygen, and left 10 ml of oxygen uncombined. Note that *the hydrogen and oxygen combined in the ratio of two volumes of hydrogen to one volume of oxygen.*

We have demonstrated by both analysis and synthesis that *water is composed of two volumes of hydrogen to one volume of oxygen.*

7. The composition of water by weight. *1. By direct weighings.* An American chemist, Dr. Edward W. Morley (1838–1923), determined the

Fig. 10–7. Eudiometer tubes like these are used to determine the composition of water by volume using the method of synthesis.

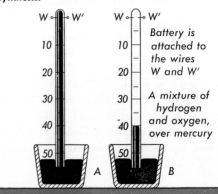

Battery is attached to the wires W and W'

A mixture of hydrogen and oxygen, over mercury

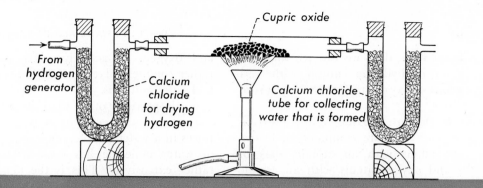

Fig. 10–8. An apparatus like this can be used to determine the composition of water by weight by the method of indirect weighing.

composition of water by weighing measured volumes of hydrogen, oxygen, and water which resulted from their union. It took him about twelve years to perfect his apparatus, purify the gases, check temperatures and pressures, and devise various precautions to secure as accurate results as possible. As a result of his painstaking experiments, he concluded that *1 part by weight of hydrogen unites with 7.94 parts by weight of oxygen*. These quantities produce 8.94 parts by weight of water. These results are accepted today as the most accurate work which has been performed for the solution of this problem. In elementary work we can "round off" these figures and say: *"One part by weight of hydrogen unites with eight parts by weight of oxygen to form nine parts by weight of water."*

2. *By indirect weighings.* The following method was devised by Jean Dumas (1800–1884), a French chemist. A weighed quantity of cupric oxide is

placed in a hard glass tube (see Fig. 10-8). Hydrogen from a generator is dried by passing it through a U-shaped tube filled with calcium chloride. Then the dry hydrogen reduces the heated cupric oxide to metallic copper. The hydrogen unites with the oxygen removed from the cupric oxide and forms water. The water thus formed is absorbed in the tube of calcium chloride at the right. Before the experiment is started, the weight of this tube of calcium chloride is accurately determined. After the experiment is completed, the tube is again weighed. The gain in weight of the calcium chloride tube is equal to the weight of the water that is formed. The loss in weight of the cupric oxide equals the weight of the oxygen taken from the cupric oxide. The difference between the weight of the water and the weight of the oxygen equals the weight of the hydrogen. We can illustrate this method by the following data:

Weight of cupric oxide tube before heating	53.80 g
Weight of cupric oxide tube after heating	45.86 g
Difference (weight of oxygen)	7.94 g
Weight of calcium chloride tube after heating	88.94 g
Weight of calcium chloride tube before heating	80.00 g
Difference (gain due to water formed)	8.94 g

From these data we can see that one gram of hydrogen unites with 7.94 grams of oxygen to form 8.94 grams of water.

8. Deuterium oxide. While most water molecules are composed of hydrogen atoms with an atomic mass of 1 and oxygen atoms with an atomic mass of 16, there are other types of water molecules possible. This is because there are three isotopes of hydrogen with atomic masses of 1, 2, and 3, and three isotopes of oxygen with atomic masses of 16, 17, and 18. The possible combinations of these six isotopes give 18 types of water molecules. In water there is also a very small proportion of hydrogen ions, hydroxide ions, and oxide ions which are formed from the various isotopes of hydrogen and oxygen. So actually water is a rather complex mixture of 33 kinds of molecules and ions.

While particles other than ordinary water molecules exist in only small traces in a water sample, one rare type of water molecule has been studied rather extensively. This is the *deuterium oxide* molecule, D_2O, in which the symbol D is used to represent an atom of the isotope of hydrogen with an atomic mass of 2. Professor G. N. Lewis (1875–1946), while he was doing research at the University of California, first separated deuterium oxide, sometimes called "heavy water," in 1932. Professor Hugh S. Taylor (1890–   ) and his co-workers at Princeton University subjected 2300 liters of water to electrolysis and finally succeeded in iso-

Fig. 10–9. Rapidly flowing water carries considerable amounts of matter in suspension and in solution.

lating 83 ml of deuterium oxide from this large volume of water. It is possible to separate D_2O from H_2O by electrolysis because D_2O molecules are not as rapidly decomposed by the passage of an electric current as are H_2O molecules.

Deuterium oxide is about 10% denser than ordinary water. It boils at 101.42° C, freezes at 3.82° C, and has its maximum density at 11.6° C. Delicate tests have been devised for detecting deuterium oxide. It has been used as a "tracer" in research work in physiology. By tracing the course of deuterium oxide molecules through living organisms, new information has been obtained concerning certain life processes. Seeds do not germinate in deuterium oxide, and rats which are given only deuterium oxide to drink will die of thirst. The most important use of deuterium oxide is as a moderator in nuclear reactors (see Chapter 39).

2. THE PURIFICATION OF WATER

9. The impurities which may be present in water. One of the important properties of water is its ability to dissolve substances. Moving water can also carry along solid particles in suspension. Consequently, the impurities present in water may be grouped in two classes: *1. matter in solution;* and *2. matter in suspension.* Each of these classes may be subdivided to include: *a. organic matter;* and *b. inorganic or mineral matter.* Organic matter consists of bacteria, sewage, and other forms of animal and vegetable matter in various stages of decay. The mineral matter which is present will depend upon the composition of the soil and rock with which the water came in contact.

10. Potable water is safe to drink. While water always contains some impurities, this does not mean that a particular sample is not safe to drink. The term *pure drinking water* does not imply water of such high purity as the chemist requires for accurate experimental work. **Potable water** is water that is clear, colorless, of pleasing taste, free of harmful bacteria, and does not contain excessive amounts of undesirable dissolved solids. Such water is safe to drink.

11. The treatment of drinking water. The most important problems in purifying drinking water are: *1.* removing the matter held in suspension; and *2.* destroying the bacteria. Three processes are used to remove suspended matter from water. They are: *a.* sedimentation or settling; *b.* the addition of chemicals followed by further settling; and *c.* filtration through layers of sand, charcoal, and gravel. The removal or destruction of bacteria is accomplished by several processes: *a.* filtration; *b.* aeration; and *c.* the addition of chemicals such as chlorine or ozone.

12. Sedimentation helps remove suspended matter. Running water usually carries considerable material in suspension. When such water is permitted to flow into basins, tanks, or reservoirs, most of the suspended matter settles to the bottom.

Very small particles of suspended matter settle slowly. Their deposition may be hastened by the addition of certain chemicals which react to form a bulky, sticky precipitate. As the precipitate settles, bacteria and other tiny

Fig. 10–10. The cylinder at the left contains turbid water. The cylinder at the right shows that the precipitate removes suspended impurities from turbid water.

particles of suspended matter become entangled in the sticky precipitate and are carried to the bottom.

The jar at the left in Fig. 10-10 was made turbid, or cloudy, by stirring into it particles of fine clay. The jar at the right was made turbid in the same manner, and then aluminum sulfate and calcium hydroxide were added. The two chemicals react to form aluminum hydroxide and calcium sulfate:

$$Al_2(SO_4)_3 + 3\ Ca(OH)_2 \rightarrow$$
$$2\ Al(OH)_3\downarrow + 3\ CaSO_4\downarrow$$

The arrows pointing downward after the aluminum hydroxide and the calcium sulfate indicate that each of these forms a *precipitate,* or solid. The alu-

minum hydroxide is bulky and sticky. The calcium sulfate is considerably denser than water. Both settle to the bottom, dragging the fine particles of clay with them, and leaving the water at the top of the jar very clear. A comparison of the two jars after 24 hours shows how effective this method is in removing suspended matter. It is the custom to add these chemicals to the water as it flows out from the first sedimentation basin. The water then flows into a second sedimentation basin where the sticky precipitate settles.

13. Water is further purified by filtration. In many cities, water is filtered through layers of sand and gravel several feet thick. Layers of charcoal may be used between the sand and gravel to adsorb coloring matter and also any gases dissolved in the water that might give it a disagreeable odor. A sticky layer from the sedimentation process soon collects at the top of the sand. This layer at first increases the efficiency of the filter because it strains out bacteria. After continued use, however, the layer retards the filtering. Then it becomes necessary to scrape it off, or to use fresh sand, charcoal, and gravel.

14. The aeration of water. After filtering, it is usual to aerate the water before it is delivered to the consumer.

Fig. 10–11. A cross section of a sand-gravel filter.

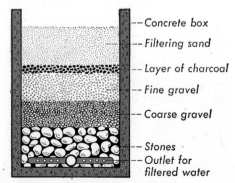

-- Concrete box

-- Filtering sand

-- Layer of charcoal

-- Fine gravel

-- Coarse gravel

-- Stones

-- Outlet for filtered water

In some reservoirs, fountains have been installed to permit the water to spout up into the air. The water then falls back in showers into the reservoir. This gives the water a chance to dissolve oxygen. Aeration oxidizes organic matter and destroys some bacteria. It also improves the taste of the water.

15. The addition of chlorine or ozone destroys the remaining bacteria. In the United States, chlorine is commonly added to water supplies in carefully controlled quantities to destroy any bacteria which remain after filtration and aeration. Sufficient chlorine is added to destroy the bacteria, and still have a small amount of chlorine remain to provide protection to the water against contamination until it reaches the consumer. Ozone is used instead of chlorine to destroy the bacteria in the water supply systems of some European cities.

16. Water can be freed from mineral matter in solution. Water can be freed from dissolved minerals by the process of *distillation*. An apparatus of the type shown in Fig. 10-13 is used in the laboratory to distill water, as well as other liquids. Water is added to the distilling flask and boiled to convert it into vapor. The vapor then passes through the inner of two concentric tubes which together are called the condenser. A stream of cold water flows continually through the outer tube of the condenser. Then the condensed water vapor flows down the inner tube into a receiving vessel. We may define *distillation as a process consisting of*

Fig. 10-12. Aeration of drinking water oxidizes organic matter, destroys some bacteria, and improves the taste of water.

evaporation followed by condensation of the vapors in a separate vessel.

One type of continuous-action water still is shown in Fig. 10-14. The water which is used for condensation is somewhat preheated before it flows into the still. This increases the amount of distilled water obtained.

Certain synthetic resins are now also being used to prepare water that is nearly free of dissolved minerals. This method, called the *ion-exchange process,* will be discussed in Chapter 25. Distilled water, or water of equivalent purity obtained by the ion-exchange process, is used for filling storage batteries, for the preparation of medicines, and in certain chemical industries.

3. HYDROGEN PEROXIDE

17. Preparation of hydrogen peroxide. Hydrogen peroxide, H_2O_2, in water solutions of less than 10% concentration may be prepared from a mixture of barium peroxide, BaO_2, and cold dilute sulfuric acid, H_2SO_4:

$$BaO_2 + H_2SO_4 \rightarrow BaSO_4\downarrow + H_2O_2$$

The precipitate, barium sulfate, can be separated from the hydrogen peroxide by filtering.

An electrolytic method is used for commercial preparation of hydrogen peroxide. Sufficient sulfuric acid is added to water to make an acid that has a specific gravity of 1.35 to 1.45. A direct current of electricity is then passed through the cold acid. At the positive terminal, persulfuric acid, $H_2S_2O_8$, is the principal product instead of oxygen as in the electrolysis of water. Persulfuric acid is not a stable compound but reacts with the water present to yield hydrogen peroxide and sulfuric acid over again:

$$H_2S_2O_8 + 2 H_2O \rightarrow H_2O_2 + 2 H_2SO_4$$

The hydrogen peroxide is then separated by distillation under reduced pressure.

Another commercial method of preparing hydrogen peroxide is assuming increased importance. In this method, hydrogen is used to reduce a complex carbon compound which has been dissolved in benzene. The reduced compound in benzene is then mixed with water and air blown through. The oxygen from the air oxidizes the carbon compound and hydrogen peroxide is formed. The hydrogen peroxide dissolves in water. This water solution of hydrogen peroxide is separated and concentrated by distillation. The oxidized carbon compound is again reduced with hydrogen, and the process repeated. This method uses only hydrogen and air as the raw materials for producing hydrogen peroxide.

18. The properties of hydrogen peroxide. Pure hydrogen peroxide is a colorless, syrupy liquid about 1.5 times as dense as water. It mixes with water in any proportion. For medicinal purposes a 3% solution of hydrogen peroxide is used. In order to prevent the decomposition of the hydrogen peroxide, the solution is kept in dark bottles, and a small quantity of acetanilide is added. The acetanilide acts as an *inhibitor,* to prevent the decomposition of hydrogen peroxide into oxygen and water.

Pure hydrogen peroxide is an unstable compound. At high temperatures it decomposes explosively. Traces

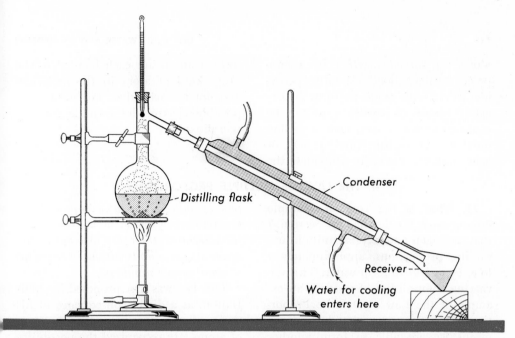

Fig. 10–13. Distillation is a process consisting of the evaporation of a liquid followed by the condensation of the vapors in a separate vessel.

of impurities in hydrogen peroxide solutions cause them to be unstable also. However, hydrogen peroxide solutions of 3%, 30%, and 85% concentration are now marketed. These solutions have been prepared by first distilling a dilute solution of hydrogen peroxide under reduced pressure to remove impurities, and then concentrating the purified solution by further evaporation of water under reduced pressure.

19. The uses of hydrogen peroxide. Hydrogen peroxide destroys the color of those organic compounds whose oxides are colorless. It will destroy bacteria, too. It is used in bleaching hair, wool, silk, ivory, and feathers. Hydrogen peroxide is an important industrial bleaching agent. It is also used in 85% concentration as a source of oxygen for rockets.

20. The peroxide group. The peroxide group found in such compounds as

barium peroxide, BaO_2, sodium peroxide, Na_2O_2, and hydrogen peroxide, H_2O_2, has the electron-dot configuration

$$\left[:\overset{..}{O}:\overset{..}{O}:\right]^{=}$$

In such compounds the two oxygen

Fig. 10–14. In a continuous-action still, the water is pre-heated by the condensing vapor, thus economizing on fuel.

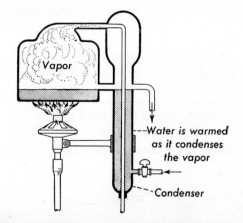

atoms are *linked together* by a non-polar covalent bond. Metallic peroxides react with acids to form hydrogen peroxide. Peroxides must not be confused with dioxides, such as carbon dioxide, CO_2, sulfur dioxide, SO_2, or lead dioxide, PbO_2. In dioxides, the oxygen atoms are each bonded to the other kind of atom in the molecule, and not to each other. For instance, a possible electron-dot formula for carbon dioxide is

$$\ddot{O}::C::\ddot{O}$$

4. THE LAW OF MULTIPLE PROPORTIONS

21. What is the Law of Multiple Proportions? We learned in Section 7 that hydrogen and oxygen unite in unvarying proportions, approximately 1 to 8, *by weight* to form water. This unvarying composition of water is an example of the Law of Definite Proportions. It is true, also, that by indirect means we are able to form another compound of hydrogen and oxygen, hydrogen peroxide. The composition of hydrogen peroxide is 1 part of hydrogen to 16 parts of oxygen by weight. It will be noted that 8 compares with 16 just as 1 is to 2, a ratio of small whole numbers. It is not uncommon in chemistry for two elements to form a series of compounds, as shown below.

From these data we observe: *1.* the weight of the hydrogen in the first pair of compounds is fixed, or constant, and the weight of iron in the second pair of compounds is also constant; *2.* the weights of oxygen, 8 and 16, in the first case are in the simple ratio of 1 to 2; the weights of chlorine, 71 and 106.5, in the second case are in the simple ratio of 2 to 3. It would be possible to give other examples, but in every case we would find the *Law of Multiple Proportions* to be true. We can state it this way: *When two elements unite to form two or more different compounds, if the amount of one element is constant, the weights of the other element in the series of compounds will be in the ratio of small whole numbers.*

This law was first proposed by John Dalton, as a direct consequence of his theory that matter existed in the form of atoms. He recognized the possibility that two kinds of atoms could combine in more than one way and in more than one proportion. But since only whole atoms could be involved in such combinations, the ratios of the weights of the second atom joining with fixed weights of the first atom would have to be in the ratio of small whole numbers. This ratio would be the same as the ratio of the actual numbers of atoms of the second element joining with a fixed number of atoms of the first element.

Today we know that the Law of Multiple Proportions arises from the fact that some elements show more than one valence or can combine in more than one way with another element. We know that iron can exist in compounds as ferrous ions with a valence of $+2$ or ferric ions with a valence of $+3$. When these forms of iron combine with chloride ions, for example, there

H_2O	1 g of H and 8 g of O	$FeCl_2$	56 g of Fe and 71 g of Cl
H_2O_2	1 g of H and 16 g of O	$FeCl_3$	56 g of Fe and 106.5 g of Cl

Fig. 10–15. A tank in which wool fibers are bleached with a solution containing hydrogen peroxide before being blended and dyed for use in making carpets.

are two possible compounds, $FeCl_2$, ferrous chloride, and $FeCl_3$, ferric chloride. The ratio of the numbers of atoms of chlorine combining with a single atom of iron is 2 to 3. And since the numbers of atoms which combine is proportional to the weights which combine, the ratio of the weights of chlorine combining with a fixed weight of iron in these two compounds is also 2 to 3.

When we compare the electron-dot formula for water

$$H\!:\!\overset{..}{\underset{..}{O}}\!:$$
$$H$$

with that for hydrogen peroxide,

$$\overset{H}{:\!\overset{..}{\underset{..}{O}}\!:\!\overset{..}{\underset{..}{O}}\!:}$$
$$H$$

we see that there are two different ways in which these two kinds of atoms can combine. In water, 2 hydrogen atoms combine with only 1 oxygen atom. In hydrogen peroxide, the 2 hydrogen atoms combine with 2 oxygen atoms. Since the numbers of atoms which combine is proportional to the weights which combine, the ratio of the weights of oxygen which combine with the same weight of hydrogen in these two compounds is 1 to 2, a ratio of small whole numbers.

Summary

Water is our most abundant and most useful liquid. Pure water is transparent, odorless, tasteless, and almost colorless. Impurities may affect its odor and taste. Water freezes at 0° C and boils at 100° C under a pressure of 760 mm of mercury. Water molecules are polar molecules, and are joined by hydrogen bonds into groups of from eight to four in liquid water. Water is used: *1.* as a standard for defining the relationship between volume and mass in the metric system; *2.* for establishing a temperature scale and graduating thermometers; *3.* for measuring heat; and *4.* as a standard of specific gravity.

Water is a very stable compound. It reacts with active metals such as sodium, potassium, and calcium. Steam reacts with red-hot iron. The oxides of very active metals are basic anhydrides, and the oxides of nonmetals are acid anhydrides. Many crystals contain water of hydration which may be driven off by heat to form anhydrous compounds. Water promotes many chemical changes.

The composition of water can be determined by: *1.* analysis; *2.* synthesis; and *3.* indirect means. By volume, water is composed of two volumes of hydrogen united with one volume of oxygen. By weight, water contains approximately one part hydrogen to eight parts oxygen.

Deuterium oxide is "heavy water." It is used in chemical and physiological research, and as a moderator in nuclear reactors.

Impurities in water may be in suspension, or in solution. Potable water is water that is fit to drink. Organic impurities include bacteria, sewage, and animal or vegetable matter in various stages of decay. Inorganic matter is made up of minerals.

Drinking water for cities is purified by: *1.* sedimentation; *2.* the addition of chemicals, followed by further settling; and *3.* filtering through layers of sand, charcoal, and gravel. Aeration improves the taste of water, and also oxidizes impurities. The addition of chlorine or ozone destroys the remaining bacteria.

Distillation separates water from nonvolatile impurities, particularly dissolved minerals.

Hydrogen peroxide is prepared: *1.* from a mixture of barium peroxide and sulfuric acid in water; *2.* by the electrolysis of sulfuric acid that has been diluted to a specific gravity of 1.35 to 1.45; or *3.* by the use of hydrogen to reduce a complex carbon compound which has been dissolved in benzene. Hydrogen peroxide is an unstable compound that decomposes into water and oxygen. It is used to destroy bacteria and for bleaching. The peroxide group consists of two oxygen atoms linked together by a nonpolar covalent bond.

The Law of Multiple Proportions: When two elements unite to form two or more different compounds, if the amount of one element is constant, the weights of the other element in the series of compounds will be in the ratio of small whole numbers.

Test yourself on these terms

acid anhydride	hydrate	potable water
aeration	hydrogen bond	precipitate
analysis	ice point	sedimentation
anhydrous	inhibitor	specific gravity
basic anhydride	Law of Multiple	stable compound
British thermal unit	Proportions	steam point
calorie	meaning of ↓	synthesis
chlorination	mineral matter	unstable compound
deuterium oxide	organic matter	water as a scientific
distillation	peroxide group	standard
filtration	polar molecule	water of hydration

Questions

Group A

1. Why is there always water vapor in the air, even over desert regions?
2. List six physical properties of water.
3. Under what conditions does one milliliter of water weigh one gram?
4. How does the volume of steam compare with the volume of water from which it was produced?
5. (a) What is a stable compound? Give an example. (b) What is an unstable compound? Give an example.
6. (a) List five metals which react with water. (b) Give the conditions under which they react.
7. (a) What is an anhydride? (b) Distinguish between a basic anhydride and an acid anhydride. (c) What type of compound may be an acid anhydride? (d) What type of compound may be a basic anhydride?
8. What is the significance of the raised dot in $BaCl_2 \cdot 2 H_2O$?
9. Give an example of a chemical change which is promoted by the presence of water.
10. What is the composition of water: (a) by volume? (b) by weight?
11. Give some uses for deuterium oxide.
12. (a) What are the two main classes of impurities in water? (b) How may each be removed from water?
13. What is a precipitate?
14. What is the function of each of the following in water purification: (a) aeration; (b) filtration; (c) chlorine; (d) charcoal?
15. Why is acetanilide added to 3% solutions of hydrogen peroxide?
16. How is it possible for two elements to form more than one compound?

Group B

17. What effect does the pressure on a water surface have on the boiling temperature of the water?
18. Describe the structure of a water molecule and tell why it is a polar molecule.

19. (*a*) What is a hydrogen bond? (*b*) What effect do the hydrogen bonds in water have on its boiling point?

20. What does the extreme stability of H_2O molecules indicate about the strength of the covalent bonds between the oxygen and hydrogen atoms?

21. How is deuterium oxide separated from ordinary water?

22. How does the addition of aluminum sulfate and calcium hydroxide assist in the sedimentation of suspended particles during water purification?

23. What chemical change does hydrogen peroxide produce in the dyes which it bleaches?

24. What conditions must be met for a series of compounds to illustrate the Law of Multiple Proportions?

25. Explain why ice occupies a greater volume than the water from which it is formed.

26. What particles are present in water beside ordinary H_2O molecules?

27. Show the difference in composition and structure between water and hydrogen peroxide by electron-dot formulas.

28. Explain why water has a point of maximum density at 4° C.

29. Distinguish between peroxides and dioxides.

30. What effect does the amount of sulfuric acid added to water have on the products of the electrolysis of this mixture?

Problems

Group A

1. A mixture of 50 ml of hydrogen and 30 ml of oxygen is ignited by an electric spark. What gas remains? What is its volume?

2. A mixture of 40 ml of oxygen and 120 ml of hydrogen is ignited. What gas remains and what is its volume?

3. What volume of hydrogen is needed for complete reaction with 37.5 ml of oxygen?

4. A mixture of equal volumes of oxygen and hydrogen has a volume of 100 ml. After the mixture is ignited, what gas remains, and what is its volume?

Group B

5. Water is 11.11% hydrogen and 88.89% oxygen. What weights of hydrogen and oxygen will be required to produce 50 g of water?

6. Hydrogen peroxide is 5.88% hydrogen and 94.12% oxygen. If one half of the oxygen is liberated when hydrogen peroxide is decomposed, what weight of hydrogen peroxide will be needed to produce 5 g of oxygen?

Some things for you to do

1. Prepare some anhydrous cupric sulfate by heating blue cupric sulfate crystals carefully. The open end of the test tube must be lower than the closed end to permit the water to run out. Examine the anhydrous cupric sulfate that results. Add a drop of water to a little of the powder to show how it can be used as a test to detect the presence of water.
2. Visit the water works in your community and learn how they purify the drinking water used in your home.
3. Prepare a quantity of distilled water, using a Liebig condenser. Note any differences in taste and appearance of the distilled water when compared with tap water.
4. Show that hydrogen peroxide produces oxygen when it decomposes. Add a pinch of manganese dioxide to a test tube half full of hydrogen peroxide solution. Hold a glowing splint above the bubbling liquid.

Check your progress in chemistry

1. Describe the structure of a calcium atom, atomic number 20, atomic mass 40.
2. Distinguish between atomic weight and atomic mass.
3. (a) In which group of the Periodic Table is oxygen placed? (b) Where is hydrogen placed on the Periodic Table?
4. (a) What is the usual valence of hydrogen? (b) What is the usual valence of oxygen?
5. What type of bonding occurs in: (a) H_2O; (b) D_2O; (c) H_2O_2?
6. The English say Priestley, the French say Lavoisier, and the Swedish people say Scheele discovered oxygen. What part did each of these scientists play in the discovery?
7. Describe two commercial methods for producing oxygen.
8. What are two laboratory methods for producing hydrogen?
9. Draw electron-dot formulas for: (a) a molecule of oxygen; (b) a molecule of hydrogen.
10. When hydrogen is passed over heated iron oxide, iron and steam are produced. (a) Was the hydrogen oxidized or reduced? (b) Was the iron oxide oxidized or reduced?
11. Draw a diagram of a laboratory burner, and use your diagram to explain its operation.
12. A wide-mouth bottle contains a colorless, odorless, and tasteless gas, which is either hydrogen or oxygen. What experiments would you conduct to establish the identity of the gas?
13. In what ways is water used as a scientific standard?
14. Describe the work of Morley and of Dumas in establishing the composition of water by weight.
15. What are the methods used to remove or destroy bacteria during the purification of water?

16. A gas has a volume of 45 ml when the barometer is 750 mm. If the temperature does not change, what will be the volume of the gas at standard pressure?

17. One hundred liters of gas is measured at 25° C and 700 mm pressure. What volume will this gas occupy at −20° C and 800 mm pressure?

★ 18. A quantity of hydrogen collected over water occupies 78.0 ml when the temperature is 23° C and the barometric pressure is 746 mm. The liquid level inside the gas collecting bottle is the same as that outside. What volume will the dry hydrogen occupy at S.T.P.?

Challenging your knowledge

1. What relationship is there between unpaired electrons in an oxygen molecule and the fact that liquid oxygen is slightly attracted by a magnet?

2. In the experiment of burning steel picture wire in pure oxygen, the end of the picture wire is sometimes dipped in powdered sulfur, and the sulfur ignited, before the wire is plunged into the oxygen. Why?

3. From a given amount of water, is it possible to prepare more hydrogen by electrolysis or by reaction with a metal such as sodium? Why?

4. Carbon dioxide is a gas which is about $1\frac{1}{2}$ times as dense as air. What would happen if this gas surrounded the unglazed porcelain cup of the apparatus shown in Fig. 8-4?

5. Scientists have not yet reached Absolute zero, yet helium has been cooled below −273° C. Explain this seeming paradox.

6. What do scientists believe happens to molecular movement as a substance is cooled to Absolute zero?

7. What are some of the probable errors in the Dumas method for determining the composition of water by weight?

8. Sand filters for drinking water have stones, pebbles, gravel, sand, and fine sand in layers from the bottom of the filter to the top. Why are they arranged in this order?

Chemical calculations

John Dalton made chemistry a mathematical science with the introduction of his Atomic Theory. Shortly thereafter he published his Law of Multiple Proportions and table of atomic weights. When we consider the crudeness of his equipment, it is not surprising that his table of relative atomic weights was mostly wrong. What is important is the fact that his bold generalizations were mostly right.

Today we have accurate tables of atomic weights. We have instruments and techniques which yield precise measurements. Given reliable experimental data, we can determine the formulas of substances and the quantitative relationships between reacting substances by means of simple calculations.

Five chapters are included in this unit: *Chemical Composition, Chemical Equations, Weight Relations in Chemical Reactions, Molecular Composition of Gases,* and *Volume Relations in Chemical Reactions.* The calculations you will learn to carry out are an essential part of the study of chemistry.

Chapter 11 CHEMICAL COMPOSITION

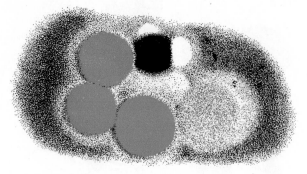

1. The significance of chemical formulas. We have learned to write formulas for compounds using our knowledge of the valence of the elements composing them. When it is known that a substance exists as simple molecules, its formula represents one molecule of the substance. Thus it is known as a *molecular formula.* In instances where the molecular structure is not known, or where it is known that the substance does not exist as simple molecules, the formula represents the simplest whole-number ratio of the atoms of the constituent elements. These are *empirical,* or simplest, *formulas.*

Let us examine some chemical formulas to learn their full significance. The compound, water, has the molecular formula H_2O. This molecular formula represents three things:

1. It represents *one* molecule of water.

2. It shows that each molecule of water is made up of *two atoms of hydrogen* and *one atom of oxygen.*

3. Since the atomic weight of hydrogen is 1 and the atomic weight of oxygen is 16, it signifies that the *formula weight* of water is 18 [(1, the atomic weight of hydrogen, $\times 2$ atoms of hydrogen) + (16,

VOCABULARY

Chemical formula. A shorthand notation using chemical symbols and numerical subscripts to represent the composition of substances.

Empirical formula. A chemical formula which denotes the constituent elements of a substance and the relative number of atoms of each.

Formula weight. The sum of the atomic weights of all of the atoms present in the chemical formula.

Molecular formula. A chemical formula which denotes the constituent elements of a substance and the number of atoms of each composing one molecule.

Molecular weight. The formula weight of a molecular substance.

the atomic weight of oxygen, $\times$ 1 atom of oxygen)].

The compound sodium chloride, table salt, has the empirical formula NaCl. It is a crystalline solid which has no simple molecular structure. Inspection of this empirical formula tells us the following:

1. It represents the relative number of atoms of each element present in the compound sodium chloride.
2. It shows that for each sodium atom there is one chlorine atom.
3. Since the atomic weight of sodium is 23 and the atomic weight of chlorine is 35.5, it signifies that the formula weight of sodium chloride is 58.5 (23 + 35.5).

The *formula weight* of any compound is merely *the sum of the atomic weights of all of the atoms present in the formula.*

2. What is the meaning of molecular weight? We have seen that a molecular formula represents 1 molecule of a substance. Since H_2O is a molecular formula and indicates 1 molecule of water, the formula weight, 18, is the relative weight of *one molecule* of water. *The formula weight of a molecular substance is its* **molecular weight.**

In the strictest sense it would be incorrect to speak of the molecular weight of a nonmolecular substance, such as sodium chloride, which is represented by an empirical formula. The term *formula weight* is more generally applicable than the term *molecular weight* and therefore is preferred by chemists. However, both terms are widely used and, in elementary chemical calculations, the distinction is not significant.

3. Finding the formula weight of a compound from its formula. If you wish to know the total weight of your chemistry class, you would add together the weights of all the individuals in the class. Similarly, if we wish to find the formula weight of any substance for which the formula is given, we must add together the atomic weights of all the atoms present, as represented by the formula. Let us use the formula of cane sugar, $C_{12}H_{22}O_{11}$, as an example.

Number of atoms	Atomic weight	Total weight
12 of C	12	12 × 12 = 144
22 of H	1	22 × 1 = 22
11 of O	16	11 × 16 = 176

formula weight (molecular weight) = 342

The formula for calcium hydroxide is $Ca(OH)_2$. The subscript $_2$ following the parentheses indicates that there are two hydroxide radicals (OH) with each calcium atom in calcium hydroxide. It is usually easier in determining formula weights of substances containing such simple radical groups to consider the *combined atomic weights* of the radical group as we would the atomic weight of a single atom of any element present. Thus we proceed as follows:

1 atom of Ca, at. wt. 40	1 × 40 = 40
2 OH radicals, combined at. wt. 17	2 × 17 = 34

formula weight = 74

The atomic weights of the elements are relative weights based on the average atom of oxygen having the assigned value of 16.0000. The formula weight of any substance is likewise a relative weight having the same base: oxygen as 16.0000. When chemical reactions are studied quantitatively the atomic weights and formula weights are exceedingly practical to use. They tell us the relative weights of elements or compounds which combine or react. We may convert these relative weights to any desired units. Thus formulas play an important part in chemical calculations.

4. Finding the percentage composition of a compound. Frequently it is important to know the composition of a compound in terms of the *percentage by weight* of each constituent element. We may want to know the weight percentage of iron in a certain pure compound. Knowledge of the percentage of oxygen in potassium chlorate will enable us to determine the amount of this compound needed to furnish enough oxygen for a laboratory experiment.

The chemical formula of a compound enables us to determine directly its formula weight simply by adding the atomic weights of all the atoms present. The formula weight represents *all*, or *100%*, of the composition of the substance as indicated by the formula. The total atomic weight (atomic weight × number of atoms) of each element present represents the *part* of the substance due to that element. The fractional part due to each element present is:

$$\frac{\text{total atomic weight of the element}}{\text{formula weight of the compound}}$$

The percentage by weight of each element present in the compound is therefore a fractional part of 100 percent of the compound and may be expressed as follows:

$$\frac{\text{at. wt.} \times \text{no. of atoms}}{\text{formula wt.}} \times 100\% =$$
$$\% \text{ of each element}$$

Let us consider the iron compound mentioned earlier. The formula is Fe_2O_3. What is the percentage of each of the elements present?

1. Formula weight of Fe_2O_3

total at. wt. of Fe = 2 × 56 = 112
total at. wt. of O = 3 × 16 = 48
formula weight of Fe_2O_3 = 160

2. Percentage of Fe

$$\frac{\text{total at. wt. of Fe}}{\text{formula wt. of Fe}_2\text{O}_3} \times 100\% = \% \text{ of Fe}$$
$$\frac{112}{160} \times 100\% = 70\%$$

3. Percentage of O

$$\frac{\text{total at. wt. of O}}{\text{formula wt. of Fe}_2\text{O}_3} \times 100\% = \% \text{ of O}$$
$$\frac{48}{160} \times 100\% = 30\%$$

Observe that, since there is no third element present, the percentage of oxygen = $100\% - 70\% = 30\%$.

As a second example, let us use crystallized sodium carbonate. From its formula, $Na_2CO_3 \cdot 10\,H_2O$, we see that 10 molecules of water have crystallized with sodium carbonate to form the hydrate. The raised period merely indicates water of hydration. To find the percentage composition we proceed as before:

1. Formula weight $Na_2CO_3 \cdot 10\,H_2O$

2 Na	2 × 23 =	46
1 C	1 × 12 =	12
3 O	3 × 16 =	48
10 H_2O	10 × 18 =	180
	formula weight =	286

2. Percentage of Na

$$\frac{46}{286} \times 100\% = 16.1\%$$

3. Percentage of C

$$\frac{12}{286} \times 100\% = 4.2\%$$

4. Percentage of O

$$\tfrac{48}{286} \times 100\% = 16.8\%$$

5. Percentage of H$_2$O

$$\tfrac{180}{286} \times 100\% = 62.9\%$$

The approximate atomic weights used have no more than two significant figures. Your accuracy cannot be improved by carrying out your computations beyond the accuracy limits of the data used. The sum of the weight percentages, therefore, may only approximate 100 percent. Such results do not detract from the validity of the chemistry involved but merely reflect the approximations employed in the computations.

5. Determining the empirical formula of a compound. When we are given the formula of a compound we may determine the percentage composition by weight of the constituent elements. So if we know the percent by weight of each element composing a compound we may calculate the ratio of the atoms of the elements combined. The elements of a compound written in their simplest whole-number ratio constitute the empirical, or simplest, formula of the compound.

This is the way in which most formulas are originally determined. A compound is analyzed to identify the elements present and determine their proportions by weight. The empirical formula is then calculated from this information by using the atomic weight of each element to reduce the weight ratios to atom ratios.

Dr. Morley of Western Reserve University (see Chapter 10, Section 7) found that 1 part by weight of hydrogen combined with 7 94 parts by weight of oxygen to form 8.94 parts by weight

of water vapor. In elementary chemistry, since we use the table of approximate atomic weights which are "rounded off," we may round off this weight ratio to 1 part of hydrogen and 8 parts of oxygen forming 9 parts of water. Thus water consists of $\tfrac{1}{9} \times 100\%$ = 11.1% hydrogen and $\tfrac{8}{9} \times 100\%$ = 88.9% oxygen.

We may find the relative number of atoms of hydrogen and oxygen in water by comparing either the relative weights or the weight percentages of the elements to their respective atomic weights.

1. From the percentage composition data

Percentage composition	Atomic weight
H = 11.1	1
O = 88.9	16

Relative number of atoms

H = 11.1 ÷ 1 = 11.1
O = 88.9 ÷ 16 = 5.55

2. From the relative weights data

Relative weight	Atomic weight
H = 1	1
O = 8	16

Relative number of atoms

H = 1 ÷ 1 = 1
O = 8 ÷ 16 = $\tfrac{1}{2}$

From these calculations we may write the empirical formula of water as $H_{11.1}O_{5.55}$ or $HO_{\frac{1}{2}}$. Both formulas show the correct ratio of hydrogen atoms to oxygen atoms in the compound, water. However, according to the Atomic Theory, only whole atoms combine chemically. We need to convert these atom ratios to their simplest whole-number values. This is accomplished by dividing each ratio by its lowest term.

$$\begin{array}{c} \text{H} \ : \ \text{O} \\ 5.55 \overline{)11.1 : 5.55} \\ 2 \ : \ 1 \end{array}$$

and

$$\begin{array}{c} \text{H} \ : \ \text{O} \\ \tfrac{1}{2} \overline{)1 \ : \ \tfrac{1}{2}} \\ 2 \ : \ 1 \end{array}$$

The empirical formula of water is therefore H_2O. See Sample Problems below and on page 157.

6. Steps for finding the empirical formula. The solutions to problems in which we are required to find the empirical formula may be summarized in the following steps: *1. Find the relative number of atoms of each element* by dividing the weight (or weight percentage) of each element by its atomic weight. *2. Find the smallest ratio of atoms* by dividing the relative number of atoms of each element by the smallest relative number. *3. Find the simplest whole-number ratio of atoms* (if

not satisfied in Step 2) by expressing as fractions and clearing. CAUTION: In some problems Step 2 may result in such ratios as $1 : 2.01 : 2.98 : 3.99$. Remembering that results obtained by using approximate atomic weights can be no more accurate than these values (see Chapter 1, Section 16), you should not attempt to clear the fractions by following Step 3. Simply round off to 2, 3, and 4 respectively.

★ **7. How may we find the molecular formula?** The analysis of a substance enables us to determine its empirical formula. This simplest formula may or may not be the molecular formula. We have calculated the empirical formula of the gas, methane, and found it to be CH_4. Any multiple of CH_4, as C_2H_8, C_3H_{12}, or C_nH_{4n}, represents the same ratio of carbon and hydrogen atoms. How then may we know which is the correct molecular formula?

It is not possible to decide which is the true formula unless the molecular weight of the substance has been determined. Some substances lend them-

---

SAMPLE PROBLEM

A compound is found by analysis to contain 75% carbon and 25% hydrogen. What is the empirical formula?

SOLUTION

We first convert the weight percentage of each element to the relative number of atoms by dividing the weight percentage by the atomic weight. The smallest ratio of these relative numbers of atoms is then found by dividing each by the smallest relative number. The smallest whole-number ratio of atoms indicates the empirical formula.

Relative number of C atoms $= \dfrac{\text{wt. \% of C}}{\text{at. wt. of C}} = \dfrac{75}{12} = 6.25$

Relative number of H atoms $= \dfrac{\text{wt. \% of H}}{\text{at. wt. of H}} = \dfrac{25}{1} = 25$

Smallest ratio of atoms $= \dfrac{6.25}{6.25} : \dfrac{25}{6.25} = 1 : 4$

Empirical formula $= CH_4$

SAMPLE PROBLEM

A compound contains carbon, 81.82%, and hydrogen, 18.18%. Find the empirical formula.

SOLUTION

Relative number of C atoms $= \dfrac{\text{wt. \% of C}}{\text{at. wt. of C}} = \dfrac{81.82}{12} = 6.82$

Relative number of H atoms $= \dfrac{\text{wt. \% of H}}{\text{at. wt. of H}} = \dfrac{18.18}{1} = 18.18$

Smallest ratio of atoms $= \dfrac{6.82}{6.82} : \dfrac{18.18}{6.82} = 1 : 2.67$

In this case it is necessary to express the atom ratio as fractions and then clear the fractions in order to arrive at the simplest whole-number ratio.

Simplest whole-number ratio $= 1 : 2.67 = 1 : 2\frac{2}{3} = 3 : 8$

Empirical formula $= C_3H_8$

SAMPLE PROBLEM

The reduction of 11.47 g of cupric oxide yields 9.16 g of copper. What is the empirical formula of the cupric oxide?

SOLUTION

As cupric oxide is composed of copper and oxygen, the weight of oxygen removed in the reduction process must be 11.47 g $-$ 9.16 g $=$ 2.31 g.

Relative number of Cu atoms $= \dfrac{\text{rel. wt. of Cu}}{\text{at. wt. of Cu}} = \dfrac{9.16}{63.5} = 0.144$

Relative number of O atoms $= \dfrac{\text{rel. wt. of O}}{\text{at. wt. of O}} = \dfrac{2.31}{16} = 0.144$

Smallest ratio of atoms $= 1 : 1$

Empirical formula $= CuO$

---

selves to known methods of determining molecular weights and some do not. These methods will be discussed in Chapters 14 and 19. If the molecular weight is known, it is a simple matter to decide which multiple of the empirical formula is the molecular formula.

Let us represent the correct multiple of the empirical formula by the subscript x. The molecular formula then becomes

$$(empirical\ formula)_x$$

which may be equated to the known molecular weight.

$$(empirical\ formula)_x = molecular\ weight$$

In the case of methane the molecular weight is known to be 16. Our equation is

$$(CH_4)_x = 16$$
$$(12 + 4)_x = 16$$
$$x = 1$$
$$molecular\ formula = (CH_4)_1\ or\ CH_4$$

★ SAMPLE PROBLEM

Hydrogen peroxide is found by analysis to consist of 5.9% hydrogen and 94.1% oxygen. Its molecular weight is determined to be 34. What is the correct formula?

SOLUTION

1. The empirical formula determined from the analysis by the method described in Section 5, is

$$HO$$

2. The molecular formula determined from the empirical formula and molecular weight is

$$(HO)_x = 34$$
$$(1 + 16)_x = 34$$
$$x = 2$$

molecular formula $= (HO)_2$ or H_2O_2

Hence the empirical formula of methane is also the molecular formula. We have seen that this is true also in the case of water. For another example, see the Sample Problem above.

The analysis of starch reveals its empirical formula to be $C_6H_{10}O_5$. No precise method has been found for determining its molecular weight. Its molecular formula could be $C_6H_{10}O_5$, $C_{60}H_{100}O_{50}$ or any other which is a multiple of the empirical formula. Chemists write the formula for starch as $(C_6H_{10}O_5)_x$, but no one knows how to find the exact value of x.

Cellulose has the same empirical formula as starch, $C_6H_{10}O_5$. Chemists are certain, however, that its molecular structure involves some multiple different from that of starch. Its formula is commonly written $(C_6H_{10}O_5)_n$, where n for cellulose and the x for starch stand for different numbers neither of which is known.

Summary

The empirical formula of a compound indicates what elements are present and the relative number of atoms of these elements. The molecular formula tells us the specific number of atoms of each element present per molecule of a compound.

The formula weight is the sum of the atomic weights of all the atoms indicated by the formula. If it is a molecular formula, the formula weight is the same as the molecular weight.

The percentage composition of a compound may be determined if the formula is known. Conversely, the empirical formula may be determined if the composition of a compound is known.

The molecular formula can be written only if the molecular weight of the substance has been determined. It will always be a whole-number multiple of the empirical formula.

Test yourself on these terms

chemical formula

empirical formula

formula weight

molecular formula

molecular weight

percentage composition

Problems

(Use the table of approximate atomic weights on the inside of the front cover.)

Group A

1. What is the formula weight of ammonia, NH_3?
2. Find the formula weight of sulfuric acid, H_2SO_4.
3. Dextrose, or grape sugar, has the formula $C_6H_{12}O_6$. Determine its formula weight.
4. Find the formula weight of ethyl alcohol, C_2H_5OH.
5. Calcium phosphate has the formula $Ca_3(PO_4)_2$. Determine the formula weight.
6. Crystallized magnesium sulfate, or Epsom salts, has the formula $MgSO_4 \cdot 7 H_2O$. What is its formula weight?
7. Vinegar contains acetic acid, $HC_2H_3O_2$. Find the percentage composition of this compound.
8. All baking powders contain sodium hydrogen carbonate, $NaHCO_3$. Calculate its percentage composition.
9. What is the percentage composition of soap having the formula $C_{17}H_{35}COONa$?
10. Which of the following compounds contains the highest percentage of nitrogen: (a) $Ca(No_3)_2$; (b) $CaCN_2$; or (c) $(NH_4)_2SO_4$?
11. A strip of pure copper weighing 6.356 g is heated in a stream of oxygen until it is completely converted to the black oxide. The weight of the oxide was found to be 7.956 g. What is the percentage composition of the cupric oxide?
12. How many kilograms of iron may be recovered from 1 metric ton (1000 kg) of Fe_3O_4?
13. Cinnabar, the ore from which mercury is extracted, has the formula HgS. Calculate the weight of mercury recovered from 1 kg of cinnabar.
14. Calculate the percentage of copper in each of the following minerals: cuprite, Cu_2O; malachite, $CuCO_3 \cdot Cu(OH)_2$; and cubanite, $CuFe_2S_4$.
15. Calculate the percentage of CaO in $CaCO_3$.

Group B

16. If 124.8 g of cupric sulfate crystals is heated to drive off the water of hydration, the loss of weight is 45 g. What is the percentage of water in hydrated cupric sulfate?
17. The anhydrous cupric sulfate produced in Problem 16 was found to contain copper, 31.8 g; sulfur, 16.0 g; and oxygen, 32.0 g. Determine the empirical formula of the hydrated cupric sulfate crystals.

18. One compound of platinum and chlorine is known to consist of 42.1% chlorine. Another consists of 26.7% chlorine. What are the two empirical formulas?

19. What is the empirical formula of silver fluoride which is found to contain 85% silver?

20. What is the percentage composition of the drug Chloromycetin, $C_{11}H_{12}N_2O_5Cl_2$?

21. Analysis: phosphorus, 43.67%; oxygen, 56.33%. What is the empirical formula?

22. Analysis: potassium, 24.58%; manganese, 34.81%; oxygen, 40.50%. What is the empirical formula?

23. Calculate the empirical formula for a compound having 37.70% sodium, 22.95% silicon, and 39.34% oxygen.

24. A compound has the following composition: sodium, 28.05%; carbon, 29.26%; hydrogen, 3.66%; oxygen, 39.02%. What is the empirical formula?

25. The analysis of a compound shows: nitrogen, 21.21%; hydrogen, 6.06%; sulfur, 24.24%; oxygen, 48.48%. Find the simplest formula.

26. What is the empirical formula of certain hydrated crystals having a composition of 56.14% $ZnSO_4$ and 43.86% water?

★ 27. The analysis of a gas reveals its composition to be carbon, 92.3%; hydrogen, 7.07%. Its molecular weight is known to be 26. What is the molecular formula?

★ 28. The percentages by weight of carbon in its two oxides are 42.8% and 27.3%. Use these data to illustrate the Law of Multiple Proportions.

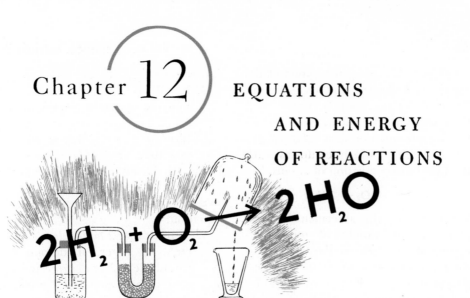

Chapter 12

EQUATIONS AND ENERGY OF REACTIONS

$$2H_2 + O_2 \rightarrow 2H_2O$$

1. CHEMICAL EQUATIONS

1. What are formula equations? The simplest way in which we may illustrate chemical action is to use *word equations*. Such equations are useful in that they enable us to state briefly what substances enter into chemical actions and what substances are produced. Word equations have *qualitative* significance.

Water is formed by the combustion of hydrogen in air. The word equation for this action is:

hydrogen + oxygen → water

We read, hydrogen *plus* oxygen *yields* water. Such an equation signifies that when hydrogen and oxygen react as indicated, water is the only product. Thus it briefly states an experimental fact. It does not tell us the circumstances under which the reaction occurs, or the quantities involved.

In our discussion of the Law of Conservation of Matter and Energy (Chapter 1, Section 11), we recognized a most useful generalization: *In ordinary chemical changes, the total weight of the reacting substances is equal to the total weight of the products.* This is sometimes referred to as the **Law of Conservation of Atoms.**

VOCABULARY

Activation energy. Energy required initially to start a reaction.

Activity series. A table of metals or nonmetals arranged in order of descending activity.

Formula equation. A concise symbolized picture of a chemical change.

Free energy. The energy of a reaction which can be converted to useful work outside the reaction.

Heat of formation. The quantity of heat energy liberated or consumed when a compound is formed from its constituent elements.

Product. An element or compound resulting from a chemical action.

Reactant. An element or compound entering into a chemical action.

Let us now replace the names of the *reactants*, hydrogen and oxygen, and the name of the *product*, water, with their respective formulas. Now we can rewrite our equation as a *balanced formula equation* which conforms with the Law of Conservation of Atoms.

$$2 H_2 + O_2 \rightarrow 2 H_2O$$

We may verify this agreement by comparing the total number of atoms of hydrogen and oxygen on the left side of the reaction sign ($\rightarrow$) to their respective totals on the right. Two molecules of hydrogen contain 4 atoms of hydrogen; 2 molecules of water also contain 4 hydrogen atoms. One molecule of oxygen contains 2 atoms of oxygen; 2 molecules of water also contain 2 oxygen atoms. Thus our chemical equation, just as any algebraic equation, *expresses an equality. Until it is balanced it cannot express an equality and is not a true equation.* The yield sign ($\rightarrow$) has the meaning of an equals sign ($=$), and in addition, indicates the direction in which the reaction proceeds.

Our formula equation now signifies much more than the original word equation.

1. It tells us the relative proportions of the reactants, hydrogen and oxygen, and the product, water.

2. It tells us that *2 molecules* of hydrogen react with *1 molecule* of oxygen to form *2 molecules* of water.

3. It tells us that *2 molecular weights* of hydrogen react with *1 molecular weight* of oxygen to form *2 molecular weights* of water.

Atomic weights, and thus molecular weights, are relative weights and may be assigned any desired weight units.

Therefore:

4. It tells us that *4 g* (or 4 kg, or 4 tons) of hydrogen react with *32 g* (or 32 kg, or 32 tons) of oxygen to form *36 g* (or 36 kg, or 36 tons) of water.

Finally, in any equation, the equality exists in both directions. If $x + y = z$, then $z = x + y$. So our chemical equation:

5. Tells us that *2 molecules* (or 36 g, etc.) of water, if decomposed, would yield *2 molecules* (or 4 g, etc.) of hydrogen and *1 molecule* (or 32 g, etc.) of oxygen.

We can see that formula equations have *quantitative* significance. They represent facts concerning reactions which have been established by experiments or other means. However, they do not tell us either the ease with which reactions proceed or the conditions under which reactions occur.

It is possible to write an equation for a reaction which does not occur. For example, hydrogen and oxygen may be shown by an equation to yield hydrogen peroxide. Such an equation can be balanced to conform to the Law of Conservation of Atoms. However, it would be a false equation and therefore useless. It would be contrary to known facts, since hydrogen and oxygen do not combine directly to form hydrogen peroxide.

2. Factors in equation writing. A chemical equation has no value unless it is correct in every detail. Three factors must be considered in writing a balanced equation.

1. The equation must represent the facts. If we are to write the equation for a reaction, we must know the facts concerning the reaction. We must know all the reactants involved and all the products formed. The chemist relies upon analysis for facts and writes equations only for those reactions that are known to occur.

2. The equation must include the symbols and formulas of all elements and compounds which are used as reactants or formed as products. We must know these symbols and formulas and must be sure that they are correctly written. In most instances your knowledge of the valence of the elements and the valence method of writing correct formulas will enable you to satisfy this requirement without extensive experience with experiments or analyses.

3. The Law of Conservation of Atoms must be satisfied. There must be the same number of atoms of each kind on each side of the equation. A new atom cannot appear on the product side and none can disappear from the reactant side. This is the *balancing factor.* It is achieved by adjusting the coefficients of the formulas of reactants and products to the smallest possible whole numbers which satisfy the Law of Conservation of Atoms.

3. Procedure in writing equations. Let us review some of the chemical reactions which we have studied and proceed to write the chemical equations which represent them. We must proceed in steps which satisfy the three factors in equation writing in their proper order. This order is as follows: *1. We must represent the facts; 2. We must balance formulas of compounds as to valence* (formulas for elementary gases with diatomic molecules must be correctly written) *; and 3. We must balance the equation as to atoms.*

We may prepare hydrogen and oxygen in the laboratory by the electrolysis of water. As the equation does not tell

the rate or conditions under which the reaction proceeds we need not concern ourselves with these matters in writing the equation.

Step 1: What are the facts? The only reactant is water and the only products are hydrogen and oxygen. We may represent these facts by the word equation:

$$\text{water} \rightarrow \text{hydrogen} + \text{oxygen}$$

Now let us substitute the formulas for these substances as accurately as we know them to be.

$$H_2O \rightarrow H_2 + O_2 \text{ (not balanced)}$$

Step 2: Are the formulas correctly written? The valence of hydrogen is $+1$ and of oxygen is -2, so the formula for water is correctly written as H_2O. Both hydrogen and oxygen exist in the free state as diatomic molecules, so the formulas of molecular hydrogen and molecular oxygen are correctly written as H_2 and O_2.

Step 3: Is the equation balanced as to atoms? Starting on the left we have 1 molecule of water consisting of 2 hydrogen atoms and 1 oxygen atom. On the right of the reaction sign $(\rightarrow)$ we have 1 molecule of hydrogen consisting of 2 atoms and 1 molecule of oxygen made up of 2 atoms. *But we had only 1 atom of oxygen on the left.* How may we adjust this difference? We cannot add a subscript $_2$ to the oxygen of the water formula for this would alter a formula which we have already established as correctly written. We can, however, increase the number of water molecules to two by placing the coefficient 2 ahead of the formula H_2O, making it $2\ H_2O$. Thus we have 2 molecules of water each with 1 oxygen giving us our necessary 2 atoms of oxygen on the left.

$$2 H_2O \rightarrow H_2 + O_2 \text{ (not balanced)}$$

Two molecules of water have a total of 4 atoms of hydrogen. We must now move to the right side of the equation and adjust the number of hydrogen atoms to 4. This may be done by placing the coefficient 2 ahead of the hydrogen molecule, making it $2 H_2$. We now have a total of 4 atoms of hydrogen on the right and our equation reads:

$$2 H_2O \rightarrow 2 H_2\uparrow + O_2\uparrow$$

We have achieved the same number of atoms of each element on both sides of the equation with the lowest whole-number ratio of coefficients possible. Thus the equation is balanced (the arrows pointing upward may be used to indicate gaseous products).

In the burning of sulfur, oxygen combines with the sulfur to form sulfur dioxide gas. These are the facts, so we may write:

sulfur + oxygen → sulfur dioxide
$$S + O_2 \rightarrow SO_2\uparrow$$

Molecular oxygen is diatomic, O_2, and the valence of sulfur and oxygen in sulfur dioxide indicate that the formula, SO_2, is correctly written. All formulas are correctly written. The numbers of atoms of sulfur and oxygen are the same on both sides of the equation. No further adjustments are required. The equation is balanced.

Priestley produced oxygen by heating mercuric oxide. The facts are: heating mercuric oxide yields metallic mercury and oxygen gas.

mercuric oxide → mercury + oxygen

Substituting the proper symbols and formulas, we write:

$$HgO \rightarrow Hg + O_2\uparrow \text{ (not balanced)}$$

Our valence check tells us that the formula of mercuric oxide is correctly written. The equation is not balanced with respect to oxygen. We can see that 2 molecules of HgO must decompose to yield the 2 atoms making up the diatomic molecule of oxygen. This will, however, produce 2 atoms of mercury. The balanced equation is:

$$2 HgO \rightarrow 2 Hg + O_2\uparrow$$

We have learned that zinc reacts with hydrochloric acid to produce hydrogen gas and zinc chloride. These facts may be represented by the word equation:

zinc + hydrochloric acid →
                    zinc chloride + hydrogen

With proper consideration for valences we may write:

$$Zn + HCl \rightarrow ZnCl_2 + H_2\uparrow \text{ (not balanced)}$$

In balancing atoms we see that 2 molecules of HCl are required to furnish the 2 chlorine atoms of $ZnCl_2$ and the 2 hydrogen atoms of the diatomic hydrogen molecule. Thus our balanced equation is:

$$Zn + 2 HCl \rightarrow ZnCl_2 + H_2\uparrow$$

One of the most common mistakes that beginners make in balancing equations is that of destroying the valence balance of a formula in order to get the required number of atoms. Do not become discouraged at this time if equations offer considerable difficulty. The trouble lies not in the method of balancing but in the large number of facts that must be known. As you continue to make progress in class and gain experience in the laboratory, the equations that now seem difficult will prove to be extremely simple.

Let us try an equation for a reaction encountered in a process of water puri-

Fig. 12–1. Most chemical reactions are of interest because of the products formed. This lightweight pipe is made of a blend of rubber and plastic.

fication. Aluminum sulfate and calcium hydroxide react to produce two insoluble products, aluminum hydroxide and calcium sulfate. These facts may be represented by the word equation:

aluminum sulfate + calcium hydroxide →
    aluminum hydroxide + calcium sulfate

By valence balancing to assure correct formulas we may write:

$Al_2(SO_4)_3 + Ca(OH)_2 \rightarrow$
    $Al(OH)_3 + CaSO_4$ (not balanced)

We now begin at the left with $Al_2(SO_4)_3$ to balance for atoms. Two Al atoms are indicated. To provide 2 Al atoms on the right we place the coefficient 2 ahead of $Al(OH)_3$. Three SO_4 groups are indicated, so we place the coefficient 3 in front of $CaSO_4$. Our equation now reads:

$Al_2(SO_4)_3 + Ca(OH)_2 \rightarrow$
    $2 Al(OH)_3 + 3 CaSO_4$ (not balanced)

Next we observe that there must be 3 Ca atoms on the left to equal the 3 Ca atoms now on the right. We place the coefficient 3 in front of $Ca(OH)_2$. This gives us 6 OH groups on the left and we observe that there are 6 OH groups on the right. We now have a balanced equation:

$Al_2(SO_4)_3 + 3 Ca(OH)_2 \rightarrow$
    $2 Al(OH)_3\downarrow + 3 CaSO_4\downarrow$

(We may add the arrows pointing down ($\downarrow$) to indicate those products which are insoluble and leave the reaction environment as precipitates.)

Your success in writing chemical equations depends on the following: *1. You must know the symbols of the common elements; 2. You must know the usual valences of the common elements and radicals; 3. You must know the facts relating to the reaction for which an equation is to be written; 4. You must insure that all formulas are correctly written* prior to any attempt to balance atoms; and 5. *You must balance the equation as to atoms of all elements present, so as to have the lowest ratio of whole-number coefficients possible.*

4. There are four general types of chemical reactions. There are various ways of classifying chemical reactions. No single scheme is entirely satisfactory. However, in elementary chemistry, four main types of reactions are generally recognized. These are:

1. Composition reactions, in which two or more substances combine to form a more complex substance. Composition reactions have the general form

$$A + X \rightarrow AX$$

Examples:

$$Fe + S \rightarrow FeS$$
$$H_2O + SO_3 \rightarrow H_2SO_4$$

2. Decomposition reactions, the reverse of the first type, in which a complex substance breaks down to form two or more simpler substances. Decomposition reactions have the general form

$$AX \rightarrow A + X$$

Examples:

$$2 H_2O \rightarrow 2 H_2\uparrow + O_2\uparrow$$
$$2 KClO_3 \rightarrow 2 KCl + 3 O_2\uparrow$$

3. Replacement reactions, in which one substance is displaced from its compound by another substance. Replacement reactions have the general form

$$A + BX \rightarrow AX + B$$

or

$$Y + BX \rightarrow BY + X$$

Examples:

$$Fe + CuSO_4 \rightarrow FeSO_4 + Cu\downarrow$$
$$Cl_2 + 2 KI \rightarrow 2 KCl + I_2$$

4. Double replacement reactions, in which the constituent substances exchange places. Double replacement reactions have the general form

$$AX + BY \rightarrow AY + BX$$

Examples:

$$NaCl + AgNO_3 \rightarrow NaNO_3 + AgCl\downarrow$$
$$(NH_4)_2S + 2 HCl \rightarrow 2 NH_4Cl + H_2S\uparrow$$

In order for double replacement reactions to proceed to completion yielding final products, one or more of the products must leave the field of action in some manner. In the examples given, AgCl is insoluble and precipitates; H_2S is volatile and escapes as a gas.

5. Six classes of decomposition reactions. These reactions are promoted by heat or electricity. The classes generally recognized are as follows:

1. Metallic carbonates, when heated, form metallic oxides and carbon dioxide. Calcium carbonate, $CaCO_3$, on being heated, will form calcium oxide, CaO. Carbon dioxide, CO_2, is given off as a gas.

$$CaCO_3 \overset{\Delta}{\rightarrow} CaO + CO_2\uparrow$$

The Greek letter Δ (delta) may be used to signify that heat energy is supplied to the action.

Ammonium carbonate, $(NH_4)_2CO_3$, because of the nonmetallic nature of the ammonium radical, decomposes in a special manner. The equation for this reaction is:

$$(NH_4)_2CO_3 \overset{\Delta}{\rightarrow} 2 NH_3\uparrow + H_2O\uparrow + CO_2\uparrow$$

Ammonia, steam, and carbon dioxide are produced.

2. Many metallic hydroxides, when heated, decompose into metallic oxides and water. If we heat calcium hydroxide, $Ca(OH)_2$, strongly, steam is given off and calcium oxide, CaO, remains.

$$Ca(OH)_2 \xrightarrow{\Delta} CaO + H_2O\uparrow$$

Sodium hydroxide is a common exception to this rule.

3. Metallic chlorates, when heated, decompose into metallic chlorides and oxygen. This is the type of reaction we used to prepare oxygen from potassium chlorate.

$$2\ KClO_3 \xrightarrow{\Delta} 2\ KCl + 3\ O_2\uparrow$$

4. Some acids, when heated, decompose into nonmetallic oxides and water. Acids may be formed by the reaction of some nonmetallic oxides, called acid anhydrides, and water. This reaction is the reverse process. Several examples are:

$$H_2CO_3 \xrightarrow{\Delta} H_2O + CO_2\uparrow$$

$$H_2SO_3 \xrightarrow{\Delta} H_2O + SO_2\uparrow$$

The two reactions above take place quite readily at room temperature. The following reaction occurs at elevated temperatures.

$$H_2SO_4 \xrightarrow{\Delta} H_2O + SO_3\uparrow$$

5. Some oxides, when heated, decompose. Most oxides are very stable compounds. There are only a few of them which will decompose on heating. Two of these oxides and the reactions for their decomposition are:

$$2\ HgO \xrightarrow{\Delta} 2\ Hg + O_2\uparrow$$

$$2\ PbO_2 \xrightarrow{\Delta} 2\ PbO + O_2\uparrow$$

6. Some decomposition reactions are produced by electricity. The following are typical:

$$2\ H_2O \xrightarrow{\text{(electricity)}} 2\ H_2\uparrow + O_2\uparrow$$

$$2\ NaCl \xrightarrow{\text{(electricity)}} 2\ Na + Cl_2\uparrow$$

6. Four classes of replacement reactions. The quantities of energy involved in replacement reactions are generally less than for composition and decomposition reactions. The action is dependent on the relative activities of the elements involved. We generally rely on an *Activity Series* such as the one discussed in Section 12 of this chapter to guide us in writing replacement equations. These reactions may be placed in four general classes.

1. Replacement of a metal in a compound by a more active metal. A reaction of this type is that of zinc and a solution of cupric sulfate, $CuSO_4$. Zinc is a more active metal than copper, thus it will replace copper from a solution of a copper compound.

$$Zn + CuSO_4 \rightarrow ZnSO_4 + Cu\downarrow$$

2. Replacement of hydrogen in water by metals. The very active metals, such as potassium, calcium, and sodium, react vigorously with water to replace half the hydrogen and form metallic hydroxides. The following reaction is typical.

$$Ca + 2\ H_2O \rightarrow Ca(OH)_2 + H_2\uparrow$$

More stable metals, such as magnesium, zinc, and iron, react at elevated temperatures with water (steam) to replace hydrogen. Because of the high temperature involved, oxides rather than hydroxides are formed. Metals less active than iron do not react appreciably with water.

3. Replacement of hydrogen in acids by metals. Many metals react with certain acids, such as hydrochloric acid and dilute sulfuric acid, to replace hydrogen and form the corresponding salt. We have used this method for the laboratory preparation of hydrogen by reacting sulfuric acid with zinc.

$$Zn + H_2SO_4 \rightarrow ZnSO_4 + H_2\uparrow$$

4. Replacement of halogens. The halogens are four elements having somewhat similar properties. They are fluorine, chlorine, bromine, and iodine. From their activity arrangement in the table in Section 12, fluorine is seen to be the most active. It will replace the other three halogens from their compounds. Chlorine will replace bromine and iodine from their compounds. Bromine will replace only iodine. An example of this type of reaction is the addition of chlorine to potassium bromide solution.

$$Cl_2 + 2 KBr \rightarrow 2 KCl + Br_2$$

7. Many reactions are reversible. It frequently happens that the products of a chemical reaction can react to produce the original reactants. We learned in Chapter 8 that hydrogen could be used as a reducing agent to separate certain metals from their oxides. If we pass dry hydrogen gas over hot mag-netic iron oxide, iron and steam are produced.

$$4 H_2 + Fe_3O_4 \rightarrow 3 Fe + 4 H_2O\uparrow$$

If we reverse the procedure and pass steam over hot iron, magnetic iron oxide and hydrogen are formed.

$$3 Fe + 4 H_2O \rightarrow Fe_3O_4 + 4 H_2\uparrow$$

Such reactions are said to be reversible and may be indicated by two reaction signs pointing in opposite directions ($\rightleftarrows$).

$$3 Fe + 4 H_2O \rightleftarrows Fe_3O_4 + 4 H_2$$

Conditions may be such as to allow both reactions to occur simultaneously. That is, if none of the products leaves the field of action, they may be able to react to form the original reactants. Under such circumstances, an *equilibrium* could develop between the two reactions after which the quantities of all the reactants would remain constant. The subject of equilibrium reactions will be discussed in Chapter 22.

2. ENERGY OF REACTIONS

8. Energy changes occur during chemical reactions. If we ignite a mixture of hydrogen and oxygen, water is produced and considerable heat energy is released. Under controlled conditions we would find the energy released during this reaction to be a characteristic amount which is directly proportional to the quantity of water produced. The source of the heat energy must be the reactants themselves since none was supplied externally other than to ignite the mixture. We may conclude that the water formed has *less* energy than did the reactants prior to the chemical action.

Conversely, if we decompose water to produce hydrogen and oxygen, we must furnish energy in the form of electricity. Since energy is absorbed in this reverse reaction we may conclude that the products, hydrogen and oxygen, have *more* energy than did the reactant, water. We may write:

$$2 H_2 + O_2 \rightarrow 2 H_2O + energy$$

and

$$2 H_2O + energy \rightarrow 2 H_2 + O_2$$

or

$$2 H_2 + O_2 \rightleftarrows 2 H_2O + energy$$

An energy change accompanies every chemical change. These energy changes may be in the form of heat, light, or electricity. Every substance has its own characteristic amount of energy by virtue of its structure and physical state. When chemical reactions occur, new substances are formed having characteristic amounts of energy greater or less than that of the reactants. If the energy of the products is less than that of the reactants, the excess energy is released. These are **exothermic reactions** and the energy of reaction is said to be *positive.* If the products possess more energy than the reactants, energy must be absorbed from an external source during the action. These are **endothermic reactions** and the energy of reaction is said to be *negative.* (Sometimes the opposite convention of signs for energy of reaction is encountered. Where it is desired to emphasize the fact that the product of an exothermic composition reaction has less *energy content* than did the reactants, the energy of reaction may be said to be negative.)

Fuels, whether for the furnace, automobile, or rocket, are energy-rich substances and the products of their combustion are energy-poor substances. In such instances the products of the chemical action may be of little concern compared to the kind and quantity of energy that is liberated.

The heat of reaction given out or absorbed when a compound is formed from its elements is called the **heat of formation** *of the compound.* Heats of formation are commonly expressed in calories per formula-weight-in-grams of the substance produced (see Chapter 10, Section 4).

Most composition reactions are exothermic, yielding compounds with positive heats of formation. In Table 6 of the Appendix you will find the heats of formation of some common compounds. You will notice that most of the heats of formation are positive. Only a few compounds such as hydrogen iodide and carbon disulfide have negative heats of formation.

9. Stability and heat of formation. A compound with a high positive heat of formation is formed with the release of considerable energy. In order to decompose such a compound into its constituent elements the same amount of energy must be supplied to the reaction. *Such compounds are very stable.* The reactions forming them proceed spontaneously, once they start, and are usually vigorous. Carbon dioxide has a high heat of formation, +94,400 calories for each 44 g of the gas produced.

Compounds with low heats of formation are generally unstable. Hydrogen sulfide, H_2S, has a heat of formation of +5300 calories. It is not very stable and decomposes when heated. Hydrogen iodide, HI, has a low negative heat of formation, −5900 calories. It is a colorless gas which undergoes some decomposition when stored at room temperatures. The presence of violet iodine vapor may be seen throughout the container of the gas.

A compound with a high negative heat of formation is likely to be explosive. Such a compound is formed only by expending a great deal of energy. Mercury fulminate, $HgC_2N_2O_2$, has a heat of formation of −64,500 calories. It is used extensively as a detonator for explosives because of its instability.

10. What is the driving force of chemical reactions? Heats of formation give an indication of the stability of substances and will aid us in predicting

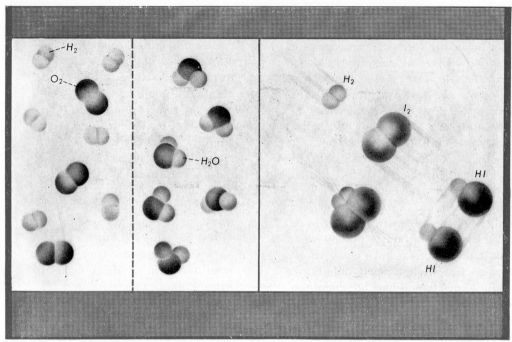

Fig. 12-2. *Left,* a mixture of hydrogen and oxygen molecules will form very stable water molecules when properly activated. *Right,* energy is required to break the bonds between atoms of diatomic molecules of hydrogen and iodine before hydrogen iodide molecules can be formed.

reactions. However, the ***driving force*** of chemical action, *the force that makes reactions go,* involves other factors in addition to heats of formation. The energy of a reaction which can be converted into useful work outside the reaction itself is a measure of this driving force. It is called the ***free energy change*** of the reaction. The free energies of substances give more accurate indications of their stability, tendency to react, and to form ions. The free energy is sometimes found to be approximately the same as the heat of formation. However, it frequently is higher or lower than the heat of formation.

11. What is the energy of activation? The heat of formation of water from its elements is quite high, +68,400 calories. The free energy change in this composition reaction is also quite high, +56,700 calories. Why then, do hydrogen and oxygen not combine spontaneously at ordinary temperatures?

Before hydrogen and oxygen atoms can combine to form water, their molecules must be broken up. The bonding forces of the atoms of the diatomic molecules, H_2 and O_2, must be counteracted. This requires an initial supply of energy from some external source. This additional energy is called the ***activation energy*** of the reactants. Once the formation of water molecules has started, the reaction energy released is more than sufficient to sustain the action. Thus a mixture of hydrogen and oxygen gases remains inert at room temperatures until the necessary activation energy is introduced by means of an electric spark. The composition equation written with electron-dot symbols will show the reaction.

$$2\,H\!:\!H + \;:\!\ddot{O}\!:\!\ddot{O}\!: \;\rightarrow\; 2\,H\!:\!\ddot{O}\!: \atop \;H$$

The energy of activation may be supplied in certain reactions by the application of heat directly to the reactants. Activation energies may also be supplied by spark discharge, by light or X rays, or by bombardment with radioactive particles. Activation energy does not always involve separating the atoms of a diatomic molecule. It may also raise certain electrons to the higher energy level necessary for a reaction.

12. What is the activity series of the elements? The quantities of energy involved in replacement reactions are generally less than those of composition or decomposition reactions. Compounds formed by replacement have higher positive heats of formation than the original compounds.

From the study of numerous electrochemical reactions, chemists are able to devise an activity series of elements to help predict the course of replacement reactions. Some composition and decomposition reactions may likewise be predicted with the aid of an activity series. The series presented here lists separately the most important common elements in descending order of their metallic and nonmetallic activities.

The relative positions of the elements in the activity series enable us to apply some of the following generalizations to appropriate composition, decomposition, and replacement reactions.

1. Each element in the list will displace from a compound any of the elements below it; the larger the interval

ACTIVITY SERIES	
Metals	Nonmetals
Lithium	Fluorine
Potassium	Chlorine
Calcium	Bromine
Sodium	Iodine
Magnesium	
Aluminum	
Zinc	
Chromium	
Iron	
Nickel	
Tin	
Lead	
HYDROGEN	
Copper	
Mercury	
Silver	
Platinum	
Gold	

between elements in the series, the more vigorous the action.

2. All metals above hydrogen will displace hydrogen from nonoxidizing acids.

3. Metals near the top of the series vigorously displace hydrogen from water. Magnesium will displace hydrogen from steam.

4. Metals above silver combine directly with oxygen; those near the top do so violently.

5. Metals below mercury may be forced to form oxides only indirectly.

6. Oxides of metals below mercury may be decomposed with mild heating.

7. Oxides of metals below chromium are easily reduced by heating with hydrogen.

8. Oxides of metals above iron resist reduction by heating with hydrogen.

9. Elements near the top of the series are never found free in nature.

10. Elements near the bottom of the series are often found free in nature.

Fig. 12–3. Some chemical reactions are of interest because of the energy released. This rocket is powered by the reaction between liquid oxygen and ethyl alcohol.

Summary

A chemical equation is a concise symbolized picture of a chemical reaction. Word equations have only qualitative significance. Formula equations have quantitative significance. An equation is useful only when it is correct in every respect.

Three factors must be satisfied in writing formula equations: *1*. The equation must represent the facts; *2*. The equation must include the symbols and formulas of all elements and compounds used as reactants and formed as products; and *3*. The Law of Conservation of Atoms must be satisfied.

There are four main types of chemical reactions: *1*. Composition; *2*. Decomposition; *3*. Replacement; and *4*. Double replacement.

Energy changes accompany all chemical reactions. In exothermic reactions energy is released, and in endothermic reactions energy is absorbed. Heats of formation of substances give an indication of their stability. Reactions occur because of a driving force. This driving force is best defined by the free energy change of a reaction. Exothermic reactions sometimes require activation energy in order to start them.

An activity series of elements is useful in predicting whether specific replacement reactions will occur. The most active element in the series is found at the top and the least active at the bottom. The greater the interval between elements of the series in a reaction, the more vigorous will be the action.

Test yourself on these terms

activation energy	double replacement	meaning of $\rightarrow$
activity series	endothermic	meaning of $\rightleftarrows$
coefficient	exothermic	meaning of $\uparrow$
composition	formula equation	meaning of $\downarrow$
decomposition	free energy	product
diatomic	heat of formation	reactant

Equations

Group A

(Write balanced formula equations for these reactions.)

1. Carbon + oxygen $\rightarrow$ carbon dioxide$\uparrow$.
2. Magnesium bromide + chlorine $\rightarrow$ magnesium chloride + bromine.
3. Zinc + hydrochloric acid (HCl) $\rightarrow$ zinc chloride + hydrogen$\uparrow$.
4. Hydrogen + nitrogen $\rightarrow$ ammonia (NH$_3$) $\uparrow$.
5. Sodium hydroxide + carbon dioxide $\rightarrow$ sodium carbonate + water.
6. Barium chloride + sodium sulfate $\rightarrow$ sodium chloride + barium sulfate$\downarrow$.
7. Zinc chloride + ammonium sulfide $\rightarrow$ zinc sulfide$\downarrow$ + ammonium chloride.
8. Ammonia + oxygen $\rightarrow$ nitric acid (HNO$_3$) + water.
9. Zinc + cupric sulfate $\rightarrow$
10. Mercuric oxide $\xrightarrow{\Delta}$
11. Sodium + water $\rightarrow$
12. Hydrogen + chlorine $\rightarrow$
13. Copper + silver sulfate $\rightarrow$ cupric sulfate +
14. Potassium + water $\rightarrow$
15. Sodium iodide + bromine $\rightarrow$
16. Carbon + steam $\rightarrow$ carbon monoxide$\uparrow$ + hydrogen$\uparrow$.
17. Zinc + lead acetate $\rightarrow$ lead$\downarrow$ + zinc acetate.
18. Potassium chlorate $\xrightarrow{\Delta}$
19. Calcium carbonate $\xrightarrow{\Delta}$
20. Ferric oxide + carbon monoxide $\rightarrow$ iron + carbon dioxide.
21. Potassium hydroxide + chlorine $\rightarrow$ potassium chloride + potassium hypochlorite (KClO) + water.
22. Calcium oxide + diphosphorus pentoxide $\rightarrow$ calcium phosphate.
23. Calcium carbonate + hydrochloric acid $\rightarrow$ calcium chloride + water + carbon dioxide$\uparrow$.
24. Copper + sulfuric acid $\rightarrow$ cupric sulfate + water + sulfur dioxide$\uparrow$.
25. Calcium hydroxide + ammonium sulfate $\rightarrow$ calcium sulfate + ammonia$\uparrow$ + water.

Group B

(In each case: 1. Write the balanced formula equation; 2. Identify the type of reaction; and 3. Tell why the reaction takes place.)

Consult the Activity Series, Section 12, and the Tables of Solubilities and Heats of Formation in the Appendix, as necessary.

26. Magnesium + oxygen →
27. Phosphorus + iodine → phosphorus tri-iodide.
28. Potassium iodide + chlorine →
29. Ferric chloride + ammonium sulfide →
30. Iron + sulfur → ferrous sulfide.
31. Nickel chlorate $\xrightarrow{\Delta}$
32. Barium carbonate $\xrightarrow{\Delta}$
33. Silver nitrate + zinc chloride →
34. Mercuric hydroxide $\xrightarrow{\Delta}$
35. Ammonia + hydrogen sulfide → ammonium sulfide.
36. Zinc + sulfuric acid →
37. Iron + cupric nitrate → ferrous nitrate +
38. Copper + silver nitrate → cupric nitrate +
39. Mercuric nitrate + ammonium sulfide →
40. Ferric hydroxide $\xrightarrow{\Delta}$
41. Phosphorus + oxygen →
42. Antimony + chlorine → antimony trichloride.
43. Sodium chlorate $\xrightarrow{\Delta}$
44. Barium chloride + magnesium sulfate →
45. Sodium bromide + chlorine →
46. Zinc chloride + phosphoric acid (H_3PO_4) →
47. Sodium sulfite + acetic acid $(HC_2H_3O_2)$ → sodium acetate + sulfur dioxide↑ + water.
48. Ammonium nitrate + potassium hydroxide → potassium nitrate + ammonia↑ + water.
49. Silver sulfate + aluminum chloride →
50. Carbonic acid $\xrightarrow{\Delta}$

Chapter 13
WEIGHT RELATIONS IN CHEMICAL REACTIONS

1. The gram-atomic weight of an element. It has been estimated that if all the people on the earth were assigned the task of counting the molecules in a tablespoon of water and were required to count at the rate of one molecule each second, approximately 8,000,000 years would be required to complete the project. However impractical this may seem, we can realize that the number of molecules involved is so large that it staggers the imagination!

Fortunately, chemists are not ordinarily faced with the problem of weighing out a certain number of molecules of a compound or atoms of an element. They do frequently need to weigh out equal numbers of atoms or molecules of different substances. A knowledge of the atomic weights of the elements allows this to be done very simply.

Atomic weights are relative weights based on oxygen as 16. As the atomic weight of hydrogen is 1, the average weight of oxygen atoms is 16 times the average weight of hydrogen atoms. It follows that 100 atoms of oxygen weigh 16 times as much as 100 hydrogen atoms. And 1 million oxygen atoms weigh 16 times as much as 1 million hydrogen atoms. Any given weights of oxygen and hydrogen which are in the ratio of 16 : 1 must have the same number of atoms.

Let us consider the atomic weights of oxygen and sulfur, 16 and 32 respectively. Oxygen atoms are one half as heavy as sulfur atoms. Thus any given weights of oxygen and sulfur which are in the ratio 1 : 2 (16 : 32) must have the same number of atoms. By similar deductions using the atomic weights of other elements, we may recognize the following important generalization: *If the weights of two elements are in the same ratio as their atomic weights, they contain the same number of atoms.*

Chemists weigh substances in gram units. It is evident that atomic weights are most useful when expressed in gram units. The **gram-atomic weight** *is that weight of an element in grams which is equal to its atomic weight.* The gram-atomic weight of an element is commonly referred to as a *gram-atom* of the element. Thus a gram-atom of oxygen

Fig. 13–1. The trip balance is used in the laboratory when accuracy to 0.1 gram is satisfactory.

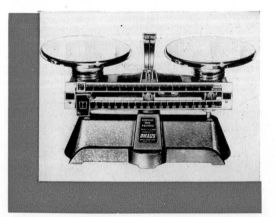

is 16 g of oxygen, a gram-atom of sulfur is 32 g of sulfur, and a gram-atom of iron is 56 g of iron.

The most significant fact concerning the gram-atomic weights of elements is that *gram-atoms of all elements contain the same number of atoms.* This number of atoms is called the **Avogadro number,** the accepted modern value of which is *6.0238 $\times$ 10²³* atoms per gram-atom of any element.

2. What is a mole of a substance? The formula weights of substances are simply the totals of atomic weights as denoted by the formulas. They too are relative weights having the same base as atomic weights, oxygen as 16. Atomic weights and formula weights are therefore fully comparable. The formula weight of a molecular substance is its molecular weight.

In a manner similar to that we used in defining the gram-atomic weight of an element, we may define the **gram-molecular weight** *as the weight of a molecular substance in grams equal to its molecular weight.* The gram-molecular weight (1 gram-molecule) of H_2O is 18 grams of water. One gram-molecule of CO_2 is 44 grams of carbon dioxide. You will readily see that 18 g of water and 44 g of carbon dioxide must consist of the same number of molecules. *Gram-molecules of all molecular substances contain the same number of molecules.* This again is the Avogadro number, 6.0238 $\times$ 10²³ molecules per gram-molecule.

The gram-molecular weight is such a useful unit to chemists that it has been given a short name, the **mole.** The concept of the mole has been extended to include those substances which do not have molecules and are expressed by empirical formulas. Thus the **gram-**

formula weight (the formula weight in grams) of sodium chloride, 58.5 g of sodium chloride, represents 1 mole of the salt. A gram-atom of an element commonly represented as monatomic constitutes 1 mole of the element. A gram-atom of zinc, 65 g of zinc, is 1 mole of that element. On the other hand, a mole of diatomic oxygen, O_2, is 32 g of oxygen. *The number of molecules in a mole of any molecular substance is the same as the number of atoms in a gram-atom of any element, the Avogadro number.*

3. Weight relations of reactants and products. When carbon is burned in air, carbon dioxide is produced. We may represent the reaction by an equation.

$$C + O_2 \rightarrow CO_2\uparrow$$

We learned in Chapter 12 that the balanced equation signifies the weight proportions of the reactants and products, as well as the composition of each substance in terms of the kinds of elements and the relative number of each kind of atom present. *These weight proportions are most conveniently expressed in terms of moles of reactants and products.* Thus our equation signifies that 1 mole of carbon combines with 1 mole of oxygen to yield 1 mole of carbon dioxide. We may indicate this as follows:

$$
\begin{array}{cccc}
C & + & O_2 & \rightarrow & CO_2\uparrow \\
\text{1 mole} & & \text{1 mole} & & \text{1 mole} \\
= 12\,g & & = 32\,g & & = 12\,g + 32\,g \\
& & & & = 44\,g
\end{array}
$$

Because the equation shows the proportions by weight of reacting substances and products, it is used when we wish to determine the weight of one substance that reacts with, or is produced from, a definite weight of another. This is one of the common problems chemists are called upon to solve.

4. Methods of solving weight-weight problems. Three general methods are

Fig. 13–2. This diagram shows the ratio of moles to volumes of different substances.

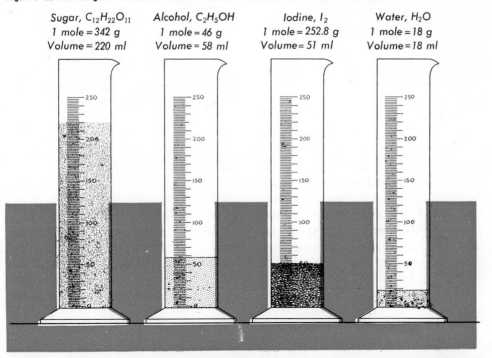

Sugar, $C_{12}H_{22}O_{11}$	Alcohol, C_2H_5OH	Iodine, I_2	Water, H_2O
1 mole = 342 g	1 mole = 46 g	1 mole = 252.8 g	1 mole = 18 g
Volume = 220 ml	Volume = 58 ml	Volume = 51 ml	Volume = 18 ml

employed in solving problems which involve weight relations of reactants and products: These are: *1. Proportion method; 2. Arithmetic method; 3. Mole method.* Each method will be demonstrated in the following sample problem illustrations. Your instructor may prefer you to use a particular method regularly in your problem work, either one of these or one of his own. Otherwise it is suggested that you study each demonstration carefully and use the method which seems most logical to you.

It is always desirable to make a preliminary mental estimate to determine the *order of magnitude* of the answer to a problem before undertaking the indicated computations. Thus you may avoid accepting an answer as correct which actually is quite absurd, due to errors in computation.

5. Solution by proportion. Let us assume that we must determine how much calcium oxide will be produced by heating 50 g of calcium carbonate. Observe that the weight of the reactant is given and the weight of a product is required. From the data in the problem and the facts known concerning the reaction, we can proceed to *set up the problem.* This may be accomplished in three steps.

The *first step* is to write the balanced equation.

The *second step* is to show the weight proportions, established by the balanced equation, which are specifically involved in the problem. This is accomplished by writing under each substance involved in the problem the number of *moles* (gram-formula weights) indicated by the equation. By converting the number of moles of each substance to grams we have the *equa-*

tion weights thus expressed in grams.

The *third step* is to show the problem specifications: what is given and what is required. To do this we write the quantity of calcium carbonate, 50 g, above the formula $CaCO_3$. Letting X represent the unknown quantity of calcium oxide produced, we write X above the formula CaO. The problem is set up ready to be solved.

$$\text{3rd step} \quad - \quad \overset{50 \text{ g}}{} \quad \overset{X}{}$$
$$\text{1st step} \quad - \quad CaCO_3 \overset{\Delta}{\rightarrow} CaO + CO_2\uparrow$$
$$\text{2nd step} - \begin{cases} 1 \text{ mole} & 1 \text{ mole} \\ = 100 \text{ g} & = 56 \text{ g} \end{cases}$$

The balanced equation tells us that 1 mole of $CaCO_3$, 100 g, yields 1 mole of CaO, 56 g. We may reason that any other weight of $CaCO_3$ used, and CaO produced, must be in the same ratio as that of the equation weights of $CaCO_3$ and CaO. This is an equality of ratios and is expressed by the *proportion:*

$$\frac{50 \text{ g}}{X} = \frac{100 \text{ g}}{56 \text{ g}}$$

Solving:

$$X = \frac{50 \text{ g} \times 56 \text{ g}}{100 \text{ g}}$$
$$X = 28 \text{ g of } CaO$$

By estimating the order of magnitude of the answer from the quantities involved we see that 28 g of CaO is a reasonable answer. See the Sample Problems on page 179.

★ **6. Solution by arithmetic.** In the arithmetic method we set up the problem in three steps as before: *1.* Write the equation; *2.* Write the equation weights in grams below the equation; and *3.* Write the problem specifications above the equation. As an example, we will use the following problem set-up in which we wish to know the number

SAMPLE PROBLEM

How many grams of potassium chlorate must be decomposed to yield 30 g of oxygen?

SOLUTION (Proportion Method)

We set up the problem by *first*, writing the balanced equation; *second*, writing the number of moles of each specified substance under its formula and expressing its equation weight in grams; and *third*, writing the specifications of the problem above the equation. We will let X represent the number of grams of potassium chlorate decomposed.

$$
\begin{array}{ccc}
X & & 30\text{ g} \\
2\text{ KClO}_3 & \rightarrow 2\text{ KCl} + & 3\text{ O}_2\uparrow \\
2\text{ moles} & & 3\text{ moles} \\
= 2[39 + 35.5 + 3(16)]\text{ g} & & = 3(32)\text{ g} \\
= 245\text{ g} & & = 96\text{ g}
\end{array}
$$

The ratio of $KClO_3$ decomposed to O_2 produced must equal the ratio of the equation weight of $KClO_3$ to the equation weight of O_2, so we may express the proportion:

$$\frac{X}{30\text{ g}} = \frac{245\text{ g}}{96\text{ g}}$$

Solving:
$$X = \frac{30\text{ g} \times 245\text{ g}}{96\text{ g}}$$
$$X = 76.6\text{ g of } KClO_3$$

SAMPLE PROBLEM

In the decomposition of water by electrolysis: a. How many moles of water must be decomposed to yield 3 moles of hydrogen? b. How many moles of oxygen are produced?

SOLUTION (Proportion Method)

a. The problem is set up as before except that we do not need to convert moles to equation-weights-in-grams since the problem specifications are in moles rather than grams. Let X represent the number of moles of water decomposed.

$$
\begin{array}{cccc}
X & 3\text{ moles} & & Y \\
2\text{ H}_2\text{O} & \rightarrow 2\text{ H}_2 & + & \text{O}_2 \\
2\text{ moles} & 2\text{ moles} & & 1\text{ mole}
\end{array}
$$

The proportion is:

$$\frac{X}{3\text{ moles}} = \frac{2\text{ moles}}{2\text{ moles}}$$

Solving: $X = 3$ moles of H_2O

b. Using the problem set-up of part a, we let Y represent the number of moles of O_2 produced.
The proportion is:

$$\frac{3\text{ moles}}{Y} = \frac{2\text{ moles}}{1\text{ mole}}$$

Solving: $Y = 1.5$ moles of O_2

Observe that
$$3\text{ moles of } H_2O = 3(18)\text{ g} = 54\text{ g of } H_2O$$
$$3\text{ moles of } H_2 = 3(2)\text{ g} = 6\text{ g of } H_2$$
$$1.5\text{ moles of } O_2 = 1.5(32)\text{ g} = 48\text{ g of } O_2$$

of grams of calcium hydroxide pro-duced from a reaction of 100 g of cal-cium oxide and water.

$$100 \text{ g} \qquad\qquad X$$
$$CaO \;+\; H_2O \;\rightarrow\; Ca(OH)_2$$
$$1 \text{ mole} \qquad\qquad 1 \text{ mole}$$
$$= 40 \text{ g} + 16 \text{ g} \qquad = 40 \text{ g} + 2(17) \text{ g}$$
$$= 56 \text{ g} \qquad\qquad = 74 \text{ g}$$

The equation indicates that 1 mole of calcium oxide reacts with water to form 1 mole of calcium hydroxide.

Thus, 56 g of CaO yields 74 g of $Ca(OH)_2$. We may reason that 1 g of CaO will yield $\frac{74}{56}$ g of $Ca(OH)_2$. So, 100 g of CaO will yield $100 \times \frac{74}{56}$ g of $Ca(OH)_2$. We may solve as follows:

$$X = 100 \text{ g CaO} \times \frac{74 \text{ g Ca(OH)}_2}{56 \text{ g CaO}}$$
$$X = 132 \text{ g of Ca(OH)}_2$$

By estimating the order of magnitude of the answer we see that 132 g is rea-sonable. See Sample Problem below.

★ SAMPLE PROBLEM

Five grams of metallic sodium is permitted to react with water to demon-strate the replacement of hydrogen. a. How much sodium hydroxide can be re-covered as a consequence of this action? b. How many moles of hydrogen are replaced from the water?

SOLUTION   (Arithmetic Method)

a. We set up the problem on the balanced equation as in earlier illustrations, letting X represent the amount of NaOH recovered.

$$\begin{array}{ccc} 5 \text{ g} & X & Y \\ 2\,Na \;+\; 2\,H_2O \rightarrow & 2\,NaOH & +\; H_2\uparrow \\ 2 \text{ moles} & 2 \text{ moles} & 1 \text{ mole} \\ = 2(23) \text{ g} & = 2(23 + 17) \text{ g} & = 2 \text{ g} \\ = 46 \text{ g} & = 80 \text{ g} & \end{array}$$

The equation indicates that 2 moles of Na produces 2 moles of NaOH,

or   46 g of Na yields 80 g of NaOH

then   1 g of Na would yield $\frac{80}{46}$ g of NaOH

and   5 g of Na must give $5 \times \frac{80}{46}$ g of NaOH

so $X = 5 \text{ g Na} \times \dfrac{80 \text{ g NaOH}}{46 \text{ g Na}}$

             $X = 8.7 \text{ g NaOH}$

b. Since the quantity of H_2 produced is to be expressed in moles, we may either convert the 5 g of Na to moles or find H_2 in grams and convert to moles. The latter plan follows more closely the solution of part a so we will let Y stand for the quantity of H_2 in grams. Using the problem set-up for part a:

$$Y = 5 \text{ g Na} \times \frac{2 \text{ g H}_2}{46 \text{ g Na}}$$
$$Y = 0.22 \text{ g H}_2$$

Now   1 mole H_2 = 1 g-mol. wt. H_2 = 2 g

so $0.22 \text{ g H}_2 = \dfrac{0.22 \text{ g H}_2}{2 \text{ g H}_2/\text{mole}} = 0.11 \text{ mole H}_2$

★ **7. Solution by moles.** The same problem set-up may be used in the mole method as in the proportion and arithmetic methods. However, in solving by moles we are interested in converting the weight of a given substance into moles of that substance. In a manner similar to the arithmetic method we may determine the moles of the substance in question since our equation tells us the mole relationship between the reactants and products.

★ SAMPLE PROBLEM

What weight of oxygen is required to oxidize 100 g of iron to ferric oxide?

SOLUTION   (Mole Method)

The problem set-up for this reaction is

$$\begin{array}{ccc} 100\text{ g} & & X \\ 4\text{ Fe} & + \quad 3\text{ O}_2 & \rightarrow 2\text{ Fe}_2\text{O}_3 \\ 4\text{ moles} & 3\text{ moles} & \\ = 4(56)\text{ g} & = 3(32)\text{ g} & \\ = 224\text{ g} & = 96\text{ g} & \end{array}$$

By definition   1 mole Fe = 1 gram-atom Fe = 56 g

and   1 mole O_2 = 1 g-mol. wt. O_2 = 32 g

The number of moles in 100 g of Fe = $\dfrac{100\text{ g}}{56\text{ g/mole}}$ = 1.78 moles

The equation shows that 1 mole of Fe combines with $\frac{3}{4}$ mole of O_2

so   1.78 moles of Fe combine with 1.78 × $\frac{3}{4}$ mole of O_2

or X = 1.78 moles of Fe × $\dfrac{3\text{ moles of O}_2}{4\text{ moles of Fe}}$

X = 1.34 moles of O_2

The number of g of O_2 in 1.34 moles = 1.34 moles × $\dfrac{32\text{ g of O}_2}{\text{mole}}$ = 43 g of O_2.

Summary

The gram-atomic weight of an element is the weight in grams which is equal to its atomic weight. The gram-formula weight of a substance is the weight in grams equal to its formula weight. For molecular substances the gram-formula weight is also its gram-molecular weight.

Gram-atoms of different elements contain equal numbers of atoms, the Avogadro number. Any weights of different elements which are in the same ratio as their atomic weights have equal numbers of atoms. Gram-molecules of different molecular substances contain equal numbers of molecules, the Avogadro number.

The mole is defined as one gram-molecular weight of a molecular substance. The mole is so useful that it has been extended to include 1 gram-formula weight of nonmolecular substances and 1 gram-atomic weight of elements commonly represented as monatomic.

Problems involving weight relations of the reactants and products in chemical reactions are usually solved by one of three methods. These are: *1.* Proportion method; *2.* Arithmetic method; and *3.* Mole method. Each method utilizes the balanced equation as the basis for the problem set-up. Whichever method is used, it is always desirable to make a preliminary mental estimate of the order of magnitude of the answer so as to avoid absurd results.

Test yourself on these terms

arithmetic method	gram-formula weight	order of magnitude
Avogadro number	gram-molecular weight	problem set-up
equation weight	gram-molecule	proportion
gram-atom	mole	proportion method
gram-atomic weight	mole method	ratio

Problems

Group A

1. How many grams of oxygen can be prepared by the decomposition of 25 grams of mercuric oxide?
2. How many grams of oxygen can be prepared by the decomposition of 25 g of potassium chlorate?
3. How many grams of zinc are required for the replacement of 0.1 gram of hydrogen from sulfuric acid?
4. How many grams of sodium chloride are needed to complete a double replacement reaction with 10 grams of silver nitrate in water solution?
5. How many grams of silver chloride are precipitated in the reaction of Problem 4?
6. In a composition reaction between sulfur and oxygen, 80 grams of sulfur dioxide is formed. How many grams of sulfur were burned?
7. How many grams of hydrogen are required to completely reduce 25 grams of hot magnetic iron oxide?
8. What quantity of cupric oxide is formed by oxidizing 1 kilogram of copper?
9. What weight of anhydrous cupric sulfate may be obtained by heating 100 grams of $CuSO_4 \cdot 5 H_2O$?
10. Suppose 10 grams of ferrous sulfide is treated with enough hydrochloric acid to complete the double replacement reaction. How many grams of hydrogen sulfide gas could be collected?

Group B

11. An excess of sulfuric acid reacts with 150 g of barium peroxide. (*a*) How many moles of hydrogen peroxide are produced? (*b*) How many moles of barium sulfate are formed?
12. Approximately 130 g of zinc was dropped into a solution containing 100 g of HCl. After the replacement action had ceased, it was found that 41 g of zinc remained. How many moles of hydrogen were produced?

13. A mixture of 10 g of powdered iron and 10 g of sulfur is heated to its reaction temperature in an open crucible. (a) How many grams of ferrous sulfide are formed? (b) The reactant in excess is oxidized. How much of its oxide is formed?

14. What weight of calcium hydroxide can be produced from 1 kg of limestone, calcium carbonate? (Decomposition of calcium carbonate by heating produces calcium oxide and carbon dioxide. Calcium hydroxide is formed by the composition reaction of calcium oxide and water.)

15. How many grams of air are required to complete the combustion of 93 g of phosphorus, assuming the air to be 23% oxygen by weight?

16. How many metric tons of carbon dioxide may be produced from the combustion of a metric ton (1000 kg) of coke which is 90% carbon?

17. What weight of a 10% solution of H_2SO_4 is required in a replacement reaction with an excess of aluminum to produce 0.5 mole of aluminum sulfate?

18. A certain rocket uses butane, C_4H_{10}, as fuel. How much liquid oxygen should be carried for the complete combustion of each kilogram of butane to carbon dioxide and water vapor?

19. When 45 g of ethane gas, C_2H_6, is burned completely in air, carbon dioxide and water vapor are formed. (a) How many moles of carbon dioxide are produced? (b) How many moles of water are produced?

20. How many grams of sodium sulfate are produced in the double replacement reaction between 150 g of sulfuric acid and an excess of sodium chloride?

Chapter 14

MOLECULAR COMPOSITION OF GASES

1. The Law of Combining Volumes of Gases. The Law of Definite Proportions, formulated by Proust in 1799, served as a basis for Dalton's Atomic Theory. While Dalton investigated the weights of combining substances, his contemporary, the Swedish chemist Berzelius, was developing methods of chemical analysis. During this same period another contemporary of Dalton, the French chemist Joseph Louis Gay-Lussac (1778–1850), became interested in the combining volumes of gaseous substances.

Gay-Lussac investigated the composition reaction between hydrogen and oxygen. He noticed that 2 liters of hydrogen was required for each liter of oxygen consumed and that 2 liters of water vapor was formed.

hydrogen + oxygen → water vapor
  2 vol.   1 vol.   2 vol.

He found that 1 liter of hydrogen combined with 1 liter of chlorine to form 2 liters of hydrogen chloride gas. Also 1 liter of hydrogen chloride combined with 1 liter of ammonia to produce a white powder with no residue of either gas remaining.

hydrogen + chlorine → hydrogen chloride
  1 vol.   1 vol.   2 vol.

hydrogen chloride + ammonia → ammonium chloride
       1 vol.   1 vol.   (a solid)

His friend, Berthollet, recognized a similar relationship in experiments with hydrogen and nitrogen. He found that 3 liters of hydrogen always com-

Fig. 14–1. Joseph Louis Gay-Lussac, a French chemist, is best known for his Law of Combining Volumes of Gases.

bined with 1 liter of nitrogen to form 2 liters of ammonia.

hydrogen + nitrogen → ammonia
3 vol.   1 vol.   2 vol.

In 1808 Gay-Lussac summarized the results of these experiments and set forth the principle which bears his name, *Gay-Lussac's Law of Combining Volumes of Gases:* *Under similar conditions, the volumes of reacting gases and of their gaseous products are expressed in ratios of small whole numbers.*

Proust had demonstrated the definite proportion of elements in a compound. Dalton's Atomic Theory had explained this regularity in the composition of substances. However, Dalton pictured the atoms of two elements combining to form *a compound atom* of the product. He could not explain why one volume of hydrogen united with one volume of chlorine to form *two* volumes of hydrogen chloride gas. To do so would require that his atoms be subdivided. He had described the atoms

of elements as "ultimate particles" and not capable of subdivision. Here was an inconsistency between Dalton's theory and Gay-Lussac's observations. Was there no explanation to resolve the difficulty?

2. Avogadro's hypothesis was proposed in 1811. Amadeo Avogadro (1776–1856) proposed a possible explanation for Gay-Lussac's simple ratios of combining gases. This *hypothesis* was to become one of the important laws of chemistry, although it was not until after his death that its implications were fully recognized.

Avogadro's hypothesis was that *equal volumes of all gases, under the same conditions of temperature and pressure, contained the same number of molecules.* He arrived at this plausible theory after studying the behavior of gases and immediately recognized its application to Gay-Lussac's volume ratios.

Avogadro reasoned that the molecules of all gases, as reactants and

Fig. 14-2. Amadeo Avogadro, an Italian physicist, is best known for his molecular hypothesis concerning gases.

products, would be in the same ratio as their respective gas volumes. Thus the composition of water vapor could be represented as 2 molecules of hydrogen combining with 1 molecule of oxygen to produce 2 molecules of water vapor.

hydrogen	+	oxygen	→	water vapor
2 volumes		1 volume		2 volumes
2 molecules		1 molecule		2 molecules

Thus each molecule of oxygen must consist of at least two identical parts (atoms) which are equally divided between the two molecules of water vapor formed. Avogadro did not repudiate the atoms of Dalton. He merely postulated that they did not exist as independent ultimate particles but were grouped into molecules which were divisible by two. The simplest such molecule would, of course, contain two atoms.

Avogadro's reasoning applied equally well to the combining volumes in the composition of hydrogen chloride gas.

hydrogen	+	chlorine	→	hydrogen chloride
1 volume		1 volume		2 volumes
1 molecule		1 molecule		2 molecules

Each molecule of hydrogen must be divisible by two, with identical parts in each of the two molecules of hydrogen chloride. Likewise, each chlorine molecule must be divisible by two with identical parts in each of the two molecules of hydrogen chloride.

By Avogadro's hypothesis the simplest molecules of hydrogen, oxygen, and chlorine each contain two atoms. The simplest possible molecule of water contains two atoms of hydrogen and one atom of oxygen. The simplest molecule of hydrogen chloride contains one atom of hydrogen and one atom of chlorine.

The correctness of Avogadro's hypothesis is widely recognized today. It is supported by the Kinetic Theory of Gases, and is employed extensively in the determination of molecular weights, atomic weights, and molecular formulas.

3. Molecules of active gaseous elements are diatomic. The application of Avogadro's hypothesis to Gay-Lussac's Law of Combining Volumes of Gases enables us to recognize the simplest possible make-up of elementary gas reactants. How may we determine whether this empirical structure is the correct one?

Fig. 14–3. As HCl is known to be the correct formula for hydrogen chloride gas, the molecules of hydrogen and chlorine are proved to be diatomic.

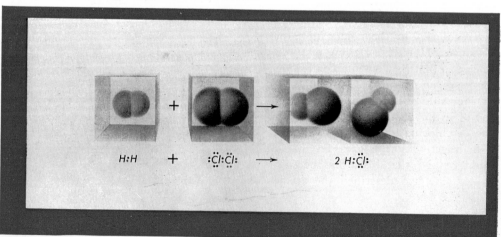

Chemists have analyzed hydrogen chloride gas and, with the aid of atomic weights, have determined the empirical formula to be HCl. By finding the molecular weight of the compound, HCl is established as the correct or molecular formula (see Chapter 11, Section 7). Thus a molecule of the compound contains *only* one atom of hydrogen and *only* one atom of chlorine. Since two molecules of HCl are formed from one molecule of hydrogen and one molecule of chlorine, each contains *only* two atoms. *Thus the hydrogen and chlorine molecules must be diatomic.* We may write the equation as follows:

$$H_2 + Cl_2 \rightarrow 2\,HCl$$

Similarly, the oxygen molecule may be proved to be diatomic since H_2O is known to be the molecular formula of water vapor.

$$2\,H_2 + O_2 \rightarrow 2\,H_2O$$

★ Let us examine one additional gaseous reaction. Berthollet found that *3 volumes* of hydrogen combined with *1 volume* of nitrogen to form *2 volumes* of ammonia. By Avogadro's hypothesis we conclude that *3 molecules* of hydrogen combine with *1 molecule* of nitrogen to form *2 molecules* of ammonia. Analysis of ammonia reveals that it is composed of 82.4% nitrogen by weight and 17.6% hydrogen by weight. The atomic weights of nitrogen and hydrogen are 14 and 1 respectively. The molecular weight of ammonia is known to be 17. Therefore the molecular formula is:

$$\text{Rel. no. of N atoms} = \frac{82.4}{14} = 5.9$$

$$\text{Rel. no. of H atoms} = \frac{17.6}{1} = 17.6$$

$$N : H = \frac{5.9}{5.9} : \frac{17.6}{5.9} = 1 : 3$$

Empirical formula $= NH_3$
Molecular formula $= (NH_3)_x$
and $(NH_3)_x = 17$
thus $x = 1$
Molecular formula $= NH_3$

★ Two molecules of NH_3 produced must contain a total of 2 nitrogen atoms which must therefore compose the 1 molecule of nitrogen reactant. Again the 2 molecules of NH_3 produced must contain a total of 6 hydrogen atoms which therefore compose the 3 molecules of hydrogen reactant. We may summarize these relations as follows:

Fig. 14–4. The application of Avogadro's Law to Gay Lussac's Combining Volumes can show the molecules of elementary gas reactants to be diatomic.

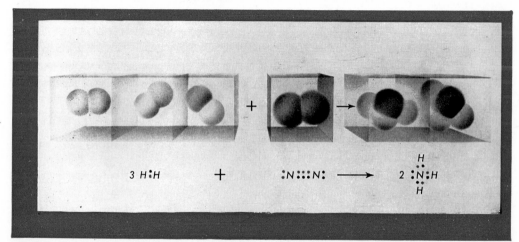

$$3\ H{:}H \quad + \quad {:}N{:}{:}{:}N{:} \longrightarrow 2\ {:}N{:}H$$

hydrogen + nitrogen → ammonia
3 volumes   1 volume   2 volumes
3 molecules   1 molecule   2 molecules
      $3 H_2$ + N_2 → $2 NH_3$

Both nitrogen and hydrogen molecules are diatomic.

4. Molecules of the inert gases are monatomic. By using the methods described in the preceding sections, we are able to show that the molecules of all ordinary gaseous elements contain two atoms. Other methods have been used to show that the inert gaseous elements, such as helium and neon, have only one atom to each molecule. The rule does not apply to solids, and it may not even apply to the vapors of certain elements which are liquid or solid at room temperature. For example, at high temperatures the molecules of mercury and iodine contain only one atom each.

5. The density and specific gravity of gases. The *density* of a substance has been defined as its *weight per unit volume*. In the case of solids and liquids the weight is expressed in *grams* and the volume in *cubic centimeters*. It is impractical, however, to express the densities of gases using the cubic-centi-

meter volume, since the weight in grams in every instance would be exceedingly small. The *liter* is a more suitable volume unit for gas-density measurements. In Chapter 9 we learned that the volume of a gas is affected by both temperature and pressure changes. The *density* of a gas is therefore given in *grams-per-liter at S.T.P.*

It is frequently convenient to compare the density of a substance to that of a suitable standard. As this is a comparison of the weights of *equal* volumes of the two, it tells us how much more (or less) dense the one is than the standard of reference. The density of water is the standard of reference for solids and liquids. Air is the most commonly used standard of reference for gases. *The ratio of the density of a substance to the density of the standard of reference* is called the **specific gravity** of the substance.

The density of oxygen is 1.43 grams per liter. Thus 1 liter of oxygen weighs 1.43 g at S.T.P. The density of air is 1.29 grams per liter. One liter of air weighs 1.29 g at S.T.P. The specific gravity of oxygen may be expressed as follows:

Fig. 14–5. At S.T.P., 22.4 liters of all gases have the same number of molecules, and the weight of each volume in grams is numerically equal to its molecular weight.

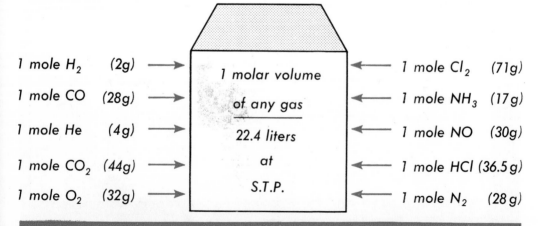

1 mole H_2 (2g) →

1 mole CO   (28g) →

1 mole He   (4g) →

1 mole CO_2 (44g) →

1 mole O_2 (32g) →

1 molar volume

of any gas

22.4 liters

at

S.T.P.

← 1 mole Cl_2 (71g)

← 1 mole NH_3 (17g)

← 1 mole NO   (30g)

← 1 mole HCl (36.5 g)

← 1 mole N_2 (28 g)

$$\text{sp gr O}_2 = \frac{\text{density of O}_2}{\text{density of air}}$$

$$\text{sp gr O}_2 = \frac{1.43 \text{ g}/l}{1.29 \text{ g}/l}$$

$$\text{sp gr O}_2 = 1.11$$

Observe that specific gravity is simply a numerical ratio which tells us that oxygen is 1.11 times denser than air. Table 10, in the Appendix, lists the density and specific gravity of many common gases.

6. What is the molar volume of a gas? Oxygen is a diatomic gas. One mole contains the Avogadro number of molecules (6.0238×10^{23}) and weighs 32 g. One mole of diatomic hydrogen contains the same number of molecules and weighs 2.016 g. Helium is a monatomic gas. One mole of helium contains the Avogadro number of monatomic molecules and weighs 4.003 g. We have learned (see Chapter 13, Section 2) that mole-quantities of all molecular substances contain the same number of molecules.

*The volume occupied by 1 mole (1 g-mol. wt.) of a gas at S.T.P. is called its **molar volume**, or its **gram-molecular volume**.* Since moles of gases have equal numbers of molecules, Avogadro's hypothesis tells us that they must occupy equal volumes under similar conditions of temperature and pressure. *The molar volumes of all gases are equal.* This has great practical significance in chemistry. Let us see how the molar volume of gases may be determined.

The densities of gases represent the weights of equal numbers of molecules measured under standard conditions of temperature and pressure. The differences in densities are due, therefore, to differences in the weights of the molecules of the different gases.

The density of hydrogen is 0.09 g/l, measured at S.T.P. A mole of hydrogen, 1 g-mol. wt., weights 2.016 g. Now 0.09 g of H_2 occupies 1 liter volume at S.T.P. What volume will 2.016 g of H_2 occupy under similar conditions? Obviously the molar volume will be as much greater than 1 liter as 2.016 g is greater than 0.09 g. This proportionality may be expressed as follows:

$$\frac{\text{molar volume of H}_2}{1 \text{ liter}} = \frac{2.016 \text{ g}}{0.09 \text{ g}}$$

Solving for molar volume:

$$\text{molar volume of H}_2 = \frac{2.016 \text{ g} \times 1 \text{ liter}}{0.09 \text{ g}}$$

$$\text{molar volume of H}_2 = 22.4 \text{ liters}$$

The density of oxygen is 1.43 g/l. A mole of oxygen weighs 32 g. Following our reasoning in the case of hydrogen, we may compute the molar volume of O_2.

$$\frac{\text{molar volume of O}_2}{1 \text{ liter}} = \frac{32 \text{ g}}{1.43 \text{ g}}$$

$$\text{molar volume of O}_2 = \frac{32 \text{ g} \times 1 \text{ liter}}{1.43 \text{ g}}$$

$$\text{molar volume of O}_2 = 22.4 \text{ liters}$$

Fig. 14–6. This is the type of glass bulb that is used in determining density of gases.

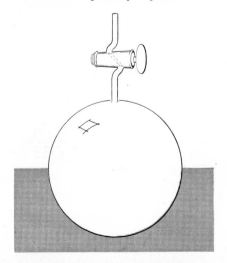

Computations with other gases would yield similar results. However, it is clear from Avogadro's hypothesis that this is unnecessary. We may generalize the proportion used above to read as follows:

$$\text{density } (D) \text{ of a gas} = \frac{1 \text{ mole of the gas}}{1 \text{ molar volume}}$$

or

$$D \text{ (of a gas)} = \frac{\text{g-mol.wt. (of the gas)}}{22.4 \; l}$$

and

$$\text{g-mol.wt.} = D \times 22.4 \; l$$

Thus we see that the *molecular weight of a gaseous substance is simply the weight, in grams, of 22.4 liters of the gas measured at S.T.P.;* or it is the density of the gas multiplied by the constant, 22.4 liters. Similarly, the density

of a gas may be found by dividing its g-mol.wt. by the constant, 22.4 liters.

If the molecular formula of a gas is known, its density may be determined directly from the formula. Let us use sulfur dioxide, SO_2, as an example. A mole of SO_2 weighs 64 g. Thus

$$D_{SO_2} = \frac{64 \text{ g}}{22.4 \; l}$$
$$D_{SO_2} = 2.85 \text{ g}/l$$

★ **7. The molecular weight of gases may be determined experimentally.** Some substances do not exist as molecules under ordinary conditions. Other substances cannot be vaporized without undergoing decomposition. Of this latter group, those which are soluble in ordinary solvents may lend themselves to molecular-weight determina-

---

★ **SAMPLE PROBLEM**

A gas sample weighing 0.35 g was measured over water at 20° C and 750 mm pressure. Its volume was 150 ml. What is its molecular weight?

SOLUTION

The partial pressure of the gas under consideration is the difference between the indicated pressure and the partial pressure due to water vapor, 750 mm − 17.5 mm, or (750 − 17.5) mm. As the temperature is lowered the volume will decrease in the ratio $\frac{273° \text{ K}}{293° \text{ K}}$. As the pressure is raised the volume will decrease in the ratio $\frac{(750 - 17.5) \text{ mm}}{760 \text{ mm}}$.

Therefore, the volume at S.T.P. is:

$$V_{\text{S.T.P.}} = 150 \text{ ml} \times \frac{273° \text{ K}}{293° \text{ K}} \times \frac{(750 - 17.5) \text{ mm}}{760 \text{ mm}}$$
$$V = 135 \text{ ml or } 0.135 \; l \text{ at S.T.P.}$$

When reduced to standard conditions, the density of the gas is proportional to 0.35 g per 0.135 liter.

Thus

$$\frac{0.35 \text{ g}}{0.135 \; l} = \frac{\text{g-mol.wt.}}{22.4 \; l}$$

Solving for g-mol.wt.:

$$\text{g-mol.wt.} = \frac{22.4 \; l \times 0.35 \text{ g}}{0.135 \; l}$$
$$\text{g-mol.wt.} = 58 \text{ g}$$
$$\text{mol.wt.} = 58$$

tions by methods which will be discussed in Chapter 19. *The molecular weights of substances which are gaseous, or which may be vaporized without decomposition, may be determined by the molar-volume method.*

It would be impractical in the laboratory to weigh directly a molar volume (22.4 l) of a gas while being held at standard conditions of temperature and pressure. Indeed, some substances, otherwise suitable for this method, are liquids or even solids under S.T.P. conditions. Consequently, any quantity of a gas which can be weighed precisely may be taken. Its volume is measured under any suitable conditions of temperature and pressure. This volume may be converted to standard temperature and pressure, and then, by proportion, the weight of 22.4 liters may be calculated. The Sample Problem on page 190 will illustrate this experimental method.

It naturally follows that the volume occupied by a known weight of a gas under any conditions of temperature and pressure can be calculated if the molecular formula of the gas is known. The molecular formula provides the weight of 1 mole of the gas which is known to occupy the molar volume, 22.4 liters, at S.T.P. By proportion, the volume of the known weight of the gas at S.T.P. can be determined. Then by application of the Gas Laws, the volume at any temperature and pressure can be computed. This is illustrated in the Sample Problem below.

★ **8. Real gases and the ideal gas.** Precise experimental determinations of molar volumes of gases reveal that all gases deviate slightly from the perfect-gas characteristics assigned to them by the Gas Laws and Avogadro's hypothesis. This does not mean that the laws are only approximately true. It does, rather, indicate that real gases do not

---

★ SAMPLE PROBLEM

What is the volume of 10 g of carbon dioxide gas, CO_2, at 20° C and 740 mm?

SOLUTION

The formula CO_2 indicates that the molecular weight is 44. Now 44 g (1 mole) of CO_2 occupies 22.4 l (1 molar volume) at S.T.P. The volume occupied by 10 g will be represented as X.

$$\frac{44 \text{ g}}{22.4 \text{ } l} = \frac{10 \text{ g}}{X}$$

Solving for X:

$$X = \frac{22.4 \text{ } l \times 10 \text{ g}}{44 \text{ g}}$$

$$X = 5.1 \text{ } l, \text{ at S.T.P.}$$

As the temperature rises the volume will increase in the ratio $\frac{293° \text{ K}}{273° \text{ K}}$.

As the pressure decreases the volume will increase in the ratio $\frac{760 \text{ mm}}{740 \text{ mm}}$.

Thus the volume at 20° C and 740 mm is:

$$V_{20°, 740 \text{ mm}} = 5.1 \text{ } l \times \frac{293° \text{ K}}{273° \text{ K}} \times \frac{760 \text{ mm}}{740 \text{ mm}}$$

$$V = 5.6 \text{ liters at } 20° \text{ C and } 740 \text{ mm}$$

behave as ideal gases over wide ranges of temperature and pressure (see Chapter 9, Section 14).

Two factors contribute to the deviation of real gases from the perfect compliance of an ideal gas: *1.* compression of a gas is *limited* by the fact that the molecules themselves occupy space; and *2.* compression is *aided* by the fact that attractive forces, however weak, do exist between the molecules.

Only when these two opposing forces within the gas exactly balance will it respond as an ideal gas. Such gases as ammonia and chlorine, which at ordinary temperatures are not far above their boiling points (condensation points), show rather marked deviations from 22.4 liters, as the molar volume. Such gases as oxygen and nitrogen, having low boiling points, behave more nearly as ideal gases under ordinary conditions. For most gases, deviations from ideal gas performance through ordinary ranges of temperature and pressure do not exceed 2 per cent. This is within the limit of accuracy obtainable in laboratory experiments.

Summary

According to the Law of Gay-Lussac, the combining volumes of gases may be expressed in small whole numbers. If the product is a gas, it bears a simple whole-number relationship to the volumes of the reacting gases.

Avogadro suggested that equal volumes of gases, under similar conditions of temperature and pressure, contained the same number of molecules. He applied this hypothesis to explain Gay-Lussac's Law of Combining Volumes of Gases. The Avogadro hypothesis, together with the Law of Gay-Lussac and molecular-weight data, may be used to show that molecules of the active elementary gases are diatomic.

The density of gases is expressed in grams per liter measured at S.T.P. The specific gravity of a gas is the numerical ratio of its density to the density of a standard of reference, usually air. Specific gravity tells us whether a gas is heavier or lighter than an equal volume of air.

The volume occupied by 1 mole of a gas at S.T.P. is called the molar volume of the gas. Molar volumes of all gases are equal and are found experimentally to be 22.4 liters. This provides a simple experimental method for determining the molecular weights of gases, and of other molecular substances which can be vaporized without undergoing decomposition.

An ideal gas conforms exactly to the proportions of the Gas Laws and Avogadro's hypothesis. Real gases deviate slightly from the behavior of an ideal gas except where the responsible molecular forces just balance out.

Test yourself on these terms

Avogadro's hypothesis	gram-molecular volume	molecular weight
density	ideal gas	monatomic molecule
diatomic molecule	molar volume	real gas
Gay-Lussac's Law	mole	specific gravity

Problems

Group A

1. Calculate the weight of one liter of hydrogen chloride gas, HCl, at S.T.P.
2. What is the weight of one liter of hydrogen sulfide, H_2S, at S.T.P.?
3. One liter of gas at S.T.P. weighs 2.5 g. What is its molecular weight?
4. One liter of nitrogen at S.T.P. weighs 1.25 g. (a) Calculate the molecular weight of nitrogen. (b) From this calculated molecular weight, determine the number of atoms in a molecule of nitrogen.
5. Hydrogen is the gas of lowest density. What is the weight of 300 ml of hydrogen at S.T.P.?
6. At standard conditions, 225 ml of sulfur dioxide gas weighs 0.6428 g. Calculate the molecular weight of sulfur dioxide.
7. What is the weight of 750 ml of CO_2 at S.T.P.?
8. Two hundred fifty milliliters of methane at S.T.P. weighs 0.179 gram. What is the molecular weight of methane?
9. The compounds HBr, PH_3, and N_2O are all gaseous at room temperature. (a) Calculate their molecular weights. (b) What is the density of each?
10. Find the weight of four liters of each of the following gases: N_2, NH_3, and C_2H_2.

Group B

11. Calculate the specific gravity of carbon monoxide, CO, air standard.
12. The specific gravity of argon, air standard, is 1.3796. What is the density of argon gas?
13. The specific gravity of a gas, air standard, is 2.695. What is the molecular weight of this gas?
14. Find the molecular weight of a gas whose specific gravity, air standard, is 1.554.
★15. A compound contains: nitrogen, 30.51%; oxygen, 69.49%. The density of the gas is 4.085 g/l. (a) What is its empirical formula? (b) What is its molecular weight? (c) What is its correct formula?
★16. One liter of a certain gas collected at a pressure of 720 mm of mercury, and at a temperature of 270° C weighs 1.30 g. Calculate its molecular weight.
★17. One liter of nitrogen combines with 1 liter of oxygen in an electric arc to form 2 liters of a gas which, by analysis, contains 46.7% nitrogen and 53.3% oxygen. Its density is determined to be 1.34 g/l. (a) Find the empirical formula of the product. (b) What is the molecular formula? (c) Using the information of this problem, and the arguments of Avogadro, determine the number of atoms per molecule of nitrogen and oxygen.
★18. What volume will 20 g of CS_2 vapor occupy at 756 mm pressure and 50° C?
★19. A liter flask filled with a gas at S.T.P. is attached to a high vacuum pump and evacuated until the pressure is only 10^{-4} mm. Assuming no temperature change, how many molecules remain in the flask?
★20. A sample of a vapor weighing 0.865 g measured 174 ml at 100° C and 745 mm. What is the molecular weight?

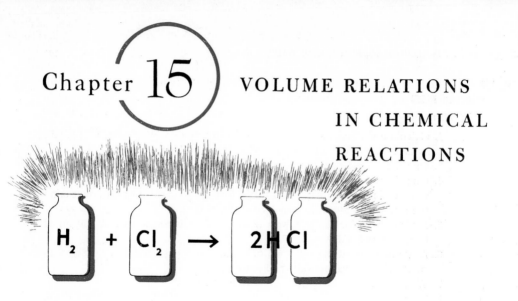

Chapter 15   VOLUME RELATIONS IN CHEMICAL REACTIONS

$$H_2 + Cl_2 \rightarrow 2HCl$$

1. Chemical problems involving gases. We have already learned the significance of the balanced equation in solving chemical problems which are concerned with the *weight relations* among reactants and products (see Chapter 13, Section 4). The equation for a reaction expresses quantities of reactants and products in *moles*. The numerical coefficients arrived at in balancing the equation tell us the number of moles of each substance involved.

It frequently happens that a reactant or product of interest in a reaction is a gas. Indeed, all reactants and products may be gaseous in certain reactions. By applying Avogadro's hypothesis we recognize that single moles of all such gases have the same volume under similar conditions of temperature and pressure. At S.T.P. a mole of any gas occupies 1 molar volume, 22.4 liters. *Consequently, the relation in moles in the equation is also the relation of volumes of gases.*

It should be remembered that real gases deviate slightly from the behavior of an ideal gas. Calculations which involve the molar volume as 22.4 liters can give only approximately correct answers.

There are two general types of problems which involve chemical equations and the volumes of gases. These are:

1. Volume-volume problems, those in which a certain *volume of a gas* reactant or product is given and the *volume of another gas* reactant or product is required.

2. Weight-volume problems, in which a certain *weight* of a reactant or product is given and the *volume of a gas* reactant or product is required, or vice versa.

2. Volume-volume problems. In this type of problem, the *volume* of one *gaseous substance* is given and we are asked to determine the *volume* of another *gaseous substance* involved in the chemical action. Since single moles of all gases at the same temperature and pressure occupy the same volume, then in a correctly balanced equation, the volumes of gases are proportional to the number of moles indicated by the numerical coefficients. To illustrate:

$$
\begin{array}{ccc}
\text{(gas)} & \text{(gas)} & \text{(gas)} \\
2\,CO & +\quad O_2 & \rightarrow\ 2\,CO_2 \\
2\ \text{moles} & 1\ \text{mole} & 2\ \text{moles} \\
2\ \text{vol.} & 1\ \text{vol.} & 2\ \text{vol.}
\end{array}
$$

The balanced equation tells us that 2 moles of CO reacts with 1 mole of O_2 to produce 2 moles of CO_2. From Avogadro's hypothesis, 2 volumes (liters, cubic feet, etc.) of carbon monoxide reacts with 1 volume (liter, cubic foot, etc.) of oxygen to produce 2 volumes (liters, cubic feet, etc.) of carbon dioxide, the temperature and pressure of all three gases being the same. Thus we can see that 10 liters of CO would require 5 liters of O_2 for combustion and would produce 10 liters of CO_2. The volume ratio is 2 : 1 : 2 under similar conditions of temperature and pressure.

Obviously, since the above reaction is exothermic, the volumes of the gases are expanded due to the rise in temperature. The volume relations apply only after the temperature of the gaseous product has been reduced to that of the reactants at the beginning of the reaction.

The conditions of temperature and pressure must be known in order to determine which substances exist as gases. Whenever the conditions are not stated they are assumed to be standard. Let us consider the combustion of methane.

$$
\begin{array}{cccc}
\text{(gas)} & \text{(gas)} & \text{(gas)} & \\
CH_4 & +\ 2\,O_2 & \rightarrow\ CO_2 & +\ 2\,H_2O \\
1\ \text{mole} & 2\ \text{moles} & 1\ \text{mole} & 2\ \text{moles} \\
1\ \text{vol.} & 2\ \text{vol.} & 1\ \text{vol.} &
\end{array}
$$

At temperatures under 100° C water is a liquid. Thus, if the volumes of the gaseous reactants are measured under ordinary conditions, water could not be included in the volume ratio. The reactants, methane and oxygen, and the product, carbon dioxide, are gases, and their volume ratio is seen to be 1 : 2 : 1.

Volume-volume problems are very simple to solve. The problem set-up is similar to that of weight-weight problems (see Chapter 13, Section 5), except that it is not necessary to use atomic weights to convert moles of the specified gases to their respective equation weights. Once set up, most volume-volume problems may be solved by inspection. The following example will show how these problems are commonly solved.

Suppose we wish to know the volume of hydrogen which will combine with 4 liters of nitrogen to form ammonia gas. We would set up the problem as follows:

$$
\begin{array}{cc}
X & 4\,l \\
3\,H_2\ +\ & N_2\ \rightarrow\ 2\,NH_3 \\
3\ \text{moles}\ & 1\ \text{mole}
\end{array}
$$

Our equation shows us that H_2 and N_2 combine in the ratio of 3 moles to 1 mole. Avogadro's hypothesis tells us that they must therefore combine in the ratio of 3 volumes to 1 volume. Thus, simply by inspection, we see that 4 liters of nitrogen requires 12 liters of hydrogen for complete reaction. Since 2 moles of NH_3 is shown, it is equally plain that 8 liters of this gas is produced. This is, in reality, a solution by the proportion method. We have the proportion:

$$
\frac{X}{4\ \text{liters}} = \frac{3\ \text{moles}}{1\ \text{mole}}
$$

Solving for X:

$$
X = \frac{3\ \text{moles} \times 4\ \text{liters}}{1\ \text{mole}}
$$

$$
X = 12\ \text{liters of } H_2
$$

SAMPLE PROBLEM

Assuming air to be 21% oxygen by volume: a. How many liters of air must enter the carburetor to complete the combustion of 60 liters of octane vapor? b. How many liters of carbon dioxide are formed? (All gases are measured at the same temperature and pressure.)

SOLUTION

Octane has the formula C_8H_{18}, and its complete oxidation produces carbon dioxide and water. Since it is the oxygen of the air which combines with octane, we must determine first the amount of oxygen required. Let X be this volume, and Y the volume of CO_2 formed. The problem set-up is:

$$\begin{array}{ccc} 60 \text{ liters} & X & Y \\ 2\ C_8H_{18} + & 25\ O_2 \rightarrow & 16\ CO_2\uparrow + 18\ H_2O\uparrow \\ 2 \text{ moles} & 25 \text{ moles} & 16 \text{ moles} \end{array}$$

a. Solving by proportion:

$$\frac{60 \text{ liters}}{X} = \frac{2 \text{ moles}}{25 \text{ moles}}$$

$$X = \frac{60 \text{ liters} \times 25 \text{ moles}}{2 \text{ moles}}$$

$$X = 750 \text{ liters of } O_2$$

Now 750 liters of O_2 is 21% of the air required.
So

$$\text{Air required} = \frac{750 \text{ liters}}{0.21} = 3570 \text{ liters}$$

b. Solving as before:

$$\frac{60 \text{ liters}}{Y} = \frac{2 \text{ moles}}{16 \text{ moles}}$$

$$Y = \frac{60 \text{ liters} \times 16 \text{ moles}}{2 \text{ moles}}$$

$$Y = 480 \text{ liters of } CO_2$$

Reminder: The volumes of air and CO_2 computed are those which would be measured at the temperature and pressure of the octane vapor prior to its combustion. Under such conditions, the water, formed as water vapor at the reaction temperature, would have condensed and could not enter the problem as a gas. The quantity of water can, of course, be computed in moles or grams using the method presented in the next section.

3. Weight-volume problems. In this type of problem, we are concerned with the relation between the *volume of gas* and the *weight* of another substance which are involved in a reaction. Either the weight of the substance is given and the volume of the gas is required, or the volume of the gas is given and the weight of the substance is required.

As an illustration let us determine the number of grams of calcium carbonate, $CaCO_3$, which must be decomposed to produce 4 liters of carbon dioxide, CO_2. The problem set-up is as follows:

$$\begin{array}{ccccc} X & & & 4\ l \\ CaCO_3 & \rightarrow & CaO & + & CO_2 \\ 1\ mole & & & & 1\ mole \\ =100\ g & & & & =44\ g \\ & & & & =22.4\ liters \end{array}$$

Observe that the molar volume (22.4 liters) is substituted for the g-mol. wt. (44 g) of CO_2. This is possible since each mole of gas occupies 22.4 liters at S.T.P. (*and only at S.T.P.*). The problem may now be solved by any of the methods used previously in connection with weight-weight relations.

1. Solution by proportion. We reason that the *ratio* of the weight of $CaCO_3$ to the volume of CO_2 is equal to the *ratio* of the equation weight of $CaCO_3$ to the volume occupied by the equation weight of CO_2 (at S.T.P.).

$$\frac{X}{4\ l}=\frac{100\ g}{22.4\ l}$$

$$X=\frac{100\ g\times 4\ l}{22.4\ l}$$

$$X=17.9\ g\ of\ CaCO_3$$

★*2. Solution by arithmetic.* We reason that 22.4 liters of CO_2 requires 100 g of $CaCO_3$ (at S.T.P.) so

$$1\ liter\ requires\ \frac{100}{22.4}\ g$$

Then,

$$4\ liters\ requires\ 4\times\frac{100}{22.4}\ g=17.9\ g$$

★*3. Solution by moles.* We reason that 4 liters of CO_2 is $\frac{4}{22.4}$ mole of CO_2 (at S.T.P.).

Since 1 mole of CO_2 requires 1 mole of $CaCO_3$

Then $\frac{4}{22.4}$ mole requires $\frac{4}{22.4}$ mole of $CaCO_3$

Number of grams in $\frac{4}{22.4}$ mole of $CaCO_3$ is:

$$\frac{4}{22.4}\times 100\ g=17.9\ g\ of\ CaCO_3$$

4. Gases not measured at S.T.P. Gases are seldom measured under standard conditions of temperature and pressure. Only gas volumes under standard conditions can be placed in a proportion with the molar volume of 22.4 liters. Therefore, *gas reactants measured under conditions other than S.T.P. must first be corrected to S.T.P.* in accordance with the Gas Laws studied in Chapter 9 before you proceed with weight-volume calculations.

If the gas in question is a *product*, and its volume is to be measured under conditions other than S.T.P., *the volume at S.T.P. is first calculated from the chemical equation.* This volume at S.T.P. is then converted to the required conditions of temperature and pressure by proper application of the Gas Laws.

Volume-volume calculations do not require S.T.P. corrections since volumes of gases are related to moles rather than to mole volumes. Thus it is only necessary that measurements of gas volumes be carried out at a constant temperature and pressure in volume-volume problems.

★**5. Gases collected over water.** The volume of a gaseous product in a weight-volume problem is calculated under S.T.P. conditions and must be corrected for any other specified conditions of temperature and pressure. If this gas is collected over water, the vapor pressure of the water must be taken into account. At the specified

What volume of oxygen, collected over water at 20° C and 750 mm pressure, can be obtained by the decomposition of 175 g of potassium chlorate?

SOLUTION

A weight is given and a gas volume is required. The volume of the gas at S.T.P. may first be found from the chemical equation. The problem set-up is as follows:

$$\begin{array}{ccc}
175 \text{ g} & & X \\
2 \text{ KClO}_3 & \rightarrow \quad 2 \text{ KCl } + & 3 \text{ O}_2\uparrow \\
2 \text{ moles} & & 3 \text{ moles} \\
= 2[39 + 35.5 + 3(16)] \text{ g} & & = 3(22.4 \; l) \\
= 245 \text{ g} & & = 67.2 \; l
\end{array}$$

Solution by proportion:

$$\frac{175 \text{ g}}{X} = \frac{245 \text{ g}}{67.2 \; l}$$

Solving for X:
$$X = \frac{175 \text{ g} \times 67.2 \; l}{245 \text{ g}} = 48 \text{ liters at S.T.P.}$$

As the temperature is increased to 20° C, the volume will increase in the ratio $\frac{293° \text{ K}}{273° \text{ K}}$. The vapor pressure of water at 20° C is found to be 17.5 mm. As the pressure is decreased to 750 mm, the volume will increase in the ratio $\frac{760 \text{ mm}}{(750 - 17.5) \text{ mm}}$. Thus the volume of O_2 at 20° C and 750 mm pressure is:

$$V_{20°, \, 750 \text{ mm}} = 48 \; l \times \frac{293° \text{ K}}{273° \text{ K}} \times \frac{760 \text{ mm}}{(750 - 17.5) \text{ mm}}$$
$$V = 53.5 \text{ liters of } O_2 \text{ at } 20° \text{ C and } 750 \text{ mm}$$

temperature, the partial pressure of the gas is the difference between the measured pressure and the partial pressure of the water vapor.

Let us suppose that the volume of a gaseous product is to be determined at 29° C and 752 mm pressure by a weight-volume calculation. The volume at S.T.P. is computed from the chemical equation. The vapor pressure of water at 29° C is found in the tables to be 30 mm. Thus

$$V_{29°, \, 752 \text{ mm}} =$$
$$V_{\text{S.T.P}} \times \frac{302° \text{ K}}{273° \text{ K}} \times \frac{760 \text{ mm}}{(752 - 30) \text{ mm}}$$

See the Sample Problem above.

Summary

There are two general types of problems involving volume relations. One, in which volumes are given and volumes are required, refers only to gases. In the other, weights are given and volumes of gases are required, or vice versa. Both types of problems are based on an application of Avogadro's hypothesis, which tells us that single moles of all gases occupy the same volume at the same temperature and pressure.

Test yourself on these terms

gaseous product   partial pressure   volume-volume prob-
gaseous reactant   proportion   lem
molar volume   volume ratio   weight-volume problem

Problems

*(In the absence of stated conditions of temperature and pressure, they are as-
sumed to be S.T.P.)*

Group A

1. Carbon monoxide burns in oxygen to form carbon dioxide. (*a*) What
volume of carbon dioxide is produced when 15 liters of carbon monoxide
burn? (*b*) What volume of oxygen is required?

2. Acetylene gas, C_2H_2, burns in oxygen to form carbon dioxide and water
vapor. (a) How many liters of oxygen are needed to burn 25 liters of
acetylene? (b) How many liters of carbon dioxide are formed?

3. Ethane gas, C_2H_6, burns in air to produce carbon dioxide and water vapor.
(*a*) How many liters of carbon dioxide are formed when 12 liters of ethane
are burned? (*b*) How many moles of water are formed?

4. How many liters of air are required to furnish the oxygen to complete
the reaction in Problem 3? (Assume the air to be 21% oxygen.)

5. How many grams of sodium are needed to liberate 4 liters of hydrogen
from water?

6. What volumes of hydrogen and nitrogen are required to produce 20 liters
of ammonia gas?

7. (*a*) How many liters of hydrogen are required to reduce 25 g of hot cupric
oxide? (*b*) How many moles of water are formed?

8. When 130 g of zinc reacts with 150 g of HCl, how many liters of hydrogen
are formed? (Note: first determine which reactant is in excess.)

9. (*a*) What volume of oxygen can be produced by the decomposition of
90 g of water? (*b*) What volume of hydrogen is produced in the same reaction?

10. If 400 ml of hydrogen and 400 ml of oxygen are mixed and ignited,
(*a*) what volume of oxygen remains uncombined? (*b*) What volume of
water vapor is formed if all gases are measured at 100° C?

Group B

11. (*a*) How many liters of sulfur dioxide gas at S.T.P. are formed when
50 g of sulfur burns? (*b*) What volume will this gas occupy at 25° C
and 745 mm pressure?

12. What weight of magnesium reacting with hydrochloric acid will be required to produce 400 ml of hydrogen at 20° C and 740 mm pressure?

★ 13. How many grams of oxygen are contained in 12 liters of the gas measured
over water at 23° C and 745 mm pressure? (The vapor pressure of water
at 23° C may be taken as 21 mm.)

★ 14. A replacement reaction between 5 g of aluminum and an excess of dilute sulfuric acid is used as a source of hydrogen gas. What volume of hydrogen is collected over water at 20° C and 765 mm pressure?

15. What volume of dry air, measured at 29° C and 744 mm pressure, is required to complete the combustion of 1 mole of carbon disulfide, CS_2, to carbon dioxide, CO_2, and sulfur dioxide, SO_2?

16. What is the volume of the mixture of CO_2 and SO_2 produced in the reaction of Problem 15, if measured under the same conditions as the air used in the reaction?

17. Chlorine gas may be generated in the laboratory by a reaction between manganese dioxide and hydrogen chloride. The equation is:

$$MnO_2 + 4\,HCl \rightarrow MnCl_2 + 2\,H_2O + Cl_2\uparrow$$

(*a*) What weight of MnO_2 is required to produce 1 liter of Cl_2 gas at S.T.P.? (*b*) What weight of HCl is required?

★ 18. In Problem 17, the HCl is available as a water solution which is 40% hydrogen chloride by weight, and the solution has a specific gravity (water standard) of 1.12. What volume of HCl solution (hydrochloric acid) must be furnished to the reaction?

Check your progress in chemistry

1. (*a*) Which term has more general application, *formula* weight or *molecular* weight? (*b*) What is the distinction between them?

2. Determine the formula weight for each of the following compounds: (*a*) H_2SO_4; (*b*) NaOH; (*c*) HgO; (*d*) $CuSO_4 \cdot 5\,H_2O$; (*e*) $HC_2H_3O_2$; (*f*) $MgBr_2$ (*g*) Al_2S_3; (*h*) $Ca(NO_3)_2$; (*i*) $Fe_2(Cr_2O_7)_3$; (*j*) $KMnO_4$.

3. A compound has the following composition: potassium 44.82%, sulfur 18.39%, oxygen 36.79%. What is the empirical formula?

4. A compound has the following composition: calcium 24.69%, hydrogen 1.23%, carbon 14.81%, oxygen 59.25%. What is the empirical formula?

5. An oxide of iron has the following composition: $Fe = 72.41\%$, $O = 27.59\%$. What is its empirical formula?

6. Write the balanced equations for the following reactions: (*a*) composition reaction between hydrogen and oxygen; (*b*) decomposition of mercuric oxide; (*c*) oxidation of sulfur; (*d*) replacement reaction between zinc and hydrochloric acid; (*e*) double replacement reaction between silver nitrate and sodium chloride; (*f*) potassium chlorate heated strongly; (*g*) complete oxidation of phosphorus; (*h*) double replacement reaction between aluminum sulfate and calcium hydroxide; (*i*) metallic zinc and cupric sulfate solution; (*j*) reduction of cupric oxide with hydrogen.

7. What is the percentage composition of each of the following compounds: (*a*) SO_2; (*b*) $Ca(OH)_2$; (*c*) NaH_2PO_4; (*d*) C_2H_5OH; (*e*) $MgSO_4 \cdot 7\,H_2O$?

8. Analysis of a compound reveals its composition to be 80% carbon and 20% hydrogen. Its molecular weight is 30. What is its molecular formula?

9. List the following elements in the order of their chemical activity: aluminum, calcium, copper, gold, hydrogen, iron, lead, potassium, silver, sodium, zinc.

10. How much ether, $(C_2H_5)_2O$, equals one mole?

11. What is the density of methane gas, CH_4, at S.T.P.?

12. What is the specific gravity (air standard) of the gas arsine, AsH_3?

13. How much copper will be produced when hydrogen is passed over 39.75 g of hot cupric oxide?

14. How many liters of hydrogen are required to reduce the cupric oxide of Problem 13?

15. An excess of copper is added to a solution containing 20 g of silver sulfate. How much silver is deposited?

16. What volume of hydrogen, measured at S.T.P., will be replaced by the action of 20 g of calcium metal and an excess of hydrochloric acid?

17. How many moles of calcium hydroxide are formed by the reaction between 60 g of calcium oxide and 20 g of water?

18. How many liters of ammonia can be prepared from 10 liters of nitrogen and 25 liters of hydrogen?

19. How many grams of charcoal, 90% carbon, must be burned to produce 100 liters of CO_2 measured at 20° C and 747 mm pressure?

★ 20. What volume of hydrogen, collected over water at 25° C and 755 mm pressure, can be obtained from 6 g of magnesium and an excess of sulfuric acid?

Challenging your knowledge

1. The compound $C_3H_5(C_{17}H_{35}CO_2)_3$ forms CO_2 and H_2O when completely oxidized. Write the balanced equation.

2. Investigate the work of the Italian chemist, Stanislao Cannizzaro (1826–1910), in which he applied Avogadro's hypothesis to the determination of atomic weights. (Your instructor may be able to recommend a suitable college text or other source.) Prepare a brief report of Cannizzaro's logic for presentation to your class.

3. If 100 liters of a perfect gas at 0° C were subjected to 100 atmospheres of pressure (temperature remaining constant) the volume would be reduced to 1 liter. Hydrogen, however, would have a volume slightly greater than 1 liter, and nitrogen would have a volume slightly less than 1 liter. Can you explain these two different deviations of real gases from ideal-gas behavior?

4. Gasoline tank additives of questionable merit appear on the market from time to time. One such additive, in the form of white tablets, was analyzed by chemists. They found that the substance burned to produce carbon dioxide and water vapor. Each gram of substance, when burned, yielded 3.44 g of CO_2 and 0.558 g of water. The density of its vapor was found to be 5.715 grams per liter. (a) What is the molecular formula? (b) What is the chemical name of the substance? (c) What is the common name?

5. A tube contains a kilogram of hot cupric oxide. Ten grams of hydrogen is passed through the tube slowly, and the water formed is expelled to the air. What remains in the tube, and in what quantities?

UNIT

5

CARBON AND ITS SIMPLE COMPOUNDS

During the time of the prehistoric forest shown above, scientists believe our tremendous natural fuel sources were being deposited. Such fuels as coal, natural gas, and petroleum were originally plants and animals which flourished on the earth many centuries ago.

One chemical element is an important constituent of each of these fuels. That is the element carbon. In fact, you will soon learn that carbon is found in all living materials, and in many other substances as well. There are so many carbon compounds that their study comprises a separate branch of chemistry, organic chemistry. This unit introduces you to the element carbon, and to some of its compounds with oxygen and with hydrogen.

Three chapters are included in the unit: *Carbon, The Oxides of Carbon,* and *Hydrocarbons.* From even this brief study, you will be amazed at the unique properties of the element carbon.

203

Chapter 16 CARBON

1. Carbon is an abundant and important element. In abundance, carbon ranks eleventh by weight among the elements in the earth's crust. But in importance, it ranks far higher than this. Carbon occurs in all living things. It is present in the tissues of our bodies and in the foods we eat. We find it in fuels, oils, wood, paper, textile fibers, and in all the plants and animals in the world. In addition, many thousands of carbon compounds have been made by synthesis in chemical laboratories. So important is the study of carbon compounds that it is a separate branch of chemistry called *organic chemistry*. Originally, organic chemistry was defined as the study of materials derived from living organisms, while inorganic chemistry was the study of materials derived from mineral sources. We have known for over a century that this is not a clear distinction. Many substances identical with those produced in plants and animals can be made also from mineral materials. As a result, *organic chemistry* today *includes the study of carbon compounds whether they are found in living organisms or not.*

In most substances containing carbon, the carbon is present in the *combined* form, usually associated with hydrogen, or with hydrogen and oxygen. However, in this chapter we shall study the solid element carbon in its *free* or *uncombined* forms.

Carbon, as an element, has been known from very early times in the forms of charcoal and soot.

2. The structure and properties of carbon atoms. Carbon is the element

VOCABULARY

Activated. Rendered more reactive.

Destructive distillation. The process of decomposing materials by heating them in a closed vessel without access to air or oxygen.

Organic chemistry. The study of carbon compounds.

Refractory. (1) Not readily melted; (2) a substance which is not readily melted.

with atomic number 6. It is located on the Periodic Table in the second period midway between the active metal lithium and the active nonmetal fluorine. It has six electrons. Two of these are in the K shell, and are tightly bound to the nucleus. The remaining four L-shell electrons are the valence electrons. In order to attain a stable outer electronic shell, we might think that carbon atoms would either lose four electrons or gain four electrons. But carbon atoms usually do neither. They show a very strong tendency to share electrons and form covalent bonds. The four valence electrons make it possible for a carbon atom to form four covalent bonds. These covalent bonds are directed in space toward the four vertices of a regular tetrahedron if we assume the center of the atom is at the center of the tetrahedron (see Fig. 16-2). The property of forming covalent bonds is so strong in carbon atoms that they not only join with other elements, but carbon atoms link together in chains, rings, plates, and even in macromolecules, such as the diamond. These varieties of ways in which carbon atoms can be linked account for the fact that there are several times as many carbon compounds as there are noncarbon compounds.

3. The allotropic forms of carbon. We have already learned that oxygen can absorb energy and form ozone, a very active allotrope of oxygen. Several other elements exist in different allotropic forms, and carbon is such an element. For example, carbon may exist: *1.* in a beautiful crystalline form as a *diamond*; *2.* in a grayish-black crystalline form called *graphite*; and *3.* as a black residue when substances which contain combined carbon are heated.

Fig. 16–1. Elementary carbon is left as a residue when sulfuric acid separates the hydrogen and oxygen from it as water. This proves that carbon is one of the elements present in sugar.

These residues are usually called *amorphous carbon* because they seem to have no definite crystalline shape when we look at them.

Such substances as charcoal, coke, boneblack, and lampblack are examples of amorphous carbon. For many years chemists believed that these forms of carbon did not have any definite crystalline shape. In recent years, however, X-ray photographs have revealed that the so-called amorphous carbon is really a mass of extremely tiny graphite crystals.

Fig. 16–2. The four covalent bonds of a carbon atom are directed in space toward the four vertices of a regular tetrahedron if the center of the atom is at the center of the tetrahedron.

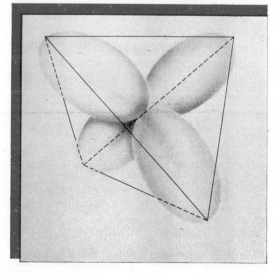

Fig. 16–3. The hydraulic press, capable of producing a pressure of 1,600,000 lb/in², in which diamonds were artificially produced at the General Electric Company, Schenectady, N.Y.

4. The occurrence of diamonds. At one time many famous diamonds were mined in India. Black diamonds are found in Brazil. Australia, too, produces diamonds, but the most famous mines in the world are located in South Africa. These mines produced the Cullinan diamond, the largest ever found. The Cullinan diamond weighed about one and one third pounds. A few diamonds are found occasionally in this country, particularly in California, Georgia, and the Carolinas.

Natural diamonds from South Africa occur usually in the shafts of extinct volcanoes, where it is believed they were formed slowly under extreme heat and pressure.

5. The artificial preparation of diamonds. In 1954, scientists at the General Electric Company proved by X-ray photographs that diamonds could be made synthetically. They started with various carbon-containing compounds and subjected them to a temperature of 5000° F and a pressure of 400 tons per square inch. While small diamonds may be crystallized in a few minutes, larger ones, up to $\frac{1}{16}$ inch in length, require as much as 16 hours. These diamonds pass all the tests used to identify natural diamonds. They have the same structure as shown by X-ray photographs, they have the same hardness, and they burn in oxygen to form carbon dioxide. The same scientists at General Electric have produced a compound of boron and nitrogen called "borazon" with a similar crystal structure and with the same hardness as a diamond (see Chapter 40).

6. The properties of diamonds. Diamonds as they are mined do not have

Fig. 16–4. One of the largest diamonds produced artificially by the General Electric scientists. It is about $\frac{1}{16}$ inch long, and is shown here beside a standard, diamond, high fidelity phonograph needle to indicate its relative size.

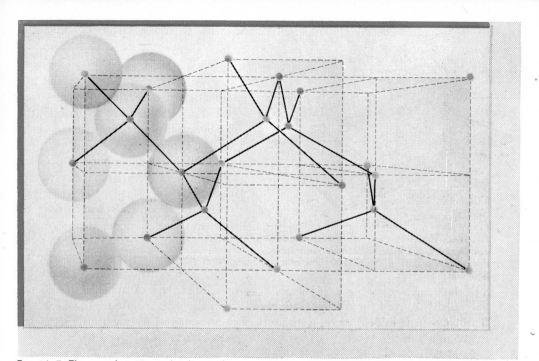

Fig. 16-5. The crystal structure of a diamond.

the same shape or luster which occurs in cut stones. They must be cut and polished to give them that appearance. The diamond is one of the hardest materials. It is the densest form of carbon, being about 3.5 times as dense as water. This hardness and density can both be explained by its structure. Fig. 16-5 shows that carbon atoms are covalently bonded to each other in a diamond in a strong, compact fashion. The rigidity of the structure gives a diamond its hardness; the compactness gives it its density. A diamond is a macromolecule. Since all the electrons are firmly bound, a diamond is a nonconductor of electricity.

Diamonds are insoluble in ordinary reagents. Lavoisier burned a clear diamond in pure oxygen and obtained carbon dioxide as a product. This proved to him that diamonds contain carbon. The English chemist Sir Humphry Davy (1778–1829) and other scientists have repeated the experiment. They found that the weight of carbon dioxide produced by burning a diamond in pure oxygen corresponds to the weight of carbon dioxide that should be produced if a diamond were pure carbon.

7. Diamonds have many uses. The great hardness of diamonds makes them useful for several purposes. Circular saws fitted with diamonds which serve as teeth are used for cutting marble. A chip diamond is used by glass cutters. A diamond with a tiny hole drilled through it serves as a die for drawing the fine tungsten wire used as the filament of electric lamps.

Black diamonds from Brazil are not suitable for gems but are used for making diamond drills. A steel shoe, set at the end of a pipe about 1.5 inches in diameter, is studded with black diamonds. As this drill is turned by the machine, it cuts through the hardest rock.

207

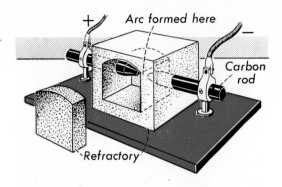

Fig. 16–6. The electric arc, conducted from one carbon rod to the other by carbon vapor, produces a temperature of about 3500° C in an arc-type electric furnace.

Such drills are used for cutting through hard rock strata in drilling oil wells and in digging tunnels.

8. Electric furnaces produce high temperatures. Several types of electric furnaces are in use. One of the simplest forms consists of two carbon rods, which serve as electrodes. The rods are mounted in a block of **refractory material,** that is—*a material which has a very high melting point.* To start the furnace, the rods are brought together momentarily, and then separated slightly. The intense heat produced by the electric current vaporizes some of the carbon and forms carbon vapor. The carbon vapor continues to conduct the electric current as an electric arc, producing a temperature of about 3500° C. Electric furnaces of this type are called *arc-type electric furnaces.* At the high temperature of such a furnace, some endothermic chemical reactions that cannot be brought about in any other way take place readily. Carbon disulfide, CS_2, and elementary phosphorus are produced in arc-type electric furnaces.

Another type of electric furnace has a central core of loose pieces of coke which, because it offers resistance to the passage of an electric current, is heated by it. The central core is surrounded by a thick bed of material which prevents the heat from escaping easily. Accumulation of heat within the central mass results finally in a high temperature. Such furnaces are called *resistance furnaces.*

9. Occurrence and preparation of graphite. Natural graphite is a mineral found in several localities. New York and Pennsylvania supply some graphite, but Ceylon and Siberia are more important sources.

Artificial graphite is made in a resistance furnace by surrounding the central core with anthracite or coke. Ferric oxide is used as a catalyst. The high temperature of 3000° C converts the anthracite into graphite.

10. The properties of graphite. Graphite is nearly as remarkable for its softness as the diamond is for its hard-

Fig. 16–7. The carbon core offers resistance to the passage of an electric current and becomes heated by it. This type of resistance furnace is used for making graphite.

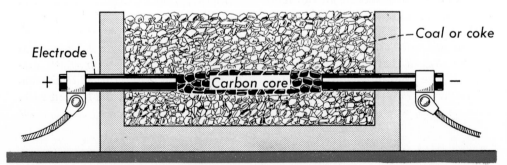

ness. Graphite, too, is a crystalline form of carbon, but its crystals are hexagonal in shape. Its specific gravity is about 2.25. It is easily crumbled and has a greasy feel. Although graphite is a nonmetal, it is a fairly good conductor of electricity.

The structure of graphite readily explains these observed properties. Fig. 16-8 shows that the carbon atoms in graphite are arranged in layers of thin hexagonal plates. Within a layer, the carbon atoms are closer together than the carbon atoms in adjacent layers. Each carbon atom in a layer is bonded to only three other carbon atoms in that layer. The fourth valence electron of each carbon atom is believed to be somewhat free to move in the space between the layers, and hold the layers together by weak bonds. The layered structure accounts for the softness and greasy feel of graphite as one layer slides over another. The wider separation of carbon atoms in graphite gives it a lower specific gravity than diamond. The free electrons between the layers of plates account for the electrical conductivity of graphite.

Like diamond, graphite does not dissolve in any ordinary reagent. It forms carbon dioxide when it is burned in oxygen.

11. Uses of graphite. Graphite makes a very good lubricant, particularly when mixed with petroleum jelly to form a graphite grease. It may be used for lubricating machine parts that are subjected to temperatures too high for the usual oil lubricants.

Graphite has a very high melting point, about 3500° C. Hence, it is an excellent refractory. If mixed with a binder to hold the particles together, artificial graphite can be made into

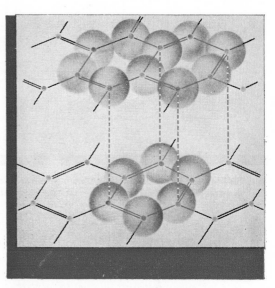

Fig. 16–8. The crystal structure of graphite.

crucibles which are used for melting steel and other metals. Artificial graphite is also used for making the electrodes of electric furnaces. Powdered graphite is dusted over a wax impression of printer's type to make the surface a conductor of electricity. When immersed in a copper-plating bath, metallic copper is deposited on the graphite and takes the outline of the type. These plates are then nickel or chrome plated to insure longer wear. Books, such as this one, are then printed from the plates, which are called *electrotypes*.

Graphite leaves a gray streak or mark when it is drawn across a sheet of paper. In making "lead" pencils, natural graphite is powdered, mixed with clay, and then formed into sticks. The hardness of a pencil depends upon the relative amount of clay that is used.

Graphite is also used as a moderator in nuclear reactors (see Chapter 39) .

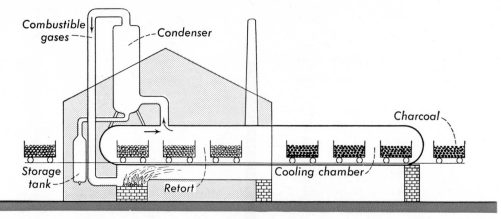

Fig. 16–9. Charcoal is made by heating wood in large closed retorts. Liquid by-products collect in the storage tank. The combustible gases are used as fuel.

12. Destructive distillation. When a complex material, such as wood or bituminous coal, is *heated in a closed retort or oven without access to air or oxygen, it becomes decomposed into simpler substances.* This process is known as **destructive distillation.** Charcoal, coke, and boneblack are prepared by destructive distillation from wood, coal, and bones respectively. Lampblack is produced by burning gas or oil in a limited supply of air.

13. The preparation of charcoal. When wood is heated strongly without access to air, combustible gases, methanol (wood alcohol), acetic acid, and other volatile products are driven off. The residue that is left is charcoal. Charcoal is prepared commercially by heating wood in iron retorts.

Charcoal has been made for many centuries by the process of destructive distillation. The combustible gases given off provide supplementary fuel. The other volatile products are condensed and sold as by-products.

14. The properties and uses of charcoal. Charcoal is a porous, black, brittle solid that is odorless and tasteless. It is denser than water, but it often adsorbs enough gas to make it float on

water. The ability to adsorb a large quantity of gas is the most remarkable physical property of charcoal. Adsorption is the accumulation of a gas on the surface of a solid. One cubic inch of freshly prepared willow charcoal adsorbs about 90 cubic inches of ammonia gas. Because of its ability to adsorb gases, charcoal is a good deodorizer. A layer of wood charcoal is often used between layers of sand and gravel in water purification for this purpose. Charcoal will also remove the color from certain liquids.

Gas masks intended for industrial or military use depend upon some form of carbon to adsorb the harmful gases from the air breathed by the wearer. Chemists have learned how to convert wood and coal into a form of carbon that is an efficient adsorbing agent. This material may be **activated,** increasing its ability to adsorb gases, by treating it with steam in retorts. It may also be impregnated with certain chemicals, which serve as catalysts, to make it more effective.

At ordinary temperatures, charcoal is inert and insoluble in all ordinary reagents. It is a good reducing agent because it unites with oxygen at a high temperature. Charcoal also makes a good fuel, but it is more expensive than other common fuels and is not widely used for this purpose. Steaks broiled over charcoal have a fine flavor.

15. The preparation of coke. When bituminous coal is heated in a hard-glass test tube, a flammable gas escapes. A tarlike liquid condenses on the upper walls of the tube. If the heating is continued until all the volatile matter is driven off, coke is left as a residue.

Commercially, coke is prepared by heating bituminous coal in the absence of air in by-product coke ovens. The volatile products which are given off are separated into: *1. coal gas,* which may be used as a fuel; *2. ammonia,* which is used in making fertilizer; and *3. coal tar.* The coal tar can be separated into many materials by distillation. These are used to make drugs, dyes, and explosives, while the black pitch produced is used to surface roads. About 50,000,000 tons of coke are produced each year in the United States.

16. The properties and uses of coke. Coke is a gray solid that is harder and denser than charcoal. It burns with little flame, but has a high heat content. It is a valuable fuel.

Coke is an excellent reducing agent. Many of the ores of iron, tin, copper, and zinc are oxides, or are converted into oxides. Millions of tons of coke are used each year to reduce these oxides to metals.

17. The preparation, properties, and uses of boneblack. Animal charcoal, or *boneblack,* is left as a residue in the retort after the destructive distillation of bones. The by-products of the process include bone oil and pyridine, which are used for denaturing alcohol (making it unfit for human consumption).

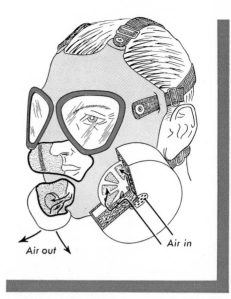

Air out   Air in

Fig. 16–10. An Army gas mask showing the passage of inspired and expired air. Activated carbon adsorbs poison gases from the air breathed by the soldier.

Boneblack usually contains considerable calcium phosphate, but this can be removed by treating the boneblack with some acid to dissolve it.

Boneblack is a good adsorbent which is used to decolorize liquids. In sugar refineries, crude sugar solutions are

Fig. 16–11. Coke is produced by the destructive distillation of bituminous coal in by-product coke ovens. Here the red-hot coke is being discharged from an oven into a waiting railroad car.

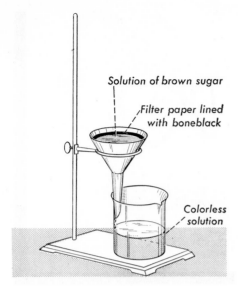

Fig. 16–12. Sugar solutions are decolorized by filtering through boneblack. The boneblack adsorbs the coloring matter and produces a water-white solution.

decolorized by filtering them through large tanks that are partially filled with boneblack. After filtering through several such tanks in succession, the liquid is changed from a brown solution to one that is water-white. The color is adsorbed by the boneblack.

18. The preparation, properties, and uses of lampblack. Finely divided particles of carbon, or soot, are set free when kerosene or light oil burns in an insufficient supply of air. The carbon may be collected as a velvety black powder, called *lampblack*, on cool surfaces near the flame. Lampblack is used in making printer's ink, shoe polish, India ink, carbon paper, black varnish, and as a black pigment in paints.

19. The preparation, properties, and uses of carbon black. *Carbon black* is made by burning natural gas in an insufficient supply of air. It is not so greasy or tarlike as lampblack. For many purposes it is more desirable than lampblack and is often substituted for

it. Carbon black is especially useful as a filler in the rubber mix for making automobile tires. It helps to preserve the life of the rubber and makes the tires wear much better on the road. In commercial practice, the carbon from the burning gas is deposited on the under side of a revolving disk. As the disk revolves, the carbon is scraped off into bags.

20. The preparation and uses of gas carbon and petroleum coke. Carbon scraped from the walls of the retorts in a coal gas plant is called *gas carbon*. A somewhat similar product, called *petroleum coke,* is scraped off the walls of the retorts in which petroleum has been distilled. Both gas carbon and petroleum coke are pressed into sticks and become fairly good conductors of electricity. They are used for making electrodes. Gas carbon electrodes are used for the positive plates of dry cells. Petroleum coke electrodes are used in the cells in which aluminum is recovered by electrolysis.

Fig. 16–13. Sectional view of a dry cell. Note that a carbon rod is used as the positive pole.

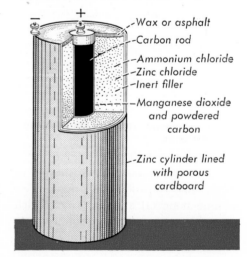

Summary

Carbon is an abundant and important element. In the combined form it occurs in all living things. Foods, fuels, paper, and textiles all contain carbon compounds. In addition, thousands of carbon compounds have been made by synthesis. Organic chemistry is the study of carbon compounds.

A carbon atom, with four valence electrons, forms covalent bonds with other elements, or with other carbon atoms. Carbon atoms may link together in chains, rings, plates, and in macromolecules like the diamond. This accounts for the tremendous number of carbon compounds.

Uncombined or free carbon occurs in the allotropic forms known as graphite and diamond. Amorphous carbon includes charcoal, coke, boneblack, and lampblack. Amorphous carbon appears to have no definite shape but is really made up of microscopic crystals of graphite.

The diamond is one of the hardest substances known. Clear diamonds are used as gems, while specimens of dark color are used for diamond drills and saws. Graphite is a crumbly solid that is a conductor of electricity. It is used as a lubricant, in paints, as electrodes, and for making "lead" pencils.

In the arc-type electric furnace, carbon disulfide and elementary phosphorus are produced. The resistance-type of electric furnace is used for making graphite.

Charcoal is made by the destructive distillation of wood. Coke is a product of the destructive distillation of soft coal. Boneblack is obtained by the destructive distillation of bones.

At ordinary temperatures, all forms of carbon are inert, but at higher temperatures they unite with oxygen to form carbon dioxide.

Carbon is a good adsorbent; thus it is suitable for use as a deodorizer, a decolorizer, and for use in gas masks. Because it is insoluble in ordinary reagents, it is useful in pigments, in paints and lacquers, and in printer's ink.

Test yourself on these terms

activated	carbon black	graphite
allotropic forms	charcoal	lampblack
amorphous carbon	coke	organic chemistry
arc-type furnace	destructive distillation	petroleum coke
artificial diamond	diamond	refractory
boneblack	gas carbon	resistance furnace

Questions

Group A

1. Why does the study of carbon compounds constitute a separate branch of chemistry?
2. How can you show that sugar contains the element carbon?
3. What property of carbon atoms makes possible the large number of carbon compounds?

4. Why is amorphous carbon no longer classified as a third allotropic form of carbon?
5. Why are diamonds so useful for industrial purposes?
6. (*a*) What are the two types of electric furnaces? (*b*) How is the heat produced from the electricity in each furnace?
7. Give several reasons why graphite is suitable as a lubricant.
8. Why is the name "lead" pencil misleading? Suggest a better name.
9. (*a*) What is destructive distillation? (*b*) Is it really destructive? Explain.
10. Why is boneblack a relatively impure form of carbon?
11. Distinguish between lampblack and carbon black.
12. What use is made of petroleum coke?

Group B

13. Why does carbon form no ionic compounds?
14. How are artificial diamonds produced?
15. When coke is used as a reducing agent, what is oxidized?
16. Why is charcoal a good adsorbent?
17. What is the orientation in space of the valence bonds of a carbon atom?
18. What proof do we have that a diamond is pure carbon?
19. How do printers make the "plates" from which books, such as this one, are printed?
20. Why will a form of carbon such as charcoal or coke remain after the destructive distillation of wood or bituminous coal?
21. Why is the specific gravity of graphite less than that of diamond?
22. Why is it so difficult to remove stains made by printer's ink?
23. Diamond is very hard and a nonconductor of electricity. Graphite is soft and is a conductor of electricity. Explain these properties in terms of the structure of diamond and graphite.
24. Powdered charcoal, cupric oxide, and manganese dioxide are all black substances. How could you identify each?

Some things for you to do

1. Examine a fine diamond with a magnifying glass. Note the shape of the different faces on the cut stone.
2. Hold a lump of natural graphite in the fingers and note the slippery feeling of the graphite. Rub it on a piece of paper and note the streak it leaves.
3. Add a drop of liquid bromine to an empty bottle, stopper it, and allow the bottle to fill with bromine vapor. CAUTION: *Bromine burns the flesh badly. Do not get any on your skin.* Now add a teaspoonful of activated carbon. What happens to the bromine vapor?
4. Prepare some carbon from sugar by the dehydrating action of concentrated sulfuric acid. Fill a tall beaker about one-third full of sugar. Add enough concentrated sulfuric acid to saturate the sugar. The action starts within a few minutes.
5. Prepare a report on the production of synthetic diamonds and other very hard materials such as boron nitride, or "borazon."

Chapter 17 THE OXIDES OF CARBON

1. CARBON DIOXIDE

1. Carbon dioxide is a common, widely distributed gas. Carbon dioxide is one of the gases found in the air. While it comprises only 0.04% of the atmosphere by volume, it is, as we shall soon see, a very important component. The water of rivers, lakes, and oceans contains between twenty and thirty times as much dissolved carbon dioxide as is found in the atmosphere. The decay of organic matter on and below the surface of the ground produces carbon dioxide. Sometimes it accumulates in considerable amounts in low-lying areas such as bogs, swamps and marshes, in coal mines, and in other underground regions. It is one of the gases spewed forth by active volcanoes. It issues, in a high degree of purity, from certain gas wells, especially those in the western states.

2. The discovery of carbon dioxide. Jan Baptista van Helmont (1577–1644), a Belgian physician, is usually credited with being the discoverer of carbon dioxide. About 1630 he recognized that a gas that would not support combustion was produced when wood burned. In addition, he discovered that this same gas was produced when acids act on limestone and when fermentation takes place.

3. The preparation of carbon dioxide. *1. By burning carbonaceous material.* We know that carbon dioxide is one of the products of the combustion of any material which contains carbon. When carbon dioxide is prepared in this way, it is mixed with other gases from the air. If these gases do not interfere with the uses for which the carbon dioxide has been prepared, this method

VOCABULARY

Enzyme. A catalyst produced by living cells.
Fermentation. A chemical change produced by the action of an enzyme.
Leavening agent. A substance which releases carbon dioxide in a dough or batter.
Sublime. To pass from the solid to the gaseous state without liquefying.

is the cheapest and easiest of them all.

2. *By heating a carbonate.* When calcium carbonate in the form of limestone, marble, or shells is heated strongly, calcium oxide and carbon dioxide are the products.

$$CaCO_3 \xrightarrow{\Delta} CaO + CO_2\uparrow$$

Calcium oxide is known as *quicklime* and is used in large quantities for making plaster and mortar. The carbon dioxide is a by-product. The gas is led off from the kiln in which the limestone is heated and is compressed into steel cylinders.

3. *By fermentation of molasses.* The enzyme *zymase,* produced by yeast, catalyzes the fermentation of the sugar, $C_6H_{12}O_6$, in molasses to produce ethanol (ethyl alcohol), C_2H_5OH, and carbon dioxide. While the process is complex, the over-all reaction is:

$$C_6H_{12}O_6 \rightarrow 2\ C_2H_5OH + 2\ CO_2\uparrow$$

This is a method by which industrial alcohol is produced, and is an important source of carbon dioxide.

4. *By the action of an acid on a carbonate.* This is the usual laboratory method for preparing carbon dioxide. The gas-generating bottle in Fig. 17-2

contains a few pieces of marble, $CaCO_3$. If we pour dilute hydrochloric acid through the funnel tube, carbon dioxide is evolved rapidly. Calcium chloride, which remains in solution in the bottle, is also formed.

This reaction proceeds in two stages. *First,* the marble and hydrochloric acid undergo a double replacement reaction, forming calcium chloride and carbonic acid:

$$CaCO_3 + 2\ HCl \rightarrow CaCl_2 + H_2CO_3$$

Second, carbonic acid is unstable and decomposes into carbon dioxide and water:

$$H_2CO_3 \rightarrow H_2O + CO_2\uparrow$$

The equation which summarizes these two reactions is:

$$CaCO_3 + 2\ HCl \rightarrow CaCl_2 + H_2O + CO_2\uparrow$$

Carbon dioxide may be collected by water displacement if it is generated rapidly. It may also be collected by displacement of air. In this case, the receiver must be kept *mouth upward* because the gas is more dense than air.

This is a general type reaction for an acid and a carbonate. Almost any acid may be used instead of hydrochloric

Fig. 17-1. Carbon dioxide is a by-product of the fermentation of the sugar in molasses to produce ethanol. The fermentation is carried out in huge tanks such as these.

acid, even a weak one such as the acetic acid in vinegar. Almost any carbonate, too, may be used. The equation for the reaction between sodium carbonate and sulfuric acid is:

$$Na_2CO_3 + H_2SO_4 \rightarrow$$
$$Na_2SO_4 + H_2O + CO_2\uparrow$$

5. By respiration and decay. This is a natural method of preparation of carbon dioxide. The foods we eat contain compounds of carbon. We inhale oxygen which is used in oxidizing our food, thus supplying us with heat and muscular energy. Carbon dioxide is one of the products of this oxidation which we exhale into the air. Both animals and plants give off carbon dioxide during respiration.

When plants and animals die, decay begins. Carbon dioxide is one of the products of complete decay of all vegetable and animal matter. This gas eventually finds its way into the surrounding air, or becomes dissolved in surface or underground streams.

4. The physical properties of carbon dioxide. Carbon dioxide is a colorless gas with a very faintly pungent odor and a slightly pungent taste. The molecular weight of carbon dioxide is 44. This causes carbon dioxide to have a density about 1.5 times that of air. The large, heavy molecules of carbon diox-

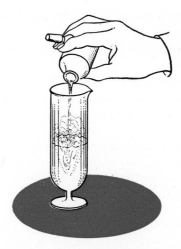

Fig. 17-3. Carbon dioxide bubbles off when an acid is added to a carbonate.

ide move more slowly than the smaller, lighter molecules of oxygen or hydrogen. Because of the higher density and slower rate of diffusion, carbon dioxide can be poured from one vessel to another. Fig. 17-4 shows how pouring carbon dioxide down an incline extinguishes successive candles. The high

Fig. 17-4. As the dense carbon dioxide flows down the inclined trough, the candles are extinguished, one after another.

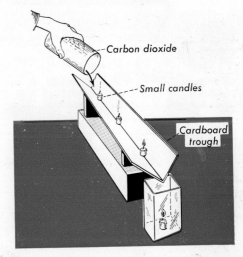

Carbon dioxide

Small candles

Cardboard trough

Fig. 17-2. Carbon dioxide is prepared in the laboratory by adding an acid to a carbonate.

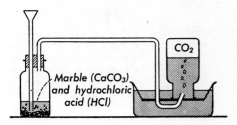

CO₂

Marble (CaCO₃) and hydrochloric acid (HCl)

density and slow rate of diffusion also explains why carbon dioxide sometimes collects at the bottom of caves, mines, or dry wells.

If carbon dioxide is compressed and yet kept at room temperature, at about 70 atmospheres pressure, the molecules are pushed close enough together for them to attract each other and condense to a liquid. If this liquid is permitted to evaporate rapidly under atmospheric pressure, part of it changes into a gas, absorbing heat from the remainder, which is thus cooled until it solidifies. Solid carbon dioxide is called *Dry Ice*.

Solid carbon dioxide has a high vapor pressure. This means that many molecules of carbon dioxide, even in the solid state, possess sufficient energy to escape from the surface of the solid into the air. The vapor pressure of solid carbon dioxide equals atmospheric pressure at $-78.5°$ C. As a result, solid carbon dioxide under atmospheric pressure sublimes (changes directly into a gas) at this temperature. Liquid carbon dioxide does not exist at atmospheric pressure. At low temperatures, but with pressures higher than 5 atmospheres, carbon dioxide may be liquefied.

5. The chemical properties of carbon dioxide. Carbon dioxide is a stable gas which neither burns nor supports combustion. Burning magnesium is hot enough to decompose carbon dioxide. For that reason, a piece of burning magnesium ribbon will continue to burn in a bottle of the gas. The magnesium unites vigorously with the oxygen that is set free by the decomposition of the carbon dioxide. Carbon is produced, as the coating of soot on the inside of the bottle shows.

$$2\ Mg + CO_2 \rightarrow 2\ MgO + C$$

Carbon dioxide dissolves readily in *cold water*. Some of the dissolved molecules also unite with the water. It is the anhydride of carbonic acid. This is a weak acid which exists only in water solution. It is easily decomposed by heat as represented by the following reversible equation:

$$H_2O + CO_2 \rightleftarrows H_2CO_3$$

Fig. 17–5. A plant in which Dry Ice is manufactured. Note the cylinders of carbon dioxide, and the insulated carts in which the Dry Ice is transported within the plant.

When carbon dioxide is passed into a water solution of a hydroxide, it reacts with it and forms a carbonate.

$$2 \, NaOH + CO_2 \rightarrow Na_2CO_3 + H_2O$$

If the positive ion of the hydroxide to which the carbon dioxide is added forms an insoluble carbonate, this carbonate will be precipitated when carbon dioxide is bubbled through the hydroxide solution. Such a reaction, using limewater, a saturated solution of $Ca(OH)_2$, and precipitating white calcium carbonate, serves as a *test for carbon dioxide.*

$$Ca(OH)_2 + CO_2 \rightarrow CaCO_3\downarrow + H_2O$$

Carbon dioxide is not considered to be poisonous, but a person will die in an atmosphere of carbon dioxide because of internal suffocation due to lack of oxygen.

6. Carbon dioxide has many uses. It combines with plaster and mortar as they harden. It reacts with a compound of lead in the making of "white lead" for paint. Baking soda and washing soda are carbonates, and carbon dioxide is required for their manufacture. Strawberries and raspberries that are to be shipped long distances to market are exposed to carbon dioxide. This treatment preserves the freshness of the berries and retards the growth of molds. Some of the more important uses of carbon dioxide that are of special interest are described in Sections 7–12 which follow.

7. Carbon dioxide is necessary for photosynthesis. *Photosynthesis means "putting together by means of light."* It is the name given to the process by which green plants manufacture carbohydrate foods with the aid of sun-light. *Chlorophyll,* the green coloring matter in the leaves, acts as a catalyst. Carbon dioxide from the air and water from the soil are the raw materials. Glucose, a simple sugar, $C_6H_{12}O_6$, is formed according to the following equation:

$$6 \, CO_2 + 6 \, H_2O \xrightarrow[\substack{\text{source of} \\ \text{energy}}]{\text{sunlight as}} C_6H_{12}O_6 + 6 \, O_2\uparrow$$

The sugar is then converted into starch and stored in various parts of the plant. Plants convert some of the starch which they produce into other foods, such as proteins and oils. However, we do not yet have a complete knowledge as to how they accomplish this conversion. The importance of photosynthesis cannot be overemphasized because *the food of all living things depends upon it.*

8. Oxygen and carbon dioxide form a cycle. All plants and animals are mutually dependent on each other. Plants remove carbon dioxide from the air and return oxygen in the process of photosynthesis. Higher animals breathe in oxygen from the air in the process called *respiration,* and exhale carbon dioxide. This dual process is called the **oxygen-carbon dioxide cycle.** Plants undergo respiration too, a process sim-

Fig. 17–6. The operation of the oxygen-carbon dioxide cycle keeps the percentage of carbon dioxide in the air fairly constant.

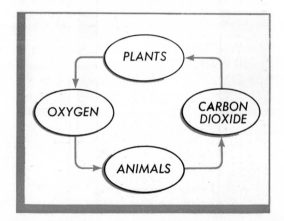

ilar to that occurring in animals, although plants have no breathing organs. However, in sunlight, the amount of carbon dioxide plants use for photosynthesis is many times greater than the amount they give off in respiration.

The large amounts of carbon dioxide which man releases to the atmosphere as a product of the combustion of carbon-containing fuels must also be counterbalanced by photosynthesis in plants. Winds keep the atmosphere mixed so that large concentrations of carbon dioxide do not build up over cities and industrial plants. The solubility of carbon dioxide in the surface waters of the earth helps to maintain a constant amount of carbon dioxide in the earth's atmosphere. If the concentration of carbon dioxide in the atmosphere temporarily becomes higher

Fig. 17-7. When a soda-acid fire extinguisher is inverted, the acid spills and reacts with the sodium hydrogen carbonate to liberate carbon dioxide.

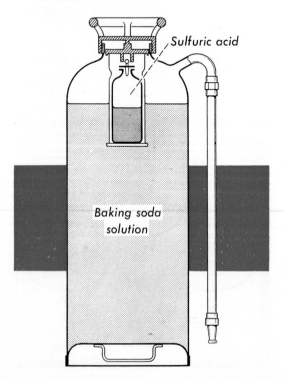

than normal, more dissolves in the surface waters. If it becomes lower than normal, carbon dioxide bubbles out of the surface waters and increases the concentration of carbon dioxide in the atmosphere.

9. Carbon dioxide is used in most fire extinguishers. In the soda-acid type of fire extinguisher shown in Fig. 17-7, about 1.5 lb of sodium hydrogen carbonate (baking soda) is dissolved in water. The small, loosely-stoppered bottle contains sulfuric acid. When such an extinguisher is inverted, the acid spills and reacts with the sodium hydrogen carbonate solution.

$$2\ NaHCO_3 + H_2SO_4 \rightarrow$$
$$Na_2SO_4 + 2\ H_2O + 2\ CO_2\uparrow$$

The pressure of the gas forces a stream of liquid a considerable distance. The carbon dioxide dissolved in the liquid is of some benefit in putting out the fire. However, the water is the principal extinguishing agent.

Liquid carbon dioxide fire extinguishers are widely used and quite efficient. The extinguisher can be carried in one hand. The valve is opened, and the flaring nozzle directs a stream of carbon dioxide "snow" against the flame. It puts out many fires very quickly. Such an extinguisher is effective against oil fires, may be used around electric switchboards, and leaves no messy residue.

In the foam type of fire extinguisher, sodium hydrogen carbonate is used to supply the carbon dioxide. A solution of aluminum sulfate, $Al_2(SO_4)_3$, which acts as an acid, is used to react with the sodium hydrogen carbonate and liberate the carbon dioxide. An extract of licorice, or some other sticky substance,

Fig. 17-8. A liquid carbon dioxide fire extinguisher is effective in putting out oil fires.

is used to prevent the escape of the gas by stabilizing the foam. The foam forms a blanket over the fire, shutting off the oxygen. Foam fire extinguishers are effective for putting out oil or gasoline fires. But they leave a frothy residue that must be cleaned up afterwards.

10. Carbonated beverages contain carbon dioxide in solution. Certain mineral springs contain considerable quantities of carbon dioxide in solution. Such springs at Vichy, France, and Seltzer, Germany, have given us the terms "Vichy" water and "Seltzer" water. Those at Saratoga Springs, New York, and Manitou Springs, Colorado, are famous.

Soft drinks are charged by forcing carbon dioxide into the beverages under increased pressure. When the bot-

tles are opened and the excess pressure is released, bubbles of carbon dioxide rapidly escape from the liquid.

Soda water in fountains is charged with carbon dioxide. The gas is forced into solution under a pressure of several atmospheres. When this beverage was first manufactured, soda (sodium carbonate) was used with an acid to produce the carbon dioxide. Hence it became known as "soda water."

11. Leavening agents produce carbon dioxide. Yeast is mixed with the flour and other ingredients in making dough for bread. The living yeast plant produces an enzyme which acts on the starches and sugars and causes fermentation. The equation for the reaction with a typical sugar, $C_6H_{12}O_6$, is:

$$C_6H_{12}O_6 \rightarrow 2\ C_2H_5OH + 2\ CO_2\uparrow$$

The bubbles of carbon dioxide which are formed by such fermentation become entangled in the plastic dough. They cause the dough to rise while they are being liberated. The alcohol, C_2H_5OH, produced by the fermentation, is vaporized and driven off during the baking process.

There are other ways of liberating carbon dioxide for use in leavening besides the use of yeast. Sour milk contains lactic acid which reacts with baking soda (sodium hydrogen carbonate) and liberates carbon dioxide. Molasses, which may be used for making cookies, contains some acids which react with baking soda, causing it to liberate carbon dioxide.

Baking powder differs from baking soda because it is always a dry mixture, not just one compound. It contains baking soda and also some powder that will form an acid when water is added. The acid compound varies with the kind of baking powder used. One type of baking powder uses a mixture of tartaric acid and cream of tartar (po-tassium hydrogen tartrate) as the acid substance. A second type uses monocalcium phosphate. A third type employs a double salt, anhydrous sodium aluminum sulfate. All three types work about equally well, although individual cooks may prefer one particular type. Dried cornstarch is used in all baking powders to keep them dry until they are used. The baking soda supplies the carbon dioxide.

12. Carbon dioxide is used as a refrigerant. Solid carbon dioxide (Dry Ice) costs more than ice for refrigeration, but is superior to ice in at least two respects: *1.* it leaves no liquid, but changes directly from a solid to a gas; and *2.* because of its low temperature, one pound of Dry Ice produces a greater cooling effect than an equal weight of ice. It is useful for shipping perishable fruits and vegetables, and for packing around ice cream that is to be delivered. The temperature of Dry Ice is so low that it must never be handled with bare hands because serious frostbite may result.

2. CARBON MONOXIDE

13. Carbon monoxide may contaminate the air we breathe. Normal air does not contain carbon monoxide. But there are several ways by which this poisonous gas may get into the air which we breathe. If a coal fire is not properly banked and the furnace door is left open, carbon monoxide may escape. It then mixes with the air in living or sleeping rooms. Carbon monoxide is one of the components of some fuel gases. Leaking gas lines are dangerous because of the fire hazard as well as the poisonous nature of the gas. Carbon monoxide is present in the exhaust of an automobile. Therefore, you should never leave the engine of an automobile running in a closed garage. Likewise, the engine of an automobile should not be kept running to provide heat to a car parked in cool weather with the windows closed. The facts that carbon monoxide has no odor and induces drowsiness before actual asphyxiation make it very hazardous. The air in city streets where automobile traffic is heavy may contain considerable amounts of this gas. Air containing as little as one part of carbon monoxide per thousand parts of air will produce nausea and headache in less than an hour if such polluted air is breathed. One part of carbon monoxide in one hundred parts of air may produce fatal results in ten minutes.

14. Preparation of carbon monoxide. Several methods are used for the preparation of this gas.

1. By reducing carbon dioxide. When carbon burns, carbon dioxide is formed. If this gas comes into contact with white-hot carbon or coke, it is reduced to carbon monoxide. The equations are:

$$C + O_2 \rightarrow CO_2\uparrow$$
$$CO_2 + C \rightarrow 2\ CO\uparrow$$

2. By action of steam on hot coke. We have already learned in Chapter 8 that passing steam over red-hot coke produces a mixture of carbon monoxide and hydrogen called *water gas*. This is an industrial method of producing carbon monoxide for use as a fuel gas.

$$C + H_2O \rightarrow CO\uparrow + H_2\uparrow$$

3. By decomposing formic acid. This is the usual laboratory method for preparing carbon monoxide. Formic acid has the formula, HCOOH. If formic acid is allowed to trickle, a drop at a time, into hot, concentrated sulfuric acid, carbon monoxide is produced as each drop strikes the hot acid (see Fig. 17-10). Concentrated sulfuric acid is an excellent dehydrating agent. It removes a molecule of water from each molecule of the formic acid. Removal of water from the formic acid molecule leaves only carbon monoxide, CO.

$$HCOOH \rightarrow H_2O + CO\uparrow$$

CAUTION: When using this method, always be sure the connections are tight so that the carbon monoxide does not escape into the room.

Fig. 17-9. Carbon monoxide is produced by the reduction of carbon dioxide in a coal stove.

Fig. 17-10. Carbon monoxide can be prepared in the laboratory by dehydrating formic acid with concentrated sulfuric acid.

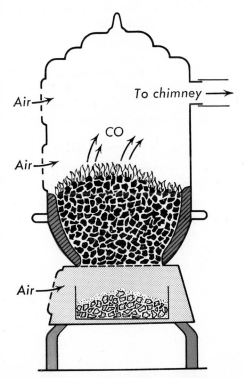

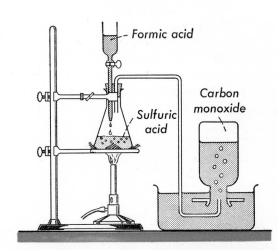

15. The physical properties of carbon monoxide. Carbon monoxide is a colorless, odorless, tasteless gas. It is very slightly less dense than air, is only slightly soluble in water, and is a rather difficult gas to liquefy. Carbon monoxide is not readily adsorbed by activated carbon. Hence, a gas mask affords no protection against the gas unless a special canister is used. These special canisters contain activated carbon which has been treated with certain oxides that oxidize the carbon monoxide to carbon dioxide.

16. The chemical properties of carbon monoxide. Carbon monoxide burns with a blue flame. Probably you have seen this blue flame above a coal fire just after a fresh supply of coal has been added. Carbon monoxide unites with oxygen so readily at high temperatures that it can take oxygen from oxide ores. Thus it is a very good reducing agent.

17. The physiological action of carbon monoxide. This gas is poisonous because it unites very readily with hemoglobin (*hee*-moh-gloh-bin). *Hemoglobin* is the red substance in blood that serves as an oxygen carrier. If the hemoglobin unites with carbon monoxide, it is not available for carrying oxygen. When sufficient carbon monoxide has been breathed, the person collapses because of oxygen starvation. The compound formed by carbon monoxide and hemoglobin is so stable that even artificial respiration is not too successful. Blood transfusions, which supply fresh hemoglobin in the veins of the patient may help. Autopsies performed on the bodies of those who have been killed by carbon monoxide reveal a peculiar red color in the blood of the victims. By this color, physicians can recognize the cause of death.

18. The uses of carbon monoxide. Carbon monoxide has three important uses.

1. As a reducing agent. In the extraction of iron, copper, and some other metals from their ores, carbon monoxide is used. It acts as a reducing agent on the hot oxides, leaving the metal uncombined. Here is a typical equation:

$$Fe_2O_3 + 3\ CO \rightarrow 2\ Fe + 3\ CO_2\uparrow$$

Our most useful heavy metals are obtained by such reactions.

2. As a fuel. Many of our fuel gases contain carbon monoxide mixed with other combustible gases. Manufactured gas, either coal gas or water gas, always contains carbon monoxide. It makes a very good fuel.

3. For making methanol. Methanol, CH_3OH, is made by synthesis from carbon monoxide and hydrogen. Under pressure the two gases unite when a mixture of zinc oxide and copper is used as a catalyst. The equation is:

$$CO + 2\ H_2 \rightarrow CH_3OH$$

Methanol has many uses, among which are its use in antifreeze for automobiles, and in the manufacture of formaldehyde.

Summary

Carbon dioxide is present in the air, although only in small amounts, because it is a product of decay, of combustion, and of the breathing of animals. Carbon dioxide can be prepared: *1.* by burning carbon or carbon compounds; *2.* by heating a carbonate; *3.* by fermentation of molasses; or *4.* by the action of an acid on a carbonate.

Carbon dioxide is a dense, colorless gas which is moderately soluble in water. Its water solution is carbonic acid. It is a stable gas that does not burn.

Carbon dioxide has several important uses: *1.* by plants during photosynthesis; *2.* in fire extinguishers; *3.* in carbonated beverages; *4.* as a leavening agent; and *5.* as Dry Ice in refrigeration.

Carbon monoxide can be prepared by the reduction of carbon dioxide, and by heating formic acid with concentrated sulfuric acid, which acts as a dehydrating agent. Carbon monoxide is a colorless, odorless, tasteless gas which is exceedingly poisonous. It burns with a blue flame.

The exhaust gases from an automobile engine always contain some carbon monoxide. For this reason an automobile engine should never be left running in a closed garage. The carbon monoxide unites with the hemoglobin of the blood, and the person dies from oxygen starvation.

Carbon monoxide is used as a fuel, since it is one of the components of coal gas and water gas. It is used as a reducing agent in the extraction of iron, copper, and other metals from their ores. Large quantities of carbon monoxide are used for making methanol.

Test yourself on these terms

decay	fermentation	photosynthesis
Dry Ice	leavening agent	respiration
enzyme	oxygen-carbon dioxide cycle	sublime

Questions

Group A

1. Why is carbon dioxide one of the important gases in the atmosphere when it occurs to only 0.04% by volume?
2. (*a*) What are the three commercial methods for preparing carbon dioxide? (*b*) What is the usual laboratory method? (*c*) Write balanced chemical equations for these methods of preparation.
3. What difficulties are experienced when collecting carbon dioxide: (*a*) by water displacement; (*b*) by air displacement?
4. How does a liquid carbon dioxide fire extinguisher put out fires?
5. What advantages does Dry Ice have over ice from water as a refrigerant?
6. What are the chemical properties of carbon dioxide?
7. What is the test for carbon dioxide?

8. (a) How is carbonic acid made? (b) Is it a strong acid?
9. (a) What part does carbon dioxide play in the oxygen-carbon dioxide cycle? (b) What is the function of the oxygen?
10. Write a balanced equation for the reaction which occurs when a soda-acid fire extinguisher is discharged.
11. (a) What is the source of carbon dioxide in most leavening agents? (b) How is it released?
12. What are the sources of carbon monoxide which contaminate the atmosphere?
13. What is the function of sulfuric acid in the preparation of carbon monoxide from formic acid?
14. What are three uses of carbon monoxide?

Group B

15. Explain the part that the earth's surface waters play in regulating the carbon dioxide content of the atmosphere.
16. Why is carbon dioxide more dense than air?
17. What physical property of a solid determines whether it will sublime or melt when heated?
18. Does magnesium ribbon actually burn in carbon dioxide? Explain.
19. What is the function of an enzyme?
20. Distinguish between baking soda and baking powder.
21. Why does carbon dioxide diffuse more slowly than oxygen or hydrogen?
22. Can carbon monoxide be prepared by direct union of the elements? Explain.
23. Both carbon dioxide and carbon monoxide will produce asphyxiation. Do they act on the body in the same manner or differently? Explain.
24. When a bottle of limewater is left unstoppered, a white ring is formed on the inside of the bottle at the surface of the liquid. Explain its cause, and tell how it can be removed.

roblems

Group A

1. How many grams of ferric oxide can be reduced by 56 g of carbon monoxide, according to the following equation:

$$Fe_2O_3 + 3\,CO \rightarrow 2\,Fe + 3\,CO_2\uparrow$$

2. Calculate the amount of iron produced in Problem 1.
3. What will be the volume of carbon dioxide at S.T.P. which is liberated in the reaction of Problem 1?
4. How much sulfuric acid is required to react with 1 kg of baking soda in a soda-acid fire extinguisher, according to the following equation:

$$2\,NaHCO_3 + H_2SO_4 \rightarrow Na_2SO_4 + 2\,H_2O + 2\,CO_2\uparrow$$

5. Calculate the volume of carbon dioxide at S.T.P. liberated during the discharge of the fire extinguisher of Problem 4.

Group B

6. How many grams of carbon monoxide can be obtained by the dehydration of 38 g of formic acid by sulfuric acid?
7. How many liters of carbon monoxide will be produced in Problem 6? The temperature is 27° C and the barometer reading is 750 mm.
8. What volume of carbon dioxide will be produced by the combustion of the carbon monoxide of Problem 7 if the product is restored to 27° C and 750 mm pressure?
9. It is desired to prepare five liters of dry carbon dioxide at 17° C and 740 mm pressure by the reaction between calcium carbonate and hydrochloric acid. How many grams of calcium carbonate will be required?
10. What weight of HCl is required for the reaction of Problem 9?

Some things for you to do

1. Fill a wide-mouth bottle with carbon dioxide and "pour" it over a candle flame. This shows two properties of carbon dioxide.
2. Siphon carbon dioxide gas from a large, elevated jar of the gas into a lower receiver. Use a rubber tube just as if you were siphoning water. When you estimate that the lower jar is full of carbon dioxide, prove it by pouring the gas over a candle flame.
3. Test a collection of minerals to find out which ones are carbonates. Add a drop of concentrated hydrochloric acid to the mineral samples. Carbonates will give off bubbles of gas.
4. Make some baking powder from 5 g baking soda, 10 g cream of tartar, and 3 g cornstarch. Add a pinch of dried egg albumin and mix the powders thoroughly in a mortar. Test it to see if it "works" by adding water to some of the powder in a dry beaker. The egg albumin makes the bubbles more lasting. (For baking purposes, a more accurate mixture of the chemicals is necessary.)
5. Prepare a report on methods used to ventilate long vehicular tunnels such as the Lincoln Tunnel under the Hudson River at New York City.
6. Compare the labels on various brands of baking powder to determine their components. What similarities and what differences do you find?

Chapter 18 HYDROCARBONS

1. There are many carbon compounds. The number of carbon compounds seems to be almost unlimited. More than 700,000 have been listed, and many new ones are being added each year. In this chapter we shall study only a very few compounds which are basic to an understanding of organic chemistry. In Unit 15, other organic compounds important in everyday life will be discussed.

The reasons for the existence of so many carbon compounds are: *1. Carbon atoms link together with covalent bonds.* In Chapter 16, we learned that carbon atoms readily form covalent bonds with other carbon atoms. This makes possible the existence of compounds in which as many as 70 carbon atoms are bonded together one after another to form a long chain. Some compounds are basically a long chain of carbon atoms, but have groups of other carbon atoms as side chains attached to the main chain. Other carbon compounds have carbon atoms linked together to form rings. Still others may consist of several such rings joined together. Not only are carbon atoms linked by single covalent bonds, but they are sometimes linked by double or triple covalent bonds.

2. The same atoms may be arranged in several different ways. One of the substances present in gasoline is an organic compound called *octane.* Its mo-

VOCABULARY

Cracking. A process of breaking down complex organic molecules by the action of heat or a catalyst or both.

Homologous series. A series of similar compounds which conform to a general formula.

Hydrocarbon. A compound consisting of only carbon and hydrogen.

Isomer. One of two or more compounds having the same composition, but different structure.

Structural formula. A formula which indicates kind, number, arrangement, and valence bonds of the atoms in a molecule.

lecular formula is C_8H_{18}, so a molecule of octane consists of 8 carbon atoms and 18 hydrogen atoms. Using an electron-dot formula, and remembering that the valence of carbon is 4 while that of hydrogen is 1, we write the straight-chain structure for an octane molecule:

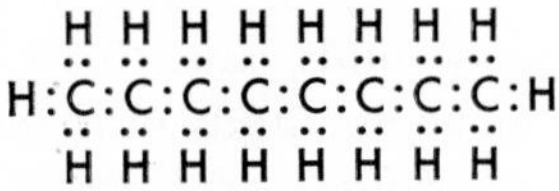

$$
\begin{array}{c}
\text{H H H H H H H H} \\
\text{H:C:C:C:C:C:C:C:C:H} \\
\text{H H H H H H H H}
\end{array}
$$

But there are other ways in which these same atoms can be arranged. For instance, here are three branched-chain formulas:

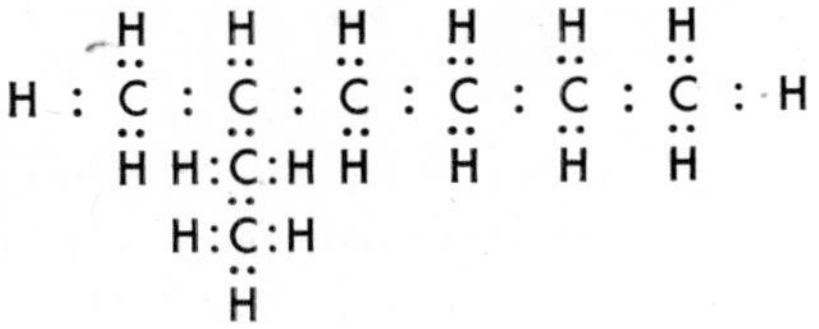

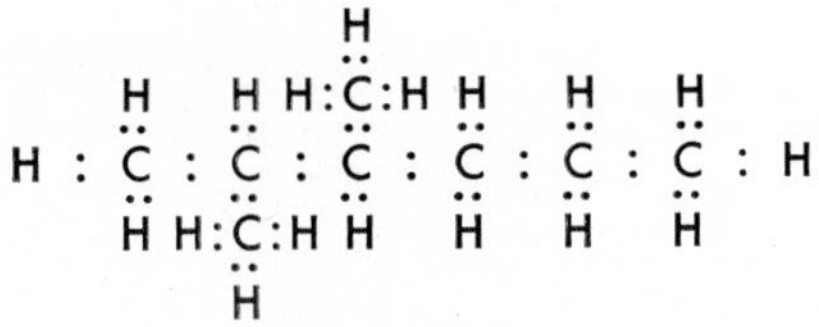

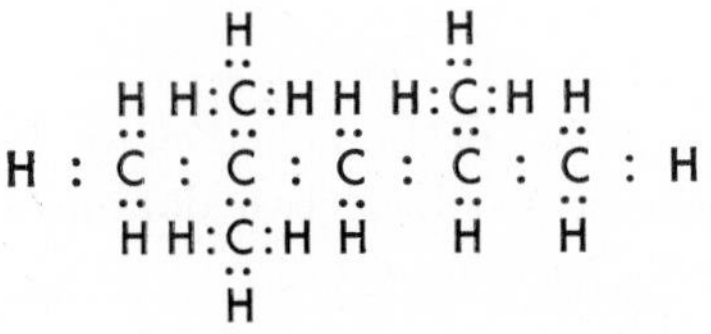

These are all arrangements of 8 carbon atoms and 18 hydrogen atoms in which each carbon atom shares four electrons and each hydrogen atom shares one electron. In addition to these four structures for octane, there are 14 others, making a total of 18 possible structures for octane. While they each have the same composition, the different arrangements of the atoms in the molecules gives each molecule slightly dif-

ferent properties. Thus each of these molecular arrangements represents a separate chemical compound. *These different compounds, all with the same composition but with different structures, are called* **isomers.**

2. Structural formulas are widely used for organic compounds. The formula H_2SO_4 for sulfuric acid is satisfactory for most purposes in inorganic chemistry. But a molecular formula such as C_8H_{18} is not at all satisfactory for organic chemistry. We have already learned that there are 18 different compounds with this same formula. In order to indicate clearly the particular isomer with which the organic chemist is dealing, he uses a *structural formula. Such a formula not only indicates what kinds of atoms and how many of each, but also indicates how they are arranged in the molecule.* We have already used electron-dot formulas in this chapter to illustrate the isomers of octane. However, electron-dot formulas are tedious to draw for routine equation work, so the organic chemist frequently substitutes a dash $(-)$ for the pair of shared electrons forming a covalent bond. Using the dash, he can represent the straight-chain structural formula for octane as:

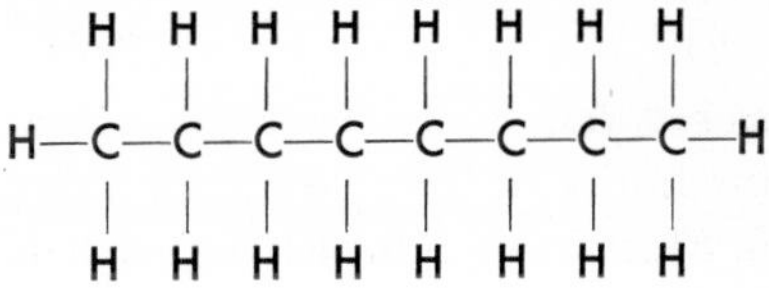

$$
\begin{array}{c}
\text{H H H H H H H H} \\
\text{| | | | | | | |} \\
\text{H—C—C—C—C—C—C—C—C—H} \\
\text{| | | | | | | |} \\
\text{H H H H H H H H}
\end{array}
$$

When we write structural formulas we must be careful to leave no dangling valence bonds. Each dash must represent an electron pair which forms the covalent bond linking two atoms. Carbon atoms must have four valence bonds. (The only exception to this statement that we shall meet in high school chemistry is the structural formula for carbon monoxide. See Chapter 6, Section 15.)

3. There are several striking differences between organic and inorganic compounds. The basic laws of chemistry hold true equally for organic chemistry as well as inorganic chemistry. The behavior of organic compounds, and the reactions between organic chemicals, however, show some differences from those of the inorganic compounds. Some of the differences are as follows:

1. Most organic compounds do not dissolve in water. The majority of inorganic compounds do dissolve more or less readily in water. Organic compounds generally dissolve in such organic liquids as alcohol, chloroform, ether, carbon disulfide, or carbon tetrachloride.

2. Organic compounds are decomposed by heat more easily than most inorganic compounds. The decomposition (charring) of sugar when it is heated moderately is familiar. Such charring on heating is often a test for organic substances. But an inorganic compound, such as common salt (sodium chloride), can be vaporized at a red heat without decomposition.

3. Organic reactions proceed at much slower rates. Such reactions often require hours or even days for completion. Most inorganic reactions occur almost as soon as the reactants are brought together in water.

4. Organic compounds exist as molecules consisting of atoms joined by covalent bonds. Many inorganic compounds have ionic structures.

4. The several series of hydrocarbons. *Hydrocarbons,* as the name suggests, *are compounds composed of only two elements—hydrogen and carbon.* Any study of organic compounds must begin with a study of the hydrocarbons, because they have the basic structures from which other organic compounds are derived. There are a tremendous number of hydrocarbons. But they can be grouped into several different series of compounds, and this grouping helps to make our study of them easier.

1. The *alkanes* (al-*kaynes*), sometimes called the paraffin series, are straight- or branched-chain hydrocarbons in which the carbon atoms are connected by only single covalent bonds.

2. The alkenes (al-*keens*), sometimes called the olefin series, are straight- or branched-chain hydrocarbons in which two carbon atoms in the molecule are connected by a double covalent bond.

3. The *alkynes* (al-*kynes*), sometimes called the acetylene series, are straight- or branched-chain hydrocarbons in which two carbon atoms in the molecule are connected by a triple covalent bond.

4. The *alkadienes* (al-kah-*dy*-eens) are straight- or branched-chain hydrocarbons which have two double bonds between carbon atoms.

5. The *aromatic hydrocarbons* have alternating single and double covalent bonds in six-membered carbon rings.

5. The alkane series of hydrocarbons. This series is sometimes called the *paraffin series.* The word "paraffin" means little affinity. The members of this series show little affinity to react with other chemicals because only single covalent bonds are present in their molecules. Hydrocarbons in which only single covalent bonds occur are *satu-*

rated hydrocarbons. Paraffin wax is a mixture of hydrocarbons of this series. The following table lists a few of the members of the alkane series. Notice that the name of each member ends in *-ane,* the same as the name of the series, alk*ane.*

NAME	FOR-MULA	STATE AT 20° C
METHANE	CH_4	gas
ETHANE	C_2H_6	gas
PROPANE	C_3H_8	gas
BUTANE	C_4H_{10}	gas
PENTANE	C_5H_{12}	liquid
HEXANE	C_6H_{14}	liquid
HEPTANE	C_7H_{16}	liquid
OCTANE	C_8H_{18}	liquid
NONANE	C_9H_{20}	liquid
DECANE	$C_{10}H_{22}$	liquid
* * * * * * * *		
EICOSANE	$C_{20}H_{42}$	solid
* * * * * * * *		
HEXACONTANE	$C_{60}H_{122}$	solid

The structural formulas for the first four members of the alkane series are:

Methane   Ethane

Propane   Butane

An examination of these formulas as well as those in the table shows that one member of the series differs from the preceding one by the group

Fig. 18–1. Propane, butane, or a mixture of both of these gases, is supplied to rural homes for use as a fuel gas.

These compounds are said to belong to an *homologous series*. It is not necessary to remember the formula of each member of an homologous series because we can make a general formula, such as C_nH_{2n+2} for the alkanes. Suppose a member of this series has 30 carbon atoms. We find the number of hydrogen atoms by multiplying 30 by 2, and then adding 2. The formula becomes $C_{30}H_{62}$.

6. Methane is the first member of the alkane series. When organic compounds decay under water, methane is formed. It occurs in coal mines, where it is known by miners as *firedamp*. It forms about 90% of natural gas. Methane is liberated when the mud at the bottom of stagnant pools is stirred. Hence, another common name for methane is *marsh gas*. Methane can be made in the laboratory by heating soda lime (which contains sodium hydroxide) and sodium acetate. The equation is:

$$NaC_2H_3O_2 + NaOH \rightarrow CH_4\uparrow + Na_2CO_3$$

Commercially, methane is obtained from natural gas.

Methane burns with a bluish flame.

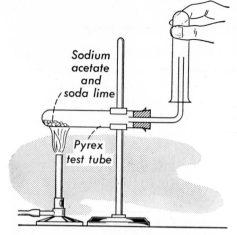

Fig. 18–3. A small quantity of methane can be prepared in the laboratory by heating a mixture of sodium acetate and soda lime.

It is used as a fuel in those places where natural gas is abundant.

$$CH_4 + 2\ O_2 \rightarrow CO_2\uparrow + 2\ H_2O\uparrow$$

Methane reacts with such halogens as chlorine or bromine to form *substitution products*. An atom of a halogen is substituted for an atom of hydrogen. For example:

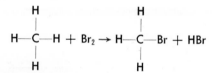

Fig. 18–2. Natural gas, which is about 90% methane, is piped long distances from the gas fields to the consumer. Pumping stations like the one shown are located at intervals along the pipe lines. They house huge compressors which keep the gas moving through the pipe lines.

By using more molecules of halogen, an atom of halogen may be substituted for each of the atoms of hydrogen.

7. Ethene (ethylene) is the first member of the alkene series. The alkenes are characterized by a double valence bond between two carbon atoms. Consequently, the simplest alkene must have two carbon atoms. Its structural formula is:

$$\begin{array}{ccc} H & & H \\ \diagdown & & \diagup \\ & C=C & \\ \diagup & & \diagdown \\ H & & H \end{array}$$

and its name is ethene. The names of the alkenes are derived from the names of the alkanes with the same number of carbon atoms by merely substituting the suffix -*ene* for the suffix -*ane*. Since eth*ane* is the alk*ane* with two carbon atoms, the alk*ene* with two carbon atoms will be named *ethene*. However, this substance is also commonly called *ethylene*. The general formula for the alkenes is C_nH_{2n}.

Alkenes are made from petroleum by *cracking*. **Cracking** *is a process by which complex organic molecules are broken up into simpler molecules by the action of heat and usually a catalyst.* Ethylene may be prepared in the laboratory by dehydrating ethyl alcohol. Hot sulfuric acid is used as the dehydrating agent.

$$C_2H_5OH \rightarrow C_2H_4\uparrow + H_2O$$

An organic compound which has a double valence bond between two carbon atoms is said to be *unsaturated,* because it is possible to add directly other atoms chemically to its molecule to form a new compound. For example, two bromine atoms may be added directly to ethylene to form 1,2-dibromoethane.

$$\begin{array}{ccccc} H & & H & & Br\ \ Br \\ \diagdown & & \diagup & & |\ \ \ | \\ & C=C & & +\ Br_2 \rightarrow H-C-C-H \\ \diagup & & \diagdown & & |\ \ \ | \\ H & & H & & H\ \ \ H \end{array}$$

It is impossible to add just one bromine atom, but two of them can be added. It seems obvious that as the double bond between the carbon atoms breaks, there is one valence bond available for each bromine atom.

Fig. 18–4. A cracking unit in a petroleum refinery. Many useful hydrocarbons, such as ethylene and butadiene, are produced by cracking petroleum.

The name of the product 1,2-dibromoethane is easily derived. The basic part of the name, *ethane,* is that of the alkane with 2 carbon atoms to which this molecule is structurally related. *Dibromo-* means 2 bromine atoms have been substituted for hydrogen atoms in ethane. *1,2-* means that one bromine atom is bonded to the first carbon atom and one bromine atom is bonded to the second carbon atom. An isomer, 1,1-dibromoethane has the structural formula

$$\begin{array}{ccc} Br & H \\ | & | \\ H-C-C-H \\ | & | \\ Br & H \end{array}$$

Ethylene is a colorless gas that burns with a bright flame. Quantities of ethylene are used for making ethyl alcohol. It is also used to make ethylene glycol, $C_2H_4(OH)_2$, a liquid which boils at a rather high temperature. Ethylene glycol is used as an antifreeze in automobile radiators. If present in the air in even minute quantities, ethylene destroys chlorophyll. For that reason, it is used in yellowing bananas, oranges, lemons, and other citrus fruits. It is useful, too, for blanching celery. An ethylene-oxygen mixture may be used as an anesthetic.

8. Ethyne (acetylene) is the first member of the alkyne series. The alkynes are characterized by a triple valence bond between two carbon atoms. The simplest alkyne must therefore have two carbon atoms and has the structural formula

$$H-C\equiv C-H$$

The names of the alkynes are derived from the names of the alkanes with the same number of carbon atoms by substituting the suffix -*yne* for -*ane.* Hence

the name of the simplest alkyne is *ethyne,* but this compound is more commonly known as *acetylene.* The general formula for the alkynes is C_nH_{2n-2}.

Acetylene, a colorless gas, may be prepared by the action of water on calcium carbide,

$$CaC_2 + 2 H_2O \rightarrow C_2H_2\uparrow + Ca(OH)_2$$

or by cracking alkanes by passing them through an electric arc.

$$2 CH_4 \rightarrow C_2H_2\uparrow + 3 H_2\uparrow$$

Acetylene is more unsaturated than ethylene because of the triple bond. It is possible chemically to add to an acetylene molecule two molecules of bromine to form 1,1,2,2-tetrabromoethane.

$$H-C\equiv C-H + 2 Br_2 \rightarrow \begin{array}{ccc} Br & Br \\ | & | \\ H-C-C-H \\ | & | \\ Br & Br \end{array}$$

Acetylene is extensively used in the synthesis of complex organic compounds in addition to its use in the oxyacetylene torch.

9. Butadiene is an important alkadiene. Alkadienes have two double bonds in each molecule. The -*ene* suffix indicates a double bond. The -*diene* suffix indicates two double bonds. The names of the alkadienes are derived in a manner similar to those of the other hydrocarbon series. Butadiene must, therefore, have four carbon atoms and contain two double bonds in its molecule. The structural formula is

$$\begin{array}{cccc} H & H & H & H \\ \diagdown & | & | & \diagup \\ C=C-C=C \\ \diagup & & & \diagdown \\ H & & & H \end{array}$$

Actually this is 1,3-butadiene, since the double bonds follow the first and third carbon atoms, but 1,2-butadiene, its isomer, is so uncommon that 1,3-butadiene is commonly called simply butadiene.

Butadiene is prepared by cracking petroleum fractions containing butane. It is used extensively in the manufacture of GR–S rubber, the most common type of synthetic rubber.

10. Benzene is the best-known aromatic hydrocarbon. Benzene has the molecular formula C_6H_6 and is represented by the structural formula

$$
\begin{array}{ccc}
& H & & H \\
& | & & | \\
& C & & C \\
\end{array}
$$

This formula shows that the bonds in benzene are not single bonds or double bonds, but each bond is a resonance hybrid bond (see Chapter 7, Section 27). All the carbon-carbon bonds in the molecule are equivalent. As a result, benzene and other aromatic hydrocarbons do not show the property of unsaturation to the extent that the alkenes do.

Because of the complexity of writing the single and double bonds when drawing the structural formula of benzene, the benzene ring is usually abbreviated as

Benzene is prepared commercially by the distillation of coal tar. It is a flammable liquid that is used as a solvent, and as a starting point in the manufacture of other chemicals, principally dyes, drugs, and explosives.

11. Other aromatic hydrocarbons. More complex hydrocarbons related to benzene have side chains leading off from the ring, as is the case with toluene. Toluene is obtained from coal tar or petroleum.

Naphthalene, $C_{10}H_8$, is a coal tar product which crystallizes in white shining scales. It is the largest single constituent of coal tar, sometimes occurring in quantities as high as 6%. The naphthalene molecule has a structure corresponding to two benzene rings joined together as shown below.

Naphthalene may be used, either as flakes or molded into balls, to kill

Fig. 18–5. A convenient method of preparing a small quantity of acetylene in the laboratory.

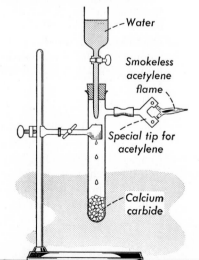

clothes moths that attack woolen garments. If used in sufficient amount in
a sealed closet or tightly closed chest,
the vapors of naphthalene are quite effective for this purpose. Naphthalene is
also used as a raw material for the manufacture of some resins and dyes.

Anthracene, $C_{14}H_{10}$, has a structure
like three benzene rings joined together.

Like naphthalene, it forms a whole
series of hydrocarbons that differ from
the compounds related to benzene in
that there is more than one ring. An-

thracene is used to prepare alizarin, a
well-known red dye.

Turpentine, $C_{10}H_{16}$, is a hydrocarbon with a complex ring structure. It
is obtained by distillation from the
longleaf pine tree. Turpentine is used
in large amounts as a thinner for
paints. It makes the paint spread more
easily and also causes it to penetrate
the wood better.

Asphalt consists chiefly of a mixture
of hydrocarbons of complex structure.
Large deposits of asphalt occur in
Texas, Oklahoma, and Utah. It is also
found on the island of Trinidad. Asphalt is used for paving streets. Petroleum pitch is often substituted for natural asphalt.

 ummary

The number of carbon compounds seems to be almost unlimited. The
great number of carbon compounds is due: 1. to the ability of carbon atoms
to join other carbon atoms forming chains or rings; and 2. to the existence of
isomers. Isomers have the same composition, but a different arrangement of
the atoms in the molecule. Structural formulas show us what atoms are present
and also how they are linked together in the molecule.

Organic compounds are, for the most part, not soluble in water, and many
of them are decomposed by heat. Organic compounds exist as molecules
consisting of atoms joined by covalent bonds, while many inorganic compounds have ionic structures. Organic reactions proceed at much slower rates
than inorganic reactions.

Hydrocarbons are compounds of carbon and hydrogen. Methane is the first
in a long series of saturated hydrocarbons known as the alkanes. Methane is
obtained from natural gas. The alkanes show little tendency to react with
other chemicals. Ethylene is the simplest of the alkenes, the hydrocarbons with
a double valence bond between two carbon atoms. Ethylene is an unsaturated
hydrocarbon which is made from petroleum by cracking. Cracking is a process
by which complex organic molecules are broken up into simpler molecules by
the action of heat and usually a catalyst. Acetylene is the first member of the
alkyne series, the series characterized by a triple valence bond between two
carbon atoms. Butadiene is an important alkadiene used in the manufacture
of one type of synthetic rubber. Benzene is a ring compound. It is obtained
commercially by distilling coal tar. Naphthalene has a structure corresponding
to two benzene rings joined together. It is also a coal tar product, and is used
as a moth preventive. Anthracene has a structure like three benzene rings
joined together. It is used in the preparation of certain dyestuffs.

Test yourself on these terms

acetylene series aromatic hydrocarbon paraffin series
alkadiene homologous series saturated
alkane hydrocarbon structural formula
alkene isomer substitution product
alkyne olefin series unsaturated

Questions

Group A

1. Give two reasons for the existence of so many carbon compounds.
2. What does a dash (—) represent in a structural formula?
3. What information do you obtain from a properly written structural formula?
4. (a) How is methane produced in nature? (b) In the laboratory?
5. How are alkenes produced from petroleum?
6. What are two uses for acetylene?
7. What do the terms *saturated* and *unsaturated* mean when applied to hydrocarbons?
8. Why must calcium carbide be sold in air-tight metal cans?
9. How are naphthalene and anthracene related structurally to benzene?
10. Name the five main series of hydrocarbons and describe the bonding in each.

Group B

11. Give four important differences between organic and inorganic compounds.
12. What are the general formulas for: (a) the alkane series; (b) the alkene series; (c) the alkyne series?
13. A hydrocarbon contains 6 carbon atoms. Give its empirical formula if it is: (a) an alkane; (b) an alkene; (c) an alkyne.
14. Draw structural formulas for the three isomers of pentane.
15. Beyond the first four members of the alkane series, how are the hydrocarbons of this series named?
16. Write a balanced formula equation for the complete combustion of: (a) methane; (b) ethylene; (c) acetylene.
17. (a) What is resonance? (b) Using structural formulas explain the resonance in the benzene molecule. (c) Is a double bond in a benzene molecule the same as a double bond in an ethylene molecule?
18. Draw a structural formula for 2,2-dichloropropane.

Some things for you to do

1. Take six paper clips and link them together, first in a straight chain, and then in a shorter chain with branch side chains. See how many different ways

you can link the paper clips together, simulating the linkages of carbon atoms in the different isomers of hexane. There are five different isomers of hexane.

2. Collect some marsh gas, which is principally methane, from the decaying vegetation along the shore of a pond, stream, or lake. Fill a bottle under water, hold it inverted and insert a funnel in the neck of the bottle to direct bubbles of gas up into the water-filled bottle. Use a stick to stir up some dead leaves at the bottom of the pond, and catch the bubbles of gas, as they rise, in the bottle. When you have a bottle full of the gas, test its combustibility with a match. Bring a full bottle of the marsh gas to class and demonstrate its combustibility.

Check your progress in chemistry

1. What type of bonding occurs in the oxides of carbon and in the hydrocarbons?

2. What is the significance of a balanced formula equation?

3. Define: (*a*) molecular weight; (*b*) formula weight; (*c*) gram-molecular weight; (*d*) gram-formula weight; (*e*) mole.

4. What two scientific laws are sometimes included with Boyle's Law and Charles' Law as the Gas Laws?

5. How do you identify: (*a*) weight-weight problems; (*b*) weight-volume problems; (*c*) volume-volume problems?

6. (*a*) Why do carbon atoms join together in chains and rings? (*b*) Do any other elements of Group IVA of the Periodic Table behave in similar fashion?

7. How does the crystal structure of graphite explain the desirability of this material as a lubricant?

8. What industrial uses are there for diamonds?

9. (*a*) What type of composition reaction is carried out in an electric furnace? (*b*) Name several compounds produced by this type of reaction.

10. (*a*) List the forms of amorphous carbon. (*b*) What is the source of each? (*c*) By what process is each prepared?

11. Why does carbon dioxide sometimes collect in low-lying regions, at the bottom of mine shafts, or in dry wells?

12. A lime kiln produces 5600 kilograms of quicklime, CaO, daily by heating limestone, $CaCO_3$. What volume of carbon dioxide is also produced each day?

13. From the formulas CO_2 and CO, calculate the weight of one liter of carbon dioxide and carbon monoxide respectively.

14. You are given four wide-mouth bottles each containing a colorless gas. If one bottle contains oxygen, another hydrogen, a third carbon dioxide, and a fourth carbon monoxide, what tests will enable you to distinguish them?

15. Explain the oxygen-carbon dioxide cycle.

16. Calculate the molecular weight of propane.

17. What is the weight of one liter of ethylene at S.T.P.?

18. When burned completely, decane, $C_{10}H_{22}$, forms carbon dioxide and water vapor. Write the chemical equation.
19. Draw structural formulas for three isomers of trichloropentane.
20. Give examples of organic and inorganic compounds which illustrate the four main differences between these two types of compounds.

Challenging your knowledge

1. Forty milliliters of dry carbon dioxide is collected over mercury at 20° C and 740 mm barometric pressure. The mercury level in the eudiometer is 20 mm above that outside. What weight of calcium carbonate was required to generate this gas?
2. The element which appears in the greatest number of compounds is hydrogen. The element forming the second greatest number of compounds is carbon. Why are there more hydrogen compounds than carbon compounds?
3. Why are so many organic compounds insoluble in water but readily soluble in a liquid like benzene?
4. Draw structural formulas for each of the 18 isomers of octane.
5. What will be the weight of one liter of butane vapor at S.T.P.?
6. How do you account for the fact that the water from certain mineral springs is carbonated in nature?

UNIT 6

IONIZATION

The theory of ionization, one of the great theories of modern chemistry, is concerned with the properties of solutions. Like other theories in science, it has been modified and reorganized as scientists have gained knowledge through its application.

In the picture above you see some of the apparatus used in handling and measuring quantities of solutions. The familiar properties of many substances in the home and the laboratory are those of solutions of these substances. The theory of ionization helps us understand the nature of solutions and the differences in their properties.

Five chapters are included in this unit: *Solution and Crystallization; The Theory of Ionization; Acids, Bases, and Salts; Chemical Equilibrium;* and *Oxidation-Reduction Reactions.* You will gain an understanding of the solution process and the nature of solutions by mastering these chapters.

Chapter 19 SOLUTION AND CRYSTALLIZATION

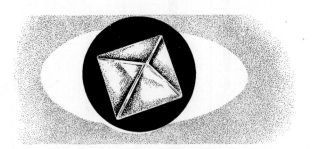

1. PROPERTIES OF SOLUTIONS

1. What is the nature of solutions? Let us drop a lump of sugar into a beaker of water. We observe that the lump of sugar gradually disappears. It is said to dissolve in the water. We may carefully examine the water with a microscope, but we are not able to see the dissolved sugar. We may add more sugar and it, too, will dissolve. But if we continue to add sugar, ultimately we reach a point where the sugar no longer will disappear into the water.

By tasting the liquid, we can tell that the sugar is still present in the water. The molecules of sugar have become mixed with the molecules of water. Eventually we can taste the same degree of sweetness in all parts of the water. We see that we have prepared a mixture of molecules of sugar and water known as a *solution*.

In general terms, *a solution is a ho-*

VOCABULARY

Deliquescence del-i-*kwes*-ens). The property of certain substances to take up water from the air to form a solution.

Effervescence (ef-er-*ves*-ens). The rapid escape of a gas from a liquid in which it was dissolved.

Efflorescence (ef-lo-*res*-ens). The property of hydrated crystals to lose water of hydration when exposed to the air.

Hygroscopic (hy-gro-*skop*-ik). Absorbing and retaining moisture from the atmosphere.

Immiscible (i-*mis*-i-b'l). Not capable of being mixed.

Miscible (*mis*-i-b'l). Capable of being mixed.

Solubility. The amount of solute dissolved in a given amount of solvent at equilibrium, under specified conditions.

Solute. The dissolved substance in a solution.

Solution. A homogeneous mixture of two or more substances, the composition of which may be varied up to a definite limit.

Solvent. The dissolving medium in a solution.

mogeneous mixture of two or more substances, the composition of which may be varied up to a definite limit. The dissolving medium is called the **solvent.** The substance dissolved is called the **solute.** The simplest solution consists of molecules of a single solute diffused throughout a single solvent.

Not all substances, when placed in water, form true solutions. If clay is mixed with water, for example, very little actually dissolves. The particles of clay are huge when compared to molecules, and a turbid, heterogeneous mixture, called a **suspension,** results. Because the components of the mixture have different densities, they readily separate into two distinct phases. It is possible, however, for particles which are very small, but larger than molecules, to be kept permanently suspended by the bombardment of the liquid molecules. Such mixtures may appear to be homogeneous, but precise examination shows that they are not true solutions. Mixtures of this type are called *colloidal suspensions* and are discussed extensively in Unit 10.

We have learned in Chapter 6, Section 5, that electrovalent solids do not exist as molecules. Each has a crystal lattice composed of ions bound together by electrostatic forces. Such substances, which form water solutions that conduct electricity, are called **electrolytes.** In general, covalent substances form molecular solutions with water which do not conduct electricity. Such substances are called **nonelectrolytes.** Acids are exceptions. When they are undissolved they are molecular, but in solution they act as electrolytes. Solutions of electrolytes have physical properties which are different from solutions of nonelectrolytes. They will be considered in detail in Chapters 20 and 21. The remainder of our present discussion of the properties of solutions will deal with solutions of nonelectrolytes.

2. Types of solutions. Matter may exist in three states: solid, liquid, and gas. Therefore, we may expect to have nine different types of solutions. These are given in the table at the top of the following page.

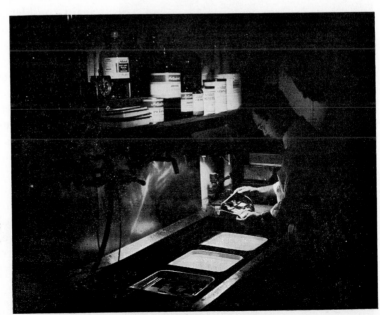

Fig. 19-1. The photographer uses a variety of carefully prepared solutions in the darkroom.

SOLUTE	SOLVENT	EXAMPLE
Gas	Gas	Air
Gas	Liquid	Soda water
Gas	Solid	Hydrogen in palladium
Liquid	Gas	Water vapor in air
Liquid	Liquid	Alcohol in water
Liquid	Solid	Mercury in copper
Solid	Gas	Sulfur vapor in air
Solid	Liquid	Sugar in water
Solid	Solid	Copper in nickel

All mixtures of gases are solutions since they consist of homogeneous mixtures of molecules. Solutions of solids in liquids are by far the most common. Since water is a liquid at ordinary temperatures, we may think of water vapor in air as a liquid-in-gas solution. Solutions of gases in solids are rare. The *occlusion* of hydrogen by palladium and platinum approaches the nature of a solution.

In general, substances of similar composition such as silver and gold, or al-

Fig. 19–2. Pharmacists are often required to prepare solutions in filling a physician's prescriptions.

cohol and water, are apt to form solutions. *When two liquids are mutually soluble in each other, they are said to be* **miscible.** Ethyl alcohol and water are miscible in all proportions. Similarly, ether and ethyl alcohol are completely miscible. Ether and water, on the other hand, are practically **immiscible.** Chemists frequently dry the inside surface of freshly washed glassware by rinsing first with distilled water, then with ethyl alcohol, and finally with ether. The ether has a high vapor pressure and quickly evaporates, leaving a dry glass surface.

3. How does solution equilibrium occur? We may think of the solution process as being *reversible*. Suppose we again consider the lump of sugar we dropped into a beaker of water. The sugar molecules which break away from the crystals and enter the water have completely random motions. Some of these molecules which broke away may come in contact with the undissolved sugar. Here they are attracted by the sugar molecules in the crystal and become a part of the crystal structure once more.

At first, since there are no sugar molecules in solution, the solution process occurs in the direction of dissolving. Molecules leave the crystal structure and diffuse throughout the water. As the concentration of dissolved sugar molecules increases, the reverse process will begin. The rate at which the sugar crystals are rebuilt will increase as the concentration of the sugar solution increases. Eventually, if undissolved sugar remains, sugar crystals will be rebuilt as fast as they dissolve. The concentration of the solution has become the greatest possible under existing conditions and the solution is said to be *saturated*. An *equilibrium* has been reached between undissolved sugar and sugar dissolved in water. *Solution equilibrium is the physical state attained in which the opposing processes of dissolving and crystallizing of a solute occur at equal rates. A saturated solution is one in which the dissolved and undissolved solutes are in equilibrium.*

If we add more water to our sugar solution, it will no longer be saturated. We have decreased the *concentration* of solute molecules, that is, the number of sugar molecules per unit volume of solution. Now more sugar will dissolve to restore the same *equilibrium concentration* of solute molecules. Solution equilibrium thus acts to limit the quantity of a solute which can dissolve in a given quantity of solvent. *The* **solubility** *of a solute is defined as the amount of that solute dissolved in a given amount of a certain solvent at equilibrium, under specified conditions.*

4. How does pressure influence solubility? Ordinary changes in pressure affect the solubility of solids and liquids so slightly that we neglect them altogether. The "solubility" of one gas in another is, of course, independent of pressure. All mixtures of gases are homogeneous and obey the Gas Laws in the same manner as individual gases.

The solubility of gases in liquids and solids, on the other hand, is appreciably affected by changes in pressure.

You know how carbonated beverages fizz or *effervesce* when you pour them into an open glass tumbler. At the bottling plant carbon dioxide gas was forced into solution in the flavored water under a pressure of from 5 to 10 atmospheres. While under such pressure the solution of gas-in-liquid was sealed in bottles. When you removed the cap, the pressure was reduced to 1 atmosphere and much of the carbon dioxide escaped from solution as gas bubbles. *This rapid evolution of a gas from a liquid in which it was dissolved* is known as **effervescence.**

Solutions of gases in liquids reach equilibrium in about the same way that solids in liquids do. The attractive forces between gas molecules are negligible and their motions are relatively great. If a gas is in contact with the surface of a liquid, gas molecules

Fig. 19–3. A saturated solution contains the equilibrium concentration of solute, under existing conditions.

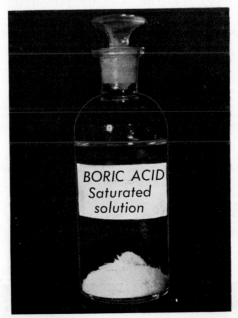

BORIC ACID
Saturated solution

may easily enter the liquid surface. As the concentration of dissolved gas molecules increases, some will begin to escape from the liquid and re-enter the gaseous phase above the liquid. An equilibrium is eventually reached between the rates at which gas molecules are dissolving and escaping from solution. After an equilibrium is attained between the gas in solution and its atmosphere above the liquid, there will be no increase in the concentration of the gaseous solute. Thus the solubility of the gas is limited to its equilibrium concentration in the liquid, under existing conditions.

If we increase the pressure of the gas above the liquid, the equilibrium is disturbed and more gas dissolves. This action, of course, increases the concentration of the dissolved gas. This, in turn, causes gas molecules to escape from the liquid surface at a faster rate. A new equilibrium with a higher concentration of solute is established at the higher pressure. Thus the solubility of the gas in the liquid is increased. *The solubility of gases in liquids is directly proportional to the pressure of the gas above the liquid.* This is a statement of **Henry's Law.** It was proposed by William Henry, an English chemist (1775–1836).

Gases which react chemically with their liquid solvents are generally more soluble than those which form no compounds with the solvent molecules.

Oxygen, hydrogen, and nitrogen are only slightly soluble in water. Ammonia, carbon dioxide, and sulfur dioxide are more soluble, probably due to the formation of unstable compounds with the water solvent. Such gases deviate from Henry's Law. If different gases are mixed in a confined space, each gas exerts the same pressure it would if it alone occupied the space. The pressure of the mixture is the *total* of the individual, or *partial,* pressures of the gases composing the mixture. The partial pressure of each gas in the mixture is proportional to the number of molecules of that gas, at a definite temperature and for a constant volume.

If a mixture of gases is in contact with a liquid, the solubility of each gas is proportional to its *partial pressure.* If we may assume that the gases present in the mixture do not react in any way when in solution, each will dissolve to the same extent it would if the other gases were not present.

Air is about 20 percent oxygen. When air is bubbled through water, only about 20 percent as much oxygen dissolves as would dissolve if pure oxygen were used, at the same pressure. Oxygen remains dissolved in the water only because it is in equilibrium with the oxygen in the air above the water. If the oxygen were removed from the atmosphere above the surface of the water, all of the dissolved oxygen would eventually escape from the water. This

Fig. 19–4. This diagram shows the amounts of three common solutes that can be dissolved in 100 g of water at 60° C.

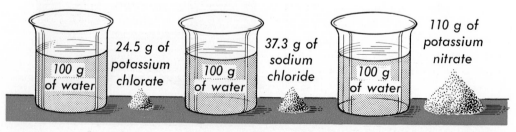

100 g of water — 24.5 g of potassium chlorate

100 g of water — 37.3 g of sodium chloride

100 g of water — 110 g of potassium nitrate

fact has great significance when we consider the abundance of life which exists in water.

5. How does temperature influence solubility? *1. Gases in liquids.* A glass of water drawn from the hot water tap often appears milky because tiny bubbles of air are suspended throughout the water. Part of the air which was dissolved in the cold water has been driven out of solution as the water was heated.

Raising the temperature of a solution increases the speed of its molecules. Molecules of dissolved gas leave the solvent at a faster rate than gas molecules enter the solvent. This lowers the equilibrium concentration of the solute. The solubility of a gas decreases as the temperature of the solvent is increased. Table 11 of the Appendix shows that the solubility of gases varies with the kind of gas, and that it decreases as the

Fig. 19–5. Solubility curves. The solubility of a solute is expressed in grams per 100 grams of solvent, at a stated temperature.

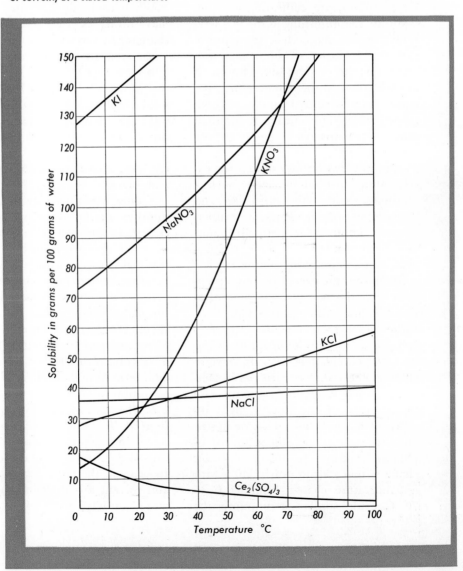

temperature of the gas is increased.

2. *Solids in liquids.* Let us add an excess of sugar to water in a beaker. When equilibrium between the sugar solute and the undissolved crystals is reached we have a saturated solution. Now let us warm the solution over a low flame. We observe that as the temperature of the solution rises, the solid sugar dissolves. It is evident that the solubility of the sugar in water has increased with the rise in temperature.

As we cool our solution, solid sugar begins to separate, indicating that the solubility is diminishing as the temperature falls. No more than the equilibrium concentration of solute may normally remain in solution. Thus with the lowering of the temperature, the equilibrium is shifted and sugar crystals separate from solution faster than solid crystals dissolve.

It is possible, however, to cool such a solution very carefully so that the excess solute does not separate. Such a solution is said to be *supersaturated.* There is a strong tendency, in a supersaturated solution, to reestablish normal equilibrium. By a slight disturbance, or by seeding the solution with a small crystal, the excess solute will separate and the equilibrium concentration of solute will be established.

Increasing the temperature usually increases the solubility of solids in liquids. Sometimes, however, the reverse effect is observed. A certain rise in temperature may result in a large increase in solubility in one case, a slight increase in another, and a decrease in still another. For example, the solubility of potassium nitrate in 100 g of water changes from 13 g to nearly 140 g with a temperature change from 0° C to 70° C. Under similar circumstances the solubility of sodium chloride increases only about 2 g. The solubility of cerium sulfate, on the other hand, decreases nearly 14 g. Typical solubility curves are shown in Fig. 19-5. If we included the solubility curve for cane sugar in water, the graph would have to be extended considerably. At 0° C, 179 g of sugar dissolves in 100 g of water. This increases to 487 g at 100° C. The solubility of solids depends upon: *1.* the nature of the solid; *2.* the solvent used; and *3.* the temperature.

When a solid dissolves in a liquid we may think of the solid as having changed in physical state to a liquid. In such a change, heat is absorbed. Thus we should expect the temperature of the solution to be lowered as the solid dissolves, and the solubility of the solid to increase as temperature is raised. Deviations from this normal pattern may indicate that some kind of chemical activity occurs between solute and solvent.

Similar reasoning may be applied to solutions of liquids in liquids. As no change in physical state occurs when we make up such solutions, we might reasonably expect little change in temperature. Where large changes in temperature are observed, as in the case of sulfuric acid in water, some type of chemical activity between solute and solvent may be occurring. When water is the solvent this chemical activity may be a form of *hydration.* The process of hydration will be studied in Chapter 20.

6. The rate of solution may be increased. The rate at which a solid dissolves in a liquid depends on the nature of the solid and that of the liquid. In general, the more nearly the solute and solvent are alike in structure the more rapidly will solution occur.

However, we may increase the rate of solution of a solid in a liquid in three ways.

1. By stirring. The diffusion of solute molecules throughout the solvent occurs rather slowly. By stirring or shaking the mixture we aid in the dispersion of the solute particles and bring fresh portions of the solvent in contact with the undissolved solid.

2. By powdering the solid. Solution action occurs only at the surface of the solid. By grinding the solid into a fine powder we greatly increase the surface area. Hence, finely powdered solids will dissolve much more rapidly than large lumps or crystals of the same substance.

3. By heating the solvent. The rate of solution rises with temperature. If we apply heat to a solvent the molecular activity increases and the solution action is speeded. At the same time, with most solids, we will increase the solubility of the substance.

7. Solutions may be dilute or concentrated. The more solute that we dissolve in a solvent the more **concentrated** our solution becomes. Conversely, the more solvent we add the more *dilute* the solution becomes. In the first instance we *increased the concentration of solute particles.* In the second, we *decreased the concentration of solute.* We may increase the concentration of solutions by one of two methods: *1.* by adding solute; or *2.* by removing solvent by evaporation.

The terms *dilute* and *concentrated* are qualitative and are useful in a general sense. However, they lack the definiteness, or quantitative significance, which chemists require in describing the precise concentration of solutions.

8. Methods of expressing concentrations. One way in which we may express the concentration of solutions quantitatively is to give the *weight of solute* and the *volume of solution.* One method expresses the weight of solute in *moles.* Another gives the solute in *equivalent weights.* The **equivalent weight** of a substance is the weight required to combine with, or replace, one gram of hydrogen. The equivalent weight of an element is found by dividing its atomic weight by its valence.

1. Molarity. The **molarity** of a solution is the number of moles of solute per liter of solution. A *molar* solution (M) is one containing *1 mole* of solute per liter of solution. Solutions of the same molarity have the same concentration of solute molecules. Equal volumes have the same number of molecules of solute.

You will recall that we have extended the meaning of the mole to include the gram-formula weight of substances represented by empirical formulas. Thus a molar solution may contain 1 gram-molecular weight of a molecular solute per liter of solution, or 1 gram-formula weight of a nonmolecular solute per liter of solution. Sometimes the terms *formality* and *formal solution* are used when we desire to distinguish the latter type of solute.

2. Normality. The **normality** of a solution is the number of equivalent weights of solute per liter of solution. A *normal* solution (N) is one containing *1 gram-equivalent weight* of solute per liter of solution. Equal volumes of solutions of the same normality are exact chemical equivalents.

The advantage of having solution concentrations expressed in molarity or normality is that any desired weight of solute may be taken in the form of its solution simply by measuring out a certain volume. The disadvantage is that the weight or volume of solvent present is not known precisely.

Another way of expressing the concentration of solutions quantitatively is to give the *weight of solute* and the *weight of solvent.*

3. Molality. The **molality** of a solution is the number of moles of solute per 1000 g of solvent. A *molal* solution (m) is one containing *1 mole* of solute per 1000 g of solvent. Molality is preferred over molarity when portions are to be weighed.

In addition to the methods listed, the concentrations of solutions are sometimes expressed in *weight percentages.* A 10% sugar-water solution consists of 1 g of sugar for every 9 g of water. Also, *grams of solute per 100 g of solvent* is a method frequently used.

9. Solvents are selective. We learned in Section 6 that, in general, the more nearly solutes and solvents are alike the more rapidly will solution occur. It is also true, in a very general sense, that the *possibility* of solvent action is in-

creased by a similarity in the composition and structure of substances. Chemists believe that the distribution of electronic forces helps to explain why solvents are selective; that is, why they will dissolve some substances readily, and others not at all.

In Chapter 10, Section 3, we described the water molecule as a polar structure with a distinct negative region (the oxygen atom) and a distinct positive region (the hydrogen atoms). The water molecule is frequently referred to as the *water dipole.* When a molecule contains polar covalent bonds which are *unsymmetrically distributed,* the molecule has dipole characteristics (a negative region and a positive region) and is said to be *polar.*

The carbon tetrachloride molecule, CCl_4, contains four polar covalent bonds. However, since these are *symmetrically* distributed, due to the regular tetrahedral structure, the molecule is *nonpolar.* Gasoline-type hydrocarbons, while very unsymmetrical in bond distribution, are practically non-

Fig. 19–6. Molecular diagrams of three common solvents. Differences in molecular structure may help to explain why they are selective.

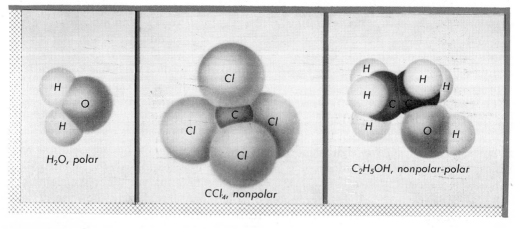

H_2O, polar

CCl_4, nonpolar

C_2H_5OH, nonpolar-polar

polar. This is because neither hydrogen nor carbon has a strong tendency to acquire electrons.

If we apply the rough rule that *like dissolves like* to these typical solvents, we would expect water to tend to dissolve polar-type substances and carbon tetrachloride to dissolve nonpolar-type substances. Polar solute molecules and charged ions of crystals are held together by strong attractive forces. They are more likely to be attracted away from the solid structure by polar water molecules than by nonpolar solvents. Thus many ionic crystalline salts and molecular solids like table salt and sugar are readily dissolved by water. Many organic compounds, such as oils and greases, which are insoluble in water, are readily dissolved by nonpolar carbon tetrachloride.

Ethyl alcohol, C_2H_5OH, is typical of a group of solvents which dissolve both polar and nonpolar substances. The structural formula is

$$H-\overset{\displaystyle\underset{|}{H}}{\underset{|}{C}}-\overset{\displaystyle\underset{|}{H}}{\underset{|}{C}}-O-H$$

We see that there are five carbon-hydrogen bonds which are essentially nonpolar. There is one carbon-carbon bond which is completely nonpolar. The carbon-oxygen bond and the hydrogen-oxygen bond are polar. The presence of distinct polar and nonpolar regions may account for the fact that alcohol is a good solvent for some polar and some nonpolar substances.

10. Hydrogen bonds affect the properties of solvents. *An electronegative*

Fig. 19–7. Ice crystals are formed by molecules of water joined by hydrogen bonds. Here the space between molecules is exaggerated to show how each hydrogen in each molecule is joined to an oxygen in a neighboring molecule.

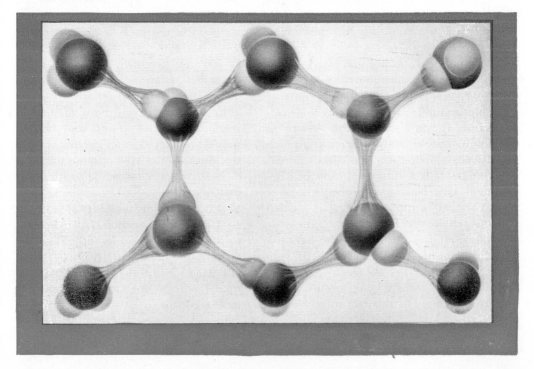

atom is one which has a great tendency to acquire electrons. Hydrogen forms distinctly polar covalent bonds with such highly electronegative elements as fluorine, oxygen, chlorine, and nitrogen. The hydrogen end of such a bond is unique in that it consists of an exposed proton. In all other elements, except hydrogen, which tend to lose electrons, the atom kernel has an electronic shell that tends to repel the highly electronegative regions of other particles. The hydrogen end of a polar bond, however, attracts the relatively negative atoms of other molecules with enough force to be recognized as a loose chemical bond. Such a bond is known as the **hydrogen bond.** By far the most common hydrogen bonds involve oxygen, although those with fluorine are generally stronger.

Such properties of water as the abnormally high boiling and melting points may be attributed in part to the presence of hydrogen bonds between molecules. The formation of hydrogen bonds between solvent and solute will increase the solubility of the solute. Hydrogen bond formation between water and ethyl alcohol may partially explain their complete miscibility.

11. Freezing and boiling points of solutions differ from those of their solvents. If you live near the ocean you know that salt water freezes at a much lower temperature than fresh water. Sea water is a dilute solution of common salt, NaCl, and other minerals. When a dilute solution is cooled enough for freezing to occur, the crystals produced are those of the *pure solvent,* not of the solution itself. In general, *solutes lower the freezing point of the solvent in which they are dissolved.* We make use of this fact when we add

alcohol or ethylene glycol to the water of an automobile radiator during the winter months.

François Raoult (rah-*oo*) (1830–1901), a French chemist, found that a molal solution of alcohol in water has a freezing point of $-1.86°$ C. Later investigations revealed that molal solutions of all nonelectrolytes in water freeze at this same temperature, $-1.86°$ C.

Experiments with different molalities proved that *the lowering of the freezing point is proportional to the molecular concentration of the solute.* Solvents other than water have their own characteristic *molal-freezing point depressions.*

The boiling point of a solution is higher than that of the pure solvent, provided the solute is not a volatile substance. Experiments have shown that, in dilute solutions of nonvolatile nonelectrolytes, *the elevation of the boiling point is proportional to the molecular concentration of the solute.* Molal solutions of nonelectrolytes in water raise the boiling point 0.52 C°. That is, the solution boils at 100.52° C at 760 mm pressure. Thus *0.52 C° is the molal-boiling point elevation of water.*

In the case of solutions of electrolytes, the freezing points and boiling points are altered in an abnormal manner. Such solutes are not molecular and do not conform to the generalizations just described.

★ **12. Molecular weights of solutes.** In Chapter 14, Section 7, we learned to apply Avogadro's hypothesis to determine the molecular weights of gases and volatile liquids by the molar-volume method. Now we shall see how molecular weights can be determined for those substances which cannot be vaporized without decomposition, *but which are soluble in water or some other common solvent.* Of course such solutes must form molecular solutions and must not react with the solvent.

We have seen in the previous section that the freezing-point depression and boiling-point elevation depend on the relative number of solute molecules mixed with a definite number of solvent molecules, rather than upon the nature of the solute. Molal solutions of all nonelectrolytes in water freeze at $-1.86°$ C and, if the solute is nonvolatile, boil at $100.52°$ C at standard pressure. Knowing this we have a method of determining the molecular weights of such substances. The freezing point depression is more frequently used.

We may dissolve a known weight of nonelectrolyte in a known weight of water. The freezing point of this solution may then be determined experimentally. Knowing the concentration of our solution and its freezing-point depression, we may readily calculate the grams of this solute which must be dissolved in 1000 g of water to give the molal-freezing point depression, which for water is 1.86 C°.

$$\frac{g \ solute/1000 \ g \ water}{observed \ depression, \ C°} = \frac{1 \ mole \ solute/1000 \ g \ water}{1.86 \ C°}$$

Suppose 5 g of a substance dissolved in 100 g of water lowers the freezing point of the water 0.37 C°. *Remember that the weight of solute dissolved in 1000 g of water, which lowers the freezing point 1.86 C°, is the molecular weight.* Then 50 g of this solute dissolved in 1000 g of water lowers the freezing point 0.37 C°. From the above proportion

$$1 \ mole = 50 \ g \times \frac{1.86 \ C°}{0.37 \ C°}$$

$$1 \ mole = 250 \ g$$

Therefore,

$$mol. \ wt. = 250$$

We may calculate the molecular weights from the boiling-point elevation in the same manner, remembering that the molal-boiling point elevation of water is 0.52 C°. Solvents other than water may be used in molecular weight determinations. Each has its own characteristic molal-freezing point depression and molal-boiling point elevation which would be used instead of those for water.

2. CRYSTALLIZATION

13. What are crystals? Many substances form crystals when they separate from solutions. *Crystals are solids having a regular geometric shape.* For example, crystals of common salt, NaCl, are *cubes.* This can be shown by sprinkling a little table salt on a black surface and examining the particles with a magnifying glass. Alum forms eight-sided, or *octahedral,* crystals. Cupric sulfate forms blue crystals that are *rhombohedral* in shape. The opposite sides of such crystals are parallel, but not all the angles are right angles, as in the case of a cube. It is possible to form crystals by the evaporation of a solution, or by the cooling of a hot, saturated solution.

Crystals are also formed when some substances change from the liquid to the solid state by freezing. Most of us are familiar with snowflake crystals

Fig. 19–8. The crystalline structure of a substance follows a characteristic pattern. Left, a garnet crystal; right, a quartz crystal.

which are formed when water vapor changes to the solid state. The hydrogen bond helps to determine the shape of ice crystals which are formed when water freezes. Molten sugar, sulfur, and iron form crystals in a similar manner when they change from the liquid to the solid state. Most solids have some kind of crystalline structure.

Electrovalent compounds have *ionic* crystalline structures. Most of the chemicals on the laboratory stock-room shelves are of this sort. Some crystalline substances are *molecular*. Iodine crystals consist of a regular pattern of I_2 molecules. Other crystalline substances are *macromolecular*. The diamond is such a crystal. The strength of structural materials is largely dependent on the nature of the metallic crystals composing them.

14. What use is made of crystals? If we look at Fig. 19-8, we see that the crystals of one substance have a definite shape. This makes it possible for a person skilled in crystallography to identify many substances by their crystalline structure. Many natural minerals can be identified by studying the shape

of the crystals they form. Several natural crystals, such as the diamond, are valuable as gems. Certain types of crystals are used to aid broadcasting stations maintain stable signal frequencies. Germanium crystals and silicon crystals are important in the new field of semi-conductors.

15. Chemists purify chemicals by crystallization. Suppose we have some impure potassium nitrate which we wish to purify. We may dissolve the potassium nitrate in distilled water, then increase the concentration of the solution by evaporation. After the saturation point is reached, crystals of potassium nitrate of a rather high degree of purity begin to separate from the solution as it is allowed to cool. By filtering out these crystals and dissolving them again in water, we can repeat the process and get crystals of still greater purity. Such crystals are said to be *recrystallized*. Crystallization and recrystallization are much used by chemists to obtain pure chemicals.

The saturated solution which is left after a "crop" of crystals has formed is known as the "mother liquor." By evaporating the mother liquor still more, a second, or even a third, crop of crystals may be obtained. Each successive crop, however, will be less pure than the crop before it.

If the solution is stirred while crystallization is taking place, smaller crystals are formed. Small crystals produced rapidly are generally purer than large crystals which are formed by slow evaporation. This is because large crystals are more likely to have some of the mother liquor incorporated in them. Crystals that contain water held mechanically will *decrepitate,* or crackle, when heated. Steam forms within the crystal, and its expansion causes the crystal to burst open. Lead nitrate crystals scattered over the bottom of an Erlenmeyer flask will show decrepitation quite strikingly, if the flask is heated gently.

Sometimes it is possible to separate two different chemicals which are dissolved in the same solution by means of fractional crystallization. When the solvent is evaporated, the less soluble chemical crystallizes first, and it may

be removed by the process of filtration.

16. Standards of purity. If you look over the supply of chemicals in your laboratory stock room, you will find several different terms used to indicate the purity of the different chemicals. Some, marked "technical," are comparatively cheap because they are not highly refined. Yet they are not supposed to contain impurities which would interfere with the commercial uses for which they are intended. Chemicals of higher purity may be marked "purified," "N.F.," "U.S.P.," "C.P.," or "reagent." The terms N.F. and U.S.P. mean the chemicals or drugs are pure enough to meet the specifications listed in the National Formulary and the United States Pharmacopoeia, respectively. The United States Pharmacopoeia is the official book which pharmacists use as a guide in compounding medicines. The letters C.P. stand for *"chemically pure"* and designate a grade which is usually much higher in

Fig. 19–10. Hydrated crystals of different substances have different aqueous vapor pressures (arrows up). In an atmosphere of normal aqueous pressure (arrows down) the crystal on the left will effloresce. The one on the right will not. In dry air both will effloresce.

Fig. 19–9. Reagent chemicals must meet rigid standards of purity.

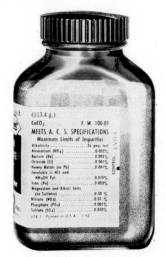

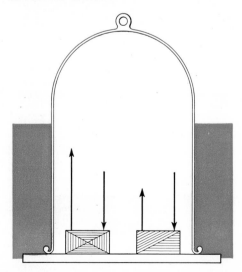

quality than U.S.P. or N.F. The letters A.C.S. are often seen on labels of highest grade chemicals, used as *analytical reagents* in chemical laboratories. These chemicals meet the specifications of the *American Chemical Society* Committee on Analytical Reagents. It is not possible, of course, for manufacturing chemists to attain absolute purity in their products.

17. Water of hydration. In Chapter 10, Section 5, we learned that some crystals unite chemically with water when they crystallize from a water solution. Such crystals are known as hydrates. The water they contain is called *water of hydration* or *water of crystallization*. Common examples are: $CuSO_4·5 H_2O$; $ZnSO_4·7 H_2O$; $CoCl_2·6 H_2O$; and $Na_2CO_3·10 H_2O$. Alum is the *double* salt $K_2SO_4·Al_2(SO_4)_3·24 H_2O$.

Each hydrate holds a definite proportion of water which is necessary for the formation of the crystal structure. Water of hydration must not be confused with the mechanically held water mentioned in Section 15. We may drive off the water of hydration by applying heat, producing the *anhydrous* form of the substance. The anhydrous form of the blue cupric sulfate crystals is a white powder.

Many compounds form hydrates when they crystallize. Some have two or more hydrated forms which are stable over different temperature ranges. Many other compounds form crystals which do not require water of hydration. Examples are: $NaCl$, KNO_3, and $KClO_3$.

18. What is efflorescence? Suppose we place ten grams of sodium sulfate crystals, $Na_2SO_4 · 10 H_2O$, on a watch glass and counterpoise it on a balance. In a few minutes the crystals begin to show a loss of weight. By the end of the laboratory period the loss in weight may amount to a gram or more.

Some hydrated crystals hold the water of hydration very loosely. Water is given off from them when they are exposed to dry air. The crystals lose their glassy luster and become powdery. *This loss of water when such crystals are exposed to the air is called efflorescence.* Actually, about 56% of the weight of freshly prepared sodium sulfate crystals is water. Efflorescence occurs much more rapidly in a warm,

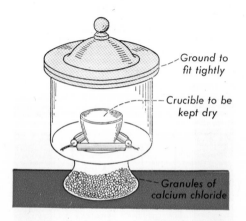

Ground to fit tightly

Crucible to be kept dry

Granules of calcium chloride

Fig. 19–11. A deliquescent substance, such as anhydrous calcium chloride, silica gel, or activated alumina, is used to maintain a dry atmosphere in a laboratory desiccator.

Fig. 19–12. Calcium chloride removes water vapor from the air to control the dust on an unpaved road.

dry atmosphere than in a cool, moist room. Hydrates which effloresce have higher vapor pressures than that of the water vapor in the air above them. Sodium carbonate decahydrate, $Na_2CO_3 \cdot 10 H_2O$, has a high aqueous vapor pressure. When exposed to the atmosphere, it effloresces forming the monohydrate, $Na_2CO_3 \cdot H_2O$. Thus a pound of freshly packaged washing soda may weigh considerably less when purchased at the neighborhood grocery.

19. What is deliquescence? Let us place a few grams of calcium chloride granules on a watch glass and counterpoise them on a balance. After the calcium chloride has been exposed to the air for half an hour, we find that it shows a decided gain in weight. The granules have become moist, or perhaps even formed a solution with water

from the air. **Deliquescence** *is the property of certain substances to take up water from the air to form a solution.* Such substances are very soluble in water and their crystals have aqueous vapor pressures which are low compared to the normal range of partial pressures of water vapor in the air.

Many materials such as silk, wool, hair, and tobacco pick up water vapor from the air. The water molecules may be held in pores and imperfections of the solid. All such materials, along with deliquescent substances, are classed as *hygroscopic.* Common table salt is hygroscopic only because it contains a small amount of magnesium chloride, a very deliquescent substance. The presence of this impurity causes table salt to "cake" and clog the holes of the salt shaker.

Summary

A solution is made up of two parts; the solute which is dissolved, and the solvent in which the solute is dissolved. Solutions are homogeneous mixtures of particles no larger than molecular size. Solutes may be classed as electrolytes or nonelectrolytes depending on the ability of their solutions to conduct electricity. The properties of the solutions of electrolytes and nonelectrolytes are quite different.

We may have solutions of gases, or liquids, or solids in other gases, liquids, and solids. Substances of similar composition are likely to form solutions.

Solution equilibrium places a limit on the quantity of solute which can dissolve in a given quantity of solvent. Equilibrium is influenced by temperature. The solubility of a solute is determined by the equilibrium concentration of solute particles.

The solubility of a gas in a liquid is influenced by pressure in accordance with Henry's Law. Gases which react with their liquid solvent are more soluble than those which do not. The solubility of a gas decreases as the temperature is raised. Solids are generally more soluble at higher temperatures. We may hasten the formation of a solution in several ways.

The concentration of a solution may be described qualitatively as either dilute or concentrated. Concentration is described precisely by stating the molarity, normality, or molality of the solution.

Molecular solutes lower the freezing point of their solvents characteristic amounts. If nonvolatile, they raise the boiling point characteristic amounts also. Each solvent has a specific molal-freezing point depression and molal-boiling point elevation. These properties are used to determine molecular weights of soluble substances which cannot be vaporized without decomposing.

Solids usually separate from solution as crystals. Crystals assume characteristic forms and are either ionic, molecular, or macromolecular in structure.

Specific amounts of water are essential to the formation of crystals of some substances. Some hydrated crystals lose water of hydration when exposed to air and are said to effloresce. Substances which remove water from the air to form solutions are said to be deliquescent.

Test yourself on these terms

anhydrous	equilibrium concentration	normality
concentrated	equivalent weight	octohedral
C.P.	Henry's Law	rhombohedral
crystals	hydrate	saturated
decrepitate	hydrogen bond	solubility
deliquescence	hygroscopic	soluble
dilute	immiscible	solute
dissolve	miscible	solution equilibrium
effervescence	molality	solvent
efflorescence	molarity	supersaturated
electronegative	mother liquor	U.S.P.

Questions

Group A

1. List, by name, five common solvents.
2. Why are the terms *dilute* and *concentrated* not entirely satisfactory as applied to solutions?
3. (a) Name the nine different types of solutions possible. (b) Which type is the most common?
4. Why does carbonated water effervesce when it is drawn from the soda fountain?
5. What action limits the amount of a solute which can dissolve in a given quantity of solvent under fixed conditions?
6. Explain the difference between *dissolve* and *melt.*
7. What is the influence of pressure on the solubility of: (a) a gas in a liquid; and (b) a solid in a liquid?
8. What is the influence of temperature on the solubility of: (a) a gas in a liquid; and (b) a solid in a liquid?
9. (a) What is the difference between *miscible* and *immiscible?* (b) Give an example of each.
10. What method of expressing the concentration of a solution would be used if the solute is given: (a) in moles per liter of solution; (b) in moles per kilogram of solvent; and (c) in equivalent weights per liter of solution?
11. What is the distinguishing characteristic of *polar* molecules?
12. Alcohol is a nonelectrolyte and is soluble in water, yet a molal solution of alcohol in water does not give the molal-boiling point elevation of water. Explain.
13. (a) Explain why anhydrous calcium chloride may be used to keep the air in a basement dry. (b) Suggest a suitable method of accomplishing this.
14. What do the letters "A.C.S." on a bottle of ferrous sulfate mean?

Group B

15. Explain the meaning of *saturated solution* in terms of solution equilibrium.
16. (a) What determines the amount of oxygen which remains dissolved in water which is at constant temperature and in contact with the atmosphere? (b) Explain what would happen if the oxygen were removed from the air above the water.
17. Suppose you wished to make a concentrated solution of cupric sulfate in water. What steps would you take to hasten the solution process?
18. The carbon tetrachloride molecule contains four polar covalent bonds yet the molecule as a whole is nonpolar. Explain.
19. How may we explain the fact that alcohol is a good solvent for both water and ether?
20. Why do caps sometimes blow off the tops of ginger ale bottles when they are exposed to direct sunlight for some time?

21. Why is cold water more appropriate than hot water for making a saturated solution of calcium hydroxide?

22. Tobacco growers prefer to handle the dried tobacco leaves during damp weather. Explain.

23. A package of washing soda $(Na_2CO_3 \cdot 10 H_2O)$ labeled "one pound" was found to weigh only 14 ounces. Was the packer necessarily dishonest? Explain.

24. A bottle of alum crystals was erroneously labeled "sodium chloride." How could the error be detected at once by an alert chemistry student?

25. From which substance, sodium nitrate or sodium chloride, could potassium nitrate be more easily separated by fractional crystallization? Explain.

26. How are solubility curves similar to those shown in Fig. 19-5 constructed?

Problems

Group B

★ 1. A solution consists of 60 g of cane sugar, $C_{12}H_{22}O_{11}$, in 150 g of water. What is the freezing point of the water?

★ 2. What is the boiling point of the solution described in Problem 1?

★ 3. The analysis of a compound shows: carbon, 32%; hydrogen, 4%; oxygen, 64%. Fifteen grams of the compound added to 1000 g of water lowered the freezing point of the water 0.186 C°. (a) Find the empirical formula. (b) What is the molecular weight of the compound? (c) What is the molecular formula?

★ 4. A compound contains: carbon, 40%; hydrogen, 6.67%; oxygen, 53.33%. Nine grams of the compound dissolved in 500 g of water raised the boiling point of the water 0.052 C°. (a) Find the empirical formula. (b) Find the molecular weight. (c) What is the molecular formula?

★ 5. The analysis of a compound shows: carbon, 30.4%; hydrogen, 1.69%; bromine, 68%. The substance is soluble in benzene and 10 g of it lowers the freezing point of 100 g of benzene 2.17 C°. The normal freezing point of benzene is 5.48° C, and the molal-freezing point depression is 5.12 C°. (a) Find the empirical formula of the compound. (b) Determine the molecular weight. (c) What is the molecular formula?

Some things for you to do

1. Prepare a supersaturated solution of "hypo" by dissolving 50 g of sodium thiosulfate in 10 ml of water with the aid of heat. Allow the solution to cool undisturbed. Add a tiny crystal of hypo and watch the crystals form.

2. Test the solubility of gum camphor or iodine crystals in both water and alcohol. Which is the better solvent?

3. See how large and nearly perfect a crystal of alum you can get to "grow" from a saturated solution. Select a well-formed, single crystal to start. Wipe the crystal each day with a soft cloth to prevent the growth of secondary crystals. In six months you should have one like that sketched for the opening of this chapter. The solution must be stored in a place of nearly uniform temperature.

Chapter 20

THE THEORY OF IONIZATION

1. Some solutions conduct electricity. In Chapter 19, Section 1, we learned that solutions of electrovalent and covalent compounds may have different properties. These are due to the differences in the chemical nature of electrovalent and covalent solutes. Electrovalent compounds are ionic, and their water solutions conduct electricity.

Let us arrange an apparatus like that shown in Fig. 20-1. An electric lamp is connected in series with a knife switch and a pair of platinum electrodes which dip into the solution in the beaker. A battery of the same voltage rating as the lamp is used as the source of current. If the liquid we are testing is a *conductor of electricity* the lamp filament will glow when the switch is closed.

If pure water is used in the beaker, the filament will not glow. Thus pure water is (for all practical purposes) a *nonconductor*. We may show that water solutions of such covalent substances as sugar, alcohol, and glycerin do not conduct electricity. These solutes are ***nonelectrolytes.***

In a similar manner we can show that solutions of electrovalent substances, such as sodium chloride, cupric sulfate, and potassium nitrate, are *conductors*. These solutes are ***electrolytes.*** Hydrogen chloride is an example of a covalent compound which, in water solution, conducts an electric current. Such

VOCABULARY

Dissociation. The separation of the ions of an electrovalent substance during the solution process.

Electrolyte. A substance whose water solution conducts the electric current.

Hydration. The attachment of water molecules to particles of the solute.

Ion. An atom or a group of atoms which carries an electric charge.

Ionization. The formation of ions from polar solute molecules by the action of a solvent.

Nonelectrolyte. A substance whose water solution does not conduct the electric current.

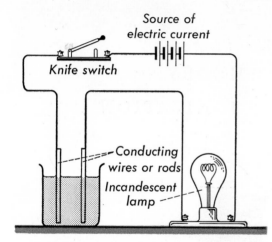

Fig. 20–1. Solutions that conduct electricity will enable the lamp to glow when the switch is closed.

substances are also called electrolytes.

2. Electrolytes lower the freezing point more than nonelectrolytes. In Chapter 19, Section 11, we learned that one mole of a nonelectrolyte dissolved in 1000 g of water lowers the freezing point of the water 1.86 C°. This is known as the *molal freezing point depression of water*. Molal solutions of electrolytes have a somewhat greater influence on the freezing point. One mole of sodium chloride dissolved in 1000 g of water lowers the freezing point *nearly twice* as much as 1 mole of sugar. One mole of potassium sulfate dissolved in 1000 g of water lowers the freezing point *nearly three times* as much as 1 mole of sugar. In general, *electrolytes in water solutions lower the freezing point nearly 2, or 3, or more times as much as nonelectrolytes in water solutions of the same molality.*

3. Electrolytes raise the boiling point more than nonelectrolytes. One mole of sugar dissolved in 1000 g of water raises the boiling point of the water 0.52 C°. This is known as the *molal boiling point elevation* of water. Molal-solutions of electrolytes have a greater effect on the boiling point of the sol-

vent than do nonelectrolytes. Sodium chloride solutions have boiling point elevations *almost twice* those of sugar solutions of equal molality. A molal solution of potassium sulfate shows *almost three times* as much rise in boiling point as a molal solution of sugar. In general, *electrolytes in water solutions raise the boiling point nearly 2, or 3, or more times as much as nonelectrolytes in water solutions of the same molality.*

4. How is the behavior of electrolytes explained? Michael Faraday, an English chemist and physicist (1791–1867), first used the terms *electrolyte* and *nonelectrolyte* in his experiments on the conductivity of solutions. He concluded that conducting solutions contained particles which carried the electricity across from one electrode to the other. Faraday called these particles *ions* and assumed that they were produced from molecules by the electrical potential difference between the electrodes. As other properties of electrolytic solutions were revealed, it became

Fig. 20–2. Svante August Arrehenius, a Swedish chemist, first proposed the theory of ionization.

apparent that they contained ions regardless of the presence of the charged electrodes.

In 1887 the Swedish chemist Svante Arrhenius (1859–1927) published a report of his study of the behavior of solutions of electrolytes. This is known as the *Theory of Ionization*. Arrhenius believed that ions were produced by the *ionization* of molecules of electrolytes in water solution. He considered the ions to be electrically charged. When molecules ionized, they produced both positive ions and negative ions. The solution as a whole contained equal numbers of positive and negative charges. He considered the ionization to be complete only in very dilute solutions. In more concentrated solutions the ions were in equilibrium with *unionized* molecules of the solute.

For many years these assumptions formed the basis of our knowledge of solutions. Recently, however, some of the concepts of Arrhenius have been modified or replaced by new and different concepts. This is largely due to two factors: *1*. modern knowledge concerning the structure of crystals; and *2*, knowledge of the structure of the water molecule.

It is a great tribute to Arrhenius that his original theory of ionization served so long as the sole guide for the studies of the properties of solutions. You must remember that present-day knowledge of the crystalline structure of electrovalent compounds was not available to him when, at the age of 28, he published his thesis on ionization.

5. The modern theory of ionization. In the modern theory of ionization the solvent plays an important part in the solution process. Water is by far the most important solvent. We studied the nature of the water molecule in Chapter 10, Section 3, and in Chapter 19, Sections 9 and 10. Presently we shall see why the polar water molecule is so important in the solution process. According to present-day concepts, the theory of ionization assumes:

1. That electrolytes in solution exist in the form of ions.

2. That an ion is an atom or a group of atoms which carries an electrical charge.

3. That the water solution of an electrolyte contains an equal number of positive and negative charges.

6. The structure of electrovalent compounds. We have already seen that electrovalent compounds result from the actual transfer of electrons from one kind of atom to another. As a result, electrovalent compounds are not made up of neutral atoms. They consist of atoms which have lost or gained electrons. Those atoms which *gained* electrons in forming the compound have a *negative* charge. Those which *lost* electrons carry a *positive* charge. *Such atoms or groups of atoms which carry an electrical charge are called ions.* In forming an ion, an atom loses electrical neutrality and gains chemical stability.

Ions have quite different properties from the atoms from which they were produced. This is reasonable because of the difference in structure and electrical characteristics resulting from the formation of ions. A neutral sodium atom with one electron revolving in its outermost M shell is different from a sodium ion. The sodium ion has one excess positive charge of electricity and eight electrons in the outermost L shell. We must remember that chemical properties are determined chiefly by the outer electron arrangement of an atom or an ion. If the outer electronic structure is different, the properties will be different. The loss of the M-shell electron gives sodium the stable electronic configuration of neon. *The charge of an ion is the same as its valence.* In fact, the charge on the ion is what determines its valence.

Electrovalent compounds usually exist in the form of crystals. These crystals are made up in a very orderly fashion. For example, the structure of crystalline sodium chloride is shown in Fig. 20-3. By X-ray analysis, the crystals are known to be composed of ions. Other electrovalent compounds crystallize in different patterns. These patterns are built up in a manner which depends on the relative size and valence of the ions.

7. The hydration of ions. Suppose we drop a few crystals of salt in water. The water dipoles immediately exert an attractive force on the ions forming the surface of the crystals. The negative oxygen end of several water dipoles exerts an attractive force on a positive

Fig. 20–3. A sodium chloride crystal consists of sodium ions and chloride ions. Each ion has six neighbors of opposite charge, this arrangement being repeated in each direction to the edge of the crystal.

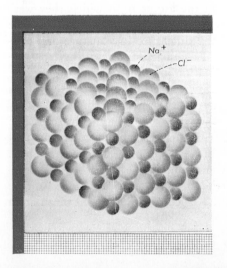

sodium ion. Likewise, the positive hydrogen end of other water dipoles exerts an attractive force on a negative chloride ion. This weakens the bond by which the sodium and chloride ions are held together in the crystals. These ions can then no longer be held in the crystalline pattern. They diffuse throughout the solution loosely bonded to these solvent molecules. Other sodium and chloride ions are similarly attracted by solvent molecules and diffuse in the solution. In this way the salt crystal is gradually dissolved and the ions take up independent existence in the solution. *The separation of ions from the crystals of electrovalent compounds during the solution process is called* **dissociation.** We may represent the dissociation of sodium chloride:

$$Na^+Cl^- \rightarrow Na^+ + Cl^-$$

Sodium chloride is said to *dissociate* when it is dissolved in water.

The number of water dipoles which attach themselves to the ions of the crystal depends largely upon the size and charge on the ion. *This attachment of water molecules to ions of the solute is called* **hydration.** The ions are said to be *hydrated.* The degree of hydration of these ions is somewhat indefinite. Water molecules may be constantly interchanging from ion to ion and between ions and solvent. In certain cases the water dipoles are not involved in reforming the crystal structure during the evaporation of the solvent. This is true of sodium chloride; we know that the crystals do not contain water of hydration. On the other hand, a characteristic number of water molecules may be retained by ions in forming the crystal lattice of a salt that is known to exist in the hydrated form.

We can see that extensive hydration of the solute ions ties up a substantial portion of the solvent molecules. This reduces the number of *free* water molecules in the spaces separating hydrated ions of opposite charge. Attraction between ions becomes stronger and the crystal begins to form again. A practical limit of solubility is reached as the tendency for hydrated ions to reform the crystal lattice reaches an *equilibrium* with the tendency of ions to be hydrated.

$$Na^+Cl^- \rightleftharpoons Na^+ + Cl^-$$

Electrovalent compounds can act as electrolytes in another way. Since they consist of ions, any effect which reduces the mutual attraction between the ions will enable them to conduct electricity. We have seen how water does this. Heating will produce the same effect. If an electrovalent compound is heated until it melts, or *fuses,* the ions become mobile. They can conduct an electric current through the molten material. Some solids, silver nitrate for example, melt at a fairly low temperature. It can easily be shown in the laboratory that fused silver nitrate conducts electricity.

Compounds such as sodium chloride must be heated to a high temperature before they melt. When melted, sodium chloride will conduct electricity.

8. Some covalent compounds ionize. We have learned that covalent bonds are formed by the sharing of electrons by two atoms. The shared electrons revolve about both atoms joined by the covalent bond. If one of the atoms is highly *electronegative,* the valence electrons spend more time revolving about this atom. In this way, one end of the covalent molecule tends to be more negative. The other end, of course, tends to be more positive. This type of molecule is said to be a *polar molecule.* How strongly polar it is depends on the relative attraction of the two atoms for the electrons forming the covalent linkage.

The covalent bond is never as strong as the electrovalent bond. When polar covalent molecules are dissolved in water, the water dipoles weaken the bonds and the molecules are pulled apart. *Thus the portions of the polar solute molecule become hydrated as ions.* Since the ions *did not exist* in the

Fig. 20-4. When sodium chloride crystals are dissolved in water, the polar water molecules exert attracting forces which weaken the ionic bonds. The solution process occurs as sodium and chloride ions become hydrated.

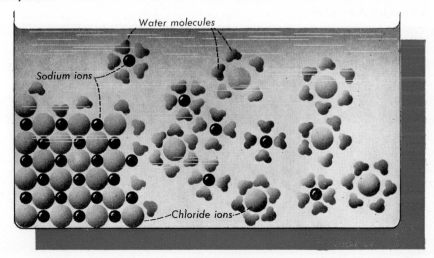

undissolved solute, but were formed by the action of the solvent, the process is called *ionization.*

Hydrogen chloride, in the liquid state, does not conduct electricity. The hydrogen and chlorine atoms are connected by a covalent bond. However, the more highly electronegative chlorine attracts the electrons forming the covalent bond. Consequently, the chlorine end of the molecule tends to be negative, while the hydrogen end tends to be positive. They are polar molecules.

Hydrogen chloride dissolved in water does, however, conduct an electric current. Under such circumstances it is an electrolyte; ions must be present. The substance is ionized in water solution.

Arrhenius believed that the process of ionization involved simply the ionization of the solute molecule on entering the solution. Thus in the case of hydrogen chloride:

$$HCl \rightarrow H^+ + Cl^-$$

Today, chemists recognize that single hydrogen ions, actually protons, do not exist *free* in a water solution. They do,

however, show a strong tendency to become hydrated. Thus the solvent plays a definite part in the separation of protons from the solute molecules.

$$HCl + H_2O \rightarrow H_3O^+ + Cl^-$$

The H_3O^+ ion is a hydrated proton $(H^+ \cdot H_2O)$ and is known as the *hydronium ion.* Because of the ionization, a solution of hydrogen chloride in water has decidedly different properties from hydrogen chloride gas. As a consequence, the solution is given the name *hydrochloric acid.*

Aluminum chloride, Al_2Cl_6 (usually represented by the empirical formula $AlCl_3$), is a nonelectrolyte in the liquid state. In water solution, however, it is a good conductor. It must, therefore, ionize during the solution process. We may represent the ionization as we did in the case of hydrogen chloride:

$$Al_2Cl_6 + 12\ H_2O \rightarrow 2\ Al(H_2O)_6^{+++} + 6\ Cl^-$$

or simply

$$AlCl_3 + 6\ H_2O \rightarrow Al(H_2O)_6^{+++} + 3\ Cl^-$$

Other hydrated aluminum ions are probably formed at the same time.

9. Some electrolytes are strong, others are weak. The strength of an elec-

Fig. 20–5. The polar hydrogen chloride molecule ionizes in water solution to form the hydronium ion and the chloride ion.

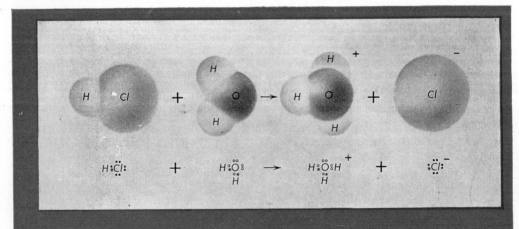

trolyte is determined by the number of its ions in solution. Electrovalent compounds are ionic as crystalline solids. Their solutions are therefore completely ionized. Hydrogen chloride has such a strong tendency to ionize in water solution that, even at ordinary dilutions, it is considered to be completely ionized. Such substances are said to be *strong electrolytes*. Their water solutions conduct electricity exceedingly well.

A water solution of acetic acid, $HC_2H_3O_2$, is a poor conductor. The fact that the solution conducts at all tells us that some ionization has occurred. This may be shown according to the reversible reaction:

$$HC_2H_3O_2 + H_2O \rightleftarrows H_3O^+ + C_2H_3O_2^-$$

We must assume that the ion concentration is low. Acetic acid molecules show only a slight tendency to hydrate as ions. Such substances are said to be *weak electrolytes*. Vinegar is a dilute solution of acetic acid. Solutions of weak electrolytes are largely molecular.

We must be sure not to confuse the terms strong and weak with the terms dilute and concentrated. *Strong* and *weak* refer to the *degree of ionization*. *Dilute* and *concentrated* refer to the *amount of solute dissolved in a solvent*. Chemically speaking, your father is incorrect when he says: "My coffee is too strong this morning." He is concerned with the amount of solute rather than with the degree of ionization.

10. Water ionizes slightly. Water is a polar covalent compound. Probably because of the influence of these polar molecules on each other, water ionizes to the extent of about two molecules in a billion. These few ions, however, are very important in chemistry as we shall see in Chapter 22. Such slight ionization may be neglected when we deal with substances such as hydrogen chloride which ionize completely. But we must take it into consideration when we deal with very weak electrolytes.

Let us consider the question, *why does water ionize?* The process probably begins with the formation of a hydrogen bond between two water molecules. Under just the right conditions

Fig. 20–6. The formation of a hydrogen bond between two water dipoles may be an intermediate step in the ionization of water.

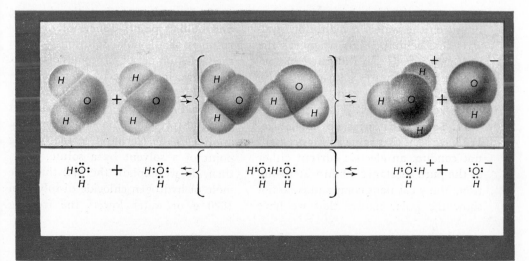

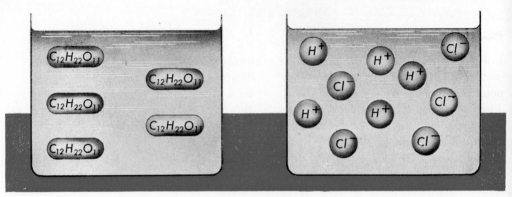

Fig. 20–7. Five sugar molecules produce only five particles in solution. Five hydrogen chloride molecules, on the other hand, produce ten particles when dissolved in water.

this bond might be stronger than the normal covalent bond of the molecule. The result of such a chance situation will be the formation of a hydrated proton and a hydroxide ion according to the reversible reaction:

$$H_2O + H_2O \rightleftarrows H_3O^+ + OH^-$$

Chemically the *hydronium ion* (H_3O^+) acts just like a hydrogen ion. *It is customary, once the hydration mechanism is understood, to drop the water of hydration from the chemical equation.* Thus we may write the equation for the ionization of water:

$$H_2O \rightleftarrows H^+ + OH^-$$

Similarly, we usually write the ionic equation for the ionization of hydrogen chloride in water solution:

$$HCl \rightarrow H^+ + Cl^-$$

In any reaction involving the hydronium ion the water of hydration is always left behind. Thus whenever the hydrogen ion, H^+, is indicated in connection with its water solution, *it is understood that it can exist only in the hydrated form, H_3O^+.*

11. Some substances do not ionize. We have seen that some substances will not conduct an electric current either as the pure substance, or in water solution. Many covalent compounds do not show the polar nature that we have

found in the hydrogen chloride molecule. The attractive force of each of the atoms for the electrons forming the covalent bond may be about the same. The valence electrons are thus almost equally shared, and little separation of electrical charge occurs. Such molecules with *symmetrical electronic fields* are not acted on by water dipoles to produce ions. Consequently, such substances are nonconductors—they are nonelectrolytes.

Carbon tetrachloride is a covalent compound with four polar bonds which are symmetrically distributed. The structure as a whole is nonpolar. Thus it is a nonelectrolyte. Furthermore, it is not acted on by water molecules because of the dissimilar nature of their electronic fields (see Chapter 19, Section 9).

12. Electrolytes affect the freezing and boiling points abnormally. Equal volumes of all molal solutions contain the same number of molecules of solute. The lowering of the freezing point of a solvent by a solute is directly proportional to the number of particles of solute present. The same reasoning applies to the elevation of the boiling point of a solvent by a solute. How, then, do we explain the fact that one mole of hydrogen chloride dissolved in 1000 g of water lowers the freezing point more than one mole of sugar does? The abnormal lowering is caused by the separation of each molecule of hydrogen chloride which ionizes into two particles. Suppose that in a concentrated solution, 90 out of every 100 molecules ionize. Then, for every 100 molecules in solution, we have formed a total of 190 particles (180 ions and 10 un-ionized molecules). Such a solution would therefore have its freezing point lowered 1.9 (190 ÷ 100) times as much as that of the solution of a solute which does not ionize. Suppose 100% of the hydrogen chloride molecules were ionized, as in a more dilute solution. We would then expect the lowering of the freezing point to be double that caused by the solute in a molal solution of a nonelectrolyte.

The following equation shows the complete ionization of sulfuric acid:

$$H_2SO_4 \rightarrow 2\ H^+ + SO_4^=$$

For every molecule of sulfuric acid which ionizes, *three ions* are formed. Two are hydrogen ions which have one positive charge each; one is a sulfate ion with two negative charges. A molal solution of sulfuric acid should, therefore, lower the freezing point of its solvent *three times* as much as the molal solution of a nonelectrolyte. Careful

experiments show that our supposition is true for very dilute solutions, where the apparent degree of ionization reaches 100%. Under these circumstances the ionization theory is in accord with the facts. Of course, the reason for the different rise in the boiling point caused by electrolytes in solution is that ionization increases the number of particles present in the solution.

13. The degree of ionization may be measured. The larger the number of ions in a given volume of a solution the better a conductor of electricity it will be. It is possible to measure the degree of ionization by measuring the electrical conductivity.

It is also possible to find the degree of ionization by measuring the lowering of the freezing point by an ionized solute in a measured amount of solvent. If a molal solution of an electrolyte of the type of sodium chloride freezes at −3.72° C (2 × −1.86° C), we may assume that the solute is 100% ionized.

Actual measurements, however, will give only an *apparent degree of ionization*. We have seen that electrovalent compounds, by the very nature of their structure, must be 100% ionized in solution. Experimental results give a degree of ionization somewhat less than

Fig. 20-8. The ions in the dilute solution on the left are far apart and act independently. The activity of the ions in the solution on the right is somewhat restricted because of the concentration. Thus the apparent number of ions present may be less than the actual number.

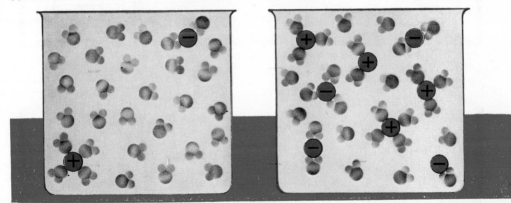

100%. We may explain this discrepancy by the attraction between ions of opposite charge, especially in concentrated solutions. Charged ions, when close together in solution, tend to interfere with each other's activities. They may tend to act as a group rather than as individual hydrated ions. In this way the *apparent* number of ions may be less than the actual number. The freezing and boiling points will be influenced accordingly. By diluting such a solution we may reduce the influence of the ions on each other and increase the *apparent degree of ionization*.

14. Ionization explains electrolysis. Electrolysis is an important method of producing chemical reactions. We have

seen one example of electrolysis in the preparation of oxygen and hydrogen by decomposing water. Now we are ready to explain what happens during that electrolysis. We know that water ionizes only slightly. In order for an adequate electric current to be conducted between the electrodes, we must supply some additional ions. Many kinds of ions will do. Sodium hydroxide can be used. Generally, however, sulfuric acid is used to supply the necessary ions.

When the electrodes are connected to a source of direct current, certain changes take place on their surfaces. In the electrolysis of our water solution, three types of ions are present. There are *hydrogen ions* from the sulfuric

Fig. 20–9. The electrolysis of water.

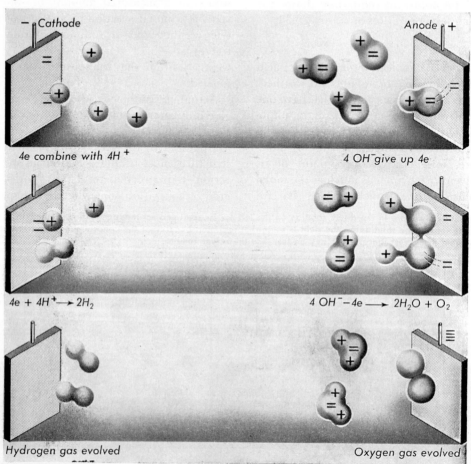

acid, and also a few hydrogen ions from the ionization of water (all are hydronium ions, of course). There are *sulfate ions* from the acid, and a few *hydroxide ions* from the ionization of water. The hydrogen ions carry a single positive charge. They are attracted to the negative electrode, which is called the *cathode*. Here each is discharged by gaining an electron, e^-, and forms a hydrogen atom. Two atoms combine to form a hydrogen molecule, and groups of these molecules bubble from the solution as hydrogen gas.

$$2\ H^+ + 2\ e^- \rightarrow H_2{}^0\uparrow$$

The reaction at the positive electrode, called the *anode,* is not as simple. There are two types of negative ions in the solution, hydroxide ions and sulfate ions. Both of these are attracted to the anode. But there are a great many more sulfate ions than hydroxide ions. Even so, the hydroxide ions give up electrons to the anode more easily than the sulfate ions. They are the ions discharged. Four hydroxide ions are required to produce a molecule of oxygen.

$$4\ OH^- - 4\ e^- \rightarrow 2\ H_2O + O_2{}^0\uparrow$$

Notice that *twice* as many electrons are involved in liberating a molecule of oxygen as are needed to liberate a molecule of hydrogen. Consequently, twice as many hydrogen molecules will be liberated as oxygen molecules. The relative volumes of the two gases liberated will be *two to one—two volumes of hydrogen to one of oxygen.*

$$4\ H^+ + 4\ OH^- \xrightarrow[\text{4 electrons}]{\text{transfer of}} 2\ H_2\uparrow + O_2\uparrow + 2\ H_2O$$

If ions other than those of sulfuric acid are used to conduct the current between the electrodes, the same electrode reactions take place in most cases, *providing very dilute solutions are used.* Under this condition, hydrogen ions take electrons more readily than many other positive ions. Therefore, they are liberated at the cathode in preference to those positive ions. Even if dilute solutions of sodium hydroxide or sodium chloride are used, hydrogen is liberated directly from the water. No metallic sodium is ever liberated from such solutions. Hydroxide ions in dilute solutions of electrolytes give up electrons more readily than many other negative ions. Therefore, in accordance with the reaction described above, oxygen is liberated at the anode in preference to these negative ions, which remain in the solution.

Summary

Substances which in water solution conduct electricity are called electrolytes. Those whose water solutions do not conduct electricity are nonelectrolytes.

Water molecules are covalent molecules. The electrons are unevenly distributed, causing the oxygen end of the molecule to be more negative, and the hydrogen end more positive.

Electrovalent compounds are composed of ions. Water dipoles exert an attracting force on these ions, weakening their bonds. The ions enter the solution as hydrated particles—that is, loosely bonded to water dipoles. The degree of hydration of ions in water solution is somewhat indefinite. Solubility is limited by the tendency of hydrated ions to reform the crystal lattice as the number of free water moleclules separating the ions diminishes.

Polar covalent molecules may ionize in water solution as hydrated ions. Strong electrolytes ionize practically completely, weak electrolytes only slightly. Water ionizes very slightly, forming hydrogen ions and hydroxide ions. Hydrogen ions are never free in water solutions but are hydrated in the form of hydronium ions.

Electrolytes affect the freezing and boiling points of solvents to a greater extent than do nonelectrolytes. They have more particles per volume of solution.

The apparent degree of ionization may be measured by electrical conductivity, or by freezing point depression or boiling point elevation. The apparent degree of ionization increases with increased dilution of an electrolyte. Electrovalent compounds are actually 100% ionized in solution.

In the electrolysis of water, hydrogen ions are discharged at the negative electrode. Hydrogen gas is given up. Hydroxide ions are discharged at the positive electrode. Oxygen gas is given up. The function of the dilute acid added to the water is to increase its conductivity.

Test yourself on these terms

anode	electrolysis	nonelectrolyte
cathode	electrovalent structure	polar molecule
covalent structure	hydrated ion	strong electrolyte
degree of ionization	hydronium ion	theory of ionization
dipole	ion	valence
dissociation	ionization	weak electrolyte

Questions

Group A

1. What is the distinction between an electrolyte and a nonelectrolyte?
2. What effect does the addition of electrolytes have on the boiling points and freezing points of solvents, such as water?
3. What theory helps to explain the behavior of electrolytes?
4. What are the important assumptions of this theory?
5. What is an ion?
6. Write the equation for the ionization of water.

Group B

7. Explain why the water molecule is a polar molecule.
8. Why is it not possible to have a molecule of an electrovalent compound?
9. What is the nature of the crystal structure of an electrovalent compound?
10. How does an atom differ from an ion?
11. How may we account for the stability of an ion?
12. (*a*) How do water molecules cause an electrovalent compound to dissociate? (*b*) How may the process be reversed?

13. Why is the dissociation of electrovalent compounds 100%?
14. Melted potassium chloride conducts an electric current. Explain.
15. (a) Explain how the action of water on a polar compound like hydrogen chloride produces ionization. (b) Write the equation for the ionization of hydrogen chloride in water solution showing the part played by the water.
16. What is the distinction between dissociation and ionization?
17. Describe the solution equilibrium in a saturated solution of sodium nitrate containing an excess of the crystals.
18. (a) What are symmetrical covalent molecules? (b) Why don't they ionize?
19. Explain the abnormal freezing point lowering and boiling point elevation of solvents produced by electrolytes in terms of the theory of ionization.
20. (a) Write an equation for the dissociation of calcium chloride. (b) What will be the freezing point of a 1-molal solution of calcium chloride in water?
21. What are two ways of measuring the apparent degree of ionization?
22. Why does the measurement of the apparent degree of ionization not coincide with the theory that electrovalent compounds are 100% dissociated in solution?
23. How does a concentrated solution of a weak electrolyte differ from a dilute solution of a strong electrolyte?
24. (a) Write equations for the electrode reactions during the electrolysis of water. (b) Why must two volumes of hydrogen be liberated for each volume of oxygen?

Some things for you to do

1. Locate a copy of the JOURNAL OF THE AMERICAN CHEMICAL SOCIETY, Vol. 34, page 353 (April 1912) and read the address of Svante Arrhenius before the Chicago Section of the American Chemical Society. Try the technical branch of your public library or the technical library of a nearby chemical industry or university.
2. Ask your instructor for permission to arrange an apparatus similar to Fig. 20-1 and test the conductivity of different solutions he may suggest. Keep a record of your results and report your findings to your class.

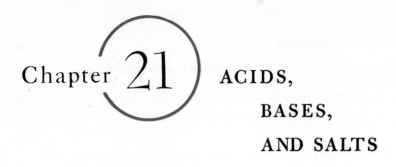

Chapter 21 ACIDS, BASES, AND SALTS

1. ACIDS

1. Acids are an important class of substances. Compounds whose water solutions contain ions are traditionally placed in three general classes: *1. acids; 2. bases;* and *3. salts.* Even in ancient times acids were recognized as a separate class of chemicals. Today we encounter them, directly or indirectly, in practically all of our normal activities.

Nearly all fruits contain acids and so do many common foods. In lemons, oranges, and grapefruit, it is citric acid. In apples, it is malic acid. The souring of milk produces lactic acid. Butter which has become rancid contains butyric acid. The fermentation of hard

VOCABULARY

Acid. A substance containing hydrogen which yields hydrogen ions as the only positive ions in water solution.

Acid anhydride. A compound derived from an acid by the removal of water from the acid.

Amphiprotic. Capable of acting either as an acid or as a base.

Base. A substance that combines with hydrogen ions.

Gram-equivalent weight. The weight of a substance, in grams, which will combine with or replace one gram of hydrogen.

Indicator. A substance which changes in color on the passage from acidity to alkalinity, or the reverse.

Neutralization. The reaction between hydrogen ions and hydroxide ions to form water.

pH. Hydrogen ion index; the common logarithm of the reciprocal of the hydrogen-ion concentration.

Salt. A compound formed by a positive ion, other than hydrogen, and a negative ion, other than hydroxide.

Standard solution. One that contains a definite concentration of solute which is known precisely.

cider forms the acetic acid of vinegar. These, because of their origin and nature, are called *organic* acids. Chemists prepare large quantities of important industrial acids synthetically. Some are made by composition reactions directly from the elements. They are often manufactured from minerals and are known as *inorganic* acids, or more commonly as *mineral* acids.

2. Important industrial acids. If you asked a manufacturing chemist to name the most important acid, he would probably say *sulfuric acid*. This is a very versatile mineral acid. It has been said that the consumption of sulfuric acid is an index to the state of civilization and prosperity of a country. If you asked a dye chemist, or one engaged in making explosives, he would tell you that *nitric acid* is important. A third important industrial acid is *hydrochloric acid*. It is used for cleaning metals before they are plated. It composes about 0.4 percent of the gastric juice of

our stomachs and aids in the preparation of food for digestion. We shall study each of these mineral acids in detail.

1. Sulfuric acid. This acid, which has the formula H_2SO_4, is a dense, oily liquid with a high boiling point. *Concentrated sulfuric acid* contains 95%–98% sulfuric acid, the balance being water. Ordinary *dilute sulfuric acid* is made by pouring 1 part of concentrated sulfuric acid into 6 parts of water.

CAUTION: *The acid may be added to water slowly with stirring, but water must never be added to concentrated sulfuric acid. This will cause a very violent reaction which will produce steam, and spatter the concentrated acid.*

The concentrated acid has a specific gravity of 1.84. Of course it is possible to dilute sulfuric acid, one part of acid to ten parts of water, or in any other desired proportion.

2. Nitric acid. This acid is a volatile

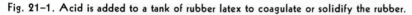

Fig. 21-1. Acid is added to a tank of rubber latex to coagulate or solidify the rubber.

liquid which has the formula HNO_3. The 100% nitric acid is too unstable to be put on the market, but the *concentrated nitric acid* of commerce is fairly stable. It contains 68% nitric acid dissolved in water. Such a solution of pure nitric acid is colorless. It may turn brown on standing, however, due to slight decomposition. Nitric acid may be mixed with water in any proportion. But ordinary *dilute nitric acid* is usually made by adding 1 part of nitric acid to 5 parts of water. It contains about 10% nitric acid. The specific gravity of concentrated nitric acid is 1.42.

3. Hydrochloric acid. Hydrogen chloride, HCl, is a gas which is extremely soluble in water. This solution is known as hydrochloric acid. *Concentrated hydrochloric acid* contains in water solution about 38% by weight of hydrogen chloride. The ordinary dilute hydrochloric acid is made by adding 1 part of concentrated hydrochloric acid to 4 parts of water. Such a solution

contains from 6% to 8% hydrogen chloride. Hydrochloric acid may be diluted to any concentration desired. Water solutions of hydrochloric acid are colorless. Concentrated hydrochloric acid is nearly 1.20 times as dense as water.

3. What is an acid? Arrhenius first gave the clue to the chemical nature of acids in his *Theory of Ionization.* He concluded that all acids ionized in water solutions to form hydrogen ions.

The three acids we have just described are essentially covalent and have one element in common, *hydrogen.* Sulfuric and nitric acids in pure form are exceedingly poor conductors, being only very slightly ionized. Liquid hydrogen chloride, as we have already learned, is considered to be a nonconductor. In water solution, however, each becomes strongly ionized due to the hydrating action of the water dipoles. We may represent their ionization by the following equations:

$$H_2SO_4 + 2\,H_2O \rightarrow 2\,H_3O^+ + SO_4^=$$
$$HNO_3 + H_2O \rightarrow H_3O^+ + NO_3^-$$
$$HCl + H_2O \rightarrow H_3O^+ + Cl^-$$

The presence of the hydronium ion, H_3O^+, is common to all of these solutions. It is apparent that the acidic properties they have in common must be the properties of this ion. When written in the more common form, in which the part played by the water dipoles is omitted, these equations become:

$$H_2SO_4 \rightarrow 2\,H^+ + SO_4^=$$
$$HNO_3 \rightarrow H^+ + NO_3^-$$
$$HCl \rightarrow H^+ + Cl^-$$

Fig. 21-2. This tank car is discharging liquid sulfuric acid into storage tanks at a sulfuric acid plant in Texas.

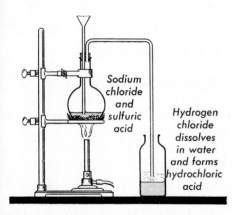

Fig. 21-3. An apparatus for the laboratory preparation of hydrogen chloride.

We may now state the simplest definition of an acid. *An **acid** is a substance which contains hydrogen and yields hydrogen ions as the only positive ions in water solutions.*

Acids which ionize completely, or nearly so, in water solution provide a high concentration of hydrogen ions. They are called *strong* acids. Sulfuric, nitric, and hydrochloric acids are strong mineral acids. Acids which furnish few hydrogen ions in water solution are known as *weak* acids. Acetic and carbonic acids are examples of weak acids.

4. Modern definition of acids. The hydrogen ion is in reality only a proton. It is not conceivable that a free proton can exist in solution. In water solution it is in the hydrated form, H_3O^+. Protons are combined with polar water molecules. *We may consider that protons (hydrogen ions) will not be released by such molecules as HCl unless there are molecules or ions present which can accept them.* This would explain why hydrogen chloride, dissolved in a nonpolar solvent such as toluene, remains a nonconductor.

Hydrogen chloride dissolved in ammonia reacts in the same way it does in water.

$$HCl + H_2O \rightarrow H_3O^+ + Cl^-$$
$$HCl + NH_3 \rightarrow NH_4^+ + Cl^-$$

We may see the way in which the reaction occurs by using electron-dot formulas.

$$H:\overset{..}{\underset{..}{Cl}}: + H:\overset{H}{\underset{H}{N}}:H \rightarrow H:\overset{H}{\underset{H}{N}}:H^+ + :\overset{..}{\underset{..}{Cl}}:^-$$

The proton is transferred directly to the ammonia structure forming the

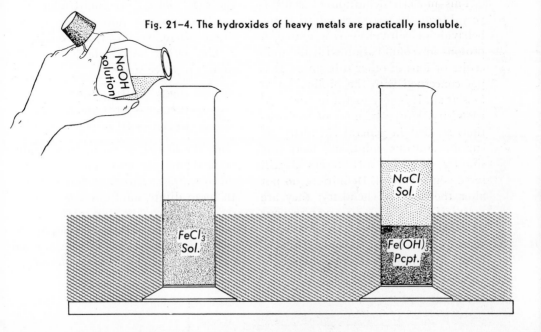

Fig. 21-4. The hydroxides of heavy metals are practically insoluble.

ammonium ion. The proton was given up by the hydrogen chloride molecule, which is said to be a **proton donor.** In the modern concept advanced by J. N. Brönsted, a Danish chemist, *an **acid** is simply a proton donor—a substance which gives up protons to another substance.* Thus hydrogen chloride is an acid, according to Brönsted's theory, even though it doesn't contain hydrogen ions when pure.

According to this more general definition, water is an acid when ammonia is dissolved in it. Some water molecules donate protons to ammonia molecules according to the following reversible reaction:

$$H\!:\!\overset{..}{\underset{H}{N}}\!:\!H + H\!:\!\overset{H}{\underset{..}{\overset{..}{O}}}\!: \rightleftarrows H\!:\!\overset{..}{\underset{H}{N}}\!:\!H^+ + :\!\overset{..}{\underset{H}{O}}\!:^-$$

$$NH_3 + H_2O \rightleftarrows NH_4^+ + OH^-$$

Furthermore, in water solutions of the strong mineral acids described in Section 3, the hydronium ion, H_3O^+, becomes the acid since it is the actual proton donor in reactions involving the solutions.

This modern definition of acids is very broad. It is concerned with the behavior of substances as a source of protons for combination with the molecules or ions of other substances. It is not concerned with the production of ions at all. It is very useful in advanced chemistry. However, most of the reactions studied in general chemistry occur in aqueous solutions. Here the simpler definition of Section 3 will serve you very well. Definitions do not alter the facts of chemistry; they are useful if they help you organize your knowledge of chemistry. In our discussions of acids, bases, and salts, the narrower and simpler concepts which hold

for water solutions will be used extensively.

5. Properties common to acids. Most acids are quite soluble in water. Other physical properties differ so widely that it is not possible to mention many general similarities. But they have several chemical properties in common.

1. Acids contain ionizable hydrogen in covalent combination with a nonmetallic element or radical. The strength of an acid depends upon the degree of ionization in water solution, not upon the *amount* of hydrogen in the molecule. Sulfuric acid ionizes in two stages, depending on the amount of dilution, according to the following ionic equations:

$$H_2SO_4 \rightarrow H^+ + HSO_4^-$$
$$HSO_4^- \rightarrow H^+ + SO_4^=$$

The first stage is completed in fairly concentrated solutions. In this form sulfuric acid may produce *acid salts,* in which the HSO_4^- ion is present. Sodium *hydrogen* sulfate, $NaHSO_4$, is an example. The second stage is completed in rather dilute solutions. Here the $SO_4^=$ ion is present. Under such conditions *normal salts* are formed. Sodium sulfate, Na_2SO_4, is an example.

The rather weak phosphoric acid ionizes in three stages.

$$H_3PO_4 \rightarrow H^+ + H_2PO_4^-$$
$$H_2PO_4^- \rightarrow H^+ + HPO_4^=$$
$$HPO_4^= \rightarrow H^+ + PO_4^{\equiv}$$

Only the first stage occurs in solutions of moderate concentrations producing the *dihydrogen phosphate ion,* $H_2PO_4^-$. In more dilute solutions the *monohydrogen phosphate ion,* $HPO_4^=$, is formed. In very dilute solutions appreciable concentrations of the normal *phosphate ion,* $PO_4^{\equiv}$, may be formed.

2. *All acids furnish hydrogen ions, or protons, when they react with bases.* Their many common properties depend on this characteristic behavior. Acids which furnish only one proton per molecule are called *monoprotic*, or *monobasic*. Examples are HCl, HNO_3, and $HC_2H_3O_2$. Sulfuric acid, H_2SO_4, is *diprotic*, or *dibasic*, giving two protons per molecule. Phosphoric acid, H_3PO_4, is *triprotic*, or *tribasic*.

3. *All acids have a sour taste.* Lemons, grapefruit, and limes are sour. These contain weak acids in solution. A solid acid tastes sour as it dissolves in the saliva forming a water solution. Most laboratory acids are very corrosive and powerful poisons. You should never use the *"taste test"* for an acid in the laboratory.

4. *Acids affect indicators.* If we touch a drop of an acid solution to a test strip of blue *litmus*, the *blue* color will change to *red*. Litmus is a dye extracted from certain lichens. Some other substances may be used as indicators. *Phenolphthalein* in the presence of acids is colorless. *Methyl orange* is another indicator. It turns red in acid solutions.

5. *Acids neutralize hydroxides.* If we mix solutions of an acid and a metallic hydroxide in equivalent quantities, each exactly cancels the properties of the other. This process is called **neutralization**. The products are a salt and water. The salt may be recovered in crystalline form by the evaporation of the water. We commonly say that an acid neutralizes a hydroxide, but it is just as accurate to say that the hydroxide neutralizes the acid.

When one mole of sodium hydroxide is treated with one mole of hydrochloric acid the following reaction occurs:

$$HCl + NaOH \rightarrow NaCl + H_2O$$

Since both reactants and the salt product are in completely ionized form, the ionic equation is more appropriate.

$$H^+ + Cl^- + Na^+ + OH^- \rightarrow$$
$$Na^+ + Cl^- + H_2O$$

We see that sodium ions and chloride ions remain in solution and actually play no part in the reaction. By writing the simplest ionic equation, we eliminate these *"spectator"* ions and show only those which actually participate in the primary action.

$$H^+ + OH^- \rightarrow H_2O$$

or

$$H_3O^+ + OH^- \rightarrow 2\ H_2O$$

This shows that the neutralization reaction is entirely between the hydrogen ion of the acid and the hydroxide ion of the soluble metallic hydroxide. In all neutralizations of very soluble hydroxides by strong acids the reaction is the same. The nonmetallic ions of the acid and the metallic ions of the hydroxide undergo no chemical change. We usually prefer to write the complete equation because it shows what salt could be recovered by evaporation of the water solvent.

6. *Acids react with many metals.* They set free hydrogen and form a salt. The equation for the action of sulfuric acid on zinc is typical:

$$Zn + H_2SO_4 \rightarrow ZnSO_4 + H_2\uparrow$$

Written ionically, the equation is:

$$Zn + 2\ H^+ + SO_4^= \rightarrow Zn^{++} + SO_4^= + H_2\uparrow$$

The salt separates as crystals of $ZnSO_4$ on evaporation of the water. You must remember that in solution, such *"salts"* are simply a dispersion of hydrated ions.

7. *Acids react with oxides of metals.*
They form salts and water. As an example, let us use cupric oxide and sulfuric acid. The equation follows:

$$CuO + H_2SO_4 \rightarrow CuSO_4 + H_2O$$

8. *Acids react with carbonates.* They
liberate carbon dioxide and produce a
salt and water.

$$CaCO_3 + 2\,HCl \rightarrow CaCl_2 + H_2O + CO_2\uparrow$$

6. How are acids named? Some
acids are *binary* compounds; others are
ternary compounds. *Binary* compounds
contain *two* elements, while *ternary*
compounds contain *three* elements.

1. Binary acids. Hydrogen chloride
in water solution is called *hydro-chlor-
ic* acid. The prefix *hydro-* shows it is a
binary acid. The root *-chlor-* is derived
from the element chlorine. Binary acids
always have the ending *-ic.* A water solution of HBr is called *hydro-brom-ic*
acid. A water solution of hydrogen sulfide, H_2S, is known as *hydro-sulfur-ic*
acid.

2. Ternary acids. Let us use the formulas and names of the various acids
of chlorine to illustrate the method of
naming acids which contain hydrogen,
oxygen, and a third element.

$HClO_4$ · · · · · · · · · · · · · · ·per-chlor-ic acid

$HClO_3$ · · · · · · · · · · · · · · · · ·chlor-ic acid

$HClO_2$ · · · · · · · · · · · · · · · ·chlor-ous acid

$HClO$ · · · · · · · · · · · · ·hypo-chlor-ous acid

In all of these acids chlorine is the
central element. For this reason the
root *chlor-* is used in each case. $HClO_3$
is named *chlor-ic acid.* No prefix is
used. The acid of chlorine which contains *more* oxygen than chloric acid is
called *per-chlor-ic* acid. The chlorine
acid containing *one less* oxygen atom
per molecule than chloric acid is called

chlor-ous acid. The acid of chlorine
which contains *still less* oxygen than
chlorous acid has the prefix *hypo-*, the
root *-chlor-*, and the suffix *-ous.*

In order to use these rules for naming acids you must know the formula
for one ternary acid containing oxygen
in any series. Chloric acid is $HClO_3$,
nitric acid is HNO_3, and bromic acid
is $HBrO_3$. But the formula for sulfuric
acid is H_2SO_4, and the formula for
phosphoric acid is H_3PO_4.

7. What are acid anhydrides? The
oxides of nonmetallic elements that react with water form acids. When carbon dioxide dissolves in water a reversible reaction occurs.

$$CO_2 + H_2O \rightleftharpoons H_2CO_3$$

If we heat the carbonic acid which is
formed, it decomposes into water and
carbon dioxide. Because we have really
dehydrated the acid, carbon dioxide is
called the *acid anhydride* of carbonic
acid. *Oxides that react with water to
form acids, or that are formed by the
removal of water from acids, are known
as* **acid anhydrides.**

There are several acids which do not
contain oxygen. The reaction between
an acid anhydride and water cannot
be considered a general method of preparing acids. However, it is an important method of preparing some oxygen-
containing acids.

Sulfur dioxide is the acid anhydride
of sulfurous acid.

$$SO_2 + H_2O \rightleftharpoons H_2SO_3$$

Sulfur trioxide is the acid anhydride
of sulfuric acid.

$$SO_3 + H_2O \rightleftharpoons H_2SO_4$$

These anhydrides are important in the
manufacture of sulfuric acid. Sulfuric

acid, because it is cheap and has a high boiling point, is used in the production of several other acids. Hydrochloric acid is an example of such a use, although important quantities of hydrochloric acid are now being produced by direct composition from the elements hydrogen and chlorine.

2. BASES

8. What is a base? There are several substances found in almost every home that have long been called bases. Household ammonia, an ammonia-water solution, is a common cleaning agent. Lye is a commercial grade of sodium hydroxide, NaOH, used for cleaning clogged sink drains. Limewater is a solution of calcium hydroxide, $Ca(OH)_2$. Milk of magnesia is a suspension of magnesium hydroxide, $Mg(OH)_2$, in water. It finds use as an antacid, a laxative, and an antidote when strong acids are swallowed.

Arrhenius considered a base to be any soluble hydroxide which destroyed the properties of an acid when their solutions were mixed. We know, of course, that the only reaction occurring in the neutralization is between hydrogen ions (hydronium ions) and hydroxide ions. The nonmetal of the acid and the metal of the hydroxide remain in solution as hydrated ions.

Bases are now defined as substances which combine with hydrogen ions. The hydroxide ion is the most common base. It combines with the hydrogen ion to form water. The soluble metallic hydroxides which yield hydroxide ions when dissolved in water, together with ammonia water, are still frequently referred to as bases. However, *it is the hydroxide ion which reacts as the base in the neutralization process.* Ammonia-water solutions are habitually referred to as ammonium hydroxide. It is questionable whether any ammonium hydroxide molecules, as such, actually exist in the solution. The most common basic solutions used in the laboratory are those of NaOH, KOH, $Ca(OH)_2$, and NH_3 in water. These solutions are said to be *alkaline* in their behavior.

In the modern concept of Brönsted, an acid is simply a proton donor. Accordingly, *a base is a proton acceptor.* Since the OH^- ion is not the only particle that combines with H^+ ions, our general use of the term base includes other substances which accept protons.

We have learned that hydrogen chloride ionizes in water solution as a result of the hydrating action of the solvent dipoles.

$$HCl + H_2O \rightarrow H_3O^+ + Cl^-$$

Here the water molecule is the base, accepting H^+ ions to form the hydronium ion H_3O^+. In the neutralization reaction between HCl and NaOH described earlier, the H_3O^+ ion may be considered to be the acid, since it, and not the HCl molecule, is the proton donor. The OH^- ion is, of course, the proton acceptor or base.

When HCl is dissolved in liquid ammonia, the NH_3 molecule acts as the base.

$$HCl + NH_3 \rightarrow NH_4^+ + Cl^-$$

When NH_3 is dissolved in water, protons are donated by the water which, therefore, acts as an acid. Ammonia accepts protons and is therefore the base. A low concentration of NH_4^+ ions and OH^- ions is produced in the reversible action.

$$NH_3 + H_2O \rightleftarrows NH_4^+ + OH^-$$

It is possible that some NH_4^+ ions and OH^- ions combine to form ammonium hydroxide molecules through hydrogen bond formation. This seems to be the only basis for the molecular formula NH_4OH.

This general concept of acids and bases is quite broad for elementary chemistry but is very useful in more advanced studies of nonaqueous solutions. We shall deal essentially with soluble metallic hydroxides and their water solutions containing the basic hydroxide ion.

9. The characteristics of hydroxides. A careful study of soluble hydroxide substances shows that they have several characteristics in common.

1. Hydroxides of the active metals furnish OH⁻ ions in solution. Sodium and potassium hydroxides are very soluble in water. They are electrovalent (ionic) compounds and so are completely ionized in water solution. Their solutions are *strongly basic* due to the high concentration of OH^- ions.

$$Na^+OH^- \rightarrow Na^+ + OH^-$$
$$K^+OH^- \rightarrow K^+ + OH^-$$

Calcium, strontium, and barium hydroxides are not very soluble in water. However, they too are ionic compounds. Their water solutions are completely ionized and are *moderately basic.*

$$Ca^{++}(OH^-)_2 \rightarrow Ca^{++} + 2\ OH^-$$
$$Sr^{++}(OH^-)_2 \rightarrow Sr^{++} + 2\ OH^-$$
$$Ba^{++}(OH^-)_2 \rightarrow Ba^{++} + 2\ OH^-$$

We can see that the strength of the base depends on the concentration of OH^- ions in solution and not on the number of hydroxide ions per formula weight of the compound.

Ammonia-water solutions are *weakly basic* due to a low concentration of OH^- ions. Ammonia, NH_3, is not a strong base and so does not acquire very many protons from water molecules when in solution. Relatively few NH_4^+ ions and OH^- ions are formed.

2. Soluble hydroxides have a bitter taste. Possibly you have tasted limewater and know that it is bitter. Soapsuds also taste bitter because of the presence of hydroxide ions. The *taste test* should never be used in the laboratory. Strongly basic solutions are very *caustic.* The accompanying metallic ions are usually quite poisonous.

3. Solutions of hydroxides feel slippery. The very soluble hydroxides, such as sodium hydroxide, attack the skin and are capable of producing severe caustic burns. Their solutions have a soapy, slippery feeling when rubbed between the thumb and fingers.

4. Soluble hydroxides affect indicators. The basic OH^- ions in solutions of the soluble hydroxides cause *litmus* to turn from *red* to *blue*. This is just the opposite color change to that caused by H^+ ions of acid solutions. In the basic solution, *phenolphthalein* turns *red*. *Methyl orange* is *yellow* in the presence of OH^- ions. The insoluble hydroxides, on the other hand, seldom produce enough OH^- ions to cause these changes. They do not affect indicators.

5. Hydroxides neutralize acids. The neutralization of HNO_3 by KOH may be represented by the ionic equation:

$$K^+ + OH^- + H^+ + NO_3^- \rightarrow$$
$$K^+ + NO_3^- + H_2O$$

Removing the *spectator* ions, those which undergo no change during the reaction, we have:

$$H^+ + OH^- \rightarrow H_2O$$

This is the only action that takes place in the neutralization reaction. The hydrated K^+ and NO_3^- ions are joined in the form of ionic crystals of the salt, KNO_3, only upon removal of the water by evaporation.

6. Hydroxides react with the oxides of nonmetals. They form salts and water. As an example, let us use carbon dioxide and sodium hydroxide. The equation for this reaction is:

$$CO_2 + 2\,NaOH \rightarrow Na_2CO_3 + H_2O$$

7. Certain hydroxides may have either acidic or basic properties. Certain hydroxide substances which are weakly basic in the presence of acids may also behave as acids in the presence of strong bases. Zinc hydroxide, $Zn(OH)_2$, reacts with hydrochloric acid to produce zinc chloride and water.

$$Zn(OH)_2 + 2\,HCl \rightarrow ZnCl_2 + 2\,H_2O$$

In the presence of a solution of sodium hydroxide it acts as an acid.

$$Zn(OH)_2 + 2\,NaOH \rightarrow Na_2ZnO_2 + 2\,H_2O$$

We may more readily understand this behavior of $Zn(OH)_2$ if we rewrite its formula as H_2ZnO_2. *Such substances which may have either acidic or basic properties under certain conditions are said to be* **amphiprotic,** *or* **amphoteric.** The hydroxides of aluminum, chromium, tin, and lead are also *amphiprotic.*

In the modern concept of acids and bases, water is an amphiprotic substance. When a water molecule accepts a proton from hydrogen chloride it acts

as a base. On the other hand, when a water molecule donates a proton to ammonia it acts as an acid. Indeed, in the slight ionization of water, one water molecule donates a proton to another water molecule. Thus, some of the water molecules behave as an acid while others behave as a base.

10. How are hydroxides named? The method of naming the hydroxides is very simple. You merely use the name of the metallic ion and follow it with the term *hydroxide.* For example, $Zn(OH)_2$ is *zinc hydroxide.* $Bi(OH)_3$ is *bismuth hydroxide.*

If two hydroxides are formed by a metal, the suffixes *-ous* and *-ic* are used to denote the lower and higher valence of the metal respectively. Thus $Fe(OH)_2$ is called *ferrous* hydroxide and $Fe(OH)_3$ is called *ferric hydroxide.*

Ammonium hydroxide is the name commonly used for a solution of ammonia in water. We know, of course, that the existence of ammonium hydroxide molecules is unlikely. Relatively few of the ammonia molecules take on protons from water molecules. The concentration of NH_4^+ ions and OH^- ions is very low compared to the molecular concentration of ammonia, NH_3.

11. What are basic anhydrides? In Chapter 8, Section 3, we learned that the active metals react with water to produce hydrogen gas and the corresponding hydroxide. These metallic hydroxides are ionic in structure and exist in solution as hydrated metallic and hydroxide ions.

The denser metals form hydroxides which are practically insoluble in water. These are produced more conveniently by indirect methods using a salt and a soluble hydroxide.

$$Fe^{+++} + 3\ Cl^- + 3\ Na^+ + 3\ OH^- \rightarrow$$
$$Fe(OH)_3\downarrow + 3\ Na^+ + 3\ Cl^-$$

As the reaction involves only the Fe^{+++} and OH^- ions, we may write the simpler equation:

$$Fe^{+++} + 3\ OH^- \rightarrow Fe(OH)_3\downarrow$$

Such precipitates are found to vary somewhat in composition, depending on the conditions under which they are formed. The actual composition is that of a *hydrated oxide*. In the case above the precipitate is more correctly represented as $Fe_2O_3 \cdot (H_2O)_n$, where n is some small integer which varies with conditions. It is a matter of convenience in equation writing to represent such precipitates as hydroxides. Aluminum, chrominum, tin, and lead also form hydrated oxides.

The oxides of active metals react with water to produce the corresponding hydroxides. If the hydroxide is soluble in water, the solution is basic due to the presence of OH^- ions. Oxides of sodium, potassium, calcium, strontium, and barium react vigorously with water. You may have seen a plasterer *slaking* quicklime, CaO, by adding water to it. He was forming *slaked lime,* $Ca(OH)_2$.

$$CaO + H_2O \rightarrow Ca(OH)_2$$

Oxides which react with water to produce solutions containing the basic OH^- ions are called **basic anhydrides.** The oxides of the active metals are *basic anhydrides.* They are electrovalent compounds which, as solids, have ionic crystalline structures. In contrast, acid anhydrides are oxides of nonmetals. They are covalent compounds which, in the solid state, have molecular crystalline structures.

★ 3. STANDARD SOLUTIONS

★ **12. The pH of a solution.** The concentration of H^+ ions (as H_3O^+ ions) in a solution may be expressed as *gram-ions* per liter. A more convenient way, however, is to indicate the concentration indirectly by a numerical scale called the *pH scale,* or *hydrogen ion index.* Numerically, *the pH of a solution is the logarithm of the number of liters of solution that contains 1 gram-atom of hydrogen as H^+ (H_3O^+) ions.*

The number of liters of solution required to furnish 1 gram-ion of H^+ is equal to the *reciprocal* of the H^+ ion concentration given in gram-ions of H^+ per liter. This is expressed by chemists as

$$\frac{1}{[H^+]}$$

where $[H^+]$ means H^+ ion concentration in *gram-ions per liter.* Thus the pH of a solution is determined by the equation:

$$pH = \log \frac{1}{[H^+]}$$

Pure water is slightly ionized. Chemists have found that it contains 0.000 0001 gram-ion of H^+ (as H_3O^+) per liter. The pH of water is therefore:

$$pH = \log \frac{1}{0.0000001}$$
$$pH = \log \frac{1}{10^{-7}}$$
$$pH = \log 10^7$$
$$pH = 7$$

The common logarithm of a number is the power to which 10 must be raised to give the number. Thus 0.0000001 is

10^{-7} and its reciprocal is 10,000,000, or 10^7. The logarithm of 10^7 is 7.

We know that the H^+ and OH^- ion concentrations in pure water are equal. Water is therefore *neutral*. *All solutions in which the H^+ and OH^- ion concentrations are equal are called* **neutral solutions.** The product of the two ionic concentrations is a *constant.* Thus, in any solution, if the concentration of one ion *decreases,* the concentration of the other must *increase.* The total range of pH values is from 0 to 14. All neutral solutions have a pH of 7.

If the H^+ ion concentration is *greater* than that in pure water, the number of liters required to provide 1 gram-ion of H^+ is *smaller.* Consequently, the pH is a *smaller* number than 7. Such a solution acts as an *acid.* Conversely, if the H^+ ion concentration is *less than* that in pure water, the pH is a *larger* number than 7. Such a solution acts as a *base.*

Special indicators, such as Hydrion paper, show varying shades of color which correspond to the whole range of pH values. To measure the *acidity* or *alkalinity* (basicity) of a solution, we place a drop of the solution on the paper. The color plate facing page 345 shows the colors obtained when using solutions of different pH values.

Gramercy Universal Indicator is a mixture of solutions of dyes that can be used to measure the pH of a solution. To 10 ml of solution, 1 ml of the indicator solution is added. By comparing the color produced with the chart facing page 345, we obtain a rather accurate determination of the pH.

★ **13. What are standard solutions?** Many chemical reactions occur in solution. We learned in Chapter 13 that just so much of one substance would

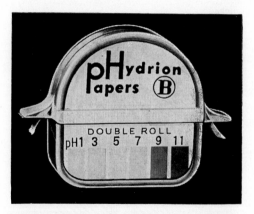

Fig. 21–5. Approximate pH values over a wide range may be determined by the use of special indicators.

react with a given quantity of another substance. If we know the concentration of one solution, it is sometimes a simple matter to determine the concentration of another solution by reacting the two solutes.

APPROXIMATE pH OF SOME COMMON SUBSTANCES	
0.1-N HCl	1.1
0.1-N H_2SO_4	1.2
gastric juice	2.0
lemons	2.3
vinegar	2.9
soft drinks	3.0
apples	3.1
grapefruit	3.1
oranges	3.5
0.1-N $HC_2H_3O_2$	3.8
tomatoes	4.2
bananas	4.6
bread	5.5
potatoes	5.8
rainwater	6.2
milk	6.5
pure water	7.0
eggs	7.8
0.1-N $NaHCO_3$	8.4
seawater	8.5
milk of magnesia	10.5
0.1-N NH_3	11.1
0.1-N Na_2CO_3	11.6
0.1-N NaOH	13.0

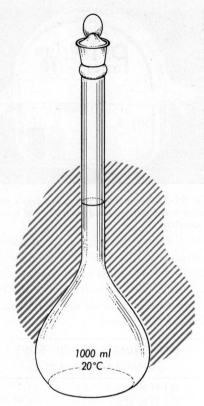

Fig. 21–6. Volumetric flask. When filled to the mark at 20° C, it contains 1000 ml.

In Chapter 19, Section 8, we expressed the concentration of solutions quantitatively in terms of *molality, molarity (formality),* and *normality.* There are certain advantages to each method. *A standard solution is one that contains a definite concentration of solute which is known precisely.*

★ **14. Standard solutions of known molality.** We can make a *molal* solution (1 m) of a substance by weighing out precisely *one mole* of the substance and then dissolving it in 1000 g of solvent. A *half-molal* solution (0.5 m) contains *one half mole* of solute per 1000 g of solvent. A *two-molal* solution (2 m) has *two moles* of solute in 1000 g of solvent.

Molal solutions are important to the chemist because *two solutions of equal molality have the same ratio between the number of solute and solvent molecules.* Molality is preferred when portions are to be weighed. This type of solution is essential in molecular weight determinations.

★ **15. Standard solutions of known molarity.** A *molar solution* (1 M) contains *1 mole* of solute per *liter* of solution. The gram-formula weight of sodium chloride, NaCl, is 58.5 g. Let us weigh out this quantity of NaCl and dissolve it in some water in a volumetric flask like that shown in Fig. 21-6. Then let us dilute the solution with water up to the mark on the neck of the flask. This flask now contains 1 liter of solution. We stopper the flask and shake it until the solution is uniform. Our solution, since it contains 1 gram-formula weight of NaCl in 1 liter of solution, is said to be *1 molar* (1 M). If we had used only one half mole, 29.25 g, in 1 liter of solution, our solution would be one half molar (0.5 M). Using two moles, or 117 g, in 1 liter of solution, makes the solution 2 M.

Taking another example, the molecular weight of H_2SO_4 is 98. To make 1 liter of a 1-M solution of H_2SO_4 requires 98 g of the solute. A 0.5-M solution needs only one half of 98 g, or 49 g, of H_2SO_4 per liter of solution. Notice that a molar solution is based on the *volume of solution.* Molal solutions are based on the *weight of solvent.* Equal *volumes of molecular solutions of equal molarity have the same number of molecules.* Molarity is preferred when volumes of solution are to be measured.

★ **16. Standard for equivalent weights.** Hydrogen is used as the standard for equivalent weight relations.

The *equivalent weight* of an element was defined in Chapter 19, Section 8, as the weight of an element which combines with, or replaces, 1 gram of hydrogen. This weight expressed in grams is called the *gram-equivalent weight* of a substance. The equivalent weight of an element is ordinarily determined by dividing its atomic weight by its valence.

The equivalent weight of oxygen is 8 (16 ÷ 2). Eight grams of oxygen combines with 1 gram of hydrogen. Sodium has a gram-equivalent weight of 23 g (23 ÷ 1). Twenty-three grams of sodium will replace 1 g of hydrogen, and will combine with 8 g of oxygen. Thus 23 g of Na, 8 g of O_2, and 1 g of H_2 are *chemical equivalents*.

The equivalent weight of a compound is determined by dividing its molecular (formula) weight by its total positive (or negative) valence. A mole of H_2SO_4 is 98 g. The total valence (positive or negative) is 2. One gram-equivalent weight of sulfuric acid is 49 g, one half mole. One mole of $Ca_3(PO_4)_2$ is 310 g. The total valence is 6. One gram-equivalent weight of $Ca_3(PO_4)_2$ is 51.7 g, one sixth mole.

★ **17. Standard solutions of known normality.** A *normal solution* (1 N) contains *1 gram-equivalent weight* of solute per *liter* of solution. Let us prepare a liter of 0.1-N HCl. The g-mol. wt. of HCl is 36.5 g. The total valence is 1, thus the g-eq. wt. is 36.5 g. We wish to have only 0.1 gram-equivalent of HCl per liter of solution. We must use 3.65 g of HCl diluted to 1 liter volume. *But this is 3.65 g of anhydrous hydrogen chloride in one liter of solution,* not 3.65 g of the concentrated hydrochloric acid on hand in the laboratory. How may we determine the volume of

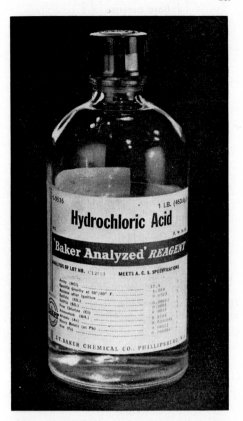

Fig. 21–7. The manufacturer's label on a reagent bottle carries information that is important to the chemist.

concentrated hydrochloric acid to be measured out which will contain 3.65 g of hydrogen chloride? This may be found very simply from the *assay* information printed on the manufacturer's label on the bottle of concentrated hydrochloric acid (see Fig. 21-7).

Let us suppose that our concentrated HCl is 37.23% HCl by weight and has a specific gravity of 1.19. One ml of the solution weighs 1.19 g of which 37.23% is HCl. One ml then contains

$$0.3723 \times 1.19 \text{ g} = 0.443 \text{ g of HCl}$$

and the volume of solution needed to provide 3.65 g of HCl is

$$3.65 \text{ g} \div 0.443 \text{ g/ml} = 8.43 \text{ ml con. HCl}$$

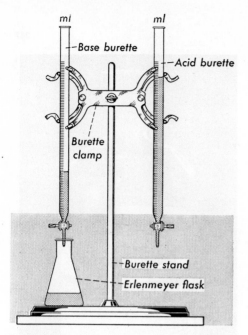

ml ml

—Base burette

—Acid burette

Burette
clamp

—Burette stand

—Erlenmeyer flask

Fig. 21–8. Burettes are used to measure standard solutions accurately.

We have already seen that 1 mole of H_2SO_4 contains 2 gram-equivalents. A normal solution (1 N) contains 49 g (98 ÷ 2) of H_2SO_4 per liter of solution. A 5-N solution contains 245 g (49 × 5) of H_2SO_4 per liter, and 0.01-N H_2SO_4 contains 0.49 g (49 ÷ 100) H_2SO_4 per liter of solution. Concentrated sulfuric acid is usually 95%–98% H_2SO_4 and has a specific gravity of about 1.84.

Crystalline salts containing water of hydration must be given special consideration in making up standard solutions. For example, crystalline cupric sulfate has the empirical formula $CuSO_4 \cdot 5 H_2O$. A 1-M $CuSO_4$ solution would contain 159.5 g of $CuSO_4$ per liter of solution. However, the formula weight of this hydrate is 249.5. Crystalline cupric sulfate is 64% $CuSO_4$. This fact must be recognized when weighing out moles or gram-equivalents of such crystalline hydrates.

If a mole of a solute contains 1 g-eq.

wt., the molarity and normality of the solution *are the same.* Thus a 1-M HCl solution is also a 1-N solution. If a mole of solute has 2 g-eq. wt., a 1-M solution is 2 N. A 1-M H_2SO_4 solution is therefore 2 N. Similarly a 1-M H_3PO_4 solution is 3 N. *The advantage of normality is that solutions of equal normality are chemically equivalent, volume for volume.*

★ **18. Standard solutions and titration.** We know that the H+ ion of an acid and the basic OH− ion combine in a neutralization reaction to form a molecule of water. One gram-ion of H+ (1 gram) and 1 gram-ion of OH− (17 grams) are chemically equivalent.

Suppose we wish to know the concentration of acetic acid in a sample of vinegar. We may *titrate* the vinegar against a sodium hydroxide solution of known normality, using a pair of burettes as shown in Fig. 21-8. The standard solution is added to a measured volume of the vinegar until the two solutions are mixed in equivalent quantities. This is shown by the color change of a suitable indicator in the vinegar.

Assume that our standard solution was 0.1-N NaOH and 50 ml was required to neutralize 10 ml of the vinegar. Since it takes 5 times as much sodium hydroxide solution as acid, it is obvious that the acid solution is 5 times as concentrated as the basic solution. Therefore, the vinegar is 0.5 N due to the amount of acetic acid present. A 1-N solution of acetic acid, $HC_2H_3O_2$, contains 60 g of solute per liter. Then the 0.5-N solution contains 30 g of $HC_2H_3O_2$ per liter. A liter of vinegar weighs approximately 1000 g. The sample of vinegar is, therefore, 3% acetic acid.

INDICATOR	ACID COLOR	pH RANGE	ALKALINE COLOR
METHYL ORANGE	red	3–5	yellow
LITMUS	pink	6–8	blue
PHENOLPHTHALEIN	colorless	8–10	red

This method of determining the concentration of a solution is called *titration*. The *end-point* of the titration is reached when the quantities of acid and hydroxide (H^+ ions and OH^- ions) are chemically equivalent. Ideally, the indicator color change should occur at a pH of 7. Actually, it may be desirable to use an indicator which changes color at a higher or lower pH.

★ **19. Indicators in titration.** Chemists have a wide choice of indicators for use in titrations. They are able to choose one which changes color over the right pH range for the reaction in question. Let us see why it is not always suitable to have our indicator change color at a pH of 7.

Solutions of soluble hydroxides and acids mixed in chemically equivalent quantities may not be exactly neutral. They will be neutral only if both solutes are ionized to the same degree. The purpose of the indicator is to show that the end-point has been reached—that is, when equivalent quantities of the two solutes are together. The accompanying table shows the color changes of three common indicators used in acid-hydroxide titrations.

The combinations of acidic and basic solutions involved in titration, which have end-points occurring in different pH ranges, are as follows:

1. Strong acid–strong hydroxide: pH is about 7. Litmus is a suitable indicator.

2. Strong acid–weak hydroxide: pH is less than 7. Methyl orange is a suitable indicator.

3. Weak acid–strong hydroxide: pH is greater than 7. Phenolphthalein is a suitable indicator.

4. Weak acid–weak hydroxide: pH may be either greater than or less than 7, depending on which solution is stronger. None of the indicators works very well.

4. SALTS

20. What is a salt? Common table salt, NaCl, is only one of a large class of compounds which the chemist calls by the name, *salt*.

An acid in water solution ionizes forming hydrogen ions which are positive. It must also form negative ions. A soluble metallic hydroxide is an ionic solid which, when dissolved in water, dissociates, releasing hydroxide ions which are negative. It must also release positive ions. The hydrogen and hydroxide ions are almost entirely removed, when two such solutions are mixed, as they form water which is only very slightly ionized. What happens to the negative ions of the acid and the positive ions of the hydroxide? *Nothing happens to them.* They have no part in the reaction which occurs, a neutralization reaction. They are simply spectator ions. For example:

$$H^+ + Cl^- + K^+ + OH^- \rightarrow$$
$$K^+ + Cl^- + H_2O$$

After the water is evaporated, the oppositely charged ions are no longer isolated from each other by water dipoles. They form a characteristic ionic crystalline structure and separate from solution as a salt. *Any compound, formed by any positive ion except hydrogen (hydronium) combining with any negative ion except hydroxide, is called a salt.* All true salts, by this definition, are electrovalent substances. They are strong electrolytes and are completely ionized in water solution.

21. Salts have varied properties. The properties of the hundreds of salts known to chemists differ widely. It is, therefore, almost impossible to list any general properties at all. We have already learned that some salts combine with water to form crystals containing water of hydration.

Probably the most important property of a salt is its solubility. In Table 7 of the Appendix, you will find a rather complete list of salts with their solubility in water and in acids. However, a few general solubility rules that are worth remembering follow for your guidance. Study the table below.

22. What reactions produce salts? There are several ways in which salts are formed, but not all of them are applicable to the formation of every salt.

1. Direct union of the elements. Sodium may be burned in chlorine to produce the salt, sodium chloride.

$$2\,Na + Cl_2 \rightarrow 2\,NaCl$$

2. Salts are formed by the replacement of the hydrogen of an acid by a metal. Zinc will react with hydrochloric acid to form zinc chloride and hydrogen.

$$Zn + 2\,HCl \rightarrow ZnCl_2 + H_2\uparrow$$

3. The oxide of a metal may react with an acid to form a salt. Sodium oxide, Na_2O, can be treated with hydrochloric acid, to form sodium chloride and water.

$$Na_2O + 2\,HCl \rightarrow 2\,NaCl + H_2O$$

4. The oxide of a nonmetal may react with a soluble hydroxide to form a salt. Carbon dioxide, in reacting with limewater, $Ca(OH)_2$, forms calcium carbonate and water.

$$CO_2 + Ca(OH)_2 \rightarrow CaCO_3\downarrow + H_2O$$

5. Acids neutralize soluble hydroxides and form salts. Sodium hydroxide and hydrochloric acid are mixed in chemically equivalent quantities. The solvent is evaporated and sodium chloride remains. Many different salts can be prepared by neutralization.

$$NaOH + HCl \rightarrow NaCl + H_2O$$

6. Two salts may be prepared at one time by double replacement. Let us add a solution of sodium sulfate, Na_2SO_4, to a solution of barium chloride, $BaCl_2$.

SOLUBILITY OF SALTS

1. Common sodium, potassium, and ammonium compounds are soluble in water.

2. Common nitrates, acetates, and chlorates are soluble.

3. Common chlorides are soluble except silver, mercurous, and lead. (Lead chloride is soluble in hot water.)

4. Common sulfates are soluble except calcium, barium, strontium, and lead.

5. Common carbonates, phosphates, and silicates are insoluble except sodium, potassium, and ammonium.

6. Common sulfides are insoluble except calcium, barium, strontium, magnesium, sodium, potassium, and ammonium.

They react according to the following equation:

$$Ba^{++} + 2\ Cl^- + 2\ Na^+ + SO_4^= \rightarrow$$
$$2\ Na^+ + 2\ Cl^- + BaSO_4\downarrow$$

It is not usually possible to separate two salts unless one of them is insoluble. In this case barium sulfate is insoluble. It can be filtered from the solution. The water may then be evaporated to obtain the other, which of course would not be in pure form.

7. Salts may be formed by the action of an acid on a carbonate. If we add some hydrochloric acid, HCl, to a solution of sodium carbonate, Na_2CO_3, the following reaction occurs:

$$2\ HCl + Na_2CO_3 \rightarrow$$
$$2\ NaCl + H_2O + CO_2\uparrow$$

Carbon dioxide bubbles out of the mixture as a gas. The sodium chloride may be recovered by evaporation.

23. How are salts named? Salts are generally named by combining the names of the ions from which they are formed. For instance, $Ba(NO_3)_2$ is barium nitrate. Ba is the symbol for barium, and NO_3 is the formula for the nitrate radical. Likewise, $FeCl_3$ is

ferric chloride. Fe, with a valence of $+3$, is the symbol for fer*ric*. Cl, with a valence of -1, is chlor*ide*. $FeCl_2$, in which Fe has a valence of $+2$, is fer*rous* chloride. Names of the positive ions are generally the same as the names of the elements from which they are derived. In the case of elements of variable valence, the Latin name often forms the root of the ion name. The suffixes *-ous* and *-ic* indicate the lower and higher valences respectively. For example, the Latin name for iron is *ferrum*. The two ions of iron are *ferrous,* with $+2$ valence, and *ferric,* with $+3$ valence. The names of the negative ions take the same root and prefix as the acid in which they occur. But the ending *-ic* is changed to *-ate,* and the ending *-ous* is changed to *-ite.* Salts derived from binary acids take the ending *-ide.* The accompanying table shows the formulas for many common acids. It also gives the names of the acids, and the names of the negative ions of the salts which are derived from these acids. By carefully studying this table and the table of valences, you should be able to name salts easily.

FORMULA	NAME OF ACID	NAME OF NEGATIVE ION OF SALT
HF	hydrofluoric	fluoride
HBr	hydrobromic	bromide
HI	hydriodic	iodide
HCl	hydrochloric	chloride
HClO	hypochlorous	hypochlorite
$HClO_2$	chlorous	chlorite
$HClO_3$	chloric	chlorate
$HClO_4$	perchloric	perchlorate
H_2S	hydrosulfuric	sulfide
H_2SO_3	sulfurous	sulfite
H_2SO_4	sulfuric	sulfate
HNO_2	nitrous	nitrite
HNO_3	nitric	nitrate
H_2CO_3	carbonic	carbonate
H_3PO_3	phosphorous	phosphite
H_3PO_4	phosphoric	phosphate

Summary

An acid, defined in its narrower sense, is a substance which contains hydrogen and yields hydrogen ions as the only positive ions in water solutions. In the more general modern sense, an acid is a proton donor. Hydrogen ions are protons and in water solution are always hydrated in the form H_3O^+. Acids are covalent molecular substances which ionize in water solution. Strong acids ionize completely in dilute solutions. Weak acids ionize incompletely. Diprotic acids ionize in two stages. Triprotic acids ionize in three stages. The last stage may make only slight progress even in very dilute solutions. Acids have many common characteristics which may be due to the formation of H_3O^+ ions in their water solutions. Nonmetallic oxides that combine with water to form acids are called acid anhydrides.

Bases are substances which combine with the hydrogen ions from acids. In the modern sense they are proton acceptors. The hydroxide ion is the most common base. Hydroxide ions are present in water solutions of soluble metallic hydroxides. The hydroxides of the active metals are ionic substances. Those which are very soluble in water form solutions which are strongly basic. Those which are moderately soluble form solutions which are moderately basic. Ammonia dissolves in water, taking some protons from the water molecules to form a low concentration of NH_4^+ and OH^- ions. Ammonia-water solutions are weakly basic. The common characteristics of soluble hydroxides are attributed to the properties of the hydroxide ion. A convenient way of indicating the concentration of hydrogen ions in a solution is to use the hydrogen-ion index, or pH. The pH range extends from 0 to 14. Numerically, the pH is the logarithm of the number of liters of a solution that contains 1 gram-atom of hydrogen as H^+ (H_3O^+) ions. The pH of pure water is 7. This is also the pH of any neutral solution. A pH less than 7 indicates an acid, greater than 7, an alkaline solution. Indicators are used to show the pH of a solution, and also to show the end-point of neutralization reactions or titrations.

Standard solutions are solutions of precisely known concentrations. Concentration is expressed in molality, molarity, or normality. Solutions of equal molality have the same ratio between the number of solute and solvent molecules. Molecular solutions of equal molarity have the same number of molecules, volume for volume. Solutions of equal normality are chemically equivalent, volume for volume.

Salts are compounds formed by any positive ion except hydrogen combined with any negative ion except hydroxide ions. Salts are ionic substances which are completely dissociated in water solution.

Test yourself on these terms

acid	equivalent weight	normal salt
acid anhydride	gram-equivalent weight	normal solution
acid salt	gram-ion	pH
amphiprotic	hydrated oxide	phenolphthalein
base	hydrogen-ion concentration	proton acceptor
basic anhydride	hydronium ion	proton donor
binary	indicator	salt
burette	molal solution	standard solution
common logarithm	molar solution	ternary
diprotic acid	monoprotic acid	titration
end point	neutralization	triprotic acid

Questions

Group A

1. Name the three most important industrial acids and tell why each is important.
2. What ion is responsible for the acidic properties of acid solutions?
3. Why is an acid thought of as a proton donor?
4. (a) What is an acid anhydride? (b) A basic anhydride? (c) Give an example of each.
5. (a) State the rules for naming binary acids. (b) For naming ternary acids.
6. Why may a base be defined as a proton acceptor?
7. Write the simplest ionic equation of the neutralization reaction.
8. Aluminum hydroxide has basic properties in the presence of a strong acid, and acidic properties in the presence of a solution which is strongly basic. (a) Write the formula of aluminum hydroxide so as to show its basic properties. (b) Rewrite the formula to show its acidic properties. (c) What term is used to describe such substances?
9. What is the nature of true salts?
10. How are salts named?
11. What method would you use to prepare a small quantity of calcium sulfate quickly and safely in the laboratory? Justify the method used and write the equation.
12. Would barium sulfate be a suitable source of the sulfate ion for a double replacement reaction with another salt? Explain.

Group B

13. Explain why a water solution of hydrogen chloride has acidic properties but pure hydrogen chloride does not, in the usual sense.
14. Hydrogen chloride, HCl, has 1 gram-atom of hydrogen per mole and hydrogen carbonate, H_2CO_3, has 2 gram-atoms of hydrogen per mole. Yet hydrochloric acid is described as a *strong* acid and carbonic acid as a *weak* acid. Explain.

15. (a) How can you justify calling hydrogen chloride an acid when it is dissolved in ammonia? (b) Write the equation.

16. (a) Explain the manner in which water may be considered to be an acid. (b) Write an equation which illustrates this behavior using electron-dot formulas.

17. (a) How would you test the soil in your lawn or garden to find out whether it is acidic or basic? (b) If you find it to be acidic, what can be added to it to remedy the condition?

18. (a) What basic solution would you use for cleaning a greasy sink? Explain. (b) For removing grease spots from clothing? Explain.

19. What basic solutions would you use for neutralizing acid stains on clothing? Explain.

20. Test your saliva with litmus paper. (a) Is the saliva acidic or alkaline? (b) Do you think that a tooth paste is likely to be acidic or basic? Test some of them.

21. Which of the following salts are soluble, and which are insoluble in water: $NaCl$, $CaCO_3$, $BaSO_4$, $(NH_4)_2S$, $Al(C_2H_3O_2)_3$, Ag_2SO_4, $Pb(NO_3)_2$, Hg_2Cl_2, $Mg_3(PO_4)_2$, CuS?

22. In a neutralization reaction between hydrochloric acid and potassium hydroxide the K^+ ion and the Cl^- ion are called *spectator* ions. (a) Explain. (b) How may potassium chloride be recovered after such a reaction?

★ 23. What indicator would you use to show the end point of the neutralization reaction described in Question 22? Justify your selection.

★ 24. (a) Explain the meaning of pH. (b) What is the range of the pH scale?

★ 25. How many moles of sodium hydroxide are needed to neutralize: (a) 1 mole of hydrochloric acid; (b) 1 mole of sulfuric acid; and (c) 1 mole of phosphoric acid? (d) Write the equation for each reaction.

★ 26. What weight of calcium hydroxide is required to make up 1 liter of 0.01-N solution?

★ 27. (a) What volume of water contains a mole of H^+ ion (as H_3O^+)? (b) How many gram-ions of hydrogen is this? (c) How many grams of H^+ ion? (d) What is the mole-concentration of OH^- ion in this volume of water? (e) How many gram-ions of hydroxide is this? (f) How many grams of OH^- ion?

★ 28. What is the normality of (a) a 0.004-M solution of phosphoric acid? (b) A 0.15-M solution of potassium hydroxide? (c) A 2-M solution of sulfuric acid?

Problems

Group A

1. How many grams of sodium hydroxide are required to neutralize 54.75 g of hydrogen chloride in water solution?

2. We may prepare nitric acid in the laboratory by reacting sodium nitrate with sulfuric acid. Sodium hydrogen sulfate is also formed. (a) How many grams of sulfuric acid are required to produce 50 g of nitric acid? (b) How many grams of sodium hydrogen sulfate are formed?

3. How many liters of carbon dioxide can be collected at 20° C and 745 mm pressure from a reaction between 25 g of calcium carbonate and an excess of hydrochloric acid?

★ 4. What quantity of potassium nitrate would you add to 500 g of water to prepare a 0.25-m solution?

★ 5. How many grams of sugar, $C_{12}H_{22}O_{11}$, are contained in 50 ml of an 0.8-M solution?

Group B

★ 6. How many solute molecules are contained in each milliliter of a 0.1-M solution?

★ 7. What is the molality of a solution that contains 2 g of sodium chloride in 100 g of water?

★ 8. (a) What is the pH of a 0.01-M solution of HCl, assuming complete ionization? (b) What is the OH^- ion concentration of a 0.01-M solution of sodium hydroxide? (c) What is the pH of this solution?

★ 9. How many milliliters of a 0.15-N solution of a metallic hydroxide are required to neutralize 30 ml of a 0.5-N solution of an acid?

★ 10. A chemistry student finds that it takes 34 ml of a 0.5-N acid solution to neutralize 10 ml of a sample of household ammonia. What is the normality of the ammonia-water solution?

★ 11. The stockroom supply of concentrated sulfuric acid is 98% H_2SO_4 by weight and has a specific gravity of 1.84. (a) How many milliliters are needed to make 1 liter of 1-N H_2SO_4 solution? (b) To make 100 ml of 0.2-N solution?

★ 12. An excess of zinc reacts with 400 ml of hydrochloric acid and 2.55 liters of H_2 gas is collected over water at 20° C and 745 mm. What was the normality of the acid? (Vapor pressure of water at 20° C is 17.5 mm.)

Some things for you to do

1. Take home some test strips of both red and blue litmus paper and Hydrion paper. Test as many different things as you can and make a list as follows: acidic, basic, neutral.

2. Using Hydrion paper determine the approximate pH of those substances.

3. Test samples of a blood-red beet and a purple cabbage to see how each one is affected by a strong acid. How is each affected by a strong hydroxide solution?

Chapter 22   CHEMICAL EQUILIBRIUM

★ **1. Reversible reactions may reach equilibrium.** Many chemical reactions are reversible—that is, the products may re-form the original reactants under suitable conditions. We have seen that mercuric oxide decomposes when heated strongly.

$$2\,HgO \rightarrow 2\,Hg + O_2\uparrow$$

But mercury and oxygen, when heated gently, combine to form mercuric oxide.

$$2\,Hg + O_2 \rightarrow 2\,HgO$$

Suppose we heat mercuric oxide in a closed container from which neither the mercury nor the oxygen can escape. It is possible, once the decomposition is under way, for the mercury and oxygen that have been liberated to recombine forming mercuric oxide again. Thus both reactions proceed at the same time. Under just the right conditions, the speed of the composition reaction may become equal to the speed of the decomposition reaction. Mercury and oxygen combine to form mercuric

VOCABULARY

Buffer. A substance which, when added to a solution, causes a resistance to any change in pH.

Buffered solution. A solution containing a relatively high concentration of a buffer salt which tends to maintain a constant pH.

Equilibrium. A dynamic state in which two opposing processes take place at the same time and at the same rate.

Equilibrium constant. The product of the concentrations of the substances produced at equilibrium divided by the product of the concentrations of reactants, each concentration raised to that power which is the coefficient of the substance in the chemical equation.

Hydrolysis. The reaction of a salt with water to form a solution which is acidic or basic.

Ionization constant. The equilibrium constant of a reversible reaction by which ions are produced from molecules.

oxide just as fast as mercuric oxide decomposes to form mercury and oxygen. We should then expect the amount of mercuric oxide, mercury, and oxygen to remain constant as long as these conditions persist. A state of *equilibrium* has been reached between the two chemical actions. *Both reactions continue but the net change is zero.* We may show the equilibrium in the following manner:

$$2\ HgO \rightleftarrows 2\ Hg + O_2$$

Chemical equilibrium is the state of balance attained in which the speeds of opposing reactions are exactly equal.

★ **2. Equilibrium is a dynamic state.** We have already seen examples of opposing processes, such as evaporation and condensation, occurring simultaneously at the same speed. The evaporation of a liquid in a closed vessel and the condensation of its saturated vapor proceed at equal rates. The equilibrium vapor pressure established is characteristic of the liquid at the prevailing temperature.

If we place an excess of sugar in water, sugar molecules go into solution and some of these in turn separate to rejoin the crystals. At saturation, molecules of sugar are separating from solution at the same rate that other crystal molecules are going into solution. These are examples of *physical equilibria*. No chemical changes are involved. The opposing physical processes occur at exactly the same speed. Equilibrium is a *dynamic* state in which two opposing processes continue to take place at the same time and at the same speed.

Electrovalent compounds, such as sodium chloride, are completely ionized in water solution. When an excess of

sodium chloride is placed in water, a saturated solution will eventually result. Equilibrium occurs as the rate of association of ions re-forming the crystal equals the rate of dissociation of ions from the crystal. This is shown in the following ionic equation.

$$Na^+Cl^- \rightleftarrows Na^+ + Cl^-$$

Polar compounds, such as acetic acid, are quite soluble in water. Molecules of acetic acid in water solution ionize forming H^+ ions (as H_3O^+) and $C_2H_3O_2^-$ ions. However, pairs of these ions tend to rejoin, forming acetic acid molecules in the solution. This tendency is so great that equilibrium is quickly established between un-ionized molecules in solution and their hydrated ions, even in fairly dilute solutions. This is an example of *ionic equilibrium*. We may represent the ionic equilibrium of acetic acid in water solution by the following equation:

$$HC_2H_3O_2 \rightleftarrows H^+ + C_2H_3O_2^-$$

If we wish to show the role played by the water dipoles we may write the equation in this manner.

$$HC_2H_3O_2 + H_2O \rightleftarrows H_3O^+ + C_2H_3O_2^-$$

Most chemical reactions reach a state of equilibrium unless prevented by the removal or escape of at least one of the substances involved. In some changes the forward reaction is nearly completed before the speed of the reverse reaction becomes high enough to establish equilibrium. *Here the products of the forward reaction (→) are favored.* In other changes the forward reaction is barely under way when equilibrium is established. *In such cases the products of the reverse reaction (←), the original reactants, are favored.* In still others, both the forward and reverse reactions occur to nearly the same extent before chemical equilibrium is established. *Neither reaction is favored; considerable concentrations of both reactants and products are present at equilibrium.*

We use chemical reactions ordinarily to convert available reactants into more desirable products. Naturally we intend to produce as much of these products as possible from the reactants used. Chemical equilibrium may seriously limit the possibilities of a seemingly useful reaction. At equilibrium the speeds of the two opposing reactions are equal. It is important that we recognize the conditions that influence the *speed* of a reaction in our study of chemical equilibrium.

★ **3. Factors affecting the speed of reaction.** Reaction speeds range all the way from those which are practically instantaneous to those which may take months, or even years, to complete. *The speed of reaction is measured by the amount of reactants converted to products in a unit of time.* In order for reactions (other than simple decompositions) to occur at all, particles (atoms, molecules, and ions) must come in contact, and this contact must result in interaction. Thus the speed of such reactions depends on: *1. the collision frequency of the reacting substances; 2. the collision efficiency.*

Any change in conditions that affects either the frequency of collisions or the collision efficiency will influence the reaction speed. Let us consider several important factors affecting the speed of reaction.

1. Nature of the reactants. Hydrogen may combine vigorously with chlorine under certain conditions. Under the same conditions it may react only feebly with nitrogen. Sodium and oxygen combine much more rapidly than iron and oxygen under similar circumstances. Platinum and oxygen will not combine directly. Atoms, ions, and molecules are the particles of substances that react. Their tendencies to react depend on their structures.

2. Amount of surface. A lump of coal will burn slowly when kindled in air. The rate of burning will be increased by breaking the lump into smaller pieces. This exposes new surfaces. We know that if the lump is powdered, suspended in the air, and ignited, it will burn explosively.

Chemical action involving a *liquid* or *solid* takes place at the exposed surfaces. Increasing the amount of surface exposed hastens the action, other conditions being the same. *Gases* and *dissolved particles* do not have surfaces in the sense just described.

3. Use of catalysts. The speed of many reactions is increased by the use of catalytic agents. Some reactions are slowed by the presence of certain catalysts (inhibitors). A catalytic agent that is effective in one reaction may have no influence in another. Many important industrial processes would not be economically feasible without catalytic action.

Chemists believe that catalytic agents influence the speed of reactions in one of two general ways. First, the catalyst may form an intermediate compound with one reactant. This compound, in turn, may react more vigorously with the second reactant to form the product and release the catalyst. Such agents are called *carrier catalysts.* Manganese dioxide is thought to behave in this manner when it is mixed with potassium

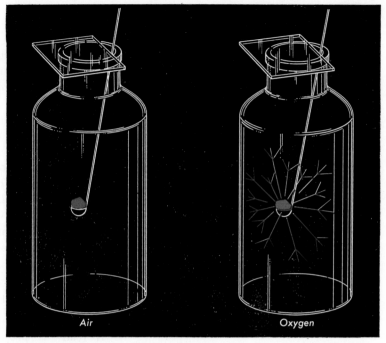

Fig. 22–1. Carbon burns faster in oxygen than in air because of the higher concentration of oxygen molecules.

Air

Oxygen

chlorate in the preparation of oxygen in the laboratory. Second, other catalytic agents may simply provide a surface on which certain gas reactants condense. Reactions are speeded by the more efficient contact between the molecules of the reactants. Such agents are called *contact catalysts*. They are usually metals in the form of thin foil, wire gauze, or fine powder. Finely divided nickel is used as a catalyst in the hydrogenation of vegetable oils to form shortenings.

4. Effect of temperature. We have already learned that a rise in temperature speeds a chemical reaction. On the average, reaction speeds are roughly doubled by a temperature increase of 10 C°.

We may account for this large increase in speed of reaction partially by the increase in collision frequency of the reactants. However, particles of reactants which collide must also react if the chemical change is to move along.

At higher temperatures more particles possess enough energy to react when collisions occur. They have the necessary *activation energy* (see Chapter 12, Section 11). A rise in temperature results in an increase in *collision efficiency* as well as *collision frequency*.

5. Effect of concentration. Let us heat a small lump of charcoal in air until combustion begins. Now let us lower the burning carbon into a bottle of pure oxygen. We observe that the reaction proceeds at a much faster rate. A substance which oxidizes in air reacts much more vigorously in pure oxygen. The partial pressure of oxygen in air is approximately one fifth of the total pressure. In pure oxygen, at the same pressure as the air, we should expect to have five times the *concentration* of oxygen molecules. If other conditions are constant, the speed of our reaction is proportional to the concentration of the oxygen.

The concentration of gases increases

with pressure according to Boyle's Law. It is not possible to change, to any appreciable extent, the concentration of pure solids and pure liquids since they are practically incompressible. The concentration of gases and substances in solution can be changed. The speed of our carbon combustion was proportional to the concentration of oxygen *only*, since the carbon was a solid.

Now we shall consider the reaction between two gases. Hydrogen combines with iodine vapor in a reversible reaction to form the gas, hydrogen iodide.

$$H_2 + I_2 \rightleftarrows 2\ HI$$

Suppose we bring together some hydrogen gas and iodine vapor in a closed vessel. *Under constant conditions,* the composition reaction proceeds at a rate proportional to the frequency of effective collisions between the two kinds of molecules. Thus *the speed of the reaction is proportional to the concentrations of both hydrogen and iodine.*

If we double the concentration of hydrogen in the vessel, the chances of a collision between hydrogen and iodine molecules will be doubled. The reaction speed is therefore *doubled.*

If the concentration of iodine is also doubled, the chances of a collision are *four times as great.* Of course, other conditions which affect the speed of the reaction must remain the same.

★ **4. The Law of Mass Action.** In 1867 two Norwegian scientists, Guldberg and Waage, stated the general principle

known as the ***Law of Mass Action.*** This law in its modern form is as follows: *The speed of a reaction is proportional to the product of the concentrations of the reacting substances.* Concentration is expressed in *moles of gas per liter of volume* or *moles of solute per liter of solution.* How does the Law of Mass Action apply to our reaction between hydrogen and iodine vapor?

Let S_1 be the speed of the forward ($\rightarrow$) reaction forming hydrogen iodide. $[H_2]$ and $[I_2]$ represent the molecular concentrations of hydrogen and iodine in moles per liter. Then

$$S_1 \propto [H_2] \times [I_2]$$

where $\propto$ is a proportionality sign and is read *"is proportional to."* If the concentrations of both hydrogen and iodine vapor are *1 mole per liter,* at a fixed temperature the speed of the reaction is a certain constant value called the *velocity constant:*

$$S_1 = k_1$$

where k_1 is the velocity constant for the forward reaction. For *any* concentration of hydrogen and iodine, the reaction speed is expressed as follows:

$$S_1 = k_1 \times [H_2] \times [I_2]$$

If $[H_2]$ is *2 moles per liter* and $[I_2]$ *is 1 mole per liter,* our equation will read

$$S_1 = k_1 \times 2 \times 1 = 2\ k_1$$

The speed of the reaction is *twice* the value for 1 mole per liter concentrations of both reactants. If now $[I_2]$ is

Fig. 22–2. Under constant conditions, the collision frequency increases with the concentration of each reactant.

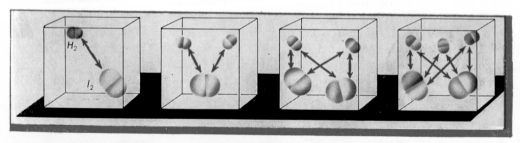

also increased to *2 moles per liter:*

$$S_1 = k_1 \times 2 \times 2 = 4k_1$$

The speed of the reaction is *four times* the value for 1 mole per liter concentrations of both reactants. Similarly, if $[H_2]$ is *3 moles per liter* and $[I_2]$ is *2 moles per liter:*

$$S_1 = k_1 \times 3 \times 2 = 6k_1$$

The speed of the reaction is *six times* the value for 1 mole per liter concentrations of both reactants.

At the fixed temperature of the forward reaction, hydrogen iodide molecules decompose. We will let this reaction speed in the reverse ($\leftarrow$) direction be S_2 for the formation of hydrogen and iodine. However, two molecules of HI must decompose to form a molecule of H_2 and a molecule of I_2. Thus the speed of the reverse reaction *is proportional to the molecular concentration of HI squared.*

$$S_2 \propto [HI] \times [HI]$$

or

$$S_2 \propto [HI]^2$$

and

$$S_2 = k_2 \times [HI]^2$$

where k_2 is the velocity constant for the decomposition of HI at the fixed temperature.

★ **5. The equilibrium constant is important to chemists.** Many chemical reactions seem to be feasible and might be expected to yield useful products. However, after they are started, they *appear* to slow down and finally stop without having run to completion. Such reactions are reversible and, under just the right conditions, reach a *state of equilibrium.* Both forward and reverse processes occur at the same rate and the concentration of products and reactants remains constant.

Chemists must understand chemical equilibria in order to determine the conditions under which such reactions will yield satisfactory results. Knowledge of equilibrium enables us to predict whether certain reactions are practical. We are then able to improve the yields of desired products formed by reversible reactions.

Suppose two substances, *A* and *B*, react to form products *C* and *D*. But *C* and *D*, in turn, react to produce *A* and *B*. Under certain conditions equilibrium occurs in this reversible reaction. This *hypothetical* equilibrium reaction may be shown by the equation:

$$A + B \rightleftarrows C + D$$

Initially, the concentration of *C* and *D* is zero and that of *A* and *B* is maximum. From the Law of Mass Action we see that the speed of the forward reaction *decreases* as *A* and *B* are used up. During the same time the speed of the reverse reaction increases, from its initial value of zero, as *C* and *D* are formed. As equilibrium is established, these two reaction rates become equal. The individual concentrations of *A*, *B*, *C*, and *D* undergo no further change as long as the same reaction conditions prevail. *At equilibrium, the ratio of the product* $[C] \times [D]$ *to the product* $[A] \times [B]$ *has a definite numerical value.* It is known as the **equilibrium constant** of the reaction and is designated by the letter *K*. Thus

$$\frac{[C] \times [D]}{[A] \times [B]} = K$$

Notice that the concentrations of substances on the right side of the chemical equation are given in the numerator. The concentrations of those on the left side of the chemical equation are in the denominator. Equilibrium concentrations are given in *moles per liter*. The constant, K, is independent of the initial concentrations but is dependent on the fixed temperature of the system.

The value of K for a given equilibrium reaction is important to the chemist. It shows him the extent to which the reactants are converted into the products of the reaction. If K is equal to 1, the products of the concentrations in the numerator and denominator have the same value. If the value of K is very small, the forward reaction occurs only very slightly before equilibrium is established. A large value of K indicates an equilibrium in which the original reactants are largely converted to products. If the values of K are known for different reaction temperatures, the chemist may select the most favorable conditions for a desired reaction. The numerical value of K for a particular equilibrium system is obtained by analyzing the equilibrium mixture and determining the concentrations of all substances present.

An equilibrium reaction may involve more than one molecule of a substance in the chemical equation. For example, in the reaction

$$3A + B \rightleftarrows 2C + 3D$$

the equilibrium constant is:

$$\frac{[C]^2[D]^3}{[A]^3[B]} = K$$

*In the general form, the **equilibrium constant** is the product of the concentrations of the substances produced at equilibrium divided by the product of the concentrations of the reacting substances, each concentration raised to that power which is the coefficient of the substance in the chemical equation.*

In Section 4, we wrote the chemical equation for the hydrogen— iodine— hydrogen iodide equilibrium as follows:

$$H_2 + I_2 \rightleftarrows 2\,HI$$

The speeds of the forward and reverse reactions are respectively:

$$S_1 = k_1[H_2][I_2]$$
$$S_2 = k_2[HI]^2$$

At equilibrium

$$S_1 = S_2$$

and

$$k_1[H_2][I_2] = k_2[HI]^2$$

or

$$\frac{k_1}{k_2} = \frac{[HI]^2}{[H_2][I_2]}$$

then

$$K = \frac{k_1}{k_2} = \frac{[HI]^2}{[H_2][I_2]}$$

★ **6. Factors that disturb equilibrium.** In systems that have attained chemical equilibrium, opposing reactions are occurring at equal speeds. Any change which alters the speed of either reaction *disturbs the equilibrium*. By displacing an equilibrium in the proper direction, chemists are often able to increase production of important industrial chemicals.

In 1888 the French chemist Henri Louis Le Chatelier (luh-*shah*-te-lyay) (1850–1936) published an important principle which is the basis for much of our knowledge of equilibria. The ***principle of Le Chatelier*** may be stated as follows: *If a system at equilibrium is subjected to a stress, the equilibrium will be displaced in such direction as to relieve the stress.* This is a general law of chemistry that applies to all kinds of dynamic equilibria, physical and ionic, as well as chemical. In applying Le Chatelier's principle to chemical equilibrium, we shall consider three important factors (stresses).

1. *Change in concentration.* We know, from the Law of Mass Action, that the speed of a reaction increases with the concentration of either reactant. Let us again consider the hypothetical equilibrium reaction:

$$A + B \rightleftarrows C + D$$

An increase in the concentration of A will displace the equilibrium to the *right*. Both A and B will be used up faster. More of C and D will be formed. The equilibrium will be re-established with a lower concentration of B. *The effect has been to shift the equilibrium in such direction as to reduce the stress caused by the increase in concentration.* Similarly, an increase in the concentration of B will drive the reaction to the *right*. An increase in either C or D will displace the equilibrium to the *left*. A

Fig. 22-3. Henri Louis Le Chatelier was professor of chemistry at the Sorbonne in Paris, France. He is well known for his contributions in metallurgy and equilibrium studies.

decrease in the concentration of either C or D will have the same effect as an *increase* in the concentration of A or B; to displace the equilibrium to the *right*. *Changes in concentration have no effect on the value of the equilibrium constant.* All concentrations will be readjusted, when equilibrium is re-established, to give the same numerical ratio for the equilibrium constant.

2. *Change in pressure.* A change in pressure can only affect equilibrium systems in which *gases* are involved. According to the principle of Le Chatelier, *if the pressure on an equilibrium system is increased, the reaction is driven in the direction which relieves the pressure.*

The Haber process for the synthesis of ammonia from its elements offers an excellent illustration of the influence of pressure.

$$N_2 + 3 H_2 \rightleftarrows 2 NH_3$$

The equation shows us that 4 molecules of the reactant gases form 2 molecules of ammonia gas. If we subject the equilibrium mixture of these three gases to an increase in pressure, the concentration of ammonia will be increased. The concentration of hydrogen and nitrogen will be decreased. *The equilibrium shifts in the direction which produces fewer molecules, consequently a lower pressure.* We see that *high* pressure is desirable in this industrial process (see Fig. 22-4).

Consider the reaction,

$$CaCO_3 \rightleftarrows CaO + CO_2$$

Carbon dioxide is the only gas in the equilibrium mixture. The products therefore are favored by a *low* pressure.

In the reaction,

$$CO + H_2O \text{ (vapor)} \rightleftarrows CO_2 + H_2$$

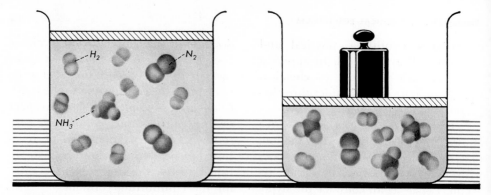

Fig. 22–4. Pressure increases the yield of ammonia since the equilibrium shifts in the direction which produces fewer molecules.

there are equal numbers of molecules of gaseous reactants and gaseous products. Pressure could not be relieved by a shift in equilibrium. Thus pressure has *no effect* on this equilibrium reaction.

We have seen that an increase in pressure on confined gases amounts to an increase in the concentration of these gases. Thus *changes in pressure do not affect the value of the equilibrium constant.*

3. *Change in temperature.* Chemical reactions are either exothermic or endothermic. Reversible reactions are exothermic in one direction and endothermic in the other. The effect of changing the temperature of an equilibrium mixture depends on which of the opposing reactions is endothermic.

The *addition* of heat, according to Le Chatelier's principle, will shift the equilibrium so that heat is absorbed. This favors the *endothermic* reaction. Conversely, the *removal* of heat favors the *exothermic reaction.* We have seen that a rise in temperature increases the speed of any reaction. In an equilibrium, the speeds of the opposing reactions are raised *unequally.* Thus, *the value of the equilibrium constant, for a given system, is affected by the operating temperature.*

The synthesis of ammonia is exothermic.

$$N_2 + 3\,H_2 \rightleftharpoons 2\,NH_3 + 24{,}000 \text{ calories}$$

We can see that a high temperature is not desirable as it favors the decomposition of ammonia, the endothermic reaction. However, at ordinary temperatures, the forward reaction is too slow to be feasible. Fortunately, it may be accelerated by the use of a suitable catalyst so that, at moderate temperatures and very high pressures, satisfactory yields of ammonia are realized.

★ **7. Some reactions run to completion.** We have seen that many reactions are reversible under suitable conditions. A state of equilibrium may be established unless at least one of the products escapes or is removed. We are able to drive an equilibrium reaction in the direction we wish it to go by applying the principle of Le Chatelier.

Some reactions appear to go to completion in the forward direction. No one has found a method of recombining potassium chloride and oxygen directly when potassium chlorate decomposes. By heating sugar we may cause it to decompose into carbon and water. Yet we know of no conditions favorable for the recombination of these products.

Many compounds are formed by the interaction of ions in solutions. If we mix solutions of two electrolytes, two pairs of ions are possible. These pairings may or may not occur. If we mix dilute solutions of sodium chloride and potassium bromide, nothing happens. We have simply a mixture of the following ions: Na^+, K^+, Cl^-, and Br^-. Association of ions occurs only if enough water is evaporated to cause crystals to separate. We would then get a mixture of NaCl, KCl, NaBr, and KBr.

In some combinations of ions, reactions do occur. *Such reactions may run to completion in the sense that the ions are almost completely removed from solution.* They are sometimes referred to as *end reactions.* Chemists can predict that certain double replacement reactions will run to completion. The extent to which the reacting ions are removed from solution depends on: *1. the solubility of the compound formed,* and *2. the degree of ionization, if it is soluble.* Thus a product which *escapes as a gas, is precipitated as a solid,* or *is only slightly ionized,* effectively removes the reacting ions from solution. We shall consider a specific example of each type of end reaction.

1. Formation of a gas. Unstable substances formed as products of double replacement reactions will decompose spontaneously. An example is carbonic acid which yields a gas as a decomposition product.

$$H_2CO_3 \rightarrow H_2O + CO_2\uparrow$$

Let us see what happens when sodium hydrogen carbonate and hydrochloric acid react. This may be shown as a double replacement.

$$Na^+ + HCO_3^- + H^+ + Cl^- \rightarrow$$
$$Na^+ + Cl^- + H_2CO_3$$

The carbonic acid decomposes into carbon dioxide and water as rapidly as it is formed. The sodium and chloride ions remain in solution and thus take no part in the action. The double replacement reaction should show the *final* products and may be properly written as follows:

$$Na^+ + HCO_3^- + H^+ + Cl^- \rightarrow$$
$$Na^+ + Cl^- + H_2O + CO_2\uparrow$$

By omitting the spectator ions, Na^+ and Cl^-, we have simply

$$H^+ + HCO_3^- \rightarrow H_2O + CO_2\uparrow$$

The reaction runs to completion because one of the products escapes as a gas. Of course, the sodium ions and chloride ions would separate as sodium chloride crystals on evaporation of the water.

The reaction between ferrous sulfide and hydrochloric acid illustrates this action more simply.

$$FeS + 2H^+ + 2Cl^- \rightarrow$$
$$Fe^{++} + 2Cl^- + H_2S\uparrow$$

The hydrogen sulfide formed is only moderately soluble and is given off as a gas.

2. Formation of a precipitate. When we mix solutions of sodium chloride and silver nitrate a white precipitate of silver chloride immediately forms.

$$Na^+ + Cl^- + Ag^+ + NO_3^- \rightarrow$$
$$Na^+ + NO_3^- + AgCl\downarrow$$

If we use equivalent quantities of the two solutes, sodium ions and nitrate ions will remain in solution. The silver ions and chloride ions will have combined to form insoluble silver chloride. *The reaction runs to completion because an insoluble product is formed.*

The only reaction that occurs is between the silver ions and chloride ions. We may omit the spectator ions, Na^+ and NO_3^-, from the equation and rewrite it in the simplest form:

$$Ag^+ + Cl^- \rightarrow AgCl\downarrow$$

Crystalline sodium nitrate is recovered only by evaporation of the water.

3. Formation of a slightly ionized product. Neutralization reactions occur between hydrogen ions (as H_3O^+) and hydroxide ions. Water molecules are formed. For example:

$$H^+ + Cl^- + Na^+ + OH^- \rightarrow$$
$$Na^+ + Cl^- + H_2O$$

or simply

$$H^+ + OH^- \rightarrow H_2O$$

Water is only very slightly ionized and exists essentially as covalent molecules. Thus hydrogen ions and hydroxide ions are effectively removed from the solution. *The reaction runs to completion because the product is very slightly ionized.* In our reaction between hydrochloric acid and sodium hydroxide, the sodium chloride crystallizes on evaporation of the water.

★ **8. What is the common ion effect?** Let us bubble hydrogen chloride gas into a saturated solution of sodium chloride. As the hydrogen chloride dissolves, sodium chloride separates as a precipitate. This is an application of the *Law of Mass Action*. The chloride ion is *common* to both solutes. The concentration of chloride ions is increased, that of the sodium ions is not. As sodium chloride crystals separate, the concentration of sodium ions in the solution is lowered. Thus an increase in the concentration of chloride ions

has the effect of decreasing the concentration of sodium ions in the solution. *This is known as the common ion effect.*

Of course, equilibrium will finally be established between the rate of dissociation of sodium chloride crystals and the rate of association of sodium and chloride ions.

$$Na^+Cl^- \rightleftarrows Na^+ + Cl^-$$

Further additions of hydrogen chloride will disturb this equilibrium and drive the reaction to the *left*. By *forcing* the reaction to the left we cause more sodium chloride to separate. This further reduces the concentration of the sodium ions in solution.

The common ion effect is also observed when *one* of the ions of a weak electrolyte is added in excess to a solution. Acetic acid is such an electrolyte. A 0.1-N $HC_2H_3O_2$ solution is about 1.3% ionized. The ionic equilibrium may be shown by this equation:

$$HC_2H_3O_2 \rightleftarrows H^+ + C_2H_3O_2^-$$

Sodium acetate is an ionic salt which is completely dissociated in water solution. Small additions of sodium acetate to a solution containing acetic acid will greatly increase the concentration of the acetate ion. The equilibrium will shift in the direction which uses acetate ions faster. More molecules of acetic acid are formed and the concentration of hydrogen ions (as H_3O^+) is reduced. In general, *the addition of a salt with an ion common to the solution of a weak electrolyte reduces the ionization of the electrolyte.* A 0.1-N $HC_2H_3O_2$ solution has a pH of 3. A solution containing 0.1-N concentrations of both acetic acid and sodium acetate has a pH of 4.6.

NH_4 OH

NH_4 Cl

H $C_2H_3O_2$

$NaC_2H_3O_2$

The pH of a weakly acidic or alkaline solution tends to remain practically constant, regardless of the addition of other ions, if the proper salts are present. The concentration of hydrogen ions will not vary appreciably in a solution of acetic acid containing a high concentration of sodium acetate. Similarly, the hydroxide-ion concentration in an ammonia-water solution will remain almost constant if the solution contains a high concentration of ammonium chloride. Salts used in this way are called *buffer salts*. The solutions are said to be *buffered* against changes in pH due to the addition or removal of small quantities of acids or alkalies.

Buffer action has many important applications in chemistry and physiology. The human blood is buffered so as to maintain a pH of about 7.3. Slight variations in pH are essential for the stimulation of certain physiological functions. However, pronounced changes would lead to serious disturbances of normal body functions, or even death.

★ **9. The ionization constant of water.** We have learned that pure water is a very poor conductor of electricity. It is therefore very slightly ionized. According to the modern concept of acids and bases, some water molecules donate protons, acting as an acid. Other water molecules which accept these protons act as a base.

$$H_2O + H_2O \rightleftarrows H_3O^+ + OH^-$$

The degree of ionization is slight and equilibrium is quickly established with a very low concentration of hydrogen (H_3O^+) and hydroxide ions.

About *one* molecule in 555,000,000 is ionized. Ten million (10^7) liters of water produce 1 gram-ion each of hydrogen and hydroxide. Thus the hydrogen-ion concentration, $[H^+]$, and hydroxide-ion concentration, $[OH^-]$, are each 10^{-7} gram-ion (mole) per liter. The product of these two concentrations is a constant known as the *ionization constant* of water.

$$[H^+] \times [OH^-] = K$$
$$10^{-7} \times 10^{-7} = 10^{-14}$$

The product (ionization constant) of the gram-ion concentrations of water (H^+ and OH^-) has this constant value not only in pure water, but in all water solutions. Thus an acid solution with a pH of 4 has a $[H^+]$ of 10^{-4} gram-ion (mole) per liter and a $[OH^-]$ of 10^{-10} gram-ion per liter. An alkaline solution with a pH of 8 has a $[H^+]$ of 10^{-8} gram-ion per liter and a $[OH^-]$ of 10^{-6} gram-ion per liter.

★ **10. Hydrolysis of salts.** In general, when we dissolve normal salts in water, we expect the solutions to remain neutral. Many salts, such as NaCl and KNO_3, behave in this way. They are formed from *strong* acids and *strong* hydroxides. Solutions of these salts have a pH of 7. When we dissolve other salts in water, we may produce solutions that are not neutral. These solutions may be either acidic (pH less than 7) or alkaline (pH greater than 7). Such salts are said to *hydrolyze* in water solution. **Hydrolysis is the action of a salt with water to form a solution which is acidic or basic.**

Let us dissolve some sodium carbonate in water and test it with litmus paper. We find that the solution turns red litmus *blue*. The solution contains an excess of OH^- ions and is basic. We shall rely somewhat on the modern concept of acids and bases to explain this phenomenon.

The sodium ion shows little tendency to combine with the hydroxide ion in solution. The carbonate ion, $CO_3^=$, is a base which accepts a proton from the water to form the slightly ionized bicarbonate ion, HCO_3^-, according to the following equation:

$$CO_3^= + H_2O \rightleftarrows HCO_3^- + OH^-$$

The OH^- ion concentration builds up until equilibrium is reached. The H^+ ion concentration becomes less since the product $[H^+][OH^-]$ must remain equal to the ionization constant of the solution, 10^{-14}. Thus the pH is *greater than 7* and the solution is *alkaline*. In general, we can say that *salts formed from weak acids and strong hydroxides hydrolyze in water to form alkaline solutions.*

A solution of ammonium chloride, NH_4Cl, turns blue litmus *red*. This tells us that hydrolysis occurs and the solution contains an excess of hydrogen (H_3O^+) ions. Chloride ions show little tendency to combine with hydrogen ions in solution. The ammonium ions donate protons to water molecules according to the following equation:

$$NH_4^+ + H_2O \rightleftarrows H_3O^+ + NH_3$$

Equilibrium is established with an increased H^+ concentration. The pH is *less than 7* and the solution is *acidic*.

The metallic ions of many salts are hydrated in water solution. Such hydrated ions may donate protons to water molecules and the solution becomes acidic. For example, aluminum chloride produces the hydrated positive ion.

$$Al(H_2O)_6^{+++}$$

Cupric sulfate in water solution yields the light blue hydrated positive ion

$$Cu(H_2O)_4^{++}$$

These ions react with water to produce hydronium ions in the following manner:

$$Al(H_2O)_6^{+++} + H_2O \rightleftarrows$$
$$Al(H_2O)_5OH^{++} + H_3O^+$$
$$Cu(H_2O)_4^{++} + H_2O \rightleftarrows$$
$$Cu(H_2O)_3OH^+ + H_3O^+$$

In general, we can say that *salts formed from strong acids and weak hydroxides hydrolyze in water to form acidic solutions.*

Let us place aluminum sulfide in water solution. We observe the formation of both precipitate and gas. The reaction is as follows:

$$Al_2S_3 + 6 H_2O \rightarrow 2 Al(OH)_3\downarrow + 3 H_2S\uparrow$$

Both products are removed from the solution. The hydrolysis therefore runs to completion. *Both ions* of a salt formed from a *weak* acid and a *weak* hydroxide will hydrolyze extensively in water. The salt may undergo complete decomposition. If both ions of the salt hydrolyze equally, the solution will be neutral. Ammonium acetate is such a salt.

Hydrolysis is often very important. Sodium carbonate, washing soda, is widely used as a cleaning agent due to the alkaline properties of the water solution. Sodium hydrogen carbonate forms a mild alkaline solution in water which finds many practical uses. Through the study of hydrolysis we are able to see clearly why the end-point of a neutralization reaction may occur at a pH other than 7 (see Chapter 21, Section 19).

Summary

A state of equilibrium is reached whenever opposing actions occur simultaneously and at equal speeds. This is true in physical, ionic, and chemical actions. Such equilibria are dynamic, as opposed to static balance.

The speed of chemical action depends on: 1. the collision frequency of the reactants; and 2. the collision efficiency. There are several factors which affect the speed of a reaction.

The Law of Mass Action is concerned with the relationship between the speed of a reaction and the concentration of reactants. Reaction speed is proportional to the product of the concentrations of the reactants.

When a reversible chemical reaction is in equilibrium, a constant relationship exists between the concentrations of products and original reactants. The ratio of the product of the concentrations of reactants to the product of the concentrations of new substances has a definite numerical value. This ratio is the equilibrium constant. It varies only with temperature for a given system.

A system in equilibrium is disturbed and the equilibrium shifts when subjected to a stress. The principle of Le Chatelier tells us that an equilibrium shifts, when subjected to a stress, in such manner as to relieve the stress. By proper application of this principle, certain equilibrium reactions are made commercially feasible.

Double replacement reactions will run to completion if at least one product escapes as a gas, is precipitated as a solid, or is only slightly ionized.

The common ion effect is an application of the Law of Mass Action to ionic equilibria. It may be applied to solutions of weak electrolytes to reduce the ionization of the electrolyte. Solutions of weak acids and alkalies may be buffered against large changes in pH by the use of proper buffer salts.

Water has an ionization constant equal to the product of the concentrations of the H^+ and OH^- ions. This constant, 10^{-14}, remains the same for water solutions as well as pure water. Salts which hydrolyze in water solution may produce an excess of either H^+ ions or OH^- ions. The solutions may be either acidic or alkaline.

Test yourself on these terms

activation energy	contact catalyst	Law of Mass Action
buffer salt	end reaction	pH
carrier catalyst	equilibrium constant	physical equilibrium
chemical equilibrium	hydrolysis	Principle of Le Chatelier
collision efficiency	ionic equilibrium	lier
collision frequency	ionization constant of	reversible reaction
common ion effect	water	velocity constant

uestions

Group A

★ 1. State three examples of physical equilibrium.

★ 2. Write the ionic equations for three examples of ionic equilibrium.

★ 3. In order for reactions, other than simple decompositions, to occur, what two conditions must be met?

★ 4. What is wrong with the following statement: When equilibrium is reached, the opposing reactions stop.

★ 5. Name five factors which influence the speed of reaction.

★ 6. State the Law of Mass Action.

★ 7. An oxidation reaction proceeding in air under standard pressure is transferred to an atmosphere of pure oxygen under the same pressure. (*a*) What is the effect on the speed of the oxidation reaction? (*b*) How can you account for this effect?

★ 8. (*a*) State the Principle of Le Chatelier. (*b*) To what kinds of equilibria does it apply?

★ 9. (*a*) Name three factors which may disturb, or shift, an equilibrium. (*b*) Which of these affects the value of the equilibrium constant?

★ 10. What are the three conditions under which double replacement reactions involving ionic substances may run to completion? Write an equation illustrating each.

Group B

★ 11. The reaction between steam and iron is reversible. Steam passed over hot iron produces magnetic iron oxide and hydrogen. Hydrogen passed over hot magnetic iron oxide reduces it to iron and forms steam. Suggest a method by which this reversible reaction may be brought to a state of equilibrium.

★ 12. What is the meaning of the term *dynamic* as applied to an equilibrium state?

★ 13. Methanol is produced synthetically as a gas by the reaction between carbon monoxide and hydrogen, in the presence of a catalyst, according to the equilibrium reaction: $CO + 2 H_2 \rightleftarrows CH_3OH + 24,000$ calories. Write the expression for the equilibrium constant of this reaction.

★ 14. How would you regulate the temperature of the equilibrium mixture of CO, H_2, and CH_3OH of Question 13 in order to increase the yield of methanol? Explain.

★ 15. How would you regulate the pressure on the equilibrium mixture of Question 13 in order to increase the yield of methanol? Explain.

★ 16. In the reaction, $A + B \rightleftarrows C$, the concentrations of A, B, and C in the equilibrium mixture were found to be 2, 3, and 1 moles per liter respectively. What is the equilibrium constant of this reaction?

★ 17. Write the balanced ionic equations for the following reactions in water solution. If a reaction does not take place, write *NO REACTION*. Omit all *spectator* ions. Show precipitates by ↓ and gases by ↑. Use solubility data in the Appendix as needed. Use a separate sheet of paper. (Do not write in this book.)

(a) $BaCO_3 + HNO_3 \rightarrow$

(b) $Pb(NO_3)_2 + NaCl \rightarrow$

(c) $CuSO_4 + HCl \rightarrow$

(d) $Ca_3(PO_4)_2 + NaNO_3 \rightarrow$

(e) $Ba(NO_3)_2 + H_2SO_4 \rightarrow$

(f) $FeS + NaCl \rightarrow$

(g) $AgC_2H_3O_2 + HCl \rightarrow$

(h) $Na_3PO_4 + CuSO_4 \rightarrow$

(i) $BaCl_2 + Na_2SO_4 \rightarrow$

(j) $CuO + H_2SO_4 \rightarrow$

★ 18. Explain why the pH of a solution containing both acetic acid and sodium acetate is higher than that of a solution containing the same concentration of acetic acid alone.

★ 19. Complete the following table, using a separate sheet of paper. (Do not write in this book.)

pH	$[H^+]$ (moles/liter)	$[OH^-]$ (moles/liter)	$[H^+][OH^-]$	Property
0				
1				
3				
5				
7	$10^{-7} = 0.0000001$	$10^{-7} = 0.0000001$	10^{-14}	Neutral
9				
11				
13				
14				

★ 20. Explain why a water solution of sodium acetate has basic properties.

Some things for you to do

1. Test the solutions of various salts, which you think hydrolyze in water, with red and blue litmus paper. See if your predictions are correct. Work out a satisfactory explanation in each case.

Chapter 23 OXIDATION-REDUCTION REACTIONS

1. What is oxidation? We have already defined oxidation as the combination of an element with oxygen. Many substances combine with oxygen to form oxides. *In all of these oxidations, electrons are lost to the oxygen, either partially or completely.* There are many reactions of similar nature which do not involve the element oxygen. Chemists have found it convenient to think of these reactions as oxidations also.

Hydrogen burns in oxygen to form water:

$$2 H_2 + O_2 \rightarrow 2 H_2O$$

Hydrogen also burns in an atmosphere of fluorine to form hydrogen fluoride:

$$H_2 + F_2 \rightarrow 2 HF$$

Hydrogen burns in chlorine to produce hydrogen chloride:

$$H_2 + Cl_2 \rightarrow 2 HCl$$

Iron, when heated, combines with chlorine, forming ferric chloride. If iron and sulfur are heated together the product is ferrous sulfide.

$$2 Fe + 3 Cl_2 \rightarrow 2 FeCl_3$$

$$Fe + S \rightarrow FeS$$

All these reactions are similar to combinations with oxygen. In each, the electropositive element loses one or

---

VOCABULARY

Electrochemical. Pertaining to spontaneous oxidation-reduction reactions used as a source of electrical energy.

Electrolytic. Pertaining to forced oxidation-reduction reactions which utilize electrical energy from an external source.

Oxidation. Loss of electrons from an ion, atom, or group of atoms.

Oxidation number. A special valence number assigned to each element to indicate the number of electrons gained, lost, or shared unequally.

Oxidizing agent. Substance which takes up electrons during a chemical reaction.

Reducing agent. Substance which supplies electrons during a chemical reaction.

Reduction. Gain of electrons by an ion, atom, or group of atoms.

more electrons, either partially or completely. These elements are said to be *oxidized*. In this general sense, **oxidation** *is the loss of electrons from an ion, atom, or group of atoms.*

The substance responsible for the removal of electrons during the oxidation process is called the *oxidizing agent*. Hydrogen is oxidized during the formation of hydrogen fluoride. Fluorine is the oxidizing agent. In the production of ferrous sulfide, iron is oxidized to the *ferrous* state, and sulfur is the oxidizing agent. Iron is oxidized to the *ferric* state in the reaction with chlorine. Here, the chlorine is the oxidizing agent. *An* **oxidizing agent** *is a substance which takes up electrons during a chemical reaction.*

2. What is reduction? You probably know that certain metals occur in nature as metallic oxides. We may produce the metal from such a compound by a process which removes the oxygen. This is the way iron is produced from iron ore in a blast furnace.

We have already defined reduction as the removal of oxygen from a compound. The substance responsible for removing the oxygen is, of course, the *reducing agent*. We now know that the only way a metal could combine with oxygen, in the first place, is by the process of losing electrons. Consequently, the only way a metal can be recovered from its oxide is by returning the lost electrons.

Chemists have extended the meaning of *reduction* to include all reactions in which electrons are gained, either partially or completely, by reacting substances. In this general sense, **reduction** *is the addition of electrons to an ion, atom, or group of atoms.* The source of these electrons is considered to be the agent responsible for the reduction. *A* **reducing agent** *is a substance which supplies electrons during a chemical action.*

3. Oxidation and reduction occur simultaneously. It is apparent that one substance cannot gain electrons unless another substance loses electrons. If *oxidation* occurs during a chemical action, then *reduction* must occur simultaneously. If one kind of particle is oxidized, another kind of particle must be reduced *to a comparable degree.*

Any chemical process in which there is a transfer of electrons, either partial or complete, is an **oxidation-reduction reaction.** This impressive name is often shortened to *"redox"* reaction. Most of the reactions that you have studied are oxidation-reduction reactions. In composition reactions having ionic products, and in single replacement reactions, the electron transfer is complete. In reactions which form *polar* covalent bonds the electron transfer is not

Fig. 23–1. The combustion of antimony in chlorine is an oxidation-reduction reaction.

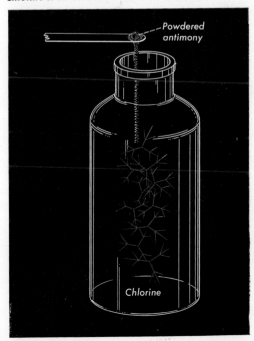
Powdered antimony

Chlorine

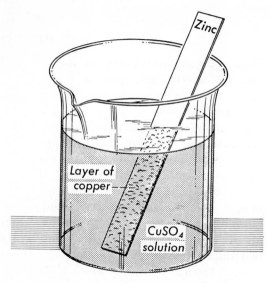

Fig. 23–2. The replacement of the cupric ion by zinc is an oxidation-reduction reaction.

complete. However, the electrons are shared unequally, with more of them moving in the space around the more highly electronegative element. We may consider the less electronegative substance to be oxidized and the more electronegative substance to be reduced. Few covalent bonds are completely nonpolar.

Reactions in which there are no changes in valence do not involve oxidation-reduction. If we add sodium chloride to a solution of silver nitrate, silver chloride precipitates.

$$Na^+ + Cl^- + Ag^+ + NO_3^- \rightarrow$$
$$Na^+ + NO_3^- + Ag^+Cl^-\downarrow$$

Silver chloride is an ionic compound. Note that the charge of each ion remains the same. No electrons have been transferred. This is *not* an oxidation-reduction reaction.

★ Oxidation-reduction reactions sometimes involve electron transfers that are not easily interpreted by our usual application of valence. For example, the *permanganate ion* in a solution of potassium permanganate has a valence of

−1, MnO_4^-. Under proper conditions this ion may be reduced to the *manganous ion,* Mn^{++}. Under other conditions the MnO_4^- ion may be reduced to the *manganate ion,* $MnO_4^=$.

★ If we are to write the equation for one of these reactions, we must know the number of electrons transferred during the chemical action. The common valence of the ion is little help if the ion consists of two or more different substances. *In order to simplify the task of balancing oxidation-reduction equations, a special kind of valence number is assigned to each element in a compound.* This valence number is commonly called the **oxidation number** of the element.

★ **4. Oxidation numbers.** We have learned that in oxidation-reduction reactions something loses electrons and is oxidized. Something else gains these electrons and is reduced to a comparable degree. The *state of oxidation* of a substance depends upon the *number of electrons lost or gained*. Loss of electrons produces a more *positive* oxidation state, and gain of electrons produces a more *negative* oxidation state. If all electrons belonging to an atom of an element are present, the oxidation state is *zero* and the atom is assigned the oxidation number 0. All atoms in their elementary form have oxidation numbers of 0. These may be written as follows: Na^0, K^0, Cu^0, H_2^0, and N_2^0.

Observe that we have assigned the oxidation number 0 to atoms of diatomic elements as well as monatomic elements. While the bond between the two hydrogen atoms of the H_2 molecule is *real*, it cannot be *polar* since both atoms are electronegative to the same degree. The electron pair is shared equally by both atoms composing the nonpolar covalent molecule.

In the following electronic equations the substances are oxidized:

$$Na^0 - e^- \rightarrow Na^{+1}$$
$$Fe^0 - 2e^- \rightarrow Fe^{+2}$$
$$Fe^{+2} - e^- \rightarrow Fe^{+3}$$
$$2Cl^{-1} - 2e^- \rightarrow Cl_2^0$$

The superscript after each symbol is the oxidation number of that particle. The difference between oxidation numbers tells us the number of electrons lost by each atom or ion. Notice that the chloride ion has the oxidation number -1, a *negative* oxidation state. *Oxidation results in an algebraic increase in the oxidation number* of a substance. A change from -1 to 0 is an algebraic increase in the oxidation number just as is a change from 0 to $+1$, or $+1$ to $+2$. Each of these changes accompanies the loss of 1 electron.

In the electronic equations which follow, the substances are reduced:

$$Na^{+1} + e^- \rightarrow Na^0$$
$$Cl_2^0 + 2e^- \rightarrow 2Cl^{-1}$$
$$Fe^{+3} + e^- \rightarrow Fe^{+2}$$
$$Cu^{+2} + 2e^- \rightarrow Cu^0$$
$$Br_2^0 + 2e^- \rightarrow 2Br^{-1}$$

The third equation illustrates the reduction of the *ferric* ion, oxidation number $+3$, to the *ferrous* state, oxidation number $+2$. Two additional electrons would be necessary to complete the reduction of the ferrous ion to the iron atom, oxidation number 0. *Reduction results in an algebraic decrease in the oxidation number of a substance.*

In the illustrations we have seen so far there appears to be no difference between the oxidation numbers assigned and the common valences to which we are accustomed. It is true that the oxidation state of each ion in a binary salt is that indicated by the ionic charge. In binary covalent compounds the oxidation number of each atom is determined by its valence. Shared electrons are arbitrarily assigned to the element having the greater attraction for electrons. The covalent bonds are polar to some degree, and occur between electropositive, or less electronegative, atoms and more highly electronegative atoms. *Positive* oxidation numbers are assigned to the electropositive atoms and *negative* oxidation numbers are assigned to the electronegative atoms. Thus, in the hydrogen chloride molecule, hydrogen is less electronegative than chlorine and is given the positive oxidation number: $H^{+1}Cl^{-1}$.

Let us examine a familiar ternary compound, H_2SO_4, with regard to the common valences. We would say that the valence of the hydrogen present is $+1$ and the valence of the sulfate radical is -2. This is evident from the ionization of a dilute solution of sulfuric acid:

$$H_2SO_4 \rightarrow 2H^+ + SO_4^=$$

Similarly, sulfurous acid, H_2SO_3, provides the sulfite ion, $SO_3^=$. Obviously all atoms in these two ternary compounds cannot have the same oxidation numbers. The common valences merely tell us that two hydrogen atoms are required for each sulfate radical, or each sulfite radical. *The oxidation state of each atom must be known if we are to balance oxidation-reduction equations involving these substances.* How may we assign the proper oxidation numbers to the elements in ternary compounds?

Metals in general are electropositive elements and nonmetals are electronegative. Of all the elements, only *fluorine* is more electronegative than oxygen. Therefore, in combinations with any of the elements except fluorine, oxygen exerts the greater force of attraction on the shared electrons. Hydrogen is the least electronegative of the nonmetals. In combination with other nonmetals, hydrogen is positive. Compounds of metals and hydrogen, called *hydrides,* are relatively unimportant and are seldom encountered in elementary chemistry.

With these facts in mind we can state a few simple rules which will enable us to assign the proper oxidation numbers to the elements in any compound.

1. The oxidation number of an atom of a free element is zero. Atoms of the same element have the same electronegativity. If bonds do occur between these atoms, they are nonpolar and bond electrons are shared equally.

2. The oxidation number of a monatomic ion is equal to its charge. Atoms of metals form ions by losing electrons to the atoms of nonmetals. The simple ions of metals are positively charged, and the simple ions of nonmetals are negatively charged.

3. In combinations of nonmetals, the oxidation number of the less electronegative element is positive and of the more electronegative element is negative. Chlorine, bromine, and iodine are the more negative elements in all of their combinations except with oxygen and fluorine.

4. The oxidation number of hydrogen is +1. The only exception to this rule is in the formation of metallic hydrides.

5. The oxidation number of oxygen is −2. There are two exceptions to this rule. In combination with fluorine, oxygen is the less electronegative nonmetal and therefore is positive. In compounds containing the *peroxide* radical, the oxidation number of oxygen is −1.

6. The algebraic sum of the oxidation numbers of the atoms in the formula of a compound is zero. We know that both molecular formulas and empirical formulas represent electrically neutral particles of matter. This rule merely tells us that the total of the positive oxidation numbers must *equal* the total of the negative oxidation numbers in any formula.

Now let us apply these rules to assign oxidation numbers to each element in the two ternary compounds, H_2SO_4 and H_2SO_3. In each, oxygen is given the oxidation number −2 and hydrogen is given the oxidation number +1. In the sulfuric acid molecule the total contribution of the 4 atoms of oxygen is 4 times −2, or −8; $4(-2) = -8$. The total contribution of the 2 atoms of hydrogen is $2(+1) = +2$. Since the H_2SO_4 molecule is neutral, the oxidation number of the single sulfur atom must be +6. We may write the appropriate oxidation number adjacent to each symbol in the formula. (The numbers are usually placed above the symbols where it is desired not to imply an ionic charge, or where it would cause undue spreading of the formula in a long equation.)

$$\overset{+1\ +6\ -2}{H_2SO_4}$$

$$2(+1) + 1(+6) + 4(-2) = 0$$

In the sulfurous acid molecule the total contribution of oxygen is $3(-2) = -6$.

That of hydrogen is $2\,(+1) = +2$. Thus the oxidation number of the single atom of sulfur must be $+4$.

$$\overset{+1\ +4\ -2}{H_2 S O_3}$$

$$2(+1) + 1(+4) + 3(-2) = 0$$

We can see that this is a reasonable assignment of oxidation numbers by examining the electronic structures of these two molecules. The electron-dot formula of sulfuric acid is as follows:

$$H \overset{..}{\underset{..}{O}} \overset{\overset{..}{O}..}{\underset{..}{S}} \overset{..}{\underset{..}{O}} H$$

Oxygen is the most electronegative element present so we shall assign to oxygen all electrons shared with oxygen. The sulfur atom must contribute all of its six electrons. Hence the oxidation number of sulfur is $+6$.

The electron-dot formula of sulfurous acid may be written as follows:

$$H \overset{..}{\underset{..}{O}} \overset{..}{\underset{\overset{..}{\underset{..}{O}}}{S}} \overset{..}{\underset{..}{O}} H$$

You will observe that one pair of electrons belonging to sulfur is unshared. The atom of sulfur contributes *four* electrons, hence the oxidation number is $+4$.

Suppose we apply our rules to a ternary salt. Potassium permanganate is composed of potassium ions, K^+, and the complex permanganate ion, MnO_4^-. The empirical formula is $KMnO_4$. Oxygen has the oxidation number -2 as before. The total contribution of the 4 oxygen atoms is $4\,(-2) = -8$. The K^+ ion is assigned the oxidation number that corresponds to its ionic charge, $+1$. The oxidation number of the manganese atom in the radical group must

then be $+7$. We could write the formula to show these oxidation states of the elements as follows:

$$K^{+1}[Mn^{+7}(O^{-2})_4]^{-1}$$

or more simply

$$\overset{+1\ +7\ -2}{KMnO_4}$$

Manganese has several important oxidation states. This oxidation number, $+7$, corresponds to the position of the element in Group VIIB of the Periodic Table and represents its highest oxidation state.

★ **5. Balancing oxidation - reduction equations.** The principal use of oxidation numbers is in balancing equations for oxidation-reduction reactions. In Chapter 12, Section 3, we learned that an orderly procedure is an essential part of equation writing. We must know the *facts:* what the reactants are and what the products are. We must then represent the reactants and products by their *correct formulas.* Finally, we must adjust the coefficients of all reactants and products to be in accord with the *conservation of atoms.* The method we use to accomplish this third step is essentially one of trial and error.

Oxidation-reduction reactions are those in which changes in oxidation number occur. *Here we must observe the* **conservation of electrons,** *as well as conservation of atoms, in writing equations.* In all but the simplest of these reactions, trial-and-error balancing is a difficult process. We may simplify this process by *balancing the electron shift* between the particles oxidized and the particles reduced *before* adjusting the coefficients for the rest of the equation. Our procedure for writing oxidation-reduction equations therefore includes the following steps:

Step 1: Write the skeleton equation for the reaction. To do this we must know the reactants and products and represent each by the correct formula (see Steps 1 and 2 of our general procedure outlined in Chapter 12, Section 3).

Step 2: Assign oxidation numbers to all elements and determine what is oxidized and what is reduced.

Step 3: Write the electronic equation for the oxidation process and the electronic equation for the reduction process.

Step 4: Adjust the coefficients in both electronic equations so that the number of electrons lost equals the number gained.

Step 5: Place these coefficients in the skeleton equation.

Step 6: Supply the proper coefficients for the rest of the equation to satisfy the conservation of atoms (see Step 3 of our general procedure outlined in Chapter 12).

We shall illustrate the application of these steps by considering a very simple oxidation-reduction reaction. Hydrogen sulfide gas burns in air to form sulfur dioxide and water. These facts, together with our knowledge of valence, enable us to write the skeleton equation.

Step 1:

$$2 \; \overset{+1}{H_2}\overset{-2}{S} + \overset{-2}{O_2} \to \overset{+4}{S}\overset{-2}{O_2} + \overset{+1}{H_2}\overset{-2}{O}$$

We now assign oxidation numbers applying the appropriate rules from Section 4. We see that sulfur is oxidized from the -2 state to the $+4$ state, and oxygen is reduced from the 0 state to the -2 state. Observe that the oxidation number of hydrogen remains the same; thus it plays no part in the primary action of oxidation-reduction.

Step 2:

$$\overset{+1 \; -2}{H_2S} + \overset{0}{O_2} \to \overset{+4 \; -2}{SO_2} + \overset{+1 \; -2}{H_2O}$$

The difference in the oxidation states of sulfur requires the loss of 6 electrons; $(-2) - (+4) = -6$. The difference in oxidation states of the oxygen requires the gain of 2 electrons; $(0) - (-2) = +2$. The electronic equations for these two actions are as follows:

Step 3:

$$S^{-2} - 6 \; e^- \to S^{+4} \; \text{(oxidation)}$$
$$O^0 + 2 \; e^- \to O^{-2} \; \text{(reduction)}$$

Free oxygen is diatomic, so 4 electrons must be gained during the reduction of a molecule of free oxygen.

$$O_2^0 + 4 \; e^- \to 2 \; O^{-2}$$

We are now in a position to adjust the coefficients of the two electronic equations so the number of electrons lost in the oxidation of sulfur equals the number gained in the reduction of oxygen. The smallest number of electrons common to both equations is 12. We can show the gain and loss of 12 electrons in the two equations by multiplying the oxidation equation by 2, and multiplying the reduction equation by 3.

Step 4:

$$2 \; S^{-2} - 12 \; e^- \to 2 \; S^{+4}$$
$$3 \; O_2^0 + 12 \; e^- \to 6 \; O^{-2}$$

Hence the coefficients of H_2S and SO_2 are both 2, and the coefficient of O_2 is 3. Notice that the 6 O^{-2} is divided between the two products SO_2 and H_2O. The coefficient, 6, is accounted for with the coefficient 2 in front of each formula. We transfer these coefficients to the skeleton equation.

Step 5:

$$2 H_2S + 3 O_2 \rightarrow 2 SO_2 + 2 H_2O$$

We are ready now to adjust the coefficients of the equation in the usual way to satisfy the Law of Conservation of Atoms. In this instance no further adjustments are needed; the equation is balanced.

Step 6:

$$2 H_2S + 3 O_2 \rightarrow 2 SO_2 + 2 H_2O$$

For a second example, let us use an oxidation-reduction equation slightly more difficult to balance. In the reaction between manganese dioxide and hydrochloric acid, water, manganous chloride, and chlorine gas are formed. The skeleton equation is:

$$\overset{+4}{Mn}\overset{-2}{O_2} + \overset{+1}{H}\overset{-1}{Cl} \rightarrow \overset{+1}{H_2}\overset{-2}{O} + \overset{+2}{Mn}\overset{-1}{Cl_2} + \overset{0}{Cl_2}$$

We assign oxidation numbers to the elements in the reaction and see that Mn^{+4} is reduced to Mn^{+2}, and some of the Cl^{-1} is oxidized to Cl^0. Hydrogen and oxygen do not take part in the primary action. The electronic equations are:

$$2 Cl^{-1} - 2 e^- \rightarrow Cl_2^0$$
$$Mn^{+4} + 2 e^- \rightarrow Mn^{+2}$$

The number of electrons lost and gained is equal, so we transfer the coefficients to the skeleton equation, which becomes:

$$MnO_2 + 2 HCl \rightarrow H_2O + MnCl_2 + Cl_2$$

The complete equation may now be balanced by inspection. Two additional molecules of HCl are required to provide the two Cl^- ions of the $MnCl_2$. This requires 2 molecules of water which then accounts for the 2 oxygens of the MnO_2. Our final equation reads:

$$MnO_2 + 4 HCl \rightarrow 2 H_2O + MnCl_2 + Cl_2$$

The equations for both of these illustrations can be balanced with little difficulty by trial and error. Let us now apply this process to a more complicated oxidation-reduction reaction. See the Sample Problem on page 320.

The method we have used to balance oxidation-reduction reactions is variously referred to as the *electron-shift, electron-transfer,* and *oxidation-state* method. The use of oxidation numbers in no way implies the existence of ions. Remember that the transfer of electrons may be partial, as in polar covalent bonds, or complete, as in ionic bonds. Oxidation numbers are assigned in either case. Some chemists prefer to use a second method, called the *ion-electron* method. It has the advantage of differentiating between ionic and molecular equations. It is, however, more difficult for students of elementary chemistry to use. For this reason it has not been presented here. Either method, used properly, leads to the correctly balanced equation.

★ **6. Oxidizing and reducing agents.** We have already defined an oxidizing agent as a substance that takes up electrons during an oxidation-reduction reaction. A reducing agent is the substance that furnishes the electrons in this action. It is obvious then that the substance oxidized is also the reducing agent, and the substance reduced is the oxidizing agent. An oxidized substance becomes a potential oxidizing agent. Similarly, a reduced substance is a potential reducing agent. It follows, however, that a very active reducing agent (one easily oxidized) becomes a very poor oxidizing agent, and conversely.

The different degrees of attraction that elements have for electrons are referred to as their differences in electro-

The oxidation-reduction reaction between hydrochloric acid and potassium permanganate yields the following products: water, potassium chloride, manganous chloride, and chlorine gas. Write the balanced equation.

SOLUTION

We first write the skeleton equation, being careful to show the correct formula of each reactant and each product. Appropriate oxidation numbers are placed above the symbols of the elements.

$$\overset{+1\;-1}{HCl} + \overset{+1\;+7\;-2}{KMnO_4} \rightarrow \overset{+1\;-2}{H_2O} + \overset{+1\;-1}{KCl} + \overset{+2\;-1}{MnCl_2} + \overset{0}{Cl_2}$$

We see that some chloride ions are oxidized to chlorine atoms, and the manganese of the permanganate ions is reduced to manganous ions. Electronic equations are written for these two actions:

$$2\,Cl^{-1} - 2\,e^- \rightarrow Cl_2^{0}$$
$$Mn^{+7} + 5\,e^- \rightarrow Mn^{+2}$$

The electron shift must involve an equal number of electrons in these two equations. This number is 10. The first equation is multiplied by 5 and the second by 2. We now have:

$$10\,Cl^{-1} - 10\,e^- \rightarrow 5\,Cl_2^{0}$$
$$2\,Mn^{+7} + 10\,e^- \rightarrow 2\,Mn^{+2}$$

These coefficients are transferred to the skeleton equation, which becomes:

$$10\,HCl + 2\,KMnO_4 \rightarrow H_2O + KCl + 2\,MnCl_2 + 5\,Cl_2$$

By inspection, $2\,KMnO_4$ produces $2\,KCl$ and $8\,H_2O$. Now $2\,KCl$ and $2\,MnCl_2$ call for 6 additional molecules of HCl. Our balanced equation then becomes:

$$16\,HCl + 2\,KMnO_4 \rightarrow 8\,H_2O + 2\,KCl + 2\,MnCl_2 + 5\,Cl_2$$

negativity. The relatively large atoms of the Sodium Family of metals, Group IA of the Periodic Table, have weak attraction for their valence electrons. They form positive ions readily and are *very active reducing agents*. The lithium atom is the most active reducing agent of all the common elements. The lithium ion, on the other hand, is the weakest oxidizing agent of the common ions.

Atoms of the Halogen Family, Group VIIA of the Periodic Table, have strong attraction for electrons. They form negative ions readily and are *very active oxidizing agents*. The fluorine atom, the most highly electronegative atom, is the most active oxidizing agent

among the elements. The fluoride ion is the weakest reducing agent.

It is possible to arrange the elements in a table according to their power as oxidizing and reducing agents. Indeed, the Activity Series in Chapter 12, Section 12, is such a table. It is arranged to show the relative abilities of metals to replace other metals from their compounds. Replacement is an oxidation-reduction process. Zinc, for example, is above copper in this series, and is therefore a more active reducing agent than copper. The cupric ion, on the other hand, is the more active oxidizing agent.

A more complete series is shown in the accompanying table. Nonmetals and some important complex ions have been added. In this series, any reducing agent will be oxidized by oxidizing agents below it. You will be interested in observing the similarity between this series and the Activity Series of Chapter 12.

RELATIVE STRENGTH OF OXIDIZING AND REDUCING AGENTS

	Reducing Agents	Oxidizing Agents	
Strong	Li	Li^+	Weak
	K	K^+	
	Ca	Ca^{++}	
	Na	Na^+	
	Mg	Mg^{++}	
	Al	Al^{+++}	
	Zn	Zn^{++}	
	Cr	Cr^{+++}	
	Fe	Fe^{++}	
	Ni	Ni^{++}	
	Sn	Sn^{++}	
	Pb	Pb^{++}	
	H_2	$H^+ (H_3O^+)$	
	H_2S	S	
	Cu	Cu^{++}	
	I^-	I_2	
	$MnO_4^=$	MnO_4^-	
	Fe^{++}	Fe^{+++}	
	Hg	Hg^+	
	Ag	Ag^+	
	Hg	Hg^{++}	
	NO_2^-	NO_3^-	
	Br^-	Br_2	
	Mn^{++}	MnO_2	
	SO_2	H_2SO_4 (conc.)	
	Cl^-	Cl_2	
	Cr^{+++}	$Cr_2O_7^=$	
	Mn^{++}	MnO_4^-	
Weak	F^-	F_2	Strong

The permanganate, MnO_4^-, ion and the dichromate, $Cr_2O_7^=$, ion are very powerful and very useful oxidizing agents. They are usually used in the form of their potassium salt. In the presence of an alkali the permanganate ion is reduced to the manganate, $MnO_4^=$, ion. In acid solutions, as we have seen, the permanganate ion is reduced to the manganous, Mn^{++}, ion. Dichromate ions, in acid solution, are reduced to chromic, Cr^{+++}, ions.

The peroxide ion, $O_2^=$, has a single covalent bond between the two oxygens. The electronic structure may be represented by the following:

$$\left[:\overset{..}{O}:\overset{..}{O}: \right]^=$$

The structure represents an intermediate state of oxidation between free oxygen and oxides. The oxidation number of oxygen in the peroxide form is -1.

Hydrogen peroxide, H_2O_2, has the interesting property of being able to act as both an oxidizing agent and a reducing agent. As an oxidizing agent, the oxidation number of oxygen changes from -1 to -2. As a reducing agent, the oxidation number of oxygen changes from -1 to 0.

In the decomposition of hydrogen peroxide, both water and molecular oxygen are formed.

$$2 H_2O_2 \rightarrow 2 H_2O + O_2\uparrow$$

The peroxide acts simultaneously as an oxidizing agent and as a reducing agent. Such a process is called *auto-oxidation*. Half of the oxygen is reduced to the oxide, forming water. The other half is oxidized to free oxygen.

★ **7. Electrochemical reactions.** *1. Electrochemical cells.* Oxidation-reduction reactions involve a transfer of electrons from the substance oxidized to the substance reduced. Such reactions, *that occur spontaneously*, can be used as a

source of electrical energy. If the reactants are in contact, the energy released during the electron transfer is
in the form of heat. By separating the
reactants in an electrolytic solution, the
transfer of electrons may take place
through a conducting wire connected
between them. Such an arrangement is
known as an **electrochemical cell.** *The
flow of electrons through the wire constitutes an electric current.*

The replacement reaction between
metallic zinc and cupric ions is the
source of electrical energy in the *Gravity cell.* The *dry cell* is a common
source of electrical energy in the laboratory. Small dry cells are familiar as
flashlight batteries. A zinc can serves as
the negative electrode or *cathode.* A
carbon rod serves as the positive electrode or *anode.* It is surrounded by a
mixture of manganese dioxide and
powdered carbon. The electrolyte is a
moist paste of ammonium chloride

which contains some zinc chloride.

When the external circuit is closed,
zinc atoms are oxidized at the cathode.

$$Zn^0 - 2\ e^- \rightarrow Zn^{++}$$

Electrons flow through the external
circuit to the carbon anode. Here, *if
manganese dioxide were not present,*
hydrogen gas would be formed.

$$2\ NH_4^+ + 2\ e^- \rightarrow 2\ NH_3^0 + H_2^0\uparrow$$

However, hydrogen is oxidized to water by the manganese dioxide, and
manganese, rather than hydrogen, *is reduced at the anode.*

$$2\ MnO_2 + 2\ NH_4^+ + 2\ e^- \rightarrow$$
$$Mn_2O_3 + 2\ NH_3 + H_2O$$

The ammonia is taken up by Zn^{++} ions
forming complex $Zn(NH_3)_4^{++}$ ions.

2. Electrolytic cells. Oxidation-
reduction reactions, *which are not spontaneous,* may be forced to occur by
means of electrical energy supplied externally. The electrolysis of water is
such a reaction (see Chapter 20, Sec-

**Fig. 23–3. The Gravity Cell. In the electrochem-
ical cell, oxidation occurs at the cathode and
reduction occurs at the anode.**

**Fig. 23–4. In the dry cell, zinc is oxidized at the
cathode and manganese is reduced at the anode.**

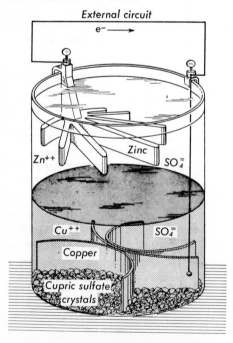

External circuit

$e^- \longrightarrow$

Zn^{++}
Zinc
$SO_4^=$

Cu^{++}
$SO_4^=$
Copper
Cupric sulfate
crystals

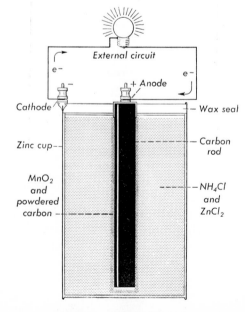

External circuit

e^-
$+$ Anode
e^-

Cathode
Wax seal

Zinc cup
Carbon rod

MnO_2
and
powdered
carbon

NH_4Cl
and
$ZnCl_2$

tion 14). The electrolytic cell for the electrolysis of water consists of two platinum electrodes immersed in a water solution of an electrolyte such as sulfuric acid. The electrodes may be connected to dry cells which supply the electric current required to force the decomposition reaction (see Fig. 23-5).

A current of electricity, as produced by a dry cell, is simply a stream of electrons flowing from the negative electrode of the dry cell, through the external circuit, to the positive electrode of the dry cell. The platinum electrode connected to the cathode of the battery acquires an excess of electrons and becomes the cathode of the electrolytic cell. The platinum electrode connected to the anode of the battery loses electrons to the battery and becomes the anode of the electrolytic cell. *Reduction of hydrogen ions occurs at the cathode* in the electrolytic cell.

$$2\,H^+ + 2\,e^- \rightarrow H_2^0\uparrow$$

Oxidation of hydroxide ions takes place at the anode.

$$4\,OH^- - 4\,e^- \rightarrow 2\,H_2O + O_2\uparrow$$

Electrolytic cells may be constructed to permit the *electroplating* of certain metals. Ions of metals below hydrogen in the electrochemical series of Section 6 are readily reduced at the cathode of an *electroplating cell*. The atoms of the metal thus formed deposit as a smooth plate on the surface of the cathode.

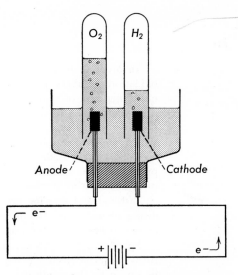

Fig. 23–5. The electrolysis of water. In the electrolytic cell, reduction occurs at the cathode, and oxidation occurs at the anode.

An electroplating cell consists of a solution of a salt of the metal to be plated, a cathode of the object to be plated, and an anode of the metal to be plated. A silver-plating cell consists essentially of a solution of a soluble silver salt, a silver anode, and a cathode of the metal object to be plated. The silver anode is connected to the positive electrode of a battery. The metal object to be plated is connected to the negative electrode. *Silver ions are reduced at the cathode* of the cell when electrons flow through the circuit.

$$Ag^+ + e^- \rightarrow Ag^0$$

Silver atoms are oxidized at the anode.

$$Ag^0 - e^- \rightarrow Ag^+$$

Thus, in effect, silver is transferred from the anode to the cathode of the cell during the electrolytic action.

Summary

A substance which loses electrons is said to be oxidized. A substance which gains electrons is said to be reduced. Both processes must occur simultaneously. Reactions of this type are known as oxidation-reduction reactions. Electrons are transferred completely between ionic substances, and partially between covalent substances.

In order to balance the more complicated oxidation-reduction reactions, oxidation numbers are assigned to each element. These numbers may be either negative or positive and are used to indicate the state of oxidation of a substance. The oxidation numbers in binary compounds are indicated by the common valence. In ternary compounds, oxidation numbers may be assigned by use of certain rules.

Complicated oxidation-reduction equations require a detailed balancing procedure. The primary reaction is balanced as to electrons lost and gained prior to adjusting the coefficients of the entire equation.

Lithium and fluorine are respectively the most active reducing and oxidizing agents. Other metals, nonmetals, and ions, arranged in order between these two substances, form an activity series of oxidizing and reducing agents.

Spontaneous oxidation-reduction reactions may be used as a source of electrical energy in electrochemical cells. Other oxidation-reduction reactions may be forced by the application of electrical energy to electrolytic cells.

Test yourself on these terms

anode	electronic equation	oxidizing agent
cathode	electropositive	polar bond
electrochemical cell	nonpolar bond	redox
electrolytic cell	oxidation	reducing agent
electronegative	oxidation number	reduction

Questions

Group A

1. (*a*) State a general definition for oxidation. (*b*) For reduction.
2. Why is a substance which undergoes oxidation a reducing agent?
3. Why may a substance which undergoes reduction be considered an oxidizing agent?
4. Which of the following are oxidation-reduction reactions?
   - (*a*) $2 Na + Cl_2 \rightarrow 2 NaCl$
   - (*b*) $C + O_2 \rightarrow CO_2$
   - (*c*) $2 H_2O \rightleftarrows 2 H_2 + O_2$
   - (*d*) $NaCl + AgNO_3 \rightarrow AgCl + NaNO_3$
   - (*e*) $NH_3 + HCl \rightarrow NH_4^+ + Cl^-$
   - (*f*) $2 KClO_3 \rightarrow 2 KCl + 3 O_2$
   - (*g*) $H_2 + Cl_2 \rightarrow 2 HCl$
   - (*h*) $2 H_2 + O_2 \rightarrow 2 H_2O$
   - (*i*) $H_2SO_4 + 2 KOH \rightarrow K_2SO_4 + 2 H_2O$
   - (*j*) $Zn + CuSO_4 \rightarrow ZnSO_4 + Cu$
5. For each oxidation-reduction reaction in Question 4 identify: (*a*) the substance oxidized; (*b*) the substance reduced; (*c*) the oxidizing agent; and (*d*) the reducing agent.

Group B

★ 6. Assuming chemical union between the following pairs, indicate in each case which element would have the positive oxidation number: (a) Hydrogen–sodium;   (b) Chlorine–fluorine;   (c) Chlorine–oxygen; (d) Hydrogen–lithium;   (e) Bromine–hydrogen.

★ 7. What is the oxidation number of each element in the following compounds: (a) MnO_2; (b) H_3PO_4; (c) HNO_3; (d) P_4O_{10}; (e) $NaOH$?

★ 8. What is the oxidation state of manganese in: (a) potassium permanganate, $KMnO_4$; (b) manganous sulfate, $MnSO_4$? (c) If manganous sulfate is one of the products of a reaction in which potassium permanganate was one of the reactants, what kind of change has it undergone? (d) What could you call manganese under such circumstances?

★ 9. The four oxygen-acids of chlorine are: hypochlorous acid, $HClO$; chlorous acid, $HClO_2$; chloric acid, $HClO_3$; and perchloric acid, $HClO_4$. What is the oxidation number of the chlorine atom in each acid of the series?

★ 10. Verify your conclusions in Question 9 by writing the electron-dot formula for each acid. Use small circles for hydrogen electrons, dots for oxygen electrons, and small crosses for chlorine electrons.

★ 11. What are the six steps involved in balancing oxidation-reduction equations? List in the proper sequence.

★ 12. Carry out the first four steps called for in Question 11 for each of the following reactions:
   (a) Zinc + hydrochloric acid → zinc chloride + hydrogen.
   (b) Iron + cupric sulfate → ferrous sulfate + copper.
   (c) Copper + sulfuric acid → cupric sulfate + sulfur dioxide + water.
   (d) Hydrochloric acid + potassium permanganate → manganous chloride + potassium chloride + chlorine + water.
   (e) Bromine + water → hydrobromic acid + hypobromous acid.

★ 13. The oxidation-reduction reaction between copper and *concentrated* nitric acid yields the following products: cupric nitrate, water, and nitrogen dioxide. Write the balanced equation.

★ 14. The oxidation-reduction reaction between copper and *dilute* nitric acid yields the following products: cupric nitrate, water, and nitric oxide. Write the balanced equation.

★ 15. Referring to the table of Section 6, the active metals down to magnesium replace hydrogen from water. Magnesium and succeeding metals replace hydrogen from steam. Metals near the bottom of the list will not replace hydrogen from steam. How does this table help to explain this behavior?

Some things for you to do

1. Ask your instructor for permission to experiment with "clock" reactions. See *Tested Demonstrations in General Chemistry*, Journal of Chemical Education, Vol. 32, No. 8 (August 1955), for some interesting reactions. Your instructor may have directions for others.

Check your progress in chemistry

1. What possible explanation can you suggest for the tendency of chemically similar substances to dissolve in each other?
2. What is the freezing point of 250 g of water containing 11.25 g of a nonelectrolyte the molecular weight of which is known to be 180?
3. Explain the dissociation of an electrovalent salt in water solution.
4. Explain the ionization of a polar molecular substance in water solution.
★ 5. What weight of each of the following chemicals would be needed to prepare one liter of 0.1-N solution of each: (a) NaOH; (b) KOH; (c) $Ba(OH)_2$; (d) H_2SO_4; (e) HCl; (f) H_3PO_4; (g) $HC_2H_3O_2$; (h) NaCl; (i) $Ca(NO_3)_2$; (j) $KMnO_4$.
★ 6. Ten milliliters of vinegar is diluted to 100 ml with distilled water and titrated against 0.01-N sodium hydroxide solution. From the burettes, 30 ml of the diluted vinegar and 25 ml of the solution of the base were withdrawn. What percentage of acetic acid, $HC_2H_3O_2$, did the vinegar contain?
★ 7. In the reversible reaction $A + B \rightleftarrows C + D$, k_1 is the velocity constant of the reaction going to the right, and k_2 is the velocity constant of the reaction going to the left for the fixed conditions of the reaction. (a) According to the Law of Mass Action, what is the speed of the reaction to the right? (b) What is the speed of the reaction to the left? (Each expressed in terms of the concentration of the reactants in moles per liter.) (c) If an equilibrium condition is reached, what is the relationship between these two reaction speeds? (d) At equilibrium, what is the value of the equilibrium constant, K, in terms of the concentrations of the reacting substances expressed in moles per liter?
★ 8. Explain the effect on the equilibrium reaction of Question 7 if the concentration of reactant A is increased.
★ 9. Assign oxidation numbers to each element in the following compounds: (a) $PbSO_4$; (b) H_2O_2; (c) $K_2Cr_2O_7$; (d) H_2SO_3; (e) $HClO_4$.
★ 10. Balance the following oxidation-reduction equation: $K_2Cr_2O_7 + HCl \rightarrow KCl + CrCl_3 + H_2O + Cl_2$.

Challenging your knowledge

1. If 1 mole of a substance dissolved in 1000 g of water lowers the freezing point 3.60 C°, what can you predict about the nature of the solution? What can you predict about the oxidation numbers of the particles of solute?
2. Name the following unfamiliar compounds: (a) H_2Se; (b) HIO_3; (c) $Ga(OH)_3$; (d) CsOH; (e) NbF_5; (f) $RaBr_2$.
★ 3. The equilibrium constant for the ionization of acetic acid (ionization constant) is 1.8×10^{-5} at 25° C. Explain the significance of this value.
★ 4. What is the pH of a 0.054-M solution of HCl?
★ 5. 25 ml of 0.15-M NaOH and 50 ml of 0.1-M HCl are mixed. What is the pH of the resulting solution?

UNIT 7

THE ACTIVE METALS

The sparkling globule of molten metal skimming over the water in the drawing above is one of the active metals, potassium. It reacts with water so vigorously that it melts and then burns with a violet flame amid a shower of sparks.

With this unit we begin a more systematic study of the elements according to family groups. The Periodic Table has the elements grouped according to similarities in atomic structure. We have already learned that elements with similar structures have similar properties.

There are two chapters in this unit. *The Sodium Family* describes the elements of Group IA, which have a single electron beyond the inert gas configuration. *The Calcium Family* describes three elements of Group IIA which have two electrons beyond the inert gas configuration. Many of our most important compounds are formed from the metals of these two chemical families.

Chapter 24 THE

SODIUM FAMILY

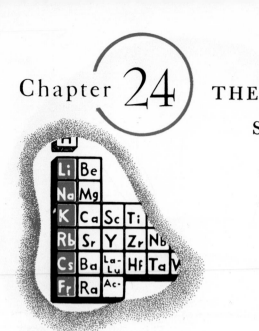

1. The Sodium Family is Group IA of the Periodic Table. This family includes the elements lithium, sodium, potassium, rubidium, cesium, and francium, as shown by the table at the top of page 329.

Each of these elements has a single electron in its outermost shell. This valence electron is easily transferred to another atom. As a result, these elements are the most active metals. The ions which are formed by the transfer of the valence electron have the configuration of the atoms of the preceding inert gas. For example, the sodium ion's electron configuration, 2, 8, is the same as that of a neon atom, while the

electron configuration of the potassium ion, 2,8,8, is the same as that of an argon atom. As a result, the ions of the elements of the Sodium Family are very stable. The members of the Sodium Family have an oxidation number of +1 and form electrovalent compounds.

The elements themselves are soft, silvery, malleable metals with low melting points and low boiling points. They are easily cut. They are good conductors of electricity. These properties are accounted for by the fact that atoms in the solid metals are rather widely spaced, and are held together by only weak attractive forces. The valence electrons are rather free to circulate

VOCABULARY

Caustic. (*1*) Capable of converting some types of animal and vegetable matter into soluble materials by chemical action; (*2*) A substance with such properties.

Spectroscope. An optical instrument consisting of a collimator tube, a glass prism, and a telescope, used for producing and viewing spectra.

Spectrum. The pattern of colors formed by passing light through a prism.

ELEMENT	ATOMIC NUMBER	ATOMIC WEIGHT	ELECTRON CONFIGURATION	OXIDATION NUMBER	MELTING POINT, ° C	BOILING POINT, ° C	DENSITY g/cm³
LITHIUM	3	6.940	2,1	+1	186.	1136	0.534
SODIUM	11	22.991	2,8,1	+1	97.5	880	0.97
POTASSIUM	19	39.100	2,8,8,1	+1	62.3	760	0.86
RUBIDIUM	37	85.48	2,8,18,8,1	+1	38.5	700	1.53
CESIUM	55	132.91	2,8,18,18,8,1	+1	28.5	670	1.873
FRANCIUM	87	223.	2,8,18,32,18,8,1	+1			

through the mass and give the metals their conductivity. These are the metals with the lowest densities because they have the largest volumes in comparison to their masses. The irregularity in density between sodium and potassium is accounted for by the fact that the increase in volume between sodium and potassium atoms is proportionally greater than the increase in mass between the two.

Because of their activity, these metals must be stored under oil or kerosene. These metals do not exist free in nature, and are produced from their melted salts only by highly endothermic reactions. They make excellent reducing agents because of the ease with which they lose an electron. They react with water, reducing it to hydrogen, and forming solutions which are strongly basic. They form no negative ions. The vapors of these metals are mostly monatomic. A very few of the vapor molecules are known to be diatomic.

1. LITHIUM

2. The properties and uses of lithium and its compounds. Lithium occurs in nature in several types of rocks of very complex composition which are found in workable deposits in South Dakota. This element was discovered in 1817 by Johan Arfvedson (1792–1841), a student of Berzelius, but was not isolated until 1855 by Robert W. Bunsen (1811–1899) and Augustus Matthiessen. Lithium is prepared by electrolyzing molten lithium chloride. It is the metal of lowest density. It reacts with oxygen, the halogens, hydrogen, and water.

Dip a clean platinum wire into a solution of a lithium compound, and then place it in the almost colorless oxidizing flame of a burner. You will see that the flame will be colored crimson by the vaporized lithium atoms. This is used as a test for lithium.

Lithium finds many uses in metallurgical processes. Its compounds are used in ceramics, welding, drugs, the manufacture of chemicals, and the synthesis of organic compounds.

2. SODIUM

3. The occurrence of sodium. Metallic sodium is never found free in nature. However, sodium compounds are widely distributed. They are found in soil, in natural waters, and in plants and animals. Sodium is such a widespread element that it is difficult to find an absolutely sodium-free material.

4. The preparation of sodium. Sir Humphry Davy was the first to prepare metallic sodium. He produced it in 1807 by the electrolysis of moist sodium hydroxide. Metallic sodium is prepared today by the electrolysis of fused sodium chloride. Since sodium chloride has such a high melting point, some other salt such as calcium chloride or sodium carbonate is mixed with it. The resulting mixture then has a lower melting point, but the added materials do not interfere with the reaction. The molten sodium is collected under oil. The apparatus in which this reaction is carried out is called a *Downs cell* (see Fig. 24-4). The chlorine produced simultaneously is a very valuable by-product.

$$2 \text{ NaCl} \rightarrow 2 \text{ Na} + \text{Cl}_2\uparrow$$

5. The physical and chemical properties of sodium. Sodium is a silvery-white, lustrous metal that tarnishes within a minute or two when exposed to air. It is so soft that it can be cut easily with a knife. It has a density lower than that of water, and also a low melting point. When you drop a pellet of sodium into water, it floats on the surface, melts, assumes a spherical shape, and spins around as it reacts with the water. The reduction of water by sodium produces sodium hydroxide and hydrogen.

$$2 \text{ Na} + 2 \text{ H}_2\text{O} \rightarrow 2 \text{ NaOH} + \text{H}_2\uparrow$$

When exposed to the air, sodium unites with the oxygen and moisture in the air to form sodium hydroxide. The sodium hydroxide, in turn, reacts with carbon dioxide and forms sodium carbonate. Metallic sodium is stored under kerosene, or some other petroleum oil. Sodium reacts with all ordinary acids. It will burn in an atmosphere of chlorine gas, uniting directly with the chlorine to form sodium chloride.

Suppose you dip a clean platinum wire into a solution of a sodium com-

Fig. 24–1. This worker is dipping molten lithium metal from the electrolytic cell in which it is produced.

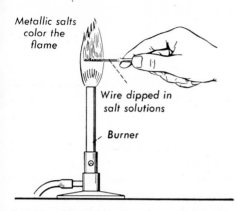

Metallic salts color the flame

Wire dipped in salt solutions

Burner

Fig. 24-2. The atoms of some metals impart a characteristic color to a colorless gas flame when they are vaporized.

pound, and then place the wire in the nearly colorless flame of a burner. You will discover that the vaporized sodium atoms impart a strong yellow-orange color to the flame. This is a test for sodium.

6. The uses of sodium. Metallic sodium has several important uses. It is used in making "Ethyl" fluid for anti-knock gasolines, in the preparation of dyes and other organic compounds, and in sodium vapor lamps. The valve stems of some internal combustion engines are filled with metallic sodium. The heat of operation melts the sodium, and this liquid metal inside the valve stem helps conduct the heat away from the head of the valve.

7. The production, properties, and uses of sodium chloride. Sodium chloride is found in sea water, in salt wells, and in deposits of rock salt. Rock salt is mined in many places in the world. One such deposit in Texas is more than 3000 ft thick. New York, Michigan, Kansas, Ohio, Utah, Louisiana, and several other states contribute to the 30 million barrels of salt produced annually in the United States.

Pure sodium chloride is not deliquescent. However, magnesium chloride, which is very deliquescent, is usu-

ally present in salt as an impurity. This fact explains why common salt becomes wet and sticky in damp weather. Sodium chloride crystallizes in cubes.

Sodium chloride is essential in our diet and is present in certain body fluids. Perspiration contains considerable amounts of it. Consequently, those who perspire freely in hot weather often find it advisable to increase their salt intake by the use of salt tablets. Many animals relish salt, also.

Thousands of tons of salt are used every year as a preservative in the packing and curing of meat and fish. Mixed with chipped ice, salt makes a good freezing mixture for homemade ice cream. Rock salt, mixed with sand, is frequently scattered on icy streets and sidewalks in the winter so as to melt the ice and make travel less hazardous. Since sodium chloride is the cheapest compound of sodium, we find it used as a starting material for making nearly all other sodium compounds. Fig. 24-6 shows some of the important uses for salt.

Fig. 24-3. Sir Humphry Davy, an English chemist, is noted particularly for his discovery of the elements sodium, potassium, calcium, strontium, and barium by electrolyzing certain of their compounds.

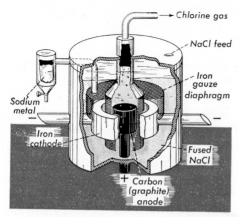

Fig. 24–4. Elementary sodium is produced by the electrolysis of fused sodium chloride in a Downs cell. Chlorine is a valuable by-product.

8. The preparation, properties, and uses of sodium hydroxide. Most of our commercial sodium hydroxide comes as a by-product from the electrolysis of sodium chloride solution to produce chlorine.

$$2\,NaCl + 2\,H_2O \rightarrow 2\,NaOH + Cl_2\uparrow + H_2\uparrow$$

Considerable amounts are also made by adding calcium hydroxide (slaked lime) to sodium carbonate solution.

$$Na_2CO_3 + Ca(OH)_2 \rightarrow 2\,NaOH + CaCO_3\downarrow$$

The precipitated calcium carbonate is filtered off, and the remaining solution of sodium hydroxide is concentrated by evaporation.

Sodium hydroxide converts some types of animal and vegetable matter into soluble materials by chemical action. Therefore, we say it is a very *caustic* substance. Acids are said to have a *corrosive* action on metals, but strong alkalies such as sodium hydroxide have a *caustic* action on skin, hair, and wool.

Sodium hydroxide is a white crystalline solid that is marketed in the form of flakes, pellets, and sticks. It is very deliquescent, taking water from the air, and then carbon dioxide, finally producing sodium carbonate. Its water solution is strongly basic.

Sodium hydroxide reacts with fats, forming soap and glycerol. Thus, one of its important uses is for making soap. Sodium hydroxide is also used in the production of rayon and cellulose film, in petroleum refining, and in the production of paper. Sodium hydroxide is sold in cans under the name lye, or caustic soda. It is used in the home for cleaning greasy sink traps.

9. The Solvay process for preparing sodium carbonate and sodium hydrogen carbonate. The great bulk of the sodium carbonate and sodium hydrogen carbonate produced in this country and abroad is manufactured by the **Solvay process**. This was developed in 1864 by Ernest Solvay (1838–1922), a Belgian.

The raw materials for the Solvay process are salt, limestone, and coal. The salt is pumped as brine from nearby salt wells. Limestone is strongly

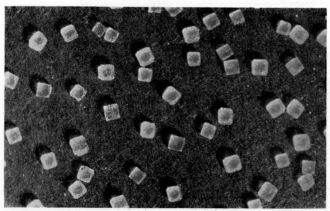

Fig. 24–5. Crystals of sodium chloride, common table salt, magnified about 80 times. Note the cubic shape of the crystals.

332

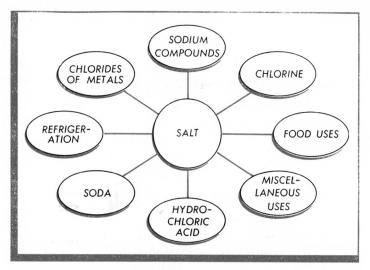

Fig. 24–6. Sodium chloride (common salt) has many important uses.

heated to yield the carbon dioxide and calcium oxide needed in the process:

Equation 1:

$$CaCO_3 \rightarrow CaO + CO_2\uparrow$$

Coal is converted into coke, gas, coal tar, and ammonia by destructive distillation. The coke and gas are used as fuel in the plant; the coal tar is sold; and the ammonia is used in the process.

In operation, a cold saturated solution of sodium chloride is treated with ammonia and carbon dioxide. The ammonia dissolves in the water and combines with the carbon dioxide to form ammonium hydrogen carbonate.

Equation 2:

$$NH_3 + H_2O + CO_2 \rightarrow NH_4HCO_3$$

The sodium chloride then reacts with the ammonium hydrogen carbonate and forms sodium hydrogen carbonate and ammonium chloride. Sodium hydrogen carbonate is only slightly soluble in this solution and precipitates.

Fig. 24–7. Flow diagram of the main reactions in the Solvay process. The success of the process depends on the re-use of the by-products, which, for simplicity, have been omitted here.

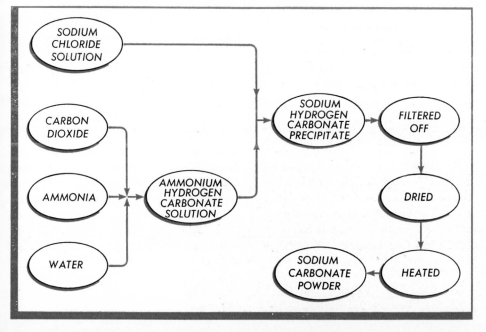

Equation 3:

$$NaCl + NH_4HCO_3 \rightarrow NaHCO_3\downarrow + NH_4Cl$$

The precipitated sodium hydrogen carbonate is filtered off, dried, and heated to convert it into sodium carbonate.

Equation 4:

$$2\,NaHCO_3 \rightarrow Na_2CO_3 + H_2O\uparrow + CO_2\uparrow$$

The dried sodium carbonate is packaged and sold. Pure baking soda (sodium hydrogen carbonate) is prepared by dissolving the sodium carbonate in water, and then forcing in carbon dioxide gas under pressure. The reaction is just the reverse of *Equation 4* above.

Equation 5:

$$Na_2CO_3 + H_2O + CO_2 \rightarrow 2\,NaHCO_3$$

The ammonia used in the process is more valuable than the sodium carbonate or sodium hydrogen carbonate. Hence it must be recovered and used over again, if the process is to be profitable. The calcium oxide produced in *Equation 1* above is slaked by adding water to form calcium hydroxide.

Equation 6:

$$CaO + H_2O \rightarrow Ca(OH)_2$$

The calcium hydroxide is reacted with the ammonium chloride that was produced in *Equation 3* above.

Equation 7:

$$Ca(OH)_2 + 2\,NH_4Cl \rightarrow$$
$$CaCl_2 + 2\,H_2O + 2\,NH_3\uparrow$$

The ammonia gas is used over again as shown in *Equation 2*. Calcium chloride produced in *Equation 7* is a by-product that can be sold, although the supply exceeds the demand because it has only limited uses (see Chapter 25, Section 20).

10. What are the properties and uses of sodium carbonate? Sodium carbonate is marketed both as colorless crystals that have the formula $Na_2CO_3 \cdot 10\,H_2O$ and also as an anhydrous white powder, Na_2CO_3. Both forms hydrolyze in water solution, producing a solution with rather strong basic properties. The crystals are sometimes used in the laundry under the name *washing soda*. Anhydrous sodium carbonate is one of the ingredients present in most scouring powders. It is also used in making glass and sodium silicate (water glass). Sodium carbonate makes an effective water softener, and is known commercially as *soda ash*.

11. The properties and uses of sodium hydrogen carbonate. Sodium hydrogen carbonate reacts with acids and liberates carbon dioxide. For this reason it is used as a leavening agent in baking and is commonly called *baking soda*. Sour milk or molasses may be added to the baking soda to set free the carbon dioxide, although baking powders that contain sodium hydrogen carbonate and some acid substance already mixed are used more commonly.

The water solution of sodium hydrogen carbonate has feebly basic properties. It is used to some extent to neutralize excess acid in the stomach. You should not confuse baking soda with washing soda, which has much stronger basic properties when it is dissolved in water.

12. Some other compounds of sodium. Sodium compounds are widely used because: *1.* they are usually cheaper; and *2.* common sodium compounds are soluble in water. The table on page 335 gives formulas, common names, and important uses of some additional familiar sodium compounds.

CHEMICAL NAME	COMMON NAME	FORMULA	COLOR	USES
SODIUM NITRATE	Chile saltpeter	$NaNO_3$	White, or colorless	As fertilizer; in making nitric acid
SODIUM SULFATE	Glauber's salt	$Na_2SO_4 \cdot 10 H_2O$	White, or colorless	In making glass; as a cathartic in medicine
SODIUM PEROXIDE	None	Na_2O_2	Yellowish white	As oxidizing and bleaching agent; as source of oxygen
SODIUM THIOSULFATE	Hypo	$Na_2S_2O_3 \cdot 5 H_2O$	White, or colorless	As fixer in photography; as antichlor
SODIUM CYANIDE (CAUTION: very poisonous.)	Prussate of soda	$NaCN$	White	To destroy vermin; to extract gold from ores; in silver and gold plating; in case-hardening of steel
SODIUM TETRABORATE	Borax	$Na_2B_4O_7 \cdot 10 H_2O$	White	As a flux; in making glass; as a water softener
SODIUM PHOSPHATE (normal)	TSP	$Na_3PO_4 \cdot 10 H_2O$	White	As a cleaning agent; as a water softener
SODIUM SULFIDE	None	Na_2S	Colorless	In the preparation of sulfur dyes; for dyeing cotton; to remove hair from hides

3. POTASSIUM

13. Where does potassium occur? Combined potassium is widely distributed. However, most deposits of potassium compounds, such as feldspar rocks, are insoluble and weather slowly, so the potassium is not readily available. Large deposits of potassium chloride, crystallized with magnesium and calcium compounds as complex salts, are found in Texas and New Mexico. These deposits, together with some potassium compounds extracted from Searles Lake in California, supply our needs for this element.

14. The discovery and preparation of potassium. Potassium was first prepared by Sir Humphry Davy in 1807 by the electrolysis of fused potassium hydroxide. Today potassium is prepared commercially by a modification of Davy's method by electrolyzing fused potassium chloride.

$$2 KCl \rightarrow 2 K + Cl_2\uparrow$$

15. Potassium metal resembles metallic sodium closely in its properties. It is soft, of low density, and has a silvery luster that acquires a bluish-gray tarnish in less than a minute when it is exposed to air. It is even more active than sodium, usually burning with a lavender flame as it spins around on the surface of water. It must be stored under oil to protect it from oxidation.

Suppose you dip a clean platinum wire into a solution of a potassium compound. Now place the wire in the almost colorless burner flame. Note the

transient violet color that is imparted
to the flame by the vaporizing potassium atoms. The presence of potassium
in a mixture containing both sodium
and potassium compounds may be detected by observing the colored flame
through cobalt-blue glass. This glass
filters out the yellow sodium flame and
permits separate observation of the
violet potassium flame.

16. The compounds of potassium.
All common potassium compounds are
soluble in water. Potassium hydroxide
is prepared by the electrolysis of a solution of potassium chloride. It has the
properties of a typical alkali. Potassium

nitrate is made by mixing hot, concentrated solutions of potassium chloride
and sodium nitrate.

$$KCl + NaNO_3 \rightarrow KNO_3 + NaCl\downarrow$$

When the solutions are mixed, sodium
chloride, being the least soluble of the
four salts, precipitates and is removed.
Then as the solution cools, the potassium nitrate which remains crystallizes
from the saturated sodium chloride solution.

The accompanying table lists a few
of the more important potassium compounds, together with their common
names, formulas, color, and their various uses.

CHEMICAL NAME	COMMON NAME	FORMULA	COLOR	USES
POTASSIUM HYDROXIDE	Caustic potash	KOH	White	In making soft soap; in the Edison battery
POTASSIUM CHLORIDE	None	KCl	White	As source of potassium; as a fertilizer
POTASSIUM SULFATE	None	K_2SO_4	White	As source of potassium; as a fertilizer
POTASSIUM CARBONATE	Potash	K_2CO_3	White	In making glass; in making soap
POTASSIUM CHLORATE	None	$KClO_3$	White	As oxidizing agent; in fireworks; in explosives
POTASSIUM NITRATE	Saltpeter	KNO_3	White	In black gunpowder; in fireworks; in curing meats
POTASSIUM BROMIDE	None	KBr	White	As a sedative; in photography
POTASSIUM IODIDE	None	KI	White	In medicine; in iodized salt; in photography
POTASSIUM PERMAN-GANATE	None	$KMnO_4$	Purple	As a germicide; as oxidizing agent

Fig. 24-8. This large machine scoops and loads potassium salts in a potash mine.

In many cases, sodium compounds can be used instead of potassium compounds. Sodium chlorate is as satisfactory as potassium chlorate for many uses. Sodium hydroxide is as useful for most purposes as potassium hydroxide. It is not only cheaper per gram, but one gram goes farther, too. Sodium has an atomic weight of 23, and potassium an atomic weight of 39. If we wish to use either one to produce a base, we find that it takes 56 grams of KOH to give us 17 grams of hydroxide ions, and only 40 grams of NaOH to furnish the same amount of hydroxide ions. Sodium carbonate is used most often for making glass, but potassium carbonate yields a more lustrous glass that is preferred for optical uses. Potassium nitrate is necessary for making black

Fig. 24-9. A cross-section through a salt deposit, showing how the different minerals have been deposited as the sea water evaporated.

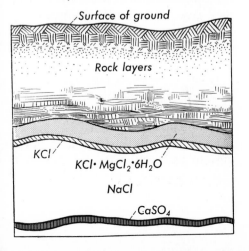

Surface of ground

Rock layers

KCl

KCl· MgCl$_2$·6H$_2$O

NaCl

CaSO$_4$

Fig. 24-10. A spectroscope is used for separating light into its various colors. Elements may be identified by their spectra.

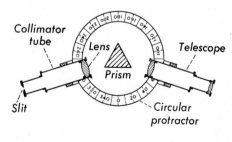

Collimator tube

Lens

Prism

Telescope

Slit

Circular protractor

gunpowder because sodium nitrate is hygroscopic and the powder would become damp and not burn properly.

There is one very important use for potassium compounds for which there is absolutely no substitution. Green plants must have these compounds to grow properly, and complete chemical fertilizers always contain a substantial percentage of this necessary element.

4. RUBIDIUM, CESIUM, AND FRANCIUM

17. Rubidium and cesium. Rubidium and cesium were discovered by Bunsen in 1860 through the use of the spectroscope. The spectrum of rubidium contains two bright lines at the red end, while the spectrum of cesium contains two bright lines at the blue end. Rubidium and cesium are prepared as metals by heating some of their compounds with metallic calcium, magnesium, or aluminum. Rubidium and cesium are used in photoelectric cells and to remove the last traces of oxygen from other electronic tubes.

18. Francium. Francium was discovered by Mlle. M. Perey in 1937, and named for her native country, France. This is a radioactive element, which is formed by the disintegration of an isotope of actinium.

5. SPECTROSCOPY

19. The use of a spectroscope. A *spectroscope* consists of a glass prism, a collimator tube to focus a narrow beam of light rays upon the prism, and a small telescope for examining the light which passes through the prism. When white light is passed through a triangular prism, a band of colors called a *continuous spectrum* is produced.

If we examine a sodium flame by means of a spectroscope, we find that it gives a bright-yellow line. Since this yellow line is always in the same relative place in the spectrum, it serves to identify sodium. Potassium produces both red and violet lines in the spectrum. From the spectrum chart facing page 344, we see the characteristic color lines of several elements and also the beautiful continuous spectrum that is produced by white light.

The stars and other heavenly bodies give characteristic spectra by means of which it is possible to determine the elements of which they are composed. Bunsen and Kirchhoff, two German chemists, introduced the spectroscope as a tool for chemical analysis. Today the spectroscope is widely used to analyze alloys during their production. The speed of this method enables the producer to alter the composition of the alloy while it is actually being made if the analysis indicates the composition is not that desired.

★ **20. The origin of spectral lines.** When atoms are heated to a high temperature and then suddenly cooled, they give off light. We have already learned that vaporized sodium atoms emit yellow light, and vaporized potassium atoms emit violet light.

When such atoms are heated, their electrons may acquire sufficient energy to move out of their normal shells into the unoccupied shells that are farther from the nucleus. Such addition of energy to an electron can be in only a certain amount—that needed for the particular change of shell which the electron makes. In the case of a sodium atom, the outer M-shell electron may move to the N-shell, or to the O-shell, or to any other unoccupied shell. The amount of energy acquired is just the amount needed for the change of shell, no more and no less. An electron which is occupying a shell of higher than normal energy level is called an *excited electron.*

When the attraction of the nucleus for this excited electron draws it back into its normal shell, it emits energy in the form of light. The energy emitted can be only a certain amount depending on the particular shell change made. Thus the light emitted has a definite wave length, and therefore a definite color. The returning of excited electrons to their normal shells in atoms produces the colored lines seen

in their spectra. The color we see with the naked eye is the combination of the separate colors of light emitted during the electrons' return.

If an electron drops back, say from the N shell to the K shell, the light which it emits is of short wave length, and may be violet. If the electron only drops back from the O shell to the N shell, the light emitted has a longer wave length, and may be red. A change of shells with energy emission between these two amounts will produce light with a wave length between violet and red. Only a relatively small amount of the energy emitted by the return of excited electrons to their normal shells is of such wave length that it falls within the visible spectrum. Much of it has a wave length which is in the ultraviolet region and can be photographed though it is not visible.

ummary

The Sodium Family includes lithium, sodium, potassium, rubidium, cesium, and francium. Each of these elements has a single electron in its outermost shell. The ions formed from these atoms are very stable. The members of the Sodium Family form electrovalent compounds.

These elements are soft, silvery metals. Because of their activity, they must be stored under oil or kerosene. They react with water, reducing it to hydrogen, and forming solutions with strong basic properties.

Metallic lithium is used in metallurgical processes, while its compounds are used in ceramics, welding, drugs, and the manufacture of chemicals.

Metallic sodium is used in making antiknock gasoline, dyes, and other organic compounds.

Sodium chloride is obtained from sea water, salt wells, and salt deposits. It is an essential in our diet. Sodium chloride is used as a preservative for meat and fish, as well as a raw material for making sodium compounds.

Sodium hydroxide, or caustic soda, is made by electrolysis of sodium chloride solution, and also by adding calcium hydroxide to sodium carbonate solution. Sodium hydroxide is used in making soap, rayon, and paper.

Sodium carbonate is made by the Solvay process. It is used in the laundry, for making glass, and as a water softener. Sodium hydrogen carbonate, baking soda, is used as a leavening agent.

Potassium compounds are absolutely essential for plant growth. Potassium salts are obtained from deposits in Texas and New Mexico, as well as from the brine of Searles Lake in California.

Flame tests are used to identify the presence of the members of the sodium family. Lithium imparts a crimson color to the flame; sodium colors the flame yellow; and potassium gives a lavender color.

Test yourself on these terms

baking soda	collimator	Solvay process
caustic	Downs cell	spectroscope
caustic potash	flame test	spectrum
caustic soda	lye	telescope
cobalt-blue glass	prism	washing soda

Questions

Group A

1. Describe the electron configuration of the atoms and ions of the elements in the Sodium Family.
2. Compare the methods of preparing lithium, sodium, and potassium.
3. List three uses for metallic sodium.
4. Distinguish between the terms *caustic* and *corrosive*.
5. (*a*) What are the raw materials for the Solvay process? (*b*) What are the products and by-products?
6. (*a*) What is caustic soda? (*b*) Washing soda? (*c*) Baking soda?
7. Why do molasses and baking soda have a leavening action in cookies?
8. What are the sources of potassium compounds in the United States?
9. (*a*) How are sodium and potassium stored in the laboratory stockroom? (*b*) Why must they be stored in this fashion?
10. Write the balanced formula equation for the reaction of potassium and water.
11. Describe the flame tests for lithium, sodium, and potassium.
12. Why were the names *rubidium* and *cesium* given to these elements?
13. Write three equations to show how sodium carbonate can be produced in the Solvay process.
14. Write three equations for the recovery of ammonia in the Solvay process.

Group B

15. Why are the members of the Sodium Family soft, malleable metals with low melting points and low boiling points?
16. Why is salt necessary in the diet of many animals and man?
17. Why is sodium chloride used as a starting material for preparing metallic sodium and other compounds of sodium?
18. (*a*) Why are sodium compounds more frequently used than potassium compounds? (*b*) For what purpose can sodium compounds not be substituted for potassium compounds?
19. What by-product of the Solvay process has such limited use and yet is produced in such quantity that disposal of it is actually a problem to the manufacturers?
20. For what purposes are spectroscopes used in chemical analysis?

21. Why does table salt become sticky in damp weather when pure sodium chloride is not deliquescent?

22. Explain why potassium has a lower density than sodium when it consists of heavier atoms.

23. Write a balanced chemical equation for the reaction which occurs when sodium hydroxide is exposed to the air.

24. In the Solvay process, why does the reaction between sodium chloride and ammonium hydrogen carbonate run to completion?

25. Why does a solution of sodium carbonate in water turn red litmus paper blue?

26. Suppose you had a tremendous quantity of acid that had to be neutralized, and that NaOH, KOH, and LiOH were all available at the same price per pound. Which of these three would you use? Why?

Problems

Group A

1. (a) How many grams of sulfuric acid in water solution can be neutralized by 10 g of sodium hydroxide? (b) By 10 g of potassium hydroxide?

2. If you have a pound of sodium nitrate and a pound of potassium chloride, theoretically how much potassium nitrate can you make by reacting these two substances?

3. If crystallized sodium carbonate, $Na_2CO_3 \cdot 10\,H_2O$, sells for 5 cents a pound, what is anhydrous sodium carbonate worth per pound?

Group B

4. How many liters of carbon dioxide can be liberated from 50 g of each of the following: (a) Na_2CO_3; (b) $NaHCO_3$; (c) K_2CO_3; (d) $KHCO_3$?

★ 5. How many pounds of sodium chloride and how many cubic feet of carbon dioxide (at S.T.P.) theoretically are required to produce a ton of anhydrous sodium carbonate?

Some things for you to do

1. Prepare a report describing the purification of sodium chloride for use as table salt. The manufacturers of table salt will usually be glad to furnish interesting pamphlets describing the process.

2. Prepare some potassium nitrate by crystallizing it from a hot solution of potassium chloride and sodium nitrate. Add 85 g of sodium nitrate to 75 g of potassium chloride, and dissolve the chemicals in as small an amount of boiling water as possible. Filter the solution to remove any suspended impurities. Allow the solution to cool, preferably in a refrigerator after it reaches room temperature. Pour off the mother liquor and examine the crystals of potassium nitrate produced. From the solubility curves given in Fig. 19-5, explain why potassium nitrate crystallized from solution. The potassium nitrate may be dried, transferred to a bottle, and added to the supplies in the stockroom.

3. Prepare a chart, similar to Fig. 24-7, but in more detail, to show all the reactants and products, as well as the recycling of ammonia and carbon dioxide, for all the reactions of the Solvay process.

Chapter 25 THE

CALCIUM FAMILY

1. The Calcium Family is Group IIA of the Periodic Table. It comprises the elements beryllium, magnesium, calcium, strontium, barium, and radium.

Because of their uses as metals and in alloys, beryllium and magnesium will be discussed with other light metals in Chapter 34. Radium's importance arises from its radioactivity. The nature of radioactivity and the properties of radium will be described in Chapter 38. The remaining three elements, calcium, strontium, and barium, have such similar properties that they are described as the Calcium Family in this chapter.

Each of the elements in the Calcium Family has two valence electrons. These electrons hold the atoms together in the solid metal. Consequently, these metals are more dense, harder, and with higher melting points and boiling points than the corresponding members of the Sodium Family, which each have only one valence electron.

The atoms and ions of the members of the Calcium Family are smaller than the corresponding members of the Sodium Family because of their higher nuclear charge. The oxides of these elements have a bonding which is more covalent, and their hydroxides are less

VOCABULARY

Hard water. Water containing ions such as calcium and magnesium which form precipitates with soap.

Ion exchange resin. A resin which can exchange hydrogen ions for positive ions; or one which can exchange hydroxide ions for negative ions.

Permanent hardness. Hardness, caused by the sulfates of calcium and magnesium, which can be removed by the addition of chemical softeners.

Temporary hardness. Hardness, caused by the bicarbonates of calcium and magnesium, which can be removed by boiling the water.

Zeolite. A sodium silico-aluminate used to soften water.

ELEMENT	ATOMIC NUMBER	ATOMIC WEIGHT	ELECTRON CONFIGURA-TION	OXIDA-TION NUMBER	MELT-ING POINT, °C	BOIL-ING POINT, °C	DEN-SITY g/cm³
BERYLLIUM	4	9.013	2,2	+2	1300	1500 (5 mm)	1.85
MAGNESIUM	12	24.32	2,8,2	+2	650	1100	1.74
CALCIUM	20	40.08	2,8,8,2	+2	810	1240	1.55
STRONTIUM	38	87.63	2,8,18,8,2	+2	800	1350	2.6
BARIUM	56	137.36	2,8,18,18,8,2	+2	850	1540	3.6
RADIUM	88	226.05	2,8,18,32,18,8,2	+2	960	1140	5

basic. The metals do not react with water as violently as the members of the Sodium Family. There is a strong electrostatic attraction between ions of this group and the negative end of the water molecule. Consequently, they form hydrates. Because of their activity, none of these elements occurs free in nature.

1. CALCIUM

2. Calcium is widely distributed. Calcium ranks fifth in abundance by weight among the elements in the earth's crust, atmosphere, and surface waters. It is widely distributed over the earth's surface in marble, limestone, dolomite, and gypsum, as well as in many other minerals.

3. The discovery of calcium. Calcium was first isolated by Sir Humphry Davy in 1808. He prepared metallic calcium by electrolyzing a moist mixture of calcium oxide and mercuric oxide, and then distilling the mercury from the resulting calcium-mercury amalgam.

4. How is metallic calcium prepared? Calcium is prepared today by electrolyzing fused calcium chloride.

$$CaCl_2 \rightarrow Ca + Cl_2\uparrow$$

A graphite crucible, which also serves as the anode, holds the fused chloride. An iron rod cathode dips into the fused salt. As metallic calcium forms on the end of the rod, the rod is slowly raised from the mass. In this way an irregular rod of metallic calcium is produced.

5. The properties and uses of calcium. Metallic calcium is silver-white in color, but a freshly-cut piece tarnishes to a bluish-gray surface within a few hours. It is somewhat harder than lead, but it is only about one-eighth as dense. If a piece of calcium is added to water, it reacts with the water and liberates hydrogen slowly.

$$Ca + 2 H_2O \rightarrow Ca(OH)_2 + H_2\uparrow$$

The reaction is much less violent than that of sodium and potassium with water. The calcium hydroxide produced in this reaction is only slightly soluble and coats the surface of the calcium. This protects the metal from the rapid interaction with the water which would be expected because of the greater electrochemical activity of calcium than of sodium. Calcium is a good reducing agent. It burns with a bright, orange-red flame in oxygen, and unites directly with chlorine, also.

Calcium is used in small amounts to deoxidize copper, and some alloy steels contain small quantities of it. Lead-calcium alloys are used for bearings in machines. Calcium is also used to harden lead for cables and storage battery grids.

6. Calcium carbonate is abundant. Calcium carbonate, $CaCO_3$, is both widely and abundantly distributed. It is found in a number of different forms.

1. Limestone. This is the most common form of calcium carbonate. It was probably formed in past geologic ages from the accumulations of the shells of clams, oysters, and other marine animals. Limestone occurs in layers as a *sedimentary rock,* and is quarried in varying amounts in almost every state in the country. A good limestone for building purposes is found in southern Indiana.

Pure calcium carbonate is white, or colorless, when crystalline. Most deposits, however, are gray because of impurities.

Limestone is used for making glass, as a flux in making iron and steel, and as a source of carbon dioxide. Much of it is used as a building stone, and considerable quantities are used for making roads. Mixed with clay, it can be converted into cement. Powdered or pulverized limestone is used to neutralize soils that are too acid. Large quantities are heated to produce *quicklime,* calcium oxide, CaO.

2. Calcite. A clear, crystalline form of calcium carbonate is known as calcite. Transparent, colorless specimens are called *Iceland spar.*

3. Marble. It is probable that this mineral was originally deposited as limestone, and later changed by heat and pressure into marble. Hence it is classed as a *metamorphic rock.* Vermont and Georgia are noted for their fine marble, but it is also quarried in many other states. Marble makes a beautiful building stone.

4. Shells. The shells of such animals as snails, clams, and oysters consist largely of calcium carbonate. In some places, large masses of such shells have become cemented together to form a mineral called *coquina* (ko-*quee*-na). This rock has been used as a building stone in the southern states. Egg shells are also made up principally of calcium carbonate. Pearls are composed of calcium carbonate. Tiny marine animals, called *polyps* (*pah*-lips), deposit limestone as they build coral reefs and islands. Chalk, such as that of the

Fig. 25–1. Limestone is an excellent building stone. Here we see a huge block of Indiana limestone being removed from the quarry.

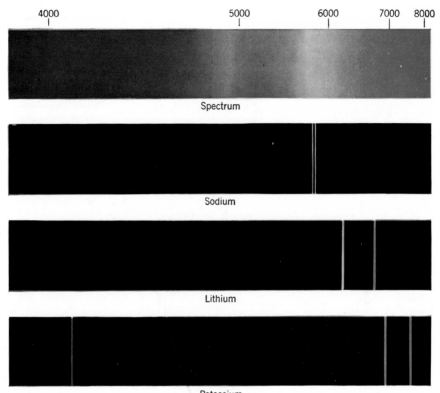

4000　　　　　　5000　　　　6000　　7000　8000

Spectrum

Sodium

Lithium

Potassium

A continuous spectrum is shown at the top. Sodium has
a double line at about 5800 angstroms wave length.
(An angstrom is 1/100,000,000 cm.)

Co　　　　Cr　　　　Mn

Fe^{++}　　　U　　　Ni

Colors obtained by adding metallic compounds to melted
borax. The presence of some elements is often detected
by this means, using a borax bead on a platinum wire.

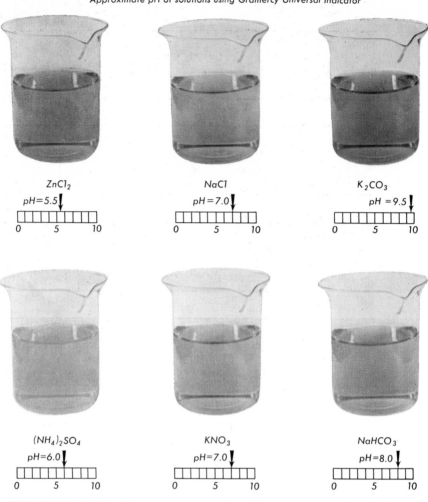

Approximate pH of solutions using Gramercy Universal Indicator

ZnCl$_2$
pH=5.5

NaCl
pH=7.0

K$_2$CO$_3$
pH=9.5

(NH$_4$)$_2$SO$_4$
pH=6.0

KNO$_3$
pH=7.0

NaHCO$_3$
pH=8.0

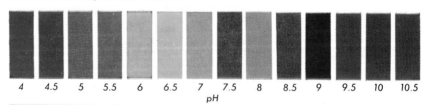

Colors with Gramercy Universal Indicator

| 4 | 4.5 | 5 | 5.5 | 6 | 6.5 | 7 | 7.5 | 8 | 8.5 | 9 | 9.5 | 10 | 10.5 |

pH

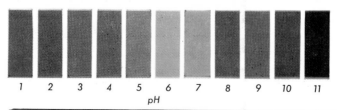

Colors with Hydrion Test Paper

| 1 | 2 | 3 | 4 | 5 | 6 | 7 | 8 | 9 | 10 | 11 |

pH

Modern indicators show that the solutions of many salts are not neutral.

Fig. 25-2. The United States Supreme Court building in Washington, D. C., is constructed of marble.

chalk cliffs of England, consists of the microscopic remains of small marine animals. Blackboard "chalk," however, contains some clay-like material mixed with calcium carbonate, and should not be confused with natural chalk.

5. Precipitated chalk. This form of calcium carbonate is made by the reaction of sodium carbonate and calcium chloride.

$$Na_2CO_3 + CaCl_2 \rightarrow CaCO_3\downarrow + 2\,NaCl$$

It is soft and finely divided. Thus it forms a nongritty scouring powder that is suitable for tooth pastes and tooth powders. Under the name of *whiting* it is used as a filler for paints. When it is ground with linseed oil, it forms putty.

7. How are limestone caves formed? Limestone reacts slowly with water that contains carbon dioxide in solution, and forms calcium hydrogen carbonate, which is slightly soluble.

$$CaCO_3 + H_2O + CO_2 \rightleftarrows Ca(HCO_3)_2$$

As the calcium hydrogen carbonate is carried away by the water in which it dissolves, caves or caverns are sometimes formed in the limestone. The Luray Caverns in Virginia, the Mammoth Cave in Kentucky, the Carlsbad Caverns in New Mexico, and the Howe Caverns in New York are famous for their size and the interesting rock formations found in them.

The chemical reaction above is reversible. For that reason, drops of water which hang from the roof of a cave may lose carbon dioxide. As a result of this reversal, limestone is redeposited in icicle-shaped masses of limestone, called *stalactites* (stah-*lack*-tytes), which hang from the roof of the cavern. Water dripping from these stalactites may then build up masses of calcium carbonate, called *stalagmites* (stah-*lag*-mytes), on the floor of the cavern. As the stalactites grow downward, and the stalagmites grow upward by long-continued deposition of material, they may meet and form columns.

A similar reaction occurs when water containing dissolved carbon dioxide comes in contact with dolomite, $CaCO_3 \cdot MgCO_3$. In this case, both calcium hydrogen carbonate and magnesium hydrogen carbonate are formed and dissolve in the water.

$$CaCO_3 \cdot MgCO_3 + 2 H_2O + 2 CO_2 \rightleftarrows$$
$$Ca(HCO_3)_2 + Mg(HCO_3)_2$$

8. Water may have temporary or permanent hardness. Limestone and dolomite are widely distributed underground. Whenever water which contains carbon dioxide in solution soaks through the ground and reaches these mineral deposits, some of the calcium carbonate and magnesium carbonate is converted to the soluble bicarbonates of these metals. This water, which contains calcium ions and magnesium ions in solution, is called *hard water*. The term "hard water" indicates that it is "hard" to get a lather when soap is added to such water. Conversely, a water that lathers readily with soap is called "soft" water. The terms are not precise, but they are in common usage. Deposits of iron and other heavy metals in the ground may also produce hard water.

Calcium hydrogen carbonate, the most frequent cause of hardness in water, is a rather unstable compound. It is decomposed by heat as follows:

$$Ca(HCO_3)_2 \rightarrow CaCO_3\downarrow + H_2O + CO_2\uparrow$$

Magnesium hydrogen carbonate is simi-

Fig. 25–3. Carlsbad Caverns contain some of the large limestone caves found in the United States. The photograph shows the entrance to the Hall of Giants in these caverns.

larly decomposed on heating. Consequently, water that contains these compounds in solution can be softened by heating it to the boiling point, and allowing the precipitated carbonates to settle. Water that can be softened in this manner is said to have *temporary hardness*.

Water frequently contains calcium sulfate, or magnesium sulfate in solution. These compounds are stable, and are not decomposed by boiling. Their presence produces water that has *permanent hardness*. Like the terms hard and soft, the terms temporary and permanent are not precise, even though they are commonly used, because all hardness can be removed from water.

9. Hard water and its action on soap. Sodium stearate, which may be considered the principal component of soap, is soluble in water. But calcium stearate, magnesium stearate, and the stearates of other metals are insoluble, sticky substances that have a greasy feeling. When soap is added to water that contains calcium, iron, or magnesium ions, a double replacement reaction occurs. For example:

sodium stearate + calcium compound →
    calcium stearate↓ + sodium compound

Thus the ions in hard water react with the soap to form precipitates until all of them are removed. Until this occurs, no lasting lather will be produced. Soft water does not contain the ions of these troublesome metals and lathers easily when soap is added.

10. The softening of hard water. Hard water is a nuisance for laundry work because of the sticky precipitate that wastes soap and collects on the fibers of the garments being laundered.

Fig. 25–4. Equal amounts of soap were added to the hard water in the bottle at the left, and to the soft water in the bottle at the right. Note how cloudy the hard water has become, while the soft water remains clear with many suds on top.

For bathing, the hard water does not lather freely, and the precipitate forms a scum on the bathtub. For generating steam in boilers, temporary hard water containing calcium hydrogen carbonate has a still more serious fault. The precipitated calcium carbonate collects as a hard scale on the inside of the boiler and on the inside of steam pipes. It may form a thick crust on these surfaces. This acts as a heat insulator and prevents efficient transfer of heat. Thus, for most purposes, hard water needs softening before it is used.

Water that has temporary hardness may be softened by heating it to the boiling point and allowing the precipitates which form to settle. The clear soft water is then drawn from the top of the container and will lather freely. Many factories use waste steam from boilers to heat large tanks of temporary hard water, prior to use in the factory. Such a method, however, is not practical for home use.

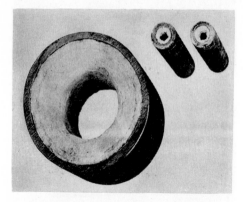

Fig. 25–5. The scale of calcium carbonate which has collected on the inside of these pipes cuts down the flow of steam through them and acts as a heat insulator. Thus, the scale prevents efficient transfer of heat.

Water that has temporary or permanent hardness, or both, may be softened by adding suitable chemicals to precipitate the troublesome metallic ions. Slaked lime, sodium carbonate, borax, and trisodium phosphate are all used for softening water. Typical reactions for sodium carbonate are:

$$Ca(HCO_3)_2 + Na_2CO_3 \rightarrow$$
$$CaCO_3\downarrow + 2\, NaHCO_3$$

$$MgSO_4 + Na_2CO_3 \rightarrow MgCO_3\downarrow + Na_2SO_4$$

The action of the sodium carbonate has produced a soft water containing sodium ions in place of calcium and magnesium ions. Only the very small concentration of calcium and magnesium ions in equilibrium with their carbonates now remains in solution. The ions which caused the hardness in the water have been removed by precipitation.

Many industrial establishments use slaked lime because it is a cheap method of softening large quantities of water. In the home, sodium carbonate or borax are more convenient to use.

11. Zeolites soften water. Some natural minerals, known as *zeolites,* contain sodium silico-aluminates. When hard water stands in contact with them, they exchange their sodium for the calcium or magnesium of the hard water. Thus the water is softened. The equation may be expressed as follows:

$$sodium\ silico\text{-}aluminate + Ca^{++} \rightarrow$$
$$calcium\ silico\text{-}aluminate + 2\, Na^+$$

Fortunately, the reaction can be reversed if one adds a concentrated solution of sodium chloride to the calcium silico-aluminate. Thus the zeolite is regenerated and used over again. "Permutit" is an artificial zeolite which acts even more rapidly than natural zeolites. The use and regeneration of such water softeners are examples of the effect of concentration on the direction of a reversible reaction.

In operation, a tank that is partly filled with a sodium zeolite is connected with the water supply. In flowing through the tank, the water is softened, while the sodium zeolite changes to calcium zeolite. In most cases, the zeolite is renewed about once a week by shutting off the water, draining the tank,

Fig. 25–6. This water softening unit enables any home to have a constant supply of soft water.

and allowing a concentrated solution of common salt to stand overnight in contact with the calcium zeolite. The sodium ions of the common salt solution regenerate the sodium zeolite as follows:

calcium silico-aluminate $+ 2\,Na^+ \rightarrow$
sodium silico-aluminate $+ Ca^{++}$

The resulting calcium chloride solution is drained off and discarded. After rinsing the zeolite, the unit is ready again for use. Many homes in areas where the water is hard are equipped with such water softeners.

12. Ion exchange resins remove minerals from water. Another method of removing minerals from solution in water employs ion exchange resins. In this process, the water flows through a tank that is partly filled with granules of an acid exchange resin that absorbs positive ions, such as calcium, magnesium, and sodium, and gives up hydrogen ions in exchange. The water is then passed through a tank that contains a base exchange resin which exchanges the negative ions in the water for hydroxide ions. After flowing through both tanks, the water is completely demineralized. Carbon dioxide may remain in solution but is harmless for most purposes. Water that has been passed through such an ion exchange unit is almost as free of minerals as distilled water. In fact, ion exchange units are now being used to supply water for many processes that formerly required distilled water, such as the preparation of medicines. Sulfuric acid and sodium carbonate, inexpensive chemicals, are used at periodic intervals to renew the ion exchange resins.

13. The preparation of calcium oxide. Calcium oxide is made by heating

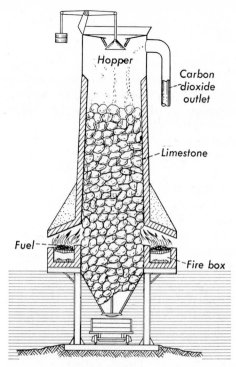

Fig. 25–7. A sectional view of a vertical lime kiln. It is operated continuously by putting limestone in at the top and withdrawing quicklime from the bottom.

calcium carbonate to a high temperature.

$$CaCO_3 \rightarrow CaO + CO_2\uparrow$$

Carbon dioxide is driven off by the heat, and calcium oxide remains. The furnace used for the process is called a kiln. It may be a vertical kiln, Fig. 25-7, or a rotary kiln, Fig. 25-8.

In the modern rotary kiln, small pieces of limestone are continuously fed into the upper end of a slowly rotating inclined cylinder. The cylinder may be 8 ft in diameter and 200 ft long. As the lumps move downward by gravity, they meet the hot gases from the burning fuel, which is usually oil or gas. By the time the lumps reach the lower end of the kiln, all the carbon dioxide has been driven off by the heat.

14. The properties of calcium oxide. Calcium oxide is a white, noncrystalline compound. It is often called quick-lime. It is very refractory since it does not melt or vaporize except at the temperature of the electric arc. It unites chemically with water to form calcium hydroxide, or *hydrated lime:*

$$CaO + H_2O \rightarrow Ca(OH)_2$$

During this process, which is called *slaking,* the mass swells and large quantities of heat are evolved.

If a lump of quicklime is exposed to the air, it gradually absorbs water, swells decidedly, cracks, and crumbles to a powder. It first forms calcium hydroxide, and then slowly unites with carbon dioxide from the air to form calcium carbonate. Thus a mixture of calcium hydroxide and calcium carbonate is formed. This is called *air-slaked lime.* Such a mixture is valuable for liming soils, but air slaking ruins lime for making mortar and plaster.

15. Calcium hydroxide has many uses. Calcium hydroxide is a white solid which is sparingly soluble in water. Its water solution, which is called limewater, has basic properties. A suspension of calcium hydroxide in water is known as milk of lime. Mixed with flour paste or glue, it makes whitewash.

Calcium hydroxide is the cheapest hydroxide. It is used to remove hair from hides before they are tanned, or converted into leather. It is useful for liming soils, for liberating ammonia from ammonium compounds, and for softening temporary hard water. Large quantities are used for making mortar and plaster.

16. What is mortar? Lime mortar, used between bricks for above ground construction, consists of slaked lime, sand, and water. The sand is used to make the mass more porous and harder, and also to prevent excessive shrinkage which might cause cracks. Although mortar of this general composition has been used for many centuries, the process by which it sets to a hard mass is still not fully understood. The first step in the setting is loss of water by evaporation. It appears that the lime and sand slowly react to some extent according to the following equation:

$$Ca(OH)_2 + SiO_2 \rightarrow CaSiO_3 + H_2O$$

Carbon dioxide from the air reacts with the lime also, as follows:

$$Ca(OH)_2 + CO_2 \rightarrow CaCO_3 + H_2O$$

Mortar becomes harder over a period

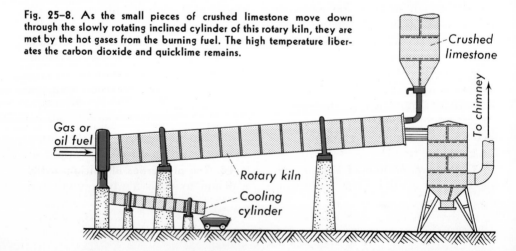

Fig. 25–8. As the small pieces of crushed limestone move down through the slowly rotating inclined cylinder of this rotary kiln, they are met by the hot gases from the burning fuel. The high temperature liberates the carbon dioxide and quicklime remains.

Crushed limestone

To chimney

Gas or oil fuel

Rotary kiln

Cooling cylinder

of many years as the chemical changes occur in the center of the mass.

Cement is sometimes added to lime mortar to make it harder and more waterproof. For some construction work, particularly underground, cement is used entirely instead of lime, making a cement mortar.

17. Plaster is a building necessity. Plaster was formerly made much like lime mortar, but with some added hair or wood fiber to make it cling together better. Such a mixture is still used for the first, or undercoat, on walls. The finish coat is a mixture of calcium hydroxide, water, and plaster of Paris. It dries quickly with a smooth hard surface.

18. The preparation of cement and concrete. Cement is made from limestone and clay. Powdered limestone and clay are mixed in the proper proportions and heated strongly in a cement kiln. Just as the mixture begins to melt, it forms into pasty masses, about the size of peas, which are called *clinker.* When the clinker is cooled and hardened, it is ground to as fine a powder as possible. The finer the grinding of the clinker, the stronger the cement will be. To prevent too rapid setting, 2% to 3% of gypsum is ground with the clinker.

Sometimes limestone deposits have clay already mixed with the calcium carbonate in about the proportions needed to serve as raw material for making cement. Such rocks are called *natural cement.* Pennsylvania has good deposits of natural cement rock. Cement is sometimes called *hydraulic cement* because it sets or hardens under water.

The hardening of cement is not completely understood. The first step ap-

Fig. 25–9. This rotary cement kiln is 12 feet in diameter and 450 feet long.

pears to be due to the union of water with some of the components of the cement to form hydrates. The hydrated crystals seem to become interlocked into a hard mass. Some chemists believe that the action is partly colloidal since the strength increases with the fineness of particle size.

Cement is mixed with sand, crushed stone, and water to make *concrete.* When concrete hardens, it forms a very

Fig. 25–10. This diagram shows how steel rods are used to reinforce concrete in the building industry.

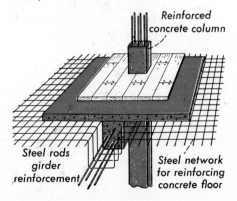

Reinforced concrete column

Steel rods girder reinforcement

Steel network for reinforcing concrete floor

hard, compact mass which is suitable for many construction purposes. *Reinforced concrete* is strengthened by embedding iron or steel rods in it.

19. The uses of calcium sulfate. Calcium sulfate occurs as the mineral *gypsum,* which is found principally in Kansas, New York, Ohio, Indiana, and Michigan. Transparent crystals of gypsum are called *selenite.*

When gypsum is heated gently, it loses part of its water of hydration and forms a white powder known as plaster of Paris.

$$2\ CaSO_4 \cdot 2\ H_2O \rightarrow$$
$$(CaSO_4)_2 \cdot H_2O + 3\ H_2O\uparrow$$

When plaster of Paris is mixed with water, it forms a paste which can be molded into any desired shape. It sets rapidly by uniting with water and forming crystals. Thus it hardens to a white solid which is useful for making casts. It is used in making decorative stucco. It is mixed with lime and used to make the finish coat of plaster. Large quantities are used in making wallboard or plasterboard.

20. Some uses of calcium chloride. Calcium chloride, $CaCl_2$, is produced as a by-product of the production of sodium carbonate by the Solvay process (see Chapter 24, Section 9). It also exists in natural brines and in sea water.

Anhydrous calcium chloride is deliquescent. Consequently, it is used as a drying agent, to lay dust on roads and in coal mines, and to prevent the too rapid drying of concrete. It is also used to melt ice and snow on roads, and in preparing brines for artificial ice plants.

Fig. 25–11. A mesh of steel rods is used to reinforce the concrete in many modern highways.

2. STRONTIUM AND BARIUM

21. Strontium compounds. The sulfate and the carbonate are the chief strontium minerals. All the compounds of strontium impart a beautiful red color to a flame. Hence they are used in fireworks displays.

Strontium nitrate, $Sr(NO_3)_2$, when mixed with powdered shellac, makes a red light for fireworks and flares.

22. Useful compounds of barium. Both the sulfate and the carbonate of barium are found in nature. The compounds of barium are similar chemically to the compounds of calcium. The following are most widely used.

1. Barium sulfate, $BaSO_4$, is a dense white solid which is used as a filler in making heavy paper and also in paints. It gives more body to paper and makes it less transparent, and it increases the durability of paint.

2. Barium peroxide, BaO_2, is used in fireworks, as a vigorous oxidizing agent, and to some extent for making hydrogen peroxide.

3. Barium nitrate, $Ba(NO_3)_2$, is a white crystalline solid. All barium compounds impart a yellowish-green color to a flame. They find considerable use in making flares and fireworks, for which the nitrate is generally used.

The oxides of both barium and strontium are used to coat the filament used in vacuum tubes. A single layer of barium atoms on the surface of the filament is said to multiply the yield of electrons given off by the filament more than one hundred million times.

Summary

The Calcium Family comprises beryllium, magnesium, calcium, strontium, barium, and radium. Each of these elements has two valence electrons. The atoms and ions of the members of the Calcium Family are smaller than the corresponding members of the Sodium Family. The bonding formed by these elements is somewhat covalent, and their hydroxides do not produce very strong bases. These elements form hydrates. None of these metals occurs free in nature.

Metallic calcium is silver-white in color, of low density, and relatively hard. It reacts with water, and burns in oxygen with an orange-red light. It is used to harden lead.

Calcium carbonate is an abundant compound that occurs in a number of different forms. Limestone caves are formed by the solvent action of water that contains dissolved carbon dioxide.

Hard water contains compounds of calcium, magnesium, or iron in solution. Water may contain temporary or permanent hardness which can be removed by various methods. The process by which hardness is removed from water is called water softening.

Calcium oxide, or quicklime, unites with water to form calcium hydroxide, or hydrated lime. Calcium hydroxide is used for making mortar, plaster, and for other uses that require the inexpensive formation of a base.

Barium and strontium compounds are used in making fireworks. Barium sulfate is used in paints and to add weight to paper.

est yourself on these terms

air-slaked lime	hydrated lime	plaster of Paris
calcite	Iceland spar	quicklime
cement	ion-exchange resin	sedimentary rock
clinker	kiln	slaking
concrete	limestone	stalactite
coquina	metamorphic rock	stalagmite
dolomite	mortar	temporary hardness
gypsum	permanent hardness	water softener
hard water	plaster	zeolite

Questions

Group A

1. Compare the preparation of elementary calcium with that of elementary sodium.
2. What are the important uses for metallic calcium?
3. In what forms is calcium carbonate found in nature?
4. (*a*) What does the term *hard water* mean? (*b*) *Soft water?*
5. How is a zeolite water softener regenerated?
6. Distinguish: (*a*) limestone; (*b*) quicklime; (*c*) slaked lime; (*d*) lime; (*e*) hydrated lime.
7. For what gas is limewater used as a test solution?
8. Distinguish between metamorphic and sedimentary rocks.
9. How could you demonstrate that a piece of coral is a carbonate?
10. Write an equation to show the action of water containing dissolved carbon dioxide on limestone.
11. Explain how cement is manufactured from clay and limestone.
12. How are "red fire" and "green fire" made for fireworks?

Group B

13. Why are the members of the Calcium Family denser and harder than the corresponding members of the Sodium Family?
14. Why does calcium chloride exist as a hydrate, $CaCl_2 \cdot 2 H_2O$, while sodium chloride does not occur as a hydrate?
15. Give two reasons why the reaction of calcium with water is not as vigorous as that of potassium and water.
16. (*a*) What metallic ions cause water to be hard? (*b*) What negative ion causes temporary hardness? (*c*) What negative ion causes permanent hardness?
17. What type of chemical reaction occurs between soap and hard water?
18. Write a balanced chemical equation to show the softening action of sodium carbonate on hard water containing: (*a*) calcium sulfate; (*b*) magnesium bicarbonate.
19. To what chemical changes is the hardening of cement believed to be due?
20. What are some uses for calcium chloride which is produced in such large quantities as a by-product of the manufacture of Solvay soda?

21. (a) How is plaster of Paris made? (b) Why does it harden?
22. What are the uses for barium sulfate?
23. What impurity may still remain in water that has been passed through both an acid exchange resin and a base exchange resin?
24. (a) Why should cement mortar be used between the cinder block of house foundations? (b) Why may lime mortar be used between the bricks?

Problems

Group A

1. How many pounds of calcium oxide can be produced from one ton of limestone which contains 10% of impurities?
2. How much weight will 86 lb of gypsum lose when it is converted into plaster of Paris?

Group B

3. How many pounds of carbon dioxide can be obtained from a ton of oyster shells that are 80% calcium carbonate?
4. How many liters will the carbon dioxide produced in Problem 3 occupy at S.T.P.?
5. If the carbon dioxide of Problem 4 is measured at 720 mm pressure and 20° C, what volume does it occupy?

Some things for you to do

1. Make a collection of as many different forms of calcium carbonate as you can find.
2. Make a paste with plaster of Paris and water. Spread it in a thin layer in a cardboard box, or on a glass square. Rub a little oil on a medal, flat key, or other metallic object, and press it into the plaster of Paris just before it hardens. After a half hour remove the metallic object, and note the clear impression it leaves in the plaster of Paris.
3. Look about your school building and list the ways in which calcium compounds have been used in its construction.
4. Visit one of the large natural caves which are located in various regions of the United States. Try to learn how the cave was formed.
5. Determine the hardness of natural waters by titrating samples of them with a standard soap solution.

Check your progress in chemistry

1. How do the structures of graphite and diamond explain the differences in their properties?
2. If you are given a bottle of nitrogen, a bottle of carbon dioxide, and a bottle of carbon monoxide, how can you distinguish them?

3. Name five series of hydrocarbons. Give the general formula for as many of these series as you can.
4. What weight of hydrated cupric sulfate, $CuSO_4 \cdot 5\,H_2O$, must be used to make up 500 ml of a 0.5-N solution?
5. Distinguish between *dissociation* and *ionization*.
6. Give the modern definitions of *acid* and *base*.
★ 7. Give the expression for the equilibrium constant for the ionization of acetic acid.
★ 8. Balance the following oxidation-reduction equation: $Hg + HNO_3 \rightarrow Hg(NO_3)_2 + H_2O + NO\uparrow$.
9. Compare potassium and calcium as to structure, physical properties, and chemical properties.
10. Why are metals generally good conductors of electricity?
11. Give several uses for elementary lithium.
12. How can you detect potassium in the presence of sodium by a flame test?
13. Write the equation for the preparation of sodium hydroxide from washing soda and slaked lime.
14. Why must the ammonia be recovered in the Solvay process?
15. Define: (a) coquina; (b) gypsum; (c) Iceland spar; (d) stalactite; (e) temporary hardness.
16. What are the principal uses for limestone?
17. Write the equation for the reaction of sodium carbonate and calcium chloride to produce precipitated chalk.
18. Explain how zeolites soften hard water and how they may be regenerated when exhausted.
19. Describe the operation of a rotary lime kiln.
20. (a) What is the composition of a plaster undercoat? (b) Of a plaster finish coat?

Challenging your knowledge

1. In the Solvay process, sodium hydrogen carbonate is prepared, converted to sodium carbonate, and then reconverted to sodium hydrogen carbonate. Why is this done rather than use the sodium hydrogen carbonate that is first prepared?
2. What optical use is made of crystals of Iceland spar?
3. For what type of solutions would the carbon dioxide which remains dissolved in water after passing through ion exchange resins be objectionable?
4. What important electrical discovery had to precede Davy's preparation of metallic sodium, metallic potassium, and metallic calcium?
5. What is *halite*?
6. Why do poultrymen add calcium carbonate to the diet of laying hens?

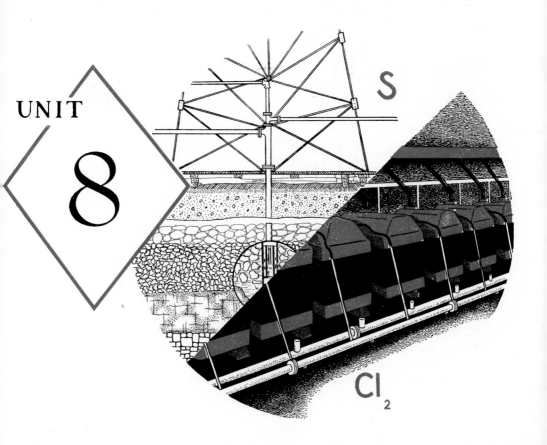

UNIT 8

THE HALOGENS AND SULFUR

In this unit we shall consider two groups of nonmetallic elements located at the right of the Periodic Table.

At the right of the drawing above is a row of Hooker cells in a plant which produces chlorine by the electrolysis of sodium chloride solution. Chlorine is an important member of the Halogen Family. The halogens are the elements with seven electrons in their outermost electronic shell.

To the left of the drawing is a cross-section of a sulfur well. Sulfur deposits in the United States occur well underground and are brought to the surface by the ingenious Frasch process. Sulfur is the starting material for the most important industrial chemical, sulfuric acid.

There are three chapters in this unit: *The Halogen Family, Sulfur and Sulfides,* and *The Oxides and Acids of Sulfur.* In these chapters you will discover the usefulness of these important nonmetals.

Chapter 26 THE

HALOGEN FAMILY

1. The Halogen Family is Group VIIA of the Periodic Table. It consists of the nonmetallic elements fluorine, chlorine, bromine, iodine, and astatine, as shown in the table on page 359.

From this table we learn that each of these elements has seven electrons in its outermost shell. In order to attain an outer octet of electrons, a halogen atom must acquire one electron. Since the atoms of these elements have such a strong affinity for electrons, they are all active elements which have never been found free in nature. In the elementary state they exist as covalent diatomic molecules. Fluorine, having the smallest atoms, shows the greatest affinity for electrons. Fluorine is consequently the most active nonmetallic

element, and cannot be prepared from its compounds by any purely chemical reduction. The other halogens, with increasingly larger atoms, show less activity than fluorine. As a result, the smaller, lighter halogens are able to replace the larger, heavier halogens from their compounds (see Activity Series, Chapter 12, Section 12). Astatine is a synthetic radioactive halogen produced in 1940 at the University of California by Corson, MacKenzie, and Segre. Very little is known of its properties. However, what study has been made of this element indicates that it is a halogen with properties which correspond to its position in the family.

We also see from the table that there is a regular change in properties shown

VOCABULARY

Antichlor. A substance used to remove traces of chlorine left in bleached goods.

Halogen (*hal*-oh-jen). The name given to the family of elements having seven valence electrons.

Mother liquor. The saturated solution remaining after the separation of a crop of crystals.

Pickling. Removing the surface impurities from a metal by dipping it into an acid bath.

ELEMENT	ATOMIC NUMBER	ATOMIC WEIGHT	ELECTRON CONFIGURA- TION	PRINCI- PAL OXIDA- TION NUMBER	MELT- ING POINT, °C	BOIL- ING POINT, °C	COLOR	DENSITY, 15°C
FLUORINE	9	19.00	2,7	−1	−223	−187	pale- yellow gas	1.69 g/l
CHLORINE	17	35.457	2,8,7	−1	−101.6	−34.6	greenish- yellow gas	3.214 g/l
BROMINE	35	79.916	2,8,18,7	−1	−7.2	58.78	reddish- brown liquid	3.12 g/ml
IODINE	53	126.91	2,8,18,18,7	−1	113.5	184.35	grayish- black crystals	4.93 g/ml
ASTATINE	85	210.	2,8,18,32,18,7					

by the members of this family as we proceed from the smallest and lightest to the largest and heaviest.

Each of the halogens combines with hydrogen. Hydrogen fluoride molecules are so polar that they associate by hydrogen bonding. The remaining hydrogen halides do not show this property.

Each of the hydrogen halides is a colorless gas which is ionized in water solution. With the exception of hydrofluoric acid, these acids are highly ionized and are strong acids.

Each of the halogens forms ionic salts with metals. Hence the name *halogens,* which means "salt producers."

1. FLUORINE

2. The preparation of fluorine. Fluorine was first prepared in 1886 by Henri Moissan (1852–1907). He prepared it by electrolyzing a solution of potassium hydrogen fluoride, KHF_2, in liquid anhydrous hydrogen fluoride in a platinum tube. He used platinum-iridium electrodes. Today it is prepared by electrolyzing a mixture of potassium fluoride and hydrogen fluoride. Stainless steel or copper is used for the electrolytic cell. The fluoride coating formed on these metals protects them from further attack. Graphite is used for the anode.

3. What are the properties of fluorine? Fluorine is the most active nonmetallic element. A fluorine atom, with seven electrons in its outer L shell, has a great affinity for an additional electron to complete its octet. An acquired electron is very strongly attracted by the positively-charged nucleus due to the small size of the fluorine atom. This accounts for its extreme electronegativity. It unites with hydrogen explosively, even in the dark. It forms compounds with all of the elements except the inert gases. There are no known positive oxidation states of fluorine. It forms salts known as *fluorides*. Fluorine attacks gold and platinum slowly. Special carbon steel containers are used to transport fluorine. These become coated with iron fluoride which resists further action.

4. Fluorine compounds are very useful. The mineral *fluorspar*, CaF_2, is used in preparing most fluorine compounds. Sodium fluoride is used as a poison for destroying roaches and vermin. Fluorides affect tooth enamel. A trace of sodium fluoride, or the cheaper sodium silico-fluoride, is added to the drinking water of many communities to help prevent tooth decay. Yet, larger quantities of fluorides in drinking water cause the enamel of the teeth to become spotted. Swabbing the teeth with a 2% solution of sodium fluoride also appears to reduce the number of cavities in children's teeth. The fluoride ion seems to react with the enamel of children's teeth, but has little effect on the teeth of adults. Fluorides have also been added to some tooth pastes to help prevent tooth decay.

Dichloro-difluoro-methane, commercially called "Freon," CCl_2F_2, is used as a refrigerant. It is odorless, nonflammable, and non-toxic. It is also used as the propellant in spray cans of insecticides. In the production of aluminum, melted cryolite, $AlF_3 \cdot 3 NaF$, is used as a solvent for aluminum oxide. Uranium is converted to the gaseous uranium hexafluoride, UF_6, for separating the uranium isotopes.

5. The preparation and properties of hydrogen fluoride. This compound, HF, is prepared by treating calcium fluoride with concentrated sulfuric acid:

$$CaF_2 + H_2SO_4 \rightarrow CaSO_4 + 2 HF\uparrow$$

The colorless gas which is set free by the reaction fumes strongly in moist air. It dissolves in water and forms hydrofluoric acid. This acid is very corrosive, attacking the flesh and forming painful sores which heal slowly. The vapor is very dangerous if inhaled. Hydrofluoric acid attacks most substances. Wax, lead, platinum, and certain plastics are important exceptions.

At ordinary room temperature, 22.4 liters of hydrogen fluoride weighs about 50 g; thus hydrogen fluoride has an average molecular weight of 50. Since the molecular weight of an HF molecule is

Fig. 26–1. Electrolytic cells used for the production of elementary fluorine from potassium fluoride and hydrogen fluoride.

only 20, this indicates that hydrogen fluoride is an approximately equal mixture of H_2F_2 and H_3F_3 molecules, having molecular weights of 40 and 60 respectively. At higher temperatures, 22.4 liters of the gas weighs only 20 g, showing that the gas dissociates into HF molecules. The association of hydrogen fluoride molecules is an example of hydrogen bonding. Only a few of the H_2F_2 molecules present in hydrofluoric acid at room temperature ionize as follows:

$$H_2F_2 \rightleftarrows H^+ + HF_2^-$$

As a result, hydrofluoric acid is a weak acid. But being a diprotic acid it forms both acid and normal salts.

$$H_2F_2 + KOH \rightarrow KHF_2 + H_2O$$
$$H_2F_2 + 2 KOH \rightarrow 2 KF + 2 H_2O$$

6. The uses of hydrofluoric acid. The chief uses of hydrofluoric acid are as a catalyst in the manufacture of high-octane gasoline, and in the manufacture of synthetic cryolite for aluminum production.

For many years hydrofluoric acid has been used for etching glass. The surface of the glass is coated with wax or paraffin. A sharp stylus is then used to

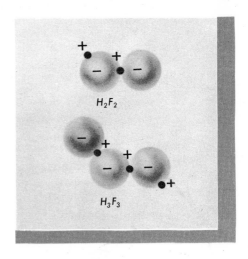

Fig. 26–2. Hydrogen fluoride at room temperature consists of H_2F_2 and H_3F_3 molecules.

scratch away the wax from that portion of the surface of the glass which is to be etched. The glass prepared in this manner is then exposed either to hydrogen fluoride gas or to a solution of the gas in water. The excess acid is washed off and the wax removed. If a solution is used for etching, the line etched is likely to be smooth and transparent. If the gas is used, the etched portion is likely to be somewhat rough and translucent. Electric light bulbs may be frosted by exposing the inside surface of the bulb to the fumes of hydrogen fluoride.

2. CHLORINE

7. Chlorine occurs widely in combined form. Because chlorine is a very active element, it never occurs free or uncombined in nature. It is found rather abundantly in the form of chlorides of sodium, potassium, and magnesium. Common table salt, or sodium chloride, is widely distributed. It is present in sea water, in salt brines underground, and in rock salt deposits. Sodium chloride is the commercial source for the preparation of chlorine.

8. The preparation of chlorine. The element chlorine was first isolated in 1774 by Scheele. There are various ways to prepare it; we shall discuss three.

1. By the electrolysis of sodium chloride. Several commercial methods for preparing chlorine by the electrolysis of sodium chloride have been developed. In all cases the concentration of the sodium chloride solution is such that hydrogen from the water is liberated at the cathode. Chlorine gas is set

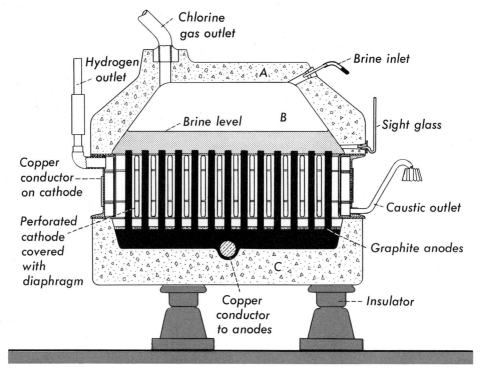

Fig. 26–3. The Hooker cell is the most efficient cell for preparing chlorine by the electrolysis of a solution of sodium chloride.

free at the anode. The gases, hydrogen and chlorine, are kept separate from each other and from the solution by asbestos diaphragms. The sodium and hydroxide ions remaining in the solution are recovered as sodium hydroxide.

$$2\ NaCl + 2\ H_2O \xrightarrow{\text{elect.}} 2\ NaOH + H_2\uparrow + Cl_2\uparrow$$

The most efficient cell for chlorine production is the *Hooker cell. Vorce cells* and *Nelson cells* are also used. A small amount of chlorine is prepared electrically from fused sodium chloride as a by-product of sodium production.

2. By the oxidation of hydrogen chloride. When you mix manganese dioxide with hydrochloric acid and heat it, the manganese oxidizes half of the chloride ions in the reacting HCl to chlorine atoms. Manganese is reduced

during the reaction from the +4 oxidation state to the +2 state.

$$MnO_2 + 4\ HCl \rightarrow MnCl_2 + 2\ H_2O + Cl_2\uparrow$$

This is the method that was used by Scheele in first preparing chlorine. It is a useful laboratory preparation.

In an alternate procedure, we mix manganese dioxide with sodium chloride and sulfuric acid, and heat the mixture. The sodium chloride and sulfuric acid react to form hydrogen chloride, as in *Equation 1* below.

Equation 1.

$$2\ NaCl + H_2SO_4 \rightarrow Na_2SO_4 + 2\ HCl$$

The hydrogen chloride is then oxidized by the manganese dioxide and free chlorine is liberated, as in *Equation 2.*

Equation 2.

$$2\ HCl + MnO_2 + H_2SO_4 \rightarrow MnSO_4 + 2\ H_2O + Cl_2\uparrow$$

Fig. 26–4. Chlorine is also prepared commercially in Vorce cells such as these.

Combining *Equations 1* and *2* gives us the following equation which represents the overall reaction:

$$2\ NaCl + 2\ H_2SO_4 + MnO_2 \rightarrow$$
$$Na_2SO_4 + MnSO_4 + 2\ H_2O + Cl_2\uparrow$$

3. By the action of hydrochloric acid on calcium hypochlorite. This is a convenient laboratory method for the preparation of chlorine, since heat is not needed. Furthermore, the chlorine can be produced in small quantities as required. Hydrochloric acid is allowed to drop onto calcium hypochlorite powder. Chlorine is liberated and calcium chloride and water are formed.

$$4\ HCl + Ca(ClO)_2 \rightarrow$$
$$CaCl_2 + 2\ Cl_2\uparrow + 2\ H_2O$$

9. The physical properties of chlorine. At room temperature chlorine is a greenish-yellow gas, which has a disagreeable, almost suffocating odor. It is about 2.5 times as dense as air, and

moderately soluble in water. It imparts to its water solution a pale-yellow color. Chlorine is easily liquefied and is usually marketed in steel cylinders.

When inhaled in small quantities, chlorine attacks the mucous membranes of the nose and throat. It produces about the same symptoms as a bad head cold. If inhaled in larger quantities, chlorine is so toxic that it causes

Fig. 26–5. One method of preparing chlorine in the laboratory is by heating a mixture of manganese dioxide, sodium chloride, and sulfuric acid.

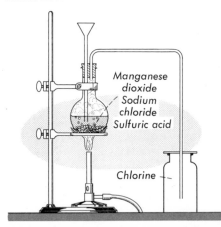

Manganese dioxide
Sodium chloride
Sulfuric acid

Chlorine

death. The bad effects from breathing chlorine are partly alleviated by inhaling either alcohol or ammonia.

10. Chlorine is very active chemically. The outer shell of a chlorine atom contains seven electrons. Chlorine undergoes many reactions as it acquires the additional electron to complete the octet. We shall study its chemical properties under the following subtopics.

1. Action with metals. We may sprinkle some powdered antimony into a jar of moist chlorine. The two elements unite spontaneously, emitting a shower of sparks. Antimony trichloride is formed, as represented by the equation

$$2\ Sb + 3\ Cl_2 \rightarrow 2\ SbCl_3$$

In a similar manner, hot metallic sodium burns in chlorine and forms sodium chloride. Chlorine combines directly with such metals as copper, iron, zinc, and arsenic, if they are heated slightly.

2. Action with hydrogen. If we mix hydrogen and chlorine in the dark, no reaction occurs. But such a mixture explodes violently if it is heated, or if it is exposed to sunlight. A jet of hydrogen, burning in air, will continue to burn if it is introduced into a bottle of chlorine. Hydrogen chloride gas is produced:

$$H_2 + Cl_2 \rightarrow 2\ HCl\uparrow$$

This is an example of combustion without the presence of oxygen.

Chlorine has such a great affinity for hydrogen that it can take hydrogen from some of its compounds. Chlorine does not support the combustion of wood or paper. A paraffin candle, however, will continue to burn in chlorine with a smoky flame. An examination of the products formed shows that the hydrogen of the paraffin united with the chlorine to form hydrogen chloride. The carbon was left uncombined. Turpentine is a hydrocarbon which has the formula $C_{10}H_{16}$. Let us moisten a strip of filter paper with hot turpentine and suspend it in a jar of chlorine. It will burn with a sooty flame. Hydrogen chloride is formed, and a dense cloud of soot is set free:

$$C_{10}H_{16} + 8\ Cl_2 \rightarrow 10\ C + 16\ HCl\uparrow$$

3. Action with water. A freshly prepared solution of chlorine in water is yellow-green in color. Suppose we let such a solution stand in sunlight for a few days. We will find that both the yellow-green color and the pronounced odor of the chlorine disappear. The

Fig. 26–6. Dyes which can be oxidized to colorless compounds are bleached successfully with chlorine.

chlorine unites with the water to form hypochlorous acid and hydrochloric acid. Hypochlorous acid is unstable and decomposes into hydrochloric acid with the liberation of oxygen. The equation is:

$$2 H_2O + 2 Cl_2 \rightarrow 2 HClO + 2 HCl$$
$$\searrow$$
$$2 HCl + O_2\uparrow$$

Because of this reaction, chlorine water is a good oxidizing agent.

If no oxidizable material is in contact with hypochlorous acid, its decomposition produces molecules of oxygen as shown by the above equation. However, if an oxidizable material is in contact with the hypochlorous acid, the liberated oxygen combines directly with the oxidizable material. In bleaching, the oxygen combines with the dye. If the dye can be oxidized to a colorless compound, the dye will be bleached successfully. However, if the dye cannot be oxidized to a colorless compound, it will not be bleached. Hypochlorous acid will not bleach all dyes or destroy all colors. Many dyestuffs are not affected by it at all. Hypochlorous acid usually removes natural colors. It takes out spots made by ordinary ink, because the compounds in the ink have white or pale-colored oxides. It does not affect printers' ink because it cannot oxidize the carbon it contains.

Thus we see that the bleaching action of chlorine in water (actually of the hypochlorous acid produced) and that of peroxides is similar (see Chapter 10, Section 19). Both decompose and liberate oxygen, which is the actual substance which produces the bleaching action.

11. The uses of chlorine. *1. For bleaching.* For use in bleaching, chlorine may be obtained from chloride of lime, commonly called bleaching powder. This product is made by passing chlorine gas into calcium hydroxide.

$$Ca(OH)_2 + Cl_2 \rightarrow Ca(ClO)Cl + H_2O$$

It is probably not a single compound but a mixture of the calcium salts of hydrochloric and hypochlorous acids, which corresponds to the formula, $Ca(ClO)Cl$.

Fig. 26–7. Chlorine is added to the water in swimming pools to destroy bacteria.

In bleaching cotton goods, the cloth is first boiled in a dilute solution of sodium hydroxide. This removes any wax from the fibers. The strip of cloth is then drawn through several vats in succession. The first and third vats contain a bleaching solution, and the second and fourth ones contain dilute sulfuric acid. A bleaching solution of chlorine in water or one of sodium hypochlorite, NaClO, is now used more often than bleaching powder. The dilute sulfuric acid liberates hypochlorous acid from the bleaching solution absorbed in the fibers of the cloth. It is at this point that the actual bleaching action occurs. The final vat contains an antichlor such as sodium thiosulfate, $Na_2S_2O_3$, to remove the last traces of chlorine which might be left in the cloth. The strip of cloth is then washed, ironed, and rolled.

Many commercial bleaches for home use are now available. Bleaching solutions are generally solutions of sodium hypochlorite. They are made by electrolyzing sodium chloride, and allowing the liberated chlorine to mix with the sodium hydroxide being produced. Or, they may be made by the reaction between chlorine and sodium carbonate. Dry powdered bleaches usually contain sodium "perborate" (see Chapter 44, Section 12).

Many ink eradicators make use of hypochlorous acid as a bleaching agent. Solution No. 1 contains citric acid or tartaric acid. Solution No. 2 contains a solution of a hypochlorite. When the two solutions are mixed, hypochlorous acid, HClO, is formed.

CAUTION: Chlorine must never be used for bleaching silk or wool, because it destroys these animal fibers. Commercial bleaches containing hypochlorites must never be used on silk or wool.

2. *As a disinfectant.* Since moist chlorine is a good oxidizing agent, it will destroy bacteria. Large quantities of chloride of lime, $Ca(ClO)Cl$, are used annually as a disinfectant. In city water systems, billions of gallons of water are treated with chlorine. This treatment kills the disease-producing bacteria, and coupled with sedimentation, filtration, and aeration, provides a potable water. The water in swimming pools is usually treated with chlorine to insure its safety for bathing. Chlorine is also used by some sewage systems to kill the bacteria in the sewage before it is discharged into lakes or rivers, so the contamination from this source will be at a minimum.

3. *For making compounds.* Because chlorine combines directly with many metals and nonmetals it is used to produce many chlorides. Among these are chloroform, $CHCl_3$; carbon tetrachloride, CCl_4; aluminum chloride, Al_2Cl_6; and sulfur chloride, S_2Cl_2.

12. How is hydrogen chloride prepared? In the laboratory, hydrogen chloride can be prepared by treating sodium chloride with sulfuric acid. The equation for this reaction is:

$$NaCl + H_2SO_4 \rightarrow NaHSO_4 + HCl\uparrow$$

This same reaction is used commercially, but it is carried out at a higher temperature. Under this condition, a second molecule of HCl may be produced if more NaCl is used.

$$2\,NaCl + H_2SO_4 \rightarrow Na_2SO_4 + 2\,HCl\uparrow$$

Hydrogen chloride is also prepared commercially by the direct union of hydrogen and chlorine. The hydrogen and chlorine used for this preparation are both obtained by the electrolysis of concentrated sodium chloride solution (see Section 8 of this chapter).

The hydrogen chloride is dissolved in pure water, and sold under the name of hydrochloric acid. Technical grade hydrochloric acid is sometimes called *muriatic acid.*

13. The physical properties of hydrogen chloride. This gas is colorless, but it has a sharp, penetrating odor. It is denser than air and extremely soluble in water. One volume of water at 0° C will dissolve more than 500 volumes of the gas at standard pressure. Hydrogen chloride fumes in moist air. It is so soluble that it condenses water vapor from the air into minute drops of hydrochloric acid.

14. The chemical properties of hydrogen chloride. Under this heading we consider two general topics. *1. Its stability.* Hydrogen chloride is a stable compound. It does not burn. Some vigorous oxidizing agents attack it and form water and chlorine. *2. It forms an acid.* The gas does not act as an acid except in the very broad modern sense that it may be a proton donor. Neither does the liquid which is formed by compressing and cooling the gas. But a water solution of the gas forms a strong acid known as *hydrochloric acid.* Hydrogen chloride is a polar covalent compound, but when it is dissolved in water the water dipoles cause it to ionize. Hydronium ions and chloride ions are formed. Thus the solution has acid properties. The concentrated acid contains about 38% hydrogen chloride by weight, and it is about 1.2 times as dense as water. Hydrochloric acid is a typical nonoxidizing acid. It reacts with many metals and oxides of metals. It neutralizes hydroxides, forming salts and water.

15. The uses of hydrochloric acid. This acid is used in preparing some of the chlorides and in cleaning metals. Many metals must be freed from their oxides and other forms of tarnish before they can be galvanized, enameled, tinned, or plated with other metals. The process of removing such a scale is called *pickling.* The metals are immersed in a mixture of acids, such as hydrochloric and sulfuric, in varying proportions.

Some hydrochloric acid is essential in the process of digestion.

16. There are many chlorides. Theoretically, it is possible to form a chloride of almost any metal. The metallic chlorides form an important group of salts. Nearly all of them are crystalline compounds, and most of them are soluble in water. The chlorides of lead

Fig. 26–8. Steel strip being drawn from an acid pickling tank. The mixture of acids in the pickling tank removes the oxide scale from the steel.

and silver, as well as mercurous chloride, are insoluble. We know sodium chloride is used for food preservation and seasoning. It is also a very important chemical raw material. Aluminum chloride is employed as a catalyst in the "cracking" of petroleum to increase the yield of gasoline. The tetrachlorides of silicon and titanium have been extensively used to make smoke screens. They are also used to produce the smoke used in sky writing. These compounds hydrolyze almost completely in moist air. The hydrogen chloride which is formed by such hydrolysis condenses the moisture of the air and forms a mist. Chlorides of carbon, sulfur, and phosphorus have some important applications. Carbon tetrachloride is used as a fire extinguisher. It is just as efficient as gasoline for removing grease spots from clothing, and it has the advantage of being nonflammable. However, good ventilation is required where it is being used because its vapors are poisonous. Sulfur chloride, S_2Cl_2, is used in one process for vulcanizing rubber.

17. The test for a chloride. To test for a soluble chloride we make use of the insolubility of silver chloride. To the solution to be tested for chloride ions, we add a solution of silver nitrate. The formation of a white precipitate which is soluble in ammonia-water solution, but is reprecipitated when excess nitric acid is added, is a test for the chloride ion.

The equations for the reactions involved in the test for the chloride ion are:

1. Forming the white silver chloride precipitate:

$$Ag^+ + Cl^- \rightarrow Ag^+Cl^-\downarrow$$

2. Dissolving the silver chloride in ammonia-water solution:

$$Ag^+Cl^- + 2\,NH_3 \rightarrow Ag(NH_3)_2^+ + Cl^-$$

3. Reprecipitating the silver chloride by adding nitric acid:

$$Ag(NH_3)_2^+ + Cl^- + 2\,H^+ + 2\,NO_3^- \rightarrow$$
$$Ag^+Cl^-\downarrow + 2\,NH_4^+ + 2\,NO_3^-$$

3. BROMINE

18. The occurrence and discovery of bromine. Several bromides, particularly those of sodium and magnesium, are found in nature. For many years the chief source of bromine was the "mother liquor" left after sodium chloride had been extracted from the brine of salt wells. Now, however, there is a great demand for bromine in manufacturing "anti-knock" fluids for gasoline. Consequently, processes have been developed to extract it from sea water.

Bromine was discovered in 1826 by the French chemist Antoine-Jerome Balard (1802–1876). He produced bromine by treating the mother liquor of a natural brine with chlorine gas.

19. Bromine is produced from bromides. In the laboratory we can prepare bromine by using manganese dioxide, sulfuric acid, and sodium bromide. The equation

$$2\,NaBr + MnO_2 + 2\,H_2SO_4 \rightarrow$$
$$Na_2SO_4 + MnSO_4 + 2\,H_2O + Br_2\uparrow$$

shows that the method is exactly analogous to that for preparing chlorine.

The commercial extraction of bromine from sea water depends on the ability of chlorine to displace bromine from solutions of its compounds, as chlorine is more highly electronegative than bromine. The equation follows:

$$2\,NaBr + Cl_2 \rightarrow 2\,NaCl + Br_2$$

Large quantities of acidified sea water are treated with chlorine. Bromine is liberated and then blown out of the solution by steam or air. It can be condensed directly. Or it may be absorbed in sodium carbonate solution, from which it can be recovered by treatment with sulfuric acid. A similar reaction is used to extract bromine from bromides found in salt wells of Michigan, Ohio, and West Virginia. Bromine may also be prepared by electrolysis of soluble bromides.

20. The physical properties of bromine. There are only two elements which are liquid at room temperature, bromine and mercury. Bromine is a dark-red liquid which is about three times as dense as water. Bromine evaporates readily. It forms a vapor which is very irritating to the eyes and throat, and very disagreeable in its odor. Bromine is moderately soluble in water. Its reddish-brown solution is used in the laboratory under the name of bromine water. It is readily soluble in carbon tet-

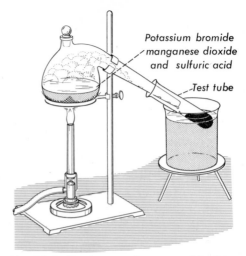

Potassium bromide
manganese dioxide
and sulfuric acid

Test tube

Fig. 26–9. Bromine may be prepared in the laboratory by heating a mixture of sodium bromide, manganese dioxide, and sulfuric acid in a glass-stoppered retort.

rachloride, carbon disulfide, and in water solutions of bromides.

CAUTION: Great care must be used in handling bromine; it burns the flesh and forms wounds which heal slowly.

21. The chemical properties of bromine. Bromine is not as electronegative an element as chlorine. It unites with hydrogen with difficulty to form hydrogen bromide. It combines with some metals to form bromides. When it is moist, it is a good bleaching agent.

Fig. 26–10. An aerial view of a large plant for the extraction of bromine from sea water. The water enters the plant through the flume at the left. The two large rectangular buildings contain the bromine extraction units. In these buildings the sea water is chlorinated and exposed to an air blast that blows out the bromine. In the cylindrical absorption towers just beyond, the bromine is recovered from the air blast.

Its water solution is a good oxidizing agent. In the presence of sunlight, such a water solution forms hydrobromic acid and liberates oxygen.

22. The preparation and properties of hydrogen bromide. Pure hydrogen bromide is prepared by the hydrolysis of phosphorus tribromide:

$$PBr_3 + 3 H_2O \rightarrow H_3PO_3 + 3 HBr\uparrow$$

We may try to prepare hydrogen bromide by a reaction similar to the laboratory preparation of hydrogen chloride:

$$NaBr + H_2SO_4 \rightarrow NaHSO_4 + HBr\uparrow$$

We do obtain some HBr. However, hydrogen bromide is a less stable compound than hydrogen chloride. Some of it is oxidized by the warm sulfuric acid. The hydrogen bromide is therefore contaminated with sulfur dioxide and free bromine.

Hydrogen bromide dissolves in water to form hydrobromic acid, a strong acid.

23. Several bromides are useful. The bromides of sodium and potassium are used in medicine as sedatives to quiet the nerves. But they should not be used unless prescribed by a physician. Silver bromide, AgBr, is a yellowish solid. It is extensively used as the sensitive salt for making photographic films or plates. Ethylene bromide, $C_2H_4Br_2$, is used to increase the efficiency of lead tetraethyl, $Pb(C_2H_5)_4$, in making antiknock gasoline. Methyl bromide is more toxic to insect larvae and moths than hydrocyanic acid. Xylyl bromide, when present to the extent of

only two or three parts per million of air, will cause a copious flow of tears. Bromine compounds, such as xylyl bromide and bromacetone, have been used as tear gases. Tear gases are now used by the police in order to quell riots, or to drive barricaded criminals out into the open. Other organic bromine compounds are used in the manufacture of dyestuffs.

24. The test for a soluble bromide. Bromine is very soluble in carbon tetrachloride, to which it imparts an orange-red color. We have learned, too, that chlorine will displace bromine from a bromide. We make use of these two facts in testing for soluble bromides.

To the solution to be tested for a bromide we add some carbon tetrachloride, and several milliliters of chlorine water. We then shake the mixture vigorously. If *bromide* ions were present, *bromine* molecules are set free by the chlorine. The bromine, being much more soluble in carbon tetrachloride than it is in water, leaves the water. It dissolves mostly in the carbon tetrachloride to which it imparts an orange-red color. The carbon tetrachloride does not mix with the water, but forms a separate layer below the water. While it is Br_2 *molecules* which color the carbon tetrachloride when the test is positive, the only form in which bromine could have existed and be oxidized to free bromine by chlorine was as Br^- *ions*. Therefore, a positive test indicates the presence of bromide ions in the original solution.

4. IODINE

25. The discovery and occurrence of iodine. The element iodine was discovered in 1811 by Bernard Courtois (1777–1838), a French chemist. He noticed the purplish vapor of iodine while investigating the ashes from seaweeds. For many years nearly all the iodine marketed was extracted from seaweeds.

At present, the most important domestic source of iodine is the iodides found in California oil well brines. The iodine is liberated from the brine by treatment with chlorine. Some iodine is obtained from Chile, where it is found in the nitrate deposits as sodium iodate, $NaIO_3$.

26. The preparation of iodine. The laboratory preparation of iodine is similar to that of chlorine and bromine. An iodide is heated with manganese dioxide and sulfuric acid.

$$2\,NaI + MnO_2 + 2\,H_2SO_4 \rightarrow$$
$$Na_2SO_4 + MnSO_4 + 2\,H_2O + I_2\uparrow$$

The iodine is driven off as a vapor. It may be condensed as a solid upon the walls of a cold dish or beaker.

Either chlorine or bromine may be used to displace iodine from a soluble iodide.

$$2\,NaI + Cl_2 \rightarrow 2\,NaCl + I_2$$
$$2\,NaI + Br_2 \rightarrow 2\,NaBr + I_2$$

27. The physical properties of iodine. Iodine is a steel-gray solid. When heated, it sublimes, or vaporizes without melting, and produces a beautiful violet-colored vapor. The odor of this vapor is irritating, resembling chlorine to some extent.

Iodine is very slightly soluble in water. But it is much more soluble in solutions of sodium or potassium iodide with which it forms the complex I_3^- ion. It dissolves readily in alcohol, forming a dark-brown solution. It is very soluble in carbon disulfide and carbon tetrachloride, to which it im-

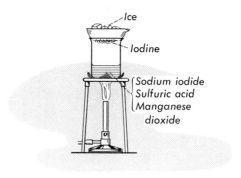

Fig. 26–11. Iodine is prepared in the laboratory by heating sodium iodide and manganese dioxide with sulfuric acid.

parts a rich purple color. Free iodine will color starch paste blue. This is caused by some of the iodine being adsorbed on the surface of the starch particles. This color change serves as a test for free iodine. If we are given an iodine solution, we may use it as a test for starch.

28. The chemical properties of iodine. Iodine is active chemically, though less so than either bromine or chlorine. It combines with metals to form iodides, and it may also unite with some nonmetals. If a crystal of iodine is placed on a small piece of white phosphorus, the two elements unite spontaneously. Light and heat are liberated.

29. The uses for iodine. Iodine is used for making certain iodides, especially those used in photography. We use iodine, too, as an antiseptic for cuts and open wounds. Surgeons sometimes use a tincture of iodine to sterilize the skin before making an incision during an operation. Tincture of iodine contains 2% iodine dissolved in 50% alcohol, to which 2.4% sodium iodide has been added.

CAUTION: Iodine is poisonous if taken internally. Starch paste or starchy foods may be used as an antidote. If a bottle containing tincture of iodine is left unstoppered, some of the solvent will evaporate. The more concentrated tincture which is left may be strong enough to blister the skin. Blistering may result, too, if a part which has been painted is covered, or if a second application is used.

30. The preparation of hydrogen iodide. Very little hydrogen iodide is obtained by heating a mixture of an iodide and sulfuric acid. Hydrogen iodide is less stable than hydrogen bromide. It decomposes and reduces the sulfuric acid to sulfur dioxide, sulfur, or even hydrogen sulfide. Any hydrogen iodide which might escape decomposition would be contaminated with iodine and the decomposition products of sulfuric acid. Pure hydrogen iodide may be prepared by hydrolysis of phosphorus tri-iodide:

$$PI_3 + 3\,H_2O \rightarrow H_3PO_3 + 3\,HI\uparrow$$

Hydrogen iodide is a colorless gas which dissolves in water and forms hydriodic acid.

31. The uses of iodides. Potassium iodide, KI, finds some use in medicine. Iodine is present in the thyroid gland of the body. The thyroid manufactures the iodine-containing compound, *thyroxine*. This substance controls the rate at which the body uses food energy. If the diet is deficient in iodine, the thyroid gland may become enlarged. This is simple goiter. Iodine compounds are added to the water in certain localities where simple goiter is common. Either sodium iodide, NaI, or potassium iodide, KI, is added to common salt to make *iodized salt*. Silver iodide, AgI, finds some use in photography. Di-iodine pentoxide, I_2O_5, is used as an indicator to detect the presence of carbon monoxide, and to determine its amount. Another iodine compound, iodoquinine sulfate, is used in making the crystals in Polaroid film.

32. The test for soluble iodides. We add to the solution to be tested a few milliliters of carbon tetrachloride and a few milliliters of chlorine water. We shake the mixture vigorously. If an iodide was present, the carbon tetrachloride globule which sinks to the bottom is colored purple. The purple color is due to free iodine. Here again, as in the test for bromides, the liberation of the *free halogen* constitutes a positive test for the presence of the corresponding *halide ion* in the solution tested.

Summary

The Halogen Family consists of fluorine, chlorine, bromine, iodine, and astatine. Each of these has seven electrons in its outermost shell. None occurs free in nature. In the elementary state they exist as covalent molecules.

Fluorine is prepared by the electrolysis of a mixture of potassium fluoride and hydrogen fluoride. The other three common halogens are prepared in the laboratory by oxidizing their binary acids with manganese dioxide. Commercially, chlorine is made by the electrolysis of brine; bromine is extracted from sea water; and iodine is obtained from oil well brines.

Hydrogen fluoride and hydrogen chloride are prepared by treating a salt of the acid with sulfuric acid. Hydrogen bromide and hydrogen iodide are prepared by the hydrolysis of phosphorus tribromide and phosphorus tri-iodide. Hydrogen fluoride molecules associate by hydrogen bonding. Each of the hydrogen halides is a colorless gas which is ionized in water solution.

Fluorine compounds are used for etching glass. Chlorine is used for bleaching, disinfecting, and for making chlorides. Bromine is used in the dye industry, for making medicines, in photography, and for making antiknock gasoline. Iodine is used in photography and in medicine.

Test yourself on these terms

antichlor	cryolite	iodized salt
bleaching action	fluorspar	mother liquor
bleaching powder	Freon	muriatic acid
chloride of lime	halogen	pickling
combustion	Hooker cell	thyroxine

Questions

Group A

1. What does the term *halogen* mean?
2. (*a*) What kind of container must be used for fluorine? (*b*) For hydrofluoric acid?
3. What are the most important uses for hydrofluoric acid?
4. Describe the physiological effects of chlorine.
5. (*a*) Define combustion. (*b*) Must oxygen be present for combustion to occur? Explain.
6. What is an *antichlor?*
7. What method of collection is used when preparing hydrogen chloride in the laboratory?
8. How can you test an unknown solution for the chloride ion?
9. Why is bromine produced in large quantities today?
10. What are the physical properties of bromine?
11. (*a*) What is xylyl bromide? (*b*) For what is it used?
12. What is the most important source of iodine in the United States?
13. What is the danger of using tincture of iodine that has been in the medicine cabinet for several years?
14. (*a*) For what purpose does the body require iodine? (*b*) From what sources may it be obtained?
15. Why are none of the halogens found free in nature?
16. List the halogens in order of increasing activity.

Group B

17. Why do hydrogen fluoride molecules exhibit hydrogen bonding?
18. Write the equation for the preparation of fluorine from hydrogen fluoride by electrolysis.
19. What is Freon?
20. Describe the process of placing the graduations on a burette.
21. Why must the hydrogen, chlorine, and sodium hydroxide produced in a Hooker cell be kept separated from each other?
22. Write the equation for the laboratory preparation of chlorine from manganese dioxide and hydrochloric acid.

23. (a) For which does chlorine have greater affinity, carbon or hydrogen? (b) What experimental evidence can you give to support your answer?
24. (a) Why is freshly prepared chlorine water yellow-green in color? (b) Why does it become colorless after standing in sunlight?
25. What element does the bleaching when chlorine is used as a bleach?
26. Is liquid hydrogen chloride an acid? Explain.
27. What type of chemical reaction is involved in the commercial preparation of bromine from sea water?
28. Why is it not possible to prepare pure hydrogen bromide from sodium bromide and sulfuric acid?
29. What constitutes a positive test for bromide ions in a solution?
30. Compare the colors of: (a) solid iodine; (b) iodine in alcohol; (c) iodine in carbon tetrachloride; (d) iodine vapor.

Problems

Group A

1. What weight of sodium hydroxide is formed while making 710 lb of chlorine by the electrolysis of sodium chloride?
2. Ten grams of bromine is needed for an experiment. What weight of sodium bromide is required to produce this bromine?
3. (a) What weight of calcium hydroxide is required for making 250 g of bleaching powder, $Ca(ClO)Cl$? (b) What weight of chlorine is also required?
4. Hydrogen bromide is to be prepared by hydrolysis of phosphorus tribromide. How much phosphorus tribromide is needed to produce 40.5 g of hydrogen bromide?

Group B

5. How many grams of hydrogen fluoride can be obtained when an excess of sulfuric acid acts on 390 g of calcium fluoride?
6. Calculate the percentage of bromine in ethylene bromide, $C_2H_4Br_2$.
7. How many liters of chlorine at S.T.P. can be obtained from 468 g of sodium chloride?
8. A laboratory experiment requires five 250-ml bottles of chlorine, the gas being measured at S.T.P. What weight of sodium chloride will be required?

Some things for you to do

1. Test pieces of colored cotton cloth with commercial bleaching solution. How do the dyes compare in fastness?
2. Visit your community water purification plant and observe how chlorine is added to kill harmful bacteria.
3. Attach a metal plate to the negative terminal of a battery of two dry cells joined in series. Cover the plate with a sheet of filter paper, and then pour over the paper a dilute solution of starch paste to which a little potassium iodide solution has been added. Attach one end of a copper wire to the positive terminal of the battery, and use the free end of that wire to write in the starch paste. What happens? Explain the action.

Chapter 27 SULFUR AND SULFIDES

1. SULFUR

1. The occurrence of sulfur. Sulfur is one of the elements known since ancient times. We naturally associate sulfur with volcanic regions, and it is true that considerable amounts of sulfur are mined in regions where volcanoes were formerly active. The sulfur mines in Sicily are of this type and have been worked for centuries. Japan and Mexico also produce some sulfur. But the United States is the greatest producer of sulfur for world markets. Sulfur occurs in nature as the free element or combined with other elements in sulfides and sulfates.

Immense deposits of nearly pure sulfur occur about 500 feet below the surface of the ground in Texas and Louisi-ana, near the Gulf of Mexico. This is a nonvolcanic region. These deposits have proved to be very valuable and are now the greatest source of sulfur in the world.

2. The mining of sulfur. The sulfur beds in Texas and Louisiana are as much as 200 feet thick. But between the surface of the ground and the sulfur there is a layer of quicksand. Several attempts were made to sink a shaft through the quicksand, but each result-ed in failure.

Herman Frasch (1852–1914), an American chemist, eventually devised a method to obtain the sulfur. He proposed driving pipes down through the quicksand to the sulfur beds below.

VOCABULARY

Fungicide. A chemical material that kills non-green, microscopic plants known as fungi.

Monoclinic. Referring to those crystals having one oblique intersection of the axes.

Rhombic. Referring to those crystals having three unequal axes at right angles to one another.

Superheated water. Water heated under pressure to a temperature above its normal boiling point.

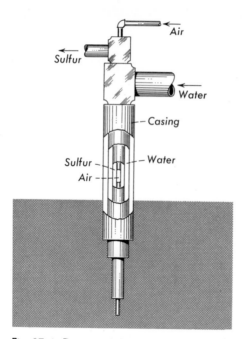

Fig. 27–1. Diagram of the system of concentric pipes used in the Frasch process of mining sulfur.

Sulfur melts at 114.5° C, and water boils at 100° C under atmospheric pressure. Obviously, water at 100° C is not hot enough to melt sulfur. However, by heating water in a closed container, it can be raised to a much higher temperature without boiling. Such water, heated above its normal boiling temperature under pressure, is **superheated water.** Frasch thought that superheated

water would melt the sulfur. He also suggested forcing compressed air down into the mass of melted sulfur to raise it to the surface. His plan was tried, and it worked.

As a casing to protect the other pipes, a 12-inch pipe is driven down to the sulfur. Inside the casing are three concentric pipes, 6 inches, 3 inches, and 1 inch in diameter, respectively. Superheated water at a temperature of 170° C is forced down the 6-inch pipe and hot air down the 1-inch pipe. As a result, a foamy mass of melted sulfur, steam, and air is forced up the 3-inch pipe (the middle one) to the surface. The melted sulfur flows into molds which may be as much as 100 feet long, 20 feet wide, and 50 feet high. After the sulfur has solidified, the sides of the mold are removed. The block is broken into pieces of convenient size for shipment.

3. The purification of sulfur. The sulfur obtained from Texas and Louisiana is about 99.5% pure. Further purification is, therefore, unnecessary for ordinary commercial purposes. But when sulfur must be further purified, the crude sulfur is distilled in large

Fig. 27–2. Liquid sulfur being sprayed into a large mold.

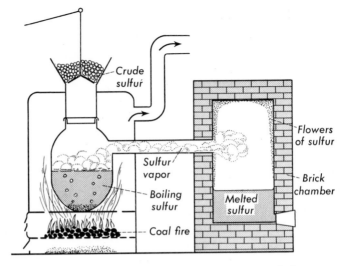

Fig. 27-3. Crude sulfur can be freed from impurities by distillation.

Crude sulfur

Flowers of sulfur

Sulfur vapor

Boiling sulfur

Melted sulfur

Brick chamber

Coal fire

iron retorts that are connected to a brick chamber. Some sulfur vapor condenses, forming a fine powder on the walls. This is called *flowers of sulfur*. A pool of liquid sulfur collects on the floor of the chamber. The liquid sulfur is poured into cylindrical molds, which, after cooling, yield *roll sulfur*.

4. The physical properties of sulfur. Ordinary sulfur is a yellow, *odorless* solid which is practically insoluble in water. It dissolves readily in carbon disulfide and in carbon tetrachloride. Sulfur is converted into soluble polysulfides by solutions of strong bases. When an acid is added to such a solution, *lac sulfur,* or *milk of sulfur* is precipitated as a fine white powder. The density of sulfur is twice that of water.

Sulfur melts at a temperature of 114.5° C, forming a pale-yellow mobile liquid. When it is heated to a still higher temperature, instead of becoming more mobile, as liquids usually do, it becomes thicker, or more viscous, and does not flow freely. At a temperature of about 250° C, the melted sulfur becomes so thick that it hardly flows from an inverted tube. At the same time that the temperature rises, the color changes from a light yellow to a reddish-brown, and then almost to black. Near the boil-

ing point the fluidity increases and the liquid again flows freely. Sulfur boils at 445° C. This unusual behavior is due to the existence of different allotropic forms of liquid sulfur at different temperatures.

5. The allotropic forms of sulfur. Sulfur is in the same family of the Periodic Table as oxygen. Just as we have learned that oxygen exists in the allotropic forms of oxygen and ozone, so sulfur also exists in several different solid and liquid allotropic forms. These are produced by different arrangements of groups of sulfur atoms.

1. Rhombic sulfur. This is the form of solid sulfur which is stable at ordinary temperatures. It consists of eight-membered puckered rings of sulfur atoms, as shown in Fig. 27-4. The sulfur atoms are connected in these rings by single covalent bonds. Crystals of rhombic sulfur may be prepared by dissolving roll sulfur in carbon disulfide, and then allowing the solvent to evaporate slowly. The crystals that are formed have the shape of an octahedron, as shown in Fig. 27-5. The specific gravity of rhombic sulfur is 2.06.

2. Monoclinic sulfur. Sulfur can also be crystallized in the form of long needle-like crystals that belong to the

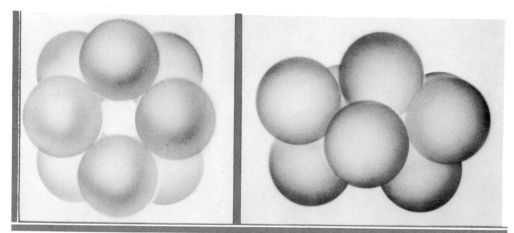

Fig. 27–4. The structure of S₈ molecules of sulfur.

monoclinic system of crystallization. Monoclinic crystals have two crystal axes at right angles to each other. The third axis is perpendicular to one of these but tilted toward the other. We can prepare monoclinic crystals by first melting some sulfur in a crucible at as low a temperature as possible. We next let it cool slowly until a crust just begins to form. If we then break the crust and pour off the liquid sulfur remaining, a mass of needle-like, monoclinic crystals will be found lining the walls of the crucible. Heat energy must be added to form this type of sulfur, and when such crystals cool, below 95° C they gradually change back into the rhombic form. However, monoclinic sulfur still consists of eight-membered rings of sulfur atoms but in a different

Fig. 27–5. These drawings show the difference between the crystal forms of rhombic and monoclinic sulfur.

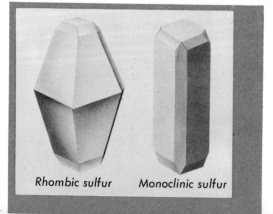

Rhombic sulfur   Monoclinic sulfur

crystalline arrangement. The specific gravity of monoclinic sulfur is 1.96.

3. λ-sulfur. (Lambda-sulfur.) This is the liquid allotropic form of sulfur which is produced at temperatures just above the melting point of sulfur. It is quite fluid and has a straw-yellow color. It, too, consists of eight-membered rings of sulfur atoms. The almost spherical shape of these S₈ molecules enables them to roll over one another easily, and gives this form of sulfur its fluidity.

4. μ-sulfur. (Mu-sulfur.) If we heat λ-sulfur to about 200° C, it darkens to a reddish, and then almost black liquid. The molten sulfur becomes so thick and viscous that it will not flow. The heating imparts enough energy to the sulfur atoms to open some of the eight-membered rings. When a ring of sulfur atoms breaks open, the sulfur atoms on either side of the break are each left with an unshared electron. These sulfur atoms with unshared electrons form bonds with similar sulfur atoms from other open rings, and produce long chains. These long chains of sulfur atoms are another allotropic form of sulfur, μ-sulfur. The color of μ-sulfur arises from the greater absorption of light falling on the sulfur. The light is absorbed by electrons which formerly

Fig. 27-6. A chain of sulfur atoms as found in mu-sulfur.

completed the ring structure but which are now free and migrate along the chain structure. The high viscosity of μ-sulfur is caused by the tangling of the chains of sulfur atoms. However, as we raise the temperature still further, these chains break up into smaller groups of atoms. The fluidity of the mass increases. But the color becomes still darker because the breaking-up of the chains produces more free electrons.

When sulfur boils at 445° C, the sulfur vapor produced consists again of S_8 molecules. If we heat sulfur vapor to a higher temperature, these molecules gradually dissociate into S_2 molecules. Monatomic molecules of sulfur are produced at very high temperatures.

5. Amorphous sulfur. Amorphous sulfur is a rubbery, plastic mass that is made when we pour boiling sulfur into cold water. It is dark-brown, or even black in color, and is elastic, like rubber. At the boiling point of sulfur, the long enmeshed chains have largely broken down, and the sulfur is fluid again. Eight-membered rings of sulfur atoms and chains are now in equilibrium. The S_8 rings are evaporating. When we suddenly cool this boiling mixture, the chains of μ-sulfur have no time to re-form into rings, and amorphous sulfur is produced. A mass of

amorphous sulfur soon loses its elasticity, becoming hard and brittle. In the cooled amorphous sulfur the transformations into successive allotropic forms proceed in reverse order. Finally, it once again becomes the S_8 ring configuration of the stable rhombic variety. Amorphous sulfur is insoluble in carbon disulfide.

6. The chemical properties of sulfur. At room temperature, sulfur is not very

Fig. 27-7. The sudden cooling of mu-sulfur produces plastic sulfur.

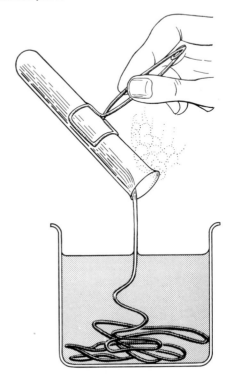

active chemically. When heated, it unites with oxygen, burning with a blue flame, and forming sulfur dioxide.

$$S + O_2 \rightarrow SO_2\uparrow$$

Traces of sulfur trioxide, SO_3, too, are formed when sulfur burns in air. Sulfur can be made to combine with non-metals such as hydrogen, carbon, and chlorine. Such compounds are formed with some difficulty, and they are not particularly stable.

From the formulas SO_3, SO_2, and H_2S, we see that sulfur may have an oxidation number of +6, or +4 when it combines with oxygen, and of −2 when it combines with hydrogen. Electron-dot formulas for these compounds are shown below. Notice that the actual molecules of sulfur trioxide and sulfur dioxide are resonance hybrids of the possible structures given.

Sulfur trioxide

Sulfur dioxide   Hydrogen sulfide

Sulfur is similar to oxygen in the manner in which it combines with other elements, as we can see by the following table.

Powdered zinc and sulfur combine explosively. The heat produced when iron filings and sulfur unite causes the whole mass to be heated to incandescence. Copper unites with the vapor of boiling sulfur to form cupric sulfide. If the oxide of any metal is insoluble, as a rule you will find that the sulfide of that metal is insoluble also.

7. Sulfur has many uses. This element is used in making sulfur dioxide, carbon disulfide, sulfuric acid, and other sulfur compounds. Several million tons are used annually in the manufacture of sulfuric acid. Matches, fireworks, and black gunpowder all contain either sulfur or sulfur compounds. Sulfur is also used in preparing certain dyes.

A mixture of four parts of sulfur and one part of lead arsenate makes an excellent fungicide for controlling blights, mildews, and other diseases of plants. Or, it may be used alone without lead arsenate. When sulfur is boiled with lime and water, it forms a red liquid which consists essentially of the polysulfides of calcium, such as CaS_x. This lime-sulfur solution is used widely to destroy scale insects, and also as a general fungicide.

Sulfur finds important uses in medicine. It is also used in the vulcanization of rubber. This process will be discussed in Chapter 45.

HYDROGEN SULFIDE	H_2S	HYDROGEN OXIDE	H_2O
CARBON DISULFIDE	CS_2	CARBON DIOXIDE	CO_2
COPPER SULFIDE	CuS and Cu_2S	COPPER OXIDE	CuO and Cu_2O
MERCURIC SULFIDE	HgS	MERCURIC OXIDE	HgO
ZINC SULFIDE	ZnS	ZINC OXIDE	ZnO

2. HYDROGEN SULFIDE

8. Hydrogen sulfide is formed by natural processes. Sulfur is present in some proteins. When such compounds decay, hydrogen sulfide is one of the products formed. The odor of decayed eggs is due to the formation of hydrogen sulfide. Coal is seldom entirely free from sulfur. As the coal burns, sulfur dioxide and some traces of hydrogen sulfide pass off into the air. Some mineral waters also contain hydrogen sulfide.

9. The preparation of hydrogen sulfide. When hydrogen is bubbled through molten sulfur, some hydrogen sulfide is formed. The action is reversible, however, and is not practical for preparing hydrogen sulfide in any considerable quantity.

We can use a metallic sulfide and either hydrochloric or sulfuric acid to prepare hydrogen sulfide. Ferrous sulfide, FeS, is suitable for the purpose. The following equations show that double replacement reactions occur when these acids are used:

$$FeS + 2\ HCl \rightarrow FeCl_2 + H_2S\uparrow$$
$$FeS + H_2SO_4 \rightarrow FeSO_4 + H_2S\uparrow$$

Hydrogen sulfide is volatile, and the double replacement reactions go to completion. The gas is usually collected by upward displacement of air since it is denser than air and moderately soluble in water (see Fig. 27-8).

10. The physical properties of hydrogen sulfide. The gas is colorless, but it has the very disagreeable odor of decayed eggs. It is denser than air, and moderately soluble in water. Hydrogen sulfide is poisonous when inhaled. When diluted with air, it causes nausea, headache, and dizziness. In concentrated form, it is a violent poison,

which may cause death if inhaled.

11. The chemical properties of hydrogen sulfide. *1. Hydrogen sulfide burns.* When hydrogen sulfide burns, the products that are formed will depend on the relative amounts of hydrogen sulfide and oxygen present. If an abundance of oxygen is available, then 2 volumes of hydrogen sulfide react with 3 volumes of oxygen.

$$2\ H_2S + 3\ O_2 \rightarrow 2\ SO_2\uparrow + 2\ H_2O\uparrow$$

When 2 volumes of hydrogen sulfide react with 2 volumes of oxygen, half the sulfur does not burn and the products formed are represented by the following equation:

$$2\ H_2S + 2\ O_2 \rightarrow 2\ H_2O\uparrow + SO_2\uparrow + S\downarrow$$

If only 1 volume of oxygen is available for burning 2 volumes of hydrogen sulfide, then the hydrogen is oxidized, and all the sulfur is set free. The equation is:

$$2\ H_2S + O_2 \rightarrow 2\ H_2O\uparrow + 2\ S\downarrow$$

2. Hydrogen sulfide is a reducing agent. Because sulfide ions give up their electrons readily to oxidizing agents, hydrogen sulfide is a good reducing agent. To show the properties of hydrogen sulfide as a reducing agent, we may bubble the gas through a solution of

Fig. 27-8. The laboratory method of preparing hydrogen sulfide.

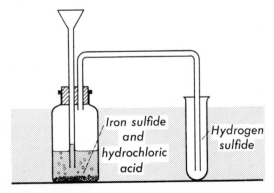

Iron sulfide and hydrochloric acid

Hydrogen sulfide

Fig. 27–9. The sulfides of many common metals are found in nature. The sulfide shown here is iron pyrites, FeS_2.

hydrogen peroxide. The hydrogen peroxide is reduced to water. Sulfur is precipitated as a fine white powder, which remains suspended in the water.

$$H_2O_2 + H_2S \rightarrow 2 H_2O + S\downarrow$$

3. Hydrogen sulfide forms a weak acid. When hydrogen sulfide dissolves in water, it forms a weak acid called hydrosulfuric acid. This weak acid will turn blue litmus red, and it will neutralize hydroxides to form sulfides and water.

$$Cu(OH)_2 + H_2S \rightarrow CuS\downarrow + 2 H_2O$$

4. Hydrogen sulfide acts on metals. The tarnishing of some metals is due to the formation of a coating of a sulfide of the metal upon the surface. A person who fails to wash the silver after a breakfast of eggs is likely to find it tarnished. Such foods as eggs and mustard form enough hydrogen sulfide to produce a stain of black silver sulfide.

12. Some tests for the presence of a sulfide. Any soluble sulfide furnishes sulfide, $S^=$, ions in solution. Such ions will unite with silver, lead, or copper to form a black precipitate. A drop of a soluble sulfide solution applied to a

silver coin will form a brownish-black stain upon the coin.

When hydrochloric acid is added to a moderately insoluble sulfide, hydrogen sulfide is set free, and it can usually be recognized by its odor.

A strip of filter paper which has been moistened with a solution of lead acetate, $Pb(C_2H_3O_2)_2$, quickly turns brownish-black when exposed to the vapors of hydrogen sulfide, or when a drop of water solution of hydrogen sulfide is placed on it.

$$Pb(C_2H_3O_2)_2 + H_2S \rightarrow PbS\downarrow + 2 HC_2H_3O_2$$

13. Hydrogen sulfide is used in chemical analysis. If you ever analyze minerals or metals, you will probably use hydrogen sulfide frequently. When it is added to a solution containing the ions of certain metals, insoluble sulfides of those metals are formed. They are deposited as precipitates. The following equations represent typical examples.

$$Cu^{++} + S^= \rightarrow CuS\downarrow$$
$$2 As^{+++} + 3S^= \rightarrow As_2S_3\downarrow$$
$$Cd^{++} + S^= \rightarrow CdS\downarrow$$
$$2 Sb^{+++} + 3S^= \rightarrow Sb_2S_3\downarrow$$

Copper, lead, silver, mercury, and some other metals form black sulfides. The sulfides of arsenic and cadmium are yellow. Antimony sulfide is orange. Zinc sulfide is white in color. But analysis is not as easy as such facts may indicate, because it is possible to have in one solution the ions of several metals. It is always necessary to separate the sulfides after they have been precipitated by finding reagents in which some of them will dissolve, but not the others. For example, the sulfides of zinc and manganese are soluble in dilute acids; the sulfides of arsenic and antimony are soluble in ammonium sulfide; the sulfides of copper and lead are soluble in hot dilute nitric acid, but mercuric sulfide is insoluble.

3. SOME OTHER SULFIDES

14. Metallic sulfides are found in nature. Many of the important ores which are found in nature are sulfides. Large quantities of copper sulfide are found in Montana. Zinc sulfide is one of the important sources of zinc; nearly all of our lead comes from lead sulfide. The sulfides of such metals as silver, nickel, arsenic, and antimony are found in nature. Several sulfides of iron also occur in nature. They serve as a source of sulfur, but are not important as a source of iron.

15. The preparation and properties of carbon disulfide. When sulfur vapor is passed over charcoal which is heated in an electric furnace, carbon and sulfur unite to form an almost colorless liquid. Its formula is CS_2, analogous to that of carbon dioxide. The commercial product has a disagreeable odor, somewhat resembling boiled cabbage. The liquid does not mix with water. It has a very low kindling temperature and it burns rapidly, its vapor burning explosively when mixed with air.

$$CS_2 + 3\ O_2 \rightarrow CO_2\uparrow + 2\ SO_2\uparrow$$

Carbon disulfide is a good solvent for rubber, phosphorus, waxes, and resins. For this reason it finds use in the manufacture of varnishes and matches. Carbon disulfide is used in one step of the process of manufacture of viscose rayon. It is also used in large quantities for the preparation of carbon tetrachloride.

Summary

Sulfur occurs both free, and combined as sulfides and sulfates. It is mined in Texas and Louisiana by the Frasch process, and may be purified by distillation. It is marketed as lump sulfur, roll sulfur, flowers of sulfur, and lac sulfur.

Sulfur exists in several allotropic forms. The solid allotropes are rhombic, monoclinic, and amorphous sulfur. The liquid allotropes are lambda and mu sulfur. Ordinary sulfur is a yellow solid which is practically insoluble in water. It dissolves in carbon disulfide and in carbon tetrachloride. Sulfur is not very active chemically, but when heated with oxygen it burns with a blue flame and forms sulfur dioxide, with traces of sulfur trioxide. Zinc, iron, and copper unite with sulfur at elevated temperatures, forming sulfides of the metals. Sulfur is used for making sulfur dioxide, carbon disulfide, sulfuric acid, and other sulfur compounds.

Hydrogen sulfide is a foul-smelling, poisonous, combustible gas. It is produced when coal which contains sulfur as an impurity is burned. It attacks silverware, forming a black tarnish of silver sulfide. In water solution, it forms a weak acid known as hydrosulfuric acid, which reacts with metallic salts to form insoluble sulfides. It is used in analysis to detect the presence of metals.

The sulfides of many metals occur in nature. Some are important ores of the metals. Carbon disulfide is a good solvent for rubber and is used in making carbon tetrachloride.

Test yourself on these terms

amorphous sulfur	lac sulfur	resonance hybrid
flowers of sulfur	λ-sulfur	rhombic sulfur
Frasch process	milk of sulfur	roll sulfur
fungicide	monoclinic sulfur	sulfides
hydrosulfuric acid	μ-sulfur	superheated water

Questions

Group A

1. Describe the location of the sulfur deposits in the United States.
2. (*a*) What is the odor of sulfur? (*b*) Of hydrogen sulfide?
3. (*a*) What is the formula for a molecule of rhombic sulfur? (*b*) Why do we not usually use this formula in equations?
4. (*a*) What is plastic sulfur? (*b*) How is it produced?
5. What are the uses of sulfur?
6. Write the formulas for: (*a*) ferric sulfide; (*b*) diarsenic pentasulfide; (*c*) cupric sulfide; (*d*) mercuric sulfide; (*e*) silver sulfide.
7. What use is made of sulfur in fungicides?
8. Describe two natural processes which release hydrogen sulfide into the air.
9. (*a*) Write the formula equation for the laboratory preparation of hydrogen sulfide. (*b*) What type of chemical reaction is this?
10. What metals have important sulfide ores?
11. (*a*) Give several uses for carbon disulfide. (*b*) What property of carbon disulfide is involved in each use?
12. (*a*) What is the function of the superheated water in the Frasch process? (*b*) The function of the compressed air?

Group B

13. Distinguish between *flowers of sulfur* and *lac sulfur*.
14. Explain the changes in color and fluidity of sulfur between its melting point and boiling point.
15. A pupil prepared some nearly-black plastic sulfur in the laboratory. The next week when he examined it, it had become brittle and much lighter in color. Explain.
16. What is meant by *resonance*?
17. Draw electron-dot formulas to show the possible resonating structures in sulfur dioxide.
18. How are the products of combustion of hydrogen sulfide related to the amount of oxygen available?
19. Explain why there is usually a yellowish-white deposit on the ground around a sulfur spring.
20. Write equations to show the reactions between hydrogen sulfide and solutions of the chlorides of mercury, lead, and antimony.

21. (a) What are the characteristics of λ-sulfur? (b) Of μ-sulfur?
22. Iron pyrites, or " fool's gold," has the formula FeS_2. How could you prove that it is not gold?
23. Look up the heat of formation of carbon disulfide in the Appendix. (a) What does this heat of formation tell you about the reaction by which it is prepared? (b) What does it tell you about the stability of carbon disulfide?
★ 24. Balance the equation for the oxidation of hydrogen sulfide by hydrogen peroxide by the electron transfer method.

Problems

Group A

1. How many pounds of sulfur dioxide may be produced by burning a ton of pure sulfur?
2. What weight of ferrous sulfide is required to prepare 170 g of hydrogen sulfide?
3. What volume of oxygen is required for the complete combustion of 5 liters of hydrogen sulfide?

Group B

4. Calculate the percentage composition of lead sulfide, PbS.
5. How many liters of carbon dioxide are formed by burning 39 g of carbon disulfide?
6. Calculate the weight in grams of 500 ml of hydrogen sulfide measured at 27° C and 740 mm pressure.

Some things for you to do

1. Write a report on the Frasch process for obtaining sulfur. Include some information about Frasch himself. Read your report to the class.
2. Bubble some hydrogen sulfide through solutions of chlorides of Co^{++}, Ni^{++}, Pb^{++}, Hg^{++}, Mn^{++}, Bi^{+++}, Sb^{+++}, Zn^{++}, Cu^{++}. If no precipitate is produced, add a little ammonia-water solution to the test tubes. Note the color of each sulfide produced.
3. Use some carbon disulfide outdoors to get rid of a pest such as a ground mole. Pour a few teaspoonfuls of the carbon disulfide down the burrow, and ignite it. Cover the burrow with earth to hold the suffocating gases within the burrow.
4. Consult an encyclopedia, college chemistry textbook, and recent scientific magazines to learn about the properties and uses of the other members of Group VIA, selenium and tellurium.

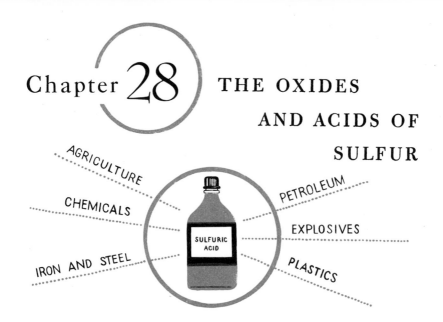

Chapter 28 THE OXIDES AND ACIDS OF SULFUR

AGRICULTURE
CHEMICALS
IRON AND STEEL
SULFURIC ACID
PETROLEUM
EXPLOSIVES
PLASTICS

1. THE OXIDES OF SULFUR

1. The occurrence of sulfur dioxide. Traces of sulfur dioxide may be found in the air for several reasons: *1*. Sulfur dioxide occurs in some volcanic gases and in some mineral waters; *2*. Coal contains sulfur as an impurity, and, as coal is burned, the sulfur is burned to sulfur dioxide also; *3*. The heating of sulfide ores in the presence of air is the first step in extracting the metal from such ores. This process, which is called *roasting,* converts the sulfur of the ore into sulfur dioxide. The sulfur dioxide is sometimes expelled into the air, although modern smelting plants convert it into sulfuric acid.

2. The preparation of sulfur dioxide. There are several ways to prepare this important gas.

1. By burning sulfur. The simplest way to prepare sulfur dioxide is to burn sulfur in air or in pure oxygen. The gas produced by burning sulfur in air will be mixed with nitrogen, but this is not objectionable for many operations.

$$S + O_2 \rightarrow SO_2\uparrow$$

2. By roasting sulfides. Enormous quantities of sulfur dioxide are produced when sulfide ores are roasted. The roasting of *sphalerite,* ZnS, is typical.

$$2\ ZnS + 3\ O_2 \rightarrow 2\ ZnO + 2\ SO_2\uparrow$$

Sulfur dioxide is a by-product in this operation. Iron pyrites, FeS_2, is roasted to produce sulfur dioxide for making sulfuric acid.

VOCABULARY

Carrier. A substance used to transfer an element or radical from one material to another.

Countercurrents. Movement of a gas and liquid in opposition to one another.

Roasting. Heating in the presence of air.

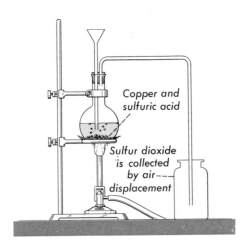

Fig. 28–1. Sulfur dioxide may be prepared in the laboratory by reducing hot, concentrated sulfuric acid with copper.

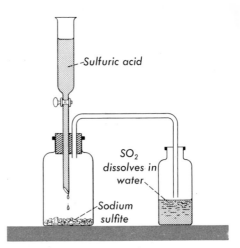

Fig. 28-2. An acid added to a sulfite forms unstable sulfurous acid which decomposes into sulfur dioxide and water.

3. By the reduction of sulfuric acid. In one of the laboratory methods of preparing this gas, a rather inactive metal such as copper is heated with concentrated sulfuric acid (see Fig. 28-1). The hot, concentrated acid is a vigorous oxidizing agent. The copper is oxidized and the sulfuric acid is reduced. Sulfur dioxide, cupric sulfate, and water are the products, as shown in the following equation:

$$Cu + 2 H_2SO_4 \rightarrow CuSO_4 + 2 H_2O + SO_2\uparrow$$

4. By the decomposition of sulfites. In this second laboratory method, pure sulfur dioxide may be prepared by the action of a strong acid on a sulfite. When sodium sulfite reacts with sulfuric acid, the following reaction occurs:

$$Na_2SO_3 + H_2SO_4 \rightarrow$$
$$Na_2SO_4 + H_2O + SO_2\uparrow$$

Sulfurous acid, H_2SO_3, is first formed. It then decomposes into water and sulfur dioxide (see Fig. 28-2).

3. The physical properties of sulfur dioxide. Pure sulfur dioxide is a colorless gas with a suffocating, choking odor. Sulfur dioxide is more than twice as dense as air, and it is very soluble in water. It is one of the easiest gases to liquefy, since it will become liquid at room temperature under a pressure of about two atmospheres. Liquid sulfur dioxide is commercially available in steel cylinders.

4. The chemical properties of sulfur dioxide. *1. It is an acid anhydride.* Sulfur dioxide is the anhydride of sulfurous acid. As it dissolves in water, it also reacts with the water:

$$H_2O + SO_2 \rightleftarrows H_2SO_3$$

This accounts, in part at least, for the high solubility of sulfur dioxide in water. Sulfurous acid is a weak acid which will turn litmus paper red, neutralize hydroxides, and form bisulfites and sulfites. The reaction is reversible, and the acid decomposes into water and sulfur dioxide again when the water solution is heated. A solution of sulfurous acid, if exposed to the air, will unite slowly with oxygen and form sulfuric acid.

If sulfur dioxide is allowed to escape into the air in the waste gases from smelting or from any other chemical operations, it combines with moisture in the air and forms sulfurous acid. This sulfurous acid, if not neutralized by alkaline dust in the air, may be oxidized to sulfuric acid. If this falls as a mist on the earth, it kills all vegetation in the area.

2. *It is a stable gas.* Sulfur dioxide does not burn. It is quite stable. In the presence of a suitable catalyst, it may be oxidized to sulfur trioxide.

$$2\,SO_2 + O_2 \rightleftarrows 2\,SO_3$$

5. The uses for sulfur dioxide and sulfurous acid. *1. For making sulfuric acid.* Tremendous quantities of sulfur dioxide are oxidized to form sulfur trioxide which can be combined with water to form sulfuric acid (see Section 7).

2. As a preservative. Dried fruits, such as apricots and prunes, are treated with sulfur dioxide which acts as a preservative.

3. In the petroleum industry. Liquid sulfur dioxide is used in the treatment of kerosene and light lubricating oils.

4. For making sulfites. Sulfurous acid is diprotic and reacts with hydroxides to form bisulfites and sulfites.

5. For bleaching. Sulfurous acid does not harm the fibers of wool, silk, straw, and paper, and can be used to bleach them. It is believed that the sulfurous acid converts the colored compounds in these materials to white sulfites. The bleaching is not permanent, however, and the natural yellow color of the fiber reappears after some time. Fig. 28-3 shows the effect of sulfur dioxide in bleaching a red carnation.

6. In preparing paper pulp. Sulfurous acid reacts with limestone to form calcium hydrogen sulfite, $Ca(HSO_3)_2$. When wood chips are heated in this bisulfite solution, the lignin which binds the cellulose fibers together is dissolved, leaving the fibers unchanged. The fibers are then processed to form paper (see Chapter 44).

6. Sulfur trioxide. Sulfur trioxide, which has the formula SO_3, is useful for one purpose. It is the anhydride of sulfuric acid. Therefore, it is the intermediate product in the manufacture of sulfuric acid. Sulfur trioxide is a white, crystalline solid at room temperature. It reacts vigorously with water to form sulfuric acid:

$$SO_3 + H_2O \rightarrow H_2SO_4$$

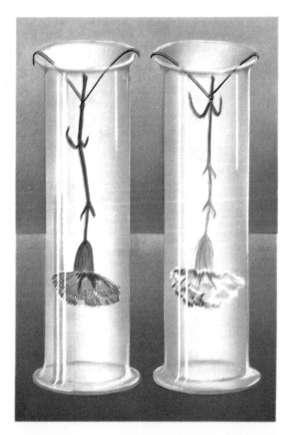

Fig. 28–3. The carnation in the jar at the left is red. The one in the jar at the right was red, but has been bleached white with sulfur dioxide.

2. SULFURIC ACID

7. The preparation of sulfuric acid. Sulfuric acid is made by two processes: *1.* the contact process; and *2.* the chamber process. Between 75% and 80% of the sulfuric acid produced in the United States is made by the contact process; the remainder is made by the chamber process.

1. The contact process. In this process, sulfur dioxide may be prepared by burning sulfur. Or, less commonly, it is prepared by roasting iron pyrites, FeS_2. The sulfur dioxide is purified to remove impurities which would quickly poison the catalyst. It is then mixed with air, and passed through heated iron pipes which contain the catalyst. It is from this close "contact" of the sulfur dioxide and the catalyst that the contact process gets its name. While in contact with the catalyst the sulfur dioxide combines with the oxygen of the air mixed with it, to form sulfur trioxide. Vanadium pentoxide, V_2O_5, is now generally used as the catalyst (see Fig. 28-4).

The oxidation of sulfur dioxide is an exothermic process. It is carried out at about 400° C. This temperature is high enough to cause the reaction to proceed at a practical rate. The heat evolved by the reaction is used to preheat the entering reactants. This prevents the temperature in the catalyzer from becoming high enough to promote the decomposition of the sulfur trioxide that is produced.

Gaseous sulfur trioxide does not unite readily with pure water. Consequently, sulfur trioxide is absorbed in 97% sulfuric acid, in which it is readily soluble. The sulfur trioxide combines with the 3% water and forms 100% sulfuric acid. Part of this may be drawn off, and the remainder diluted with water to make 97% acid for the absorption of more sulfur trioxide.

Very pure, highly concentrated sulfuric acid is produced by the contact process.

2. The chamber process. This method is used for making sulfuric acid for commercial uses that do not require very pure or highly concentrated acid. Sulfur dioxide is converted to sulfuric acid by the action of nitrogen dioxide, NO_2, and water.

$$H_2O + SO_2 + NO_2 \rightarrow H_2SO_4 + NO\uparrow$$

Fig. 28–4. In making sulfuric acid by the contact process, sulfur is burned to form sulfur dioxide. The gas is freed from dust, scrubbed, dried, and passed through a catalyst where it is converted into sulfur trioxide. The sulfur trioxide is then absorbed in sulfuric acid.

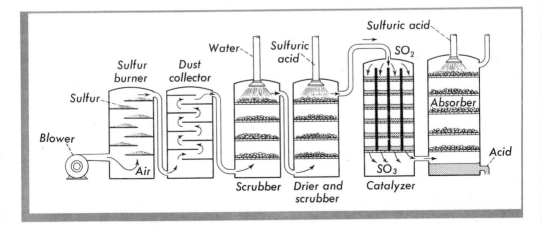

The nitric oxide, NO, which is produced, is recovered. It is allowed to react with oxygen to produce nitrogen dioxide for use over again.

$$2\ NO + O_2 \rightarrow 2\ NO_2\uparrow$$

Thus the nitric oxide serves as a *carrier* of oxygen, taking it from the air and giving it up to the sulfur dioxide to form sulfuric acid. The chemical reactions take place in huge lead-lined chambers into which steam is introduced. Concentrated sulfuric acid is used to dissolve the oxides of nitrogen and prevent their escape, so that they can be used again.

Let us refer to Fig. 28-5. The sulfur dioxide, which is formed by burning sulfur or by roasting iron pyrites, enters the Glover tower. As it rises through the tower, it meets a shower of moderately concentrated sulfuric acid mixed with oxides of nitrogen. The tower is filled with lumps of quartz, or some acid-resisting brick, to retard the upward flow of gas and expose it for a longer time to the sulfuric acid which trickles down. This is an example of the use of *countercurrents* in industrial chemistry. Some sulfuric acid is formed in the Glover tower, and it becomes quite concentrated by the time it reaches the bottom of the tower. It is drawn off into a container called an *acid egg*.

The main reactions occur in the lead chambers, which may be 100 ft long, 40 ft high, and 20 ft wide. During the complicated reactions, the exact course of which we are not sure, sulfur dioxide, air, and oxides of nitrogen from the Glover tower react with steam introduced into the lead chamber to form sulfuric acid. The acid collects in the bottom of the lead chambers. Sulfuric acid does not act upon the lead until it becomes fairly concentrated, about 75%. For many industrial purposes, sulfuric acid of this strength is sufficient, and no further concentration is necessary.

Those reactions which are not completed in the first lead chamber are continued in the second, third, and fourth chambers. The Gay-Lussac tower is used to recover the oxides of nitrogen. In this tower, sulfuric acid which is made in the Glover tower and forced by compressed air from the acid egg to the top of this tower, trickles down over layers of coke. It meets the oxides of nitrogen and reacts with them forming nitrosylsulfuric acid, which remains dissolved in the excess sulfuric acid.

Fig. 28–5. The chamber process for producing sulfuric acid is used to manufacture acid that is moderately concentrated and suitable for commercial use, but not chemically pure.

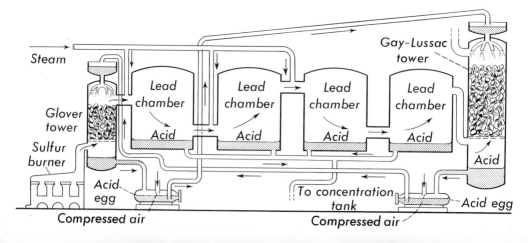

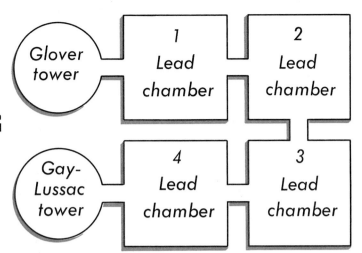

Fig. 28–6. The floor plan of a chamber process sulfuric acid plant.

$$NO + NO_2 + 2\ H_2SO_4 \rightarrow$$
$$2\ SO_2(OH)(ONO) + H_2O$$

This mixture of acids called "nitrose acid" flows into another acid egg. From this egg, the "nitrose acid" is forced to the top of the Glover tower where it is diluted with water which releases the oxides of nitrogen. While care is taken to prevent the loss of oxides of nitrogen, some must continually be replaced. They are prepared from ammonia, NH_3, by oxidation.

8. The physical properties of sulfuric acid. Concentrated sulfuric acid is a dense, oily liquid which is sometimes called *oil of vitriol*. The concentrated acid, which contains only about 2% water, has a specific gravity of about 1.84 and a boiling point of 338° C. Pure sulfuric acid is colorless, but commercial acid may have a yellow color, or it may be brown or almost black because of the presence of impurities, especially organic matter.

When sulfuric acid is added to water (*you must never add water to sulfuric acid*) a great deal of heat is evolved because of the formation of the hydrates $H_2SO_4 \cdot H_2O$ and $H_2SO_4 \cdot 2\ H_2O$.

9. The chemical properties of sulfuric acid. *1. Its acid properties.* Sulfuric acid, being a diprotic acid, ionizes in dilute water solution in two stages:

$$H_2SO_4 + H_2O \rightleftharpoons H_3O^+ + HSO_4^-$$
$$HSO_4^- + H_2O \rightleftharpoons H_3O^+ + SO_4^=$$

The reaction represented by the first equation is complete in dilute solutions. That represented by the second equation occurs to a considerable extent in dilute solution. Sulfuric acid can react with hydroxides to form bisulfates and sulfates. It attacks metals and reacts with the oxides of metals. Because it is more highly ionized, *dilute* sulfuric acid reacts with metals above hydrogen in the activity series more vigorously than *cold, concentrated* sulfuric acid does.

2. Its oxidizing properties. Hot, concentrated sulfuric acid is a vigorous oxidizing agent. It is reduced to either sulfur dioxide or hydrogen sulfide depending on the strength of the acid and the reducing agent with which it reacts. Thus, with copper, sulfur dioxide is produced (see Section 2). With zinc and hot, slightly diluted acid, hydrogen sulfide is the gaseous product.

$$4\ Zn + 5\ H_2SO_4 \rightarrow$$
$$4\ ZnSO_4 + H_2S\uparrow + 4\ H_2O$$

3. Its dehydrating properties. The strong affinity of sulfuric acid for water

Fig. 28–7. Aerial view of a plant for producing contact process sulfuric acid. Note the stockpile of sulfur at the top of the picture; the maze of tanks, pipes, and buildings of the plant itself; and the storage tanks where the sulfuric acid is kept before being transferred to the waiting railroad cars.

makes it an excellent *dehydrating* agent. Gases may be dried by bubbling them through concentrated sulfuric acid. Lumps of pumice stone soaked in sulfuric acid may be used in the lower part of a desiccator. In fact, sulfuric acid is such an active dehydrating agent that it will take hydrogen and oxygen, in the proportion needed to form water, from such substances as sugar, $C_{12}H_{22}O_{11}$, or cellulose, $(C_6H_{10}O_5)_n$, leaving the carbon uncombined.

$$C_{12}H_{22}O_{11} + 11\ H_2SO_4 \rightarrow$$
$$12\ C + 11\ H_2SO_4 \cdot H_2O$$

In the same manner, concentrated sulfuric acid chars wood, paper, cotton, starch, and other organic compounds.

In making some products commercially, water is formed as a by-product. Let us illustrate this with the reaction for making nitroglycerin, $C_3H_5(NO_3)_3$.

$$C_3H_5(OH)_3 + 3\ HNO_3 \rightarrow$$
$$C_3H_5(NO_3)_3 + 3\ H_2O$$

In the manufacture of this explosive, concentrated nitric acid is used. Since the nitric acid is reacting with a non-electrolyte, the reaction is slow. To prevent dilution of the acid, which would cause the reaction to proceed more slowly, sulfuric acid is always mixed with the nitric acid. The sulfuric acid acts as a dehydrating agent. It absorbs the water as fast as it is formed and greatly speeds the rate of the reaction.

This same principle is applied to many other reactions involving nonelectrolytes where water, formed as a product, would slow down the rate of reaction.

In the laboratory preparation of carbon monoxide, sulfuric acid is used to dehydrate formic acid (see Chapter 17, Section 14).

CAUTION: Sulfuric acid burns the flesh severely. Great care must be used in the handling of sulfuric acid so that it does not come in contact with the skin.

10. The uses of sulfuric acid. Sulfuric acid is used in a wide variety of chemical industries.

Calcium phosphate, $Ca_3(PO_4)_2$, is quarried in great amounts in Florida, Tennessee, and other states, for use as a fertilizer. The rock phosphate, even when finely pulverized, is too insoluble to be of immediate use to growing plants. Sulfuric acid is used to convert the rock phosphate into a more soluble product. About four million tons of the acid are used each year to make *superphosphate* fertilizer.

Sulfuric acid is used also in the preparation of other acids and various sulfates. For example, hydrochloric acid may be made by treating common salt with sulfuric acid. Cupric sulfate, sodium aluminum sulfate (alum), and ferrous sulfate have wide uses. Many other chemicals are made from sulfuric acid.

The iron and steel industries are large users of sulfuric acid. It is used to remove a coating of oxide from the surface of iron or steel before the metal is plated, or before it is coated with an enamel. Your bathtub was "pickled" in sulfuric acid before it was glazed. The enamelware used for kitchen utensils is similarly treated.

Sulfuric acid is used in the refining of petroleum products to remove certain organic impurities. The electrolyte used in automobile batteries is dilute sulfuric acid.

Sulfuric acid is necessary in the manufacture of many explosives. It serves as a dehydrating agent in the manufacture of smokeless powder and nitroglycerin. It is used in the manufacture of photographic film. It is used in making nitrocellulose plastics, in manufacturing rayon, paints and pigments, cellophane, and in innumerable articles of commerce.

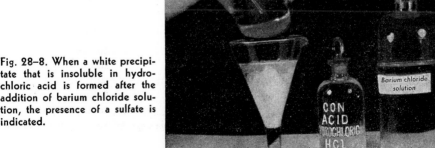

Fig. 28–8. When a white precipitate that is insoluble in hydrochloric acid is formed after the addition of barium chloride solution, the presence of a sulfate is indicated.

11. Some sulfates are important.
Sulfuric acid reacts with many metals
to form sulfates. Some of the most important sulfates are those of copper,
iron, zinc, calcium, barium, and aluminum. Cupric sulfate is used in copper plating and to produce mordants
in dyeing. Ferrous sulfate finds use in
water purification and in the manufacture of ink. Zinc sulfate is used to
make lithopone, a white paint pigment. Hydrated calcium sulfate is the
mineral gypsum. Barium sulfate and
aluminum sulfate are used in preparing other compounds of these elements.
Nearly all sulfates are soluble in water,
those of calcium, strontium, barium,
and lead being the chief exceptions.

The bisulfates are not very important.
12. The test for a sulfate. When a
solution of barium chloride is added to
sulfuric acid or to any soluble sulfate,
a white precipitate of barium sulfate
is formed, as shown in the equation:

$$Ba^{++} + SO_4^{=} \rightarrow BaSO_4\downarrow$$

The precipitate of barium sulfate is insoluble in hydrochloric acid. White
precipitates of barium oxalate or barium phosphate which might be confused with the barium sulfate precipitate are soluble in hydrochloric acid.
Thus the addition of hydrochloric acid
when performing the test prevents the
formation of these interfering precipitates.

Summary

Sulfur dioxide may be prepared: *1.* by burning sulfur; *2.* by roasting
sulfides; *3.* by the reduction of sulfuric acid; *4.* by the decomposition of
sulfites. It is a dense, suffocating gas that is extremely soluble in water and is
easily liquefied. Sulfur dioxide is the anhydride of sulfurous acid. It does not
burn and is a fairly stable compound. In the presence of a suitable catalyst,
sulfur dioxide can be oxidized to sulfur trioxide.

Sulfur dioxide is used for making sulfuric acid and sulfites. It is used as a
preservative, for treating kerosene and light oils, for bleaching, and in preparing paper pulp.

Sulfur trioxide is useful as the anhydride of sulfuric acid.

Sulfuric acid may be made by the contact process or by the chamber process. It is a dense, oily liquid which mixes with water in all proportions. When
dilute it acts as an acid; when hot and concentrated, it is a vigorous oxidizing
agent. It is also a good dehydrating agent. Sulfuric acid is one of the most
important industrial chemicals. Many sulfates are common chemical compounds.

Test yourself on these terms

acid anhydride	countercurrents	sulfate
bisulfate	dehydrating agent	sulfite
bisulfite	diprotic acid	sulfuric acid
carrier	"nitrose" acid	sulfurous acid
chamber process	oil of vitriol	superphosphate
contact process	roasting	vanadium pentoxide

Questions

Group A

1. From what sources does sulfur dioxide as an impurity in the air come?
2. What is meant by *roasting* an ore?
3. Write balanced chemical equations for: (*a*) a commercial preparation of sulfur dioxide; (*b*) a laboratory preparation of sulfur dioxide.
4. (*a*) What method of gas collection is used in a laboratory preparation of sulfur dioxide? (*b*) What properties of sulfur dioxide determine this choice?
5. What is the principal use for sulfur dioxide?
6. Why is the contact process for producing sulfuric acid so named?
7. Compare contact sulfuric acid with chamber sulfuric acid.
8. Why is sulfur trioxide absorbed in sulfuric acid rather than in water in the contact process?
9. What is the proper method of diluting sulfuric acid?
10. Why are large quantities of sulfuric acid used in the iron and steel industry?
11. Name four important sulfates and give their uses.
12. Give two reasons why boiling concentrated sulfuric acid burns the flesh so badly.

Group B

13. Is sulfur dioxide easy to liquefy or hard to liquefy? Explain.
14. Why is sulfur dioxide so soluble in water?
15. How does nitric oxide act as a carrier of oxygen in the chamber process?
16. Why is a mixture of nitric acid *and sulfuric acid* used in making nitroglycerin?
17. Write balanced chemical equations to show the formation from sulfurous acid and sodium hydroxide of: (*a*) sodium hydrogen sulfite; (*b*) sodium sulfite.
18. How is sulfuric acid used in making superphosphate?
19. How can you test a soluble salt to determine whether it is a sulfate?
20. What is meant by the *countercurrent principle* in industrial processes?
21. Compare the bleaching action of sulfur dioxide with that of hydrogen peroxide.
22. Explain the heat exchange needed in the catalyst chamber of a contact sulfuric acid plant.
23. What is the function of the Gay-Lussac tower in the chamber process?
★24. Using the electron-transfer method, balance the following equation: $Hg + H_2SO_4 \rightarrow HgSO_4 + SO_2\uparrow + H_2O.$

Problems

Group A

1. How many pounds of sulfuric acid can be prepared from one ton of sulfur that is 99.5% pure?

2. How many liters of sulfur dioxide may be produced by the roasting of 1200 kg of iron pyrites, FeS_2?

3. If 140 lb of scrap iron is added to a large vat of dilute sulfuric acid, how many pounds of ferrous sulfate can be produced?

4. Calculate the percentage composition of H_2SO_4.

Group B

5. How many grams of sodium sulfite are required for the production of 1 liter of sulfur dioxide by reaction with sulfuric acid?

6. How many liters of sulfur dioxide can be prepared from a mixture of 100 g of copper and 100 g of H_2SO_4?

7. A lead smelter processes 500 tons of zinc sulfide, ZnS, each day. If no sulfur dioxide is lost, how much sulfuric acid could be made in the plant daily?

Some things for you to do

1. Bleach a moist red carnation in a bottle of sulfur dioxide gas. The flower must be dripping wet to bleach well. Why?

2. Make a solution of sulfur dioxide in water. Put one or two dried apricots in the solution and allow it to stand for a day or two. What color change do you notice in the apricots?

3. Sulfuric acid usually comes to the laboratory in five-pint bottles with plastic tops that hold nine pounds of sulfuric acid. Examine such a bottle of concentrated acid. Note how heavy it is, but be careful not to drop it. Read the label closely and see how much information is given as to quantity, specific gravity, impurities, etc.

Check your progress in chemistry

1. In making a solution of cupric sulfate from coarse lumps of $CuSO_4 \cdot 5\,H_2O$, what procedures could you follow to shorten the time required?

2. Explain the anode and cathode reactions which occur in the electrolysis of very dilute sulfuric acid solution.

3. Write equations showing the stages in the ionization of the triprotic acid, H_3PO_4.

★ 4. How are catalysts believed to alter the rate of chemical reactions?

★ 5. What is the oxidation number of sulfur in: (a) H_2S; (b) $NaHSO_3$; (c) $KHSO_4$; (d) H_2SO_3; (e) H_2SO_4?

6. Which furnishes more carbon dioxide, 50 g of Na_2CO_3 or 50 g of $NaHCO_3$?

7. Write the equations for the production of hydrated lime from limestone.

8. Draw electron-dot formulas for molecules of fluorine, chlorine, bromine, and iodine.

9. For what purpose are fluoride ions added to drinking water?

10. How does an ink eradicator work?

11. What are the sources of bromine in the United States?

12. What do we mean when we say that iodine *sublimes?*
13. Draw a sketch showing a cross-section of the pipes which go down to a sulfur deposit. Indicate what flows through each pipe and the direction in which it goes.
14. (*a*) What are the solid allotropic forms of sulfur? (*b*) How do they differ in crystal structure?
15. Draw electron-dot formulas to show the possible resonating structures in sulfur trioxide.
16. How can you test for the presence of a sulfide?
17. Show by an equation that sulfur dioxide is an acid anhydride.
18. Sulfur trioxide is an important compound to chemical manufacturers, yet it is rarely seen in laboratory stockrooms. Why?
19. What catalyst is used in the contact process for making sulfuric acid?
20. How can you demonstrate the dehydrating property of sulfuric acid?

Challenging your knowledge

1. What do you believe was the reason for the relatively late isolation of fluorine as compared with the other common halogens?
2. (*a*) What effect will freshly prepared chlorine water have on blue litmus paper? (*b*) What effect will chlorine water stored in a clear glass bottle on a shelf in the laboratory for a week have on blue litmus paper?
3. How do reactions of metals with oxygen and metals with sulfur compare in the amount of energy evolved?
4. Why is white lead, a basic carbonate of lead, never used for making the paint to be used on the walls of a chemical laboratory?
5. What deviations from ideal gas behavior would you expect to be shown by chlorine, hydrogen sulfide, and sulfur dioxide?
6. Sulfuric acid is made by both the contact and the chamber processes. Why can both processes persist in competition with each other?
7. If equal weights of $NaCl$ and $CaCl_2 \cdot 2 H_2O$ are used with equal volumes of water, which produces the greater freezing point lowering?

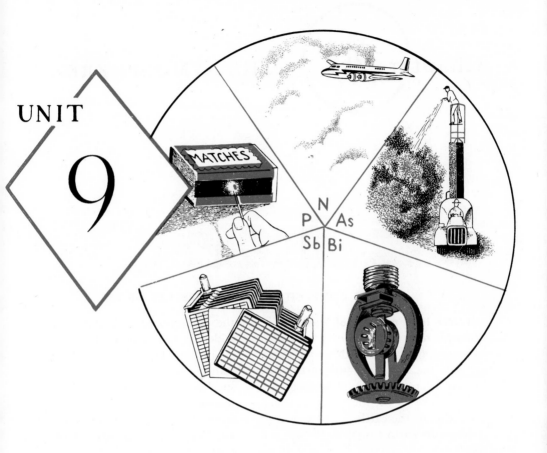

UNIT 9

THE NITROGEN FAMILY

The Nitrogen Family comprises five elements, nitrogen, phosphorus, arsenic, antimony, and bismuth. An important use for each of these elements is shown in the diagram above. Nitrogen comprises almost 80% of the air by volume; phosphorus is an important ingredient of matches; arsenic is used in agricultural sprays; antimony gives hardness to storage battery plates; and a bismuth alloy controls the valves in automatic sprinkler systems.

Because nitrogen is such a large part of the atmosphere, it is natural for us to include a study of the atmosphere and the other gases which comprise it in this unit. Thus, it is here that we include the Inert Gases, the family of unreactive elements.

There are three chapters in this unit: *The Atmosphere; Nitrogen and Its Compounds;* and *Phosphorus, Arsenic, Antimony, and Bismuth.*

Chapter 29 THE ATMOSPHERE

1. THE COMPOSITION AND PROPERTIES OF AIR

1. Air is a mixture of gases. *The atmosphere is the layer of gases which surrounds the earth.* Its density is greatest near the surface of the earth. The density decreases with increasing altitude because of the lower gravitational attraction of the earth.

Near the earth's surface, *the air is a mixture of oxygen, nitrogen, carbon dioxide, and argon and several other inert gases,* of rather constant composition. It is colorless, odorless, and tasteless. At high altitudes, its composition gradually changes. The outer limit of the atmosphere probably consists of widely scattered molecules of hydrogen.

Since smoke and other gases are constantly escaping into the air, traces of such impurities as carbon monoxide, hydrogen sulfide, sulfur dioxide, and ammonia are likely to be found in the air. Water vapor in varying quantities is always present in it. Ozone is formed in small quantities during thunderstorms. Particles of dust, bacteria, and the spores of plants are also nearly always present. The table on the next page shows the percentage composi-

VOCABULARY

Atmosphere. The layer of gases which surrounds the earth.

Critical pressure. The pressure required to liquefy a gas at its critical temperature.

Critical temperature. The highest temperature at which it is possible to liquefy a gas with any amount of pressure.

Critical volume. The volume occupied by one mole of a gas at its critical temperature and critical pressure.

Fractional distillation. The separation of the components of a mixture which have slightly different boiling points by carefully controlled vaporization.

Liquefaction. The process of converting a gas or solid to a liquid.

Relative humidity. The amount of moisture present in the air as vapor compared with the amount in saturated air at that temperature.

COMPONENT	PERCENTAGE BY VOLUME	PERCENTAGE BY WEIGHT
NITROGEN	78	75.5
OXYGEN	21	23.2
ARGON AND OTHER INERT GASES	0.94	1.3
CARBON DIOXIDE	0.04	0.05
WATER VAPOR	Varies, small fraction to 2% or more	Varies

tion of air near the earth's surface.

One liter of dry air at S.T.P. weighs 1.29 g. This is slightly less than the weight of one liter of oxygen. Dry air is $\frac{1}{773}$ as dense as water.

2. Here are some proofs that air is a mixture. There are several ways to prove that air is a mixture of gases and not a single compound.

1. The composition of the air varies slightly in different localities, and in the same locality at different times. If it were a compound, it would always have a definite composition by weight.

2. There is no evidence of any chemical action taking place when we mix the components of air in the same proportion in which they are present in air. No heat or light is produced.

3. The air which surrounds us is about one fifth oxygen by volume. When cold water is slowly warmed, we see bubbles of gas coming out of the solution. If we analyze these bubbles, we find that they consist of about one third oxygen by volume. The change in composition is due to the difference in the solubility of the gases which make up the air. If air were a single compound, the bubbles which escape from the water would have the same composition as undissolved air.

4. When liquid air boils, the nitrogen boils off first, leaving nearly pure liquid oxygen. The liquid oxygen then boils off at a somewhat higher temperature. Air must be a mixture because we can separate it into its components by this purely physical method.

5. The gases in the air react chemically with other substances the same way the pure gases do. Carbon burns in air, combining with the oxygen of the air to produce carbon dioxide. Carbon burns in pure oxygen to form carbon dioxide. Burning magnesium ribbon in air produces a mixture of magnesium oxide and magnesium nitride. Magnesium burns in pure oxygen to form magnesium oxide. Heated magnesium combines with pure nitrogen to form magnesium nitride. If air were a compound, different products would be formed by the reactions of a single substance with air and with the gases which air contains.

3. The liquefaction of gases. Michael Faraday (1791–1867) discovered that it is possible to liquefy certain gases by cooling them and compressing them at the same time. He used a thick-walled sealed tube of the type shown in Fig. 29-1 to liquefy chlorine, sulfur dioxide, and some other gases. One end

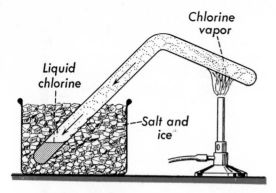

Chlorine vapor

Liquid chlorine

Salt and ice

Fig. 29–1. By using a tube like the one above, Faraday succeeded in liquefying chlorine, sulfur dioxide, and several other gases which have high critical temperatures.

of the glass tube containing the chlorine gas was strongly heated. That caused the gas in the heated end of the tube to expand and exert pressure on the gas in the other end of the tube, which was cooled by being packed in a freezing mixture. Such cooling and compression converted the gaseous chlorine into liquid chlorine.

In order to liquefy a gas, it is necessary first to compress the gas and then to absorb the heat of compression. The second step is to permit the cool, compressed gas to expand rapidly. If the expansion is sufficiently rapid, it will cool the remaining part of the gas to a temperature at which some of it will liquefy.

Compressing a gas always raises its temperature since energy is acquired by the molecules of a gas when they are pushed closer together. In liquefying gases this heat of compression is absorbed by a suitable refrigerant. The gas molecules thereby lose the energy acquired during compression. Thus the compressed gas is reduced to the same temperature that it had before compression. The molecules possess the same energy they had prior to compression.

When a compressed gas is permitted to expand, the molecules lose energy as

they spread apart. This energy loss by the molecules lowers the temperature of the gas. Since the temperature of the compressed gas was that which it had before compression, the expanded gas is now at a much lower temperature than originally. By repetition of this compression, cooling, and expansion cycle the temperature of the gas will be reduced still further.

The liquefaction of gases is accomplished by the combined efforts of lowered temperature and increased pressure. The increased pressure crowds the gas molecules together. The lowered temperature slows their movement. Ultimately, they are slowed down and crowded together so closely that the attractive forces between the molecules cause them to condense to a liquid.

Scientists have found that above a certain temperature it is impossible to liquefy a gas by pressure alone. Above this temperature the kinetic energy of the molecules is great enough to overcome the attracting forces between them. Thus the gas will not liquefy however great the pressure we apply. *The highest temperature at which it is possible to liquefy a gas with any amount of pressure is called its **critical temperature**. The pressure required to liquefy a gas at its critical temperature is called its **critical pressure**. The volume occupied by one mole of a gas under these conditions is called its **critical volume**.* The critical temperature and critical pressure of several common gases is given in the table on the next page.

From these data it is easy to see that in order to liquefy a gas we must lower its temperature below its critical temperature. Simultaneously we must

GAS	CRITICAL TEMPERATURE (° C)	CRITICAL PRESSURE (atm)
AIR	−140.7	37.2
OXYGEN	−118.8	49.7
NITROGEN	−147.1	33.5
CARBON DIOXIDE	31.1	73.0
CHLORINE	144.0	76.1
SULFUR DIOXIDE	157.2	77.7

raise its pressure above the vapor pressure of the liquefied gas at this temperature.

4. The production of liquid air. Air will change into a liquid if we cool it sufficiently. Small amounts of liquid air were first produced in France in 1877. Today it is produced in large amounts as a preliminary step in separating the components of the air.

Fig. 29-2 is a simplified diagram of a liquid air machine. By means of a compressor, the air is first put under a pressure of from 3000 to 4000 lb/in². This hot, compressed air then flows through a coiled pipe in a condenser through which water circulates to absorb the heat of compression. In the liquefier, the gas flows out through a needle valve, and expands rapidly.

Fig. 29-2. This diagram shows how a liquid air machine operates.

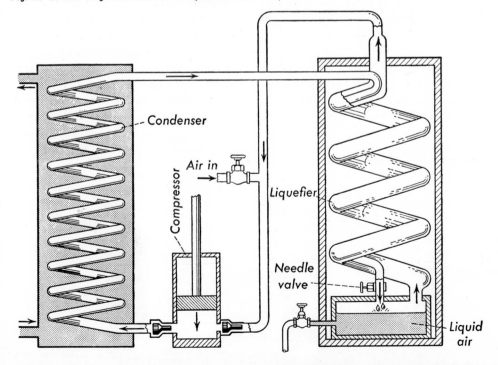

This expansion cools the gas decidedly. The cool gas then flows back through the outer of the two pipes of the liquefier. This cools still more the gas which is in the inner tube of the liquefier. The expanded gas is recycled. The continuous expansion of cooler and cooler gas in the liquefier finally produces a low enough temperature to liquefy some of the gas. The liquid air collects in the reservoir at the bottom of the liquefier.

5. The properties of liquid air. Liquid air resembles water in appearance. Under ordinary atmospheric pressure, liquid air boils at a temperature of about $-190°$ C. Its boiling temperature is not constant, because it is a mixture of liquid nitrogen which boils at $-195.8°$ C, and of liquid oxygen which boils at $-182.7°$ C. Because it has the lower boiling point, the nitrogen boils away first and leaves nearly pure oxygen.

A test tube of alcohol immersed in liquid air will soon be frozen solid. Mercury freezes so hard that it can be used as a hammer for driving nails. Carbon dioxide solidifies in liquid air. A rubber ball immersed in liquid air, and then thrown on the floor, breaks as if it were glass. Tin becomes brittle and lead becomes elastic.

To get an idea of how cold liquid air really is, we may place a vessel of liquid air upon a cake of ice. We find that the ice is so hot, comparatively, that the liquid air is likely to boil over. Remember that boiling water is only 100 Centigrade degrees hotter than ice, and that ice is about 190 Centigrade degrees hotter than liquid air. These facts will give you a clearer idea of the extremely low temperature of liquid air.

6. The storage of liquid air. Large vacuum bottles are used to store liquid air. These glass bottles are double-walled, with the space between the walls evacuated. This vacuum prevents the conduction of heat from the outside through the walls of the flask to the liquid inside. The glass is silvered to prevent radiant heat rays from passing through. Even with these precautions, enough heat gets in to keep the liquid boiling slowly. Liquid air containers should never be stoppered. The pressure of the air as it vaporizes would either blow out the stopper or burst the container.

7. The uses of liquid air. Liquid air is useful for producing low temperatures. It is a commercial source of both oxygen and nitrogen. Processors who prepare oxygen and nitrogen for the market also separate from the liquid air such products as neon and argon.

Fig. 29-3. Liquid air boils vigorously when placed on a cake of ice.

Fig. 29-4. A well insulated container for transporting or storing a small quantity of liquid air under atmospheric pressure.

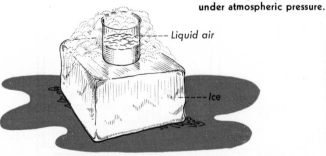

2. THE AIR WE BREATHE

8. Carbon dioxide in the air. Air usually contains between 0.03% and 0.04% carbon dioxide. However, the air in a crowded, poorly ventilated room will have more of this gas. Similarly, the air above tall chimneys in factory areas, where much fuel is consumed, will show a greater percentage of the gas.

All plants, animals, and man release carbon dioxide which is produced as a result of the oxidation of food. While the inhaled air contains only traces, exhaled air may contain as much as 5% carbon dioxide. When we consider all the factors that add carbon dioxide to the air, it is remarkable that the atmosphere does not show wider variations in composition. This comparatively even composition of the air may be accounted for in two ways.

1. Plants remove carbon dioxide from the air and use it in the photosynthesis process. They return oxygen to the air as a by-product of this process. Tests indicate that plants grow more vigorously when they are surrounded by an atmosphere with a greater amount of carbon dioxide than usual. Thus plant life maintains a balance and keeps the percentage of carbon dioxide nearly constant.

2. Winds and convection currents keep the air stirred. The total volume of the atmosphere is so enormous that slight changes produced by burning or breathing in a limited area are nullified by the mixing action of the wind. Eventually, plants utilize the carbon dioxide and the balance is thus maintained.

9. Air always contains some water vapor. Near the sea, air contains much water vapor. Even the air over the driest desert has small amounts. We may prove the existence of water vapor in the air by exposing a deliquescent substance like calcium chloride crystals to the air in a room. The crystals soon become wet when spread out on a watch glass. The outside surface of a glass of ice water standing in a warm room soon becomes covered with a film of water. Some of the water vapor in the air has condensed on the cooler surface of the glass.

10. What is relative humidity? Humidity refers to the moisture content of the air. *Relative humidity is the amount of moisture present in the air as vapor compared with the amount in saturated air at that temperature.* It is expressed as a percentage. Thus a relative humidity of 50% means that the air is 50% saturated with water vapor. The relative humidity varies greatly in different places or in the same place on different days.

11. The discomfort of poorly ventilated rooms. Dr. J. S. Haldane (1860–1936), an English scientist, conducted extensive experiments to find out what makes people uncomfortable in a crowded, poorly ventilated room. He made many analyses of the air in rooms filled with people. He concluded that discomfort in such rooms is due to an increase in the relative humidity. The water vapor which produces this increase in the humidity comes from perspiration and exhaled air. The physical discomfort is due neither to a lack of oxygen nor to an increase in the percentage of carbon dioxide.

12. Air conditioning. Engineers have found a way to control the purity and humidity of the air in buildings so we can live in rooms which are ideally adapted to our various daily activities. *Air conditioning* is the term applied to the treatment of the air in buildings so that the occupants will be comfortable.

At least four factors must be taken into consideration in air conditioning.

1. The air must be warmed in winter and cooled in summer. You can adapt yourself to extremes of temperature, of course, but you work best when the temperature ranges from 68° to 78° F.

2. If the relative humidity is above 60%, some of the moisture should be removed from the air. If the relative humidity is below 40%, then the air should be humidified.

3. The air must be filtered to remove particles of dust, pollen, and bacteria which are always present.

4. A fan must be used to keep the air in gentle motion, but not so much that it creates strong drafts.

Various methods of meeting each of these conditions have been devised. The result is that many office buildings, theatres, hotels, and homes are now comfortable and healthful at all times of the year. Railroad trains, buses, and airplanes are also air-conditioned.

3. THE INERT GASES

13. Several inert gases are present in the air. In 1893 Lord Rayleigh (1842–1919), an English physicist, was investigating nitrogen prepared by removing oxygen and the other known gases from the air. He found that the density of nitrogen prepared in this way was slightly higher than that of the nitrogen chemically prepared from nitrogen compounds. Lord Rayleigh suspected that there must be some other substance mixed with the nitrogen from the air which produced this discrepancy. He turned the problem over to his friend, Sir William Ramsay (1852–1916), who was a chemist. Ramsay carefully analyzed the air, and found that about 1% of an air sample could not be removed by chemical methods. Later Ramsay and his co-workers found that this unreactive residue of the air consisted of five inert gases, helium, neon, argon, krypton, and xenon. These gases, along with radon, which is formed by radioactive disintegration of radium, constitute Group VIIIA of the Periodic Table. Each has an outer shell consisting of a stable electron configuration. For helium this is an electron pair; for the

Fig. 29–5. Sir William Ramsay, an English scientist, discovered the inert gases, neon, argon, krypton, and xenon.

others it is an octet composed of four electron pairs. These elements show no tendency to form chemical compounds by the usual methods of electron transfer or electron sharing. As a consequence also, each of these gases is monatomic. Their atomic weights and molecular weights are the same. See the table at the bottom of this page.

14. The discovery and production of helium. Helium was first discovered through spectrographic analysis of the sun's atmosphere in 1868 by Sir Norman Lockyer (1836–1920). It was named *helium* from the Greek word meaning sun. Later, Sir William Ramsay found it in small amounts in the earth's atmosphere.

The natural gas from some wells in Texas, Oklahoma, and Kansas contains as much as 2% helium. By the use of compressors, everything except helium in such natural gases is liquefied by compression and cooling. In this way, the helium is separated from the other components of the gas and compressed into steel cylinders for storage or shipment.

15. The properties of helium. This colorless, odorless, and tasteless gas has two special properties which make it useful. It is only one-seventh as dense as air, and it does not burn. In spite of the fact that helium is twice as dense as hydrogen, it is still 93% as efficient as hydrogen as a buoyant agent (refer to Chapter 8, Section 7). Remember that the buoyancy of any gas is equal to the difference between the weight of a given volume of gas and that of the same volume of air. Helium is the most difficult gas to liquefy. Its boiling point is $-268.9°$ C.

16. The uses of helium. The importance of helium for filling balloons and airships depends on the fact that it is nonflammable and has a low density. Helium is less soluble in the blood stream than nitrogen. Accordingly, divers and men who work in tunnels in an atmosphere of compressed air breathe a special mixture of helium and oxygen. This prevents the common disease of such occupations known as "the bends," which is caused by the formation of gas bubbles in the blood when the pressure on the body is reduced. Helium is also used as an inert atmosphere to surround magnesium while it is being electrically welded. This prevents oxidation of the magnesium. Liquid helium is used in the study of the properties of materials at very low temperatures.

17. Neon is used in advertising signs. Neon is present in the air to the

ELEMENT	ATOMIC NUM-BER	ATOMIC WEIGHT	ELECTRON CONFIGURA-TION	OXIDA-TION NUM-BER	MELT-ING POINT, °C	BOIL-ING POINT, °C	DEN-SITY g/l
HELIUM	2	4.003	2	0	− 272.2	− 268.9	0.177
NEON	10	20.183	2,8	0	− 248.7	− 245.9	0.899
ARGON	18	39.944	2,8,8	0	− 189.2	− 185.7	1.784
KRYPTON	36	83.80	2,8,18,8	0	− 157	− 152.9	3.708
XENON	54	131.30	2,8,18,18,8	0	− 112	− 107.1	5.85
RADON	86	222.	2,8,18,32,18,8	0	− 71	− 61.8	9.73

extent of about 18 parts per million by weight. It is produced by the fractional distillation of liquid air. *Fractional distillation is the separation of the components of a mixture which have slightly different boiling points by carefully controlled vaporization.*

Neon signs are usually manufactured on special order for a particular purpose. First, electrodes are sealed into the ends of glass tubes which are bent to the desired shape. Then the air is pumped out of the tubes. Finally, neon gas under a pressure of about 10 mm is introduced into the tube. As the neon vapor conducts electricity through the tube, the tube is filled with an orange-red light. The electricity energizes the electrons of the neon atoms. This increase in energy causes the electrons to move away from the nucleus and temporarily occupy normally vacant energy levels. As these electrons return to their usual energy levels, they give up their energy as light energy. Neon tubes are used not only in signs but also on airport landing fields as runway and boundary markers.

18. The preparation, properties, and uses of argon. Argon is prepared commercially from liquid air by fractional distillation. The impure argon which is obtained by this process is passed over hot copper to remove any remaining traces of oxygen.

Argon is a colorless, odorless, and tasteless gas. It is present in the air to the extent of about 10,000 parts per million by weight, or about 1% by volume.

Argon is used in electric light bulbs. The gas-filled tungsten filament bulbs contain a mixture of nitrogen and argon, in some cases as much as 80% argon. The argon does not combine with the tungsten wire used for the filament, and it keeps the hot tungsten from evaporating rapidly. Its pressure inside the bulb equalizes the atmospheric pressure outside and helps prevent the seepage of air into the bulb. Such seepage would oxidize the tungsten and make the lamp less efficient. Argon is used for filling the tubes of tungar rectifiers which are used in charging storage batteries. It is also used, together with mercury vapor, in fluorescent tubes.

19. The other inert gases. *Krypton* (*krip*-ton) is present in the atmosphere to the extent of about 1 part per million by weight, while *xenon* (*zee*-non) occurs only to the extent of about 0.1 part per million by weight. Some flash tubes for use in high speed photography contain a mixture of these gases. The gases are produced by fractional distillation of liquid air.

Radon (*ray*-don) is so closely connected in its chemistry with radium that it will be studied in Chapter 38.

Fig. 29–6. This worker is welding magnesium by using a helium-shielded electric arc. The helium prevents oxidation of the magnesium during the welding process.

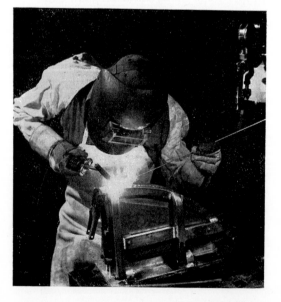

Fig. 29-7. Argon provides an inert atmosphere in this equipment for producing titanium metal from titanium tetrachloride by reduction with metallic sodium.

Summary

Air is a mixture of colorless, odorless, and tasteless gases. About 99% of it is a mixture of nitrogen and oxygen. Argon comprises about 0.9%. Smaller amounts of neon, helium, krypton, and xenon are present, together with carbon dioxide and variable amounts of water vapor. By compression and cooling, air can be liquefied. Liquid air has a very low temperature. It is used as a commercial source of nitrogen, oxygen, argon, and neon.

The highest temperature at which it is possible to liquefy a gas with any amount of pressure is called its critical temperature. The pressure required to liquefy a gas at its critical temperature is called its critical pressure.

Plants use carbon dioxide in the process of photosynthesis. Water vapor in the air is known as humidity. Air conditioning is the control of the temperature, purity, humidity, and circulation of the air in buildings.

The Inert Gases are elements with stable outer shell configurations. They show no tendency to form chemical compounds by the usual methods of electron transfer or electron sharing. Each gas is monatomic. Helium is used for balloons, and, mixed with oxygen, is breathed by divers. Neon is used for neon signs and for airplane beacons. Argon is used in electric light bulbs.

Test yourself on these terms

air conditioning	critical temperature	liquid air
argon	critical volume	neon
atmosphere	fractional distillation	proofs that air is a mix-
composition of the at-	helium	ture
mosphere	inert gas	relative humidity
critical pressure	liquefaction	the bends

Questions

Group A

1. What are the important gases in the air?
2. Name the gases which are present as impurities in the air.
3. What non-gaseous impurities are there in the air?
4. What proofs do we have that air is a mixture and not a single compound?
5. (a) Which has the higher boiling point, liquid nitrogen or liquid oxygen? (b) What practical use is made of this difference in boiling points?
6. Define: (a) critical temperature; (b) critical pressure; (c) critical volume.
7. Why will a beaker of liquid air boil very rapidly when placed on a cake of ice?
8. How are liquid air containers constructed to prevent heat transfer to the liquid air?
9. What experiment can you conduct to show that the air contains water vapor?
10. The weather report states that the relative humidity is 72%. What does this mean?
11. What four conditions are controlled in properly conditioned air?
12. (a) To which group of the Periodic Table do the inert gases belong? (b) Why are they placed in this group?
13. (a) What is an important aeronautical use for helium? (b) What properties make it so useful for this purpose?
14. Why is argon used in electric light bulbs?

Group B

15. Why does air which has been dissolved in water consist of about one third oxygen, when the atmosphere contains only about one fifth oxygen?
16. (a) Why does compressing a gas raise its temperature? (b) Why does a gas become colder when it is allowed to expand?
17. What conditions must be met in order for us to liquefy a gas?
18. Where, in a liquid air machine, is the heat actually removed from the air?
19. Why does the composition of the air remain so constant when such large quantities of carbon dioxide are added to it?
20. To what is the discomfort of a poorly ventilated room probably due?
21. What evidence caused Rayleigh to suspect that there were yet undiscovered gases in the air?

22. Why are the inert gases monatomic, while other common gases are diatomic?

23. Distinguish: *fractional distillation, destructive distillation,* and *distillation.*

24. (*a*) Can carbon dioxide be liquefied at 100° C? (*b*) Can chlorine be liquefied at 100° C?

25. Why must a difference in a physical property, such as boiling point, be used in separating neon from liquid air?

26. How is the light produced by the neon gas in advertising signs?

Problems

1. What is the weight of 22.4 liters of air at S.T.P.?

2. What is the weight of 22.4 liters of helium at S.T.P.?

3. What is the lifting power of 22.4 liters of helium?

Some things for you to do

1. Measure the relative humidity of your classroom using a sling psychrometer, or an ordinary wet and dry bulb thermometer on the wall. A chart accompanies such instruments so that the relative humidity can be determined from the difference in the readings of the two thermometers.

2. Examine an air conditioning unit and see how it filters and humidifies or dehumidifies the air.

3. Visit a plant where neon signs are made. Note the skill of the workmen in shaping the glass tubes into intricate designs.

4. Read Part IV, "The Canopy of Air," in the Life Magazine book, *The World We Live In,* and report to the class on the sections related to chemistry.

Chapter 30 — NITROGEN AND ITS COMPOUNDS

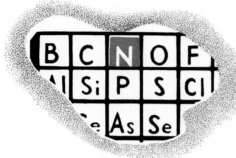

1. NITROGEN

1. The occurrence of nitrogen. We have already learned that about four-fifths of the air is *elementary nitrogen*. *Combined nitrogen* is also widely distributed. It is found in the proteins of both plants and animals. Natural deposits of both potassium nitrate and sodium nitrate are raw materials for the production of other nitrogen compounds.

2. The discovery of nitrogen. Several scientists played a part in the discovery of nitrogen. In 1772 Daniel Rutherford (1749–1819), a Scottish physician, published an account of his study on the products of breathing of small animals in a closed vessel. After he had separated the gas which we know as carbon dioxide from the exhaled air, he found that a colorless gas remained. This remaining gas would support neither life nor burning. This was the first separation of relatively pure nitrogen from the air.

Priestley, Cavendish, Scheele, and Lavoisier also made contributions to the discovery of nitrogen. Lavoisier was the first to recognize it as a distinct element present in the air. He called it *azote*, which means "without life," but the name was later changed to nitrogen because it is present in *niter*, which is the common name for potassium nitrate.

3. The preparation of nitrogen.
1. By fractional distillation of liquid air. This is the commercial method for producing nitrogen (see Chapter 29, Section 7).
2. By chemically removing oxygen

VOCABULARY

Explosive. A compound or mixture which decomposes suddenly with the production of a large volume of gas.

Nitride. A compound of nitrogen and a more positive element.

Nitrogen fixation. The process of converting elementary nitrogen into nitrogen compounds.

from the air. This laboratory method produces nitrogen which is still contaminated with carbon dioxide and the inert gases. Let us put a small piece of phosphorus in a small crucible and float the crucible on water, as shown in Fig. 30-1. We ignite the phosphorus and immediately place a bell jar over it. As the phosphorus combines with the oxygen of the air in the bell jar, the water rises in the bell jar to take the place of the oxygen which was removed. Impure nitrogen remains in the bell jar. The diphosphorus pentoxide which is formed dissolves in the water and does not contaminate the nitrogen.

Several other substances can be used to remove the oxygen from the air in similar experiments. Heated mercury can be used. So can iron filings, steel wool, hot copper gauze, or hot carbon.

3. By decomposing ammonium nitrite. Pure nitrogen can be prepared in the laboratory by gently heating ammonium nitrite, NH_4NO_2, which decomposes into nitrogen and water.

$$NH_4NO_2 \rightarrow N_2\uparrow + 2\,H_2O$$

Ammonium nitrite is too unstable to store in the laboratory. Usually, we prepare it by heating gently a mixture of ammonium chloride and sodium nitrite solutions. The ions form ammonium nitrite which then decomposes to yield nitrogen.

$$NH_4Cl + NaNO_2 \rightarrow NH_4NO_2 + NaCl$$
$$\searrow$$
$$N_2\uparrow + 2\,H_2O$$

4. The physical properties of nitrogen. Nitrogen is a colorless, odorless, and tasteless gas. It is slightly less dense than air, and is only slightly soluble in water. Its density shows that its molecules are diatomic, N_2.

5. The chemical properties of nitrogen. The triple covalent bond between the atoms of nitrogen in a molecule

$$:N:::N:$$

is a very strong one. As a result, elementary nitrogen is rather inactive. It unites with other elements with difficulty. Here are four other chemical properties of this gas.

1. Nitrogen does not burn in oxygen. However, when a lightning discharge passes through the air, or when nitrogen and oxygen are passed through an electric arc, nitric oxide, NO, is formed.

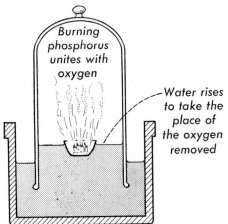

Fig. 30–1. The gas remaining after oxygen is removed from air by burning phosphorus is nitrogen contaminated with small amounts of carbon dioxide and inert gases.

Burning phosphorus unites with oxygen

Water rises to take the place of the oxygen removed

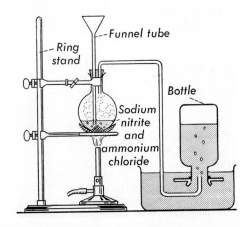

Fig. 30–2. Pure nitrogen can be prepared by the decomposition of ammonium nitrite. The flask must be heated gently to prevent too rapid decomposition.

Ring stand

Funnel tube

Bottle

Sodium nitrite and ammonium chloride

2. By the use of a catalyst, nitrogen can be made to combine with hydrogen to form ammonia, NH_3. This method of making ammonia will be described later in Section 12.

3. At a high temperature, nitrogen combines directly with such metals as magnesium, titanium, and aluminum to form *nitrides.*

4. Nitrogen is not poisonous, but animals die in an atmosphere of nitrogen due to oxygen starvation.

6. The uses of elementary nitrogen. Substances burn rapidly in pure oxygen. The nitrogen present in the air serves as a diluting agent and makes combustion much less rapid. Nitrogen gives bulk to the air and helps increase both its pressure and its buoyant force.

Nitrogen is used with argon for filling electric lamps. It is also used above mercury in thermometers to be used

Fig. 30–3. The nodules attached to the roots of this clover plant contain nitrogen-fixing bacteria. These bacteria produce nitrates from the nitrogen of the air which surrounds the soil particles through which the roots grow.

for measuring high temperatures. Large amounts of nitrogen are taken from the air for use in making ammonia, nitric acid, and other nitrogen compounds.

7. The test for nitrogen. The best test for nitrogen depends on the fact that magnesium combines with it when heated and forms magnesium nitride, Mg_3N_2. If water is added to magnesium nitride, ammonia is produced and can be detected by its odor.

$$Mg_3N_2 + 3 H_2O \rightarrow 3 MgO + 2 NH_3\uparrow$$

8. Nitrogen fixation is an important process. Besides *free or elementary nitrogen,* which is in the air, all living things contain nitrogen compounds. The nitrogen in these compounds is called *combined or fixed nitrogen. The process that converts free nitrogen into nitrogen compounds is called* **nitrogen fixation.** Such a process is important because nitrogen compounds in the soil make it possible to grow more food plants.

Green plants have their stems and leaves exposed to the air, which contains 78% free nitrogen. But they are unable to utilize this nitrogen in making essential protein foods. The problem of the agricultural chemist is to put back into the soil those nitrogen compounds which are soluble in water. Then the plants can utilize them.

Besides their use in agriculture, nitrogen compounds are necessary in the explosives industry, for making dyestuffs, and in the preparation of certain plastics.

9. Some processes of nitrogen fixation. *1. A natural method* is to grow certain crops which will put nitrogen compounds into the soil. Many crops, like wheat, corn, oats, and lettuce, remove nitrogen compounds from the soil rapidly. They cannot utilize the free nitrogen of the air. On the other hand, certain other crop plants, belonging to the bean and pea family, have small *nodules,* or swellings, on their roots (see Fig. 30-3). Special types of bacteria known as **nitrogen-fixing bacteria** grow in these nodules. If the soil is alkaline rather than acid, these bacteria have the ability to take free nitrogen from the air and convert it into nitrogen compounds which the plants can use. By growing one of these crops (beans, peas, clover, alfalfa, or lespedeza) on a field every three or four years, a farmer can keep his soil reasonably fertile. Cultures of these nitrogen-fixing bacteria are now available commercially. The grower inoculates the soil with them by treating the seeds with cultures before planting.

2. Another natural method of nitrogen fixation occurs whenever there is an electrical storm. The lightning discharges furnish sufficient energy to cause some of the nitrogen and oxygen of the air to unite. This forms an oxide of nitrogen. After a series of changes, nitrogen compounds are washed down into the soil in the ensuing rain. It is estimated that millions of tons of nitrogen compounds are produced during each year as a result of electrical storms.

3. The chief artificial method of nitrogen fixation is the manufacture of ammonia from a mixture of nitrogen and hydrogen. The ammonia so produced in chemical works can then be oxidized to nitric acid. The nitric acid, in turn, can be converted into nitrates suitable for fertilizer. This method of nitrogen fixation is of vital importance to agriculture because it makes nitrogen fertilizers available in unlimited amounts.

4. Another artificial method is the manufacture of calcium cyanamid, $CaCN_2$. In this process, nitrogen from liquid air is passed over white-hot calcium carbide.

$$CaC_2 + N_2 \rightarrow CaCN_2 + C$$

The cyanamid may be used directly as a nitrogen fertilizer, or it may be converted into ammonia by means of superheated steam.

$$CaCN_2 + 3 H_2O \rightarrow CaCO_3 + 2 NH_3\uparrow$$

10. The nitrogen cycle. In addition to the carbon dioxide and water from which plants make starch in the presence of sunlight and chlorophyll, plants also require nitrogen compounds from the soil. They need these nitrogen compounds to form complex food substances called *proteins.* Proteins are essential for life and are present in all living things, plant, animal, and man.

When plants die, proteins, which are

Fig. 30–4. The nitrogen cycle occurs over and over again, playing an important part in the life cycles of plants and animals.

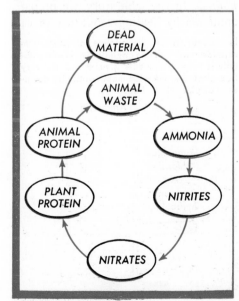

rich in nitrogen, are broken down into simpler compounds, of which ammonia is one. Certain kinds of bacteria aid in this decomposition. The ammonia is oxidized into nitrates, which then are available in the soil for succeeding generations of plants. This process of building up proteins and then breaking them down into nitrates occurs over and over again. It is called the *nitrogen cycle.*

The nitrogen cycle is of the greatest

importance for maintaining soil fertility. Corn quickly depletes the soil of nitrogen compounds when it is grown year after year in the same field. Therefore, the wise farmer will alternate his corn with another crop, preferably one containing nodules of nitrogen-fixing bacteria. He will plow this crop under and allow the nitrogen cycle to operate normally. He will also have the added nitrates from nitrogen in the air which the nitrogen-fixing bacteria form.

2. AMMONIA AND AMMONIUM COMPOUNDS

11. The occurrence of ammonia. Very small traces of ammonia, NH_3, are found in the air. This is because ammonia is formed when the complex proteins in plant and animal bodies are decomposed in the operation of the nitrogen cycle. An odor of ammonia is always noticeable around barns and stables where farm animals are housed. Bacteria break down the nitrogen compounds in manures and form ammonia.

12. The preparation of ammonia. There are three general methods used for the preparation of ammonia.

1. By decomposing ammonium compounds. In the laboratory, we prepare ammonia by heating a mixture of cal-

Fig. 30-5. When the mixture of ammonium chloride and calcium hydroxide in the test tube is heated, ammonia is produced and may be collected in the wide mouth bottle by downward displacement of air.

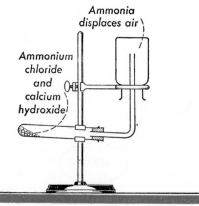

Ammonia displaces air

Ammonium chloride and calcium hydroxide

cium hydroxide and an ammonium compound, usually ammonium chloride or ammonium sulfate.

$$Ca(OH)_2 + 2\,NH_4Cl \rightarrow$$
$$CaCl_2 + 2\,NH_3\uparrow + 2\,H_2O$$

$$Ca(OH)_2 + (NH_4)_2SO_4 \rightarrow$$
$$CaSO_4 + 2\,NH_3\uparrow + 2\,H_2O$$

The mixture may be heated in a test tube fitted with an L-shaped delivery tube, as shown in Fig. 30-5. Ammonia is so soluble that it cannot be collected by water displacement. But it can be collected by downward displacement of air in an inverted container.

In either reaction, the ammonium ion, NH_4^+, from the ammonium salt, reacts with the hydroxide ion, OH^-, from the calcium hydroxide, to form ammonia and water.

$$NH_4^+ + OH^- \rightarrow NH_3\uparrow + H_2O$$

The heating drives the reaction to the right since ammonia is a gas.

Any strong hydroxide may be used instead of calcium hydroxide. For example, sodium hydroxide and ammonium chloride react as follows:

$$NaOH + NH_4Cl \rightarrow NaCl + NH_3\uparrow + H_2O$$

Fig. 30–6. These absorbing and scrubbing towers are used for purifying nitrogen and hydrogen before their synthesis into ammonia.

2. By destructive distillation of bituminous coal. When bituminous coal is heated in a closed container without access to air, ammonia is one of the gaseous products which are evolved. The ammonia is converted to ammonium sulfate by treatment with sulfuric acid.

$$2\ NH_3 + H_2SO_4 \rightarrow (NH_4)_2SO_4$$

3. By the Haber process. Chemists have long known that some ammonia can be prepared by passing an electric spark through a mixture of nitrogen and hydrogen. But the reaction is reversible:

$$N_2 + 3\ H_2 \rightleftarrows 2\ NH_3$$

Only a very small percentage of ammonia is produced. The problem of increasing that percentage was solved in 1913 by Fritz Haber (1868–1934), a German chemist.

The reaction between nitrogen and hydrogen is exothermic, and higher temperatures, which would be desirable for increasing the rate at which the molecules of nitrogen and hydrogen react, shift the equilibrium toward the left. However, four volumes of reactants produce only two volumes of products, so increased pressure shifts the equilibrium toward the right. Haber found that by using a catalyst to increase the speed of reaction, and by using a temperature of about 600° C and a pressure of about 200 atmospheres, he could obtain a yield of about 8% ammonia.

Today, the yield from the Haber process has been improved to about 40%. This has been brought about by using pressures as high as 1000 atmospheres, and an improved catalyst. This catalyst is a specially prepared mixture of porous iron and the oxides of potassium and aluminum.

The ammonia, which is produced in the special chrome-vanadium steel bombs which are needed to withstand the tremendous pressure, is separated from the unreacted nitrogen and hydrogen by being dissolved in water, or by being cooled until it liquefies. The uncombined gases are returned to the bombs to be exposed again to the action of the catalyst.

13. The physical properties of ammonia. Ammonia is a colorless gas with a characteristic, penetrating odor. It is less dense than air and is easily liquefied when sufficiently cooled. Liquid ammonia, which has a boiling point of $-34°$ C at atmospheric pressure, is sold in steel cylinders.

One of the unusual properties of ammonia is its great solubility in water. One liter of water at $20°$ C dissolves about 700 liters of ammonia. At $0°$ C nearly 1200 volumes of ammonia can be dissolved in one volume of water.

The structural formula for ammonia:

$$H : \overset{\cdot\cdot}{N} : H$$
$$\overset{\cdot\cdot}{H}$$

For a compound with such a simple molecular structure, ammonia has an unusually high melting point and a high boiling point. You will remember from your study of water that water shows these properties to an even more marked extent. Just as in the case of water, the high melting point and high boiling point are explained by the formation of hydrogen bonds between molecules of ammonia when in the solid and liquid states. The three hydrogen atoms are not symmetrically bonded to the nitrogen atom. Consequently, ammonia molecules are polar molecules. Hydrogen atoms from one ammonia molecule form hydrogen

Fig. 30–8. When a few drops of water are squeezed from the medicine dropper into the flask, the ammonia dissolves in them and reduces the pressure in the flask. The atmospheric pressure forces water with phenolphthalein solution up the glass tube. More ammonia dissolves in this water, further reducing the pressure and causing the fountain action to continue. Since ammonia-water solution has basic properties, the phenolphthalein turns red.

Fig. 30–7. Flow diagram of the Haber process. Ammonia gas produced in the catalyst chamber is condensed into a liquid in the cooler. The uncombined nitrogen and hydrogen are recirculated through the catalyst chamber.

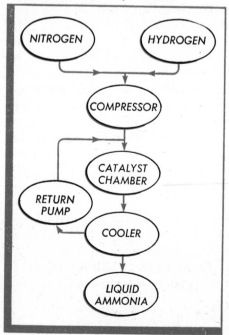

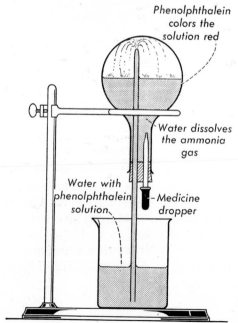

Phenolphthalein colors the solution red

Water dissolves the ammonia gas

Water with phenolphthalein solution

Medicine dropper

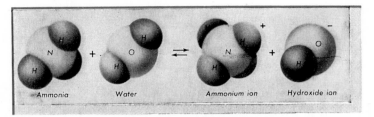

Fig. 30–9. Ammonia reacts with water to form ammonium ion and hydroxide ion.

bonds to the nitrogen atom in adjacent ammonia molecules. The polar nature of both water and ammonia molecules is also believed to be the reason for the high solubility of ammonia in water.

14. The chemical properties of ammonia. Gaseous ammonia does not burn in air, but it will burn in pure oxygen. At ordinary temperatures it is a stable compound, although it is decomposed into nitrogen and hydrogen at high temperatures. When ammonia is dissolved in water, most of the ammonia forms a simple solution. A small part of the ammonia reacts with water

and ionizes to NH_4^+ and OH^- ions.

$$NH_3 + H_2O \rightleftarrows NH_4^+ + OH^-$$

This mixture of molecules and ions is commonly called *ammonium hydroxide,* even though it is questionable whether NH_4OH molecules exist therein. A better name is *ammonia-water solution.* Ammonia-water solution is weakly basic.

We must not confuse the *ammonium ion,* NH_4^+, with the *ammonia molecule.* While the ammonium ion may act like a metallic ion such as sodium ion or potassium ion in its compounds, it

Fig. 30–10. The direct addition of synthetic ammonia to irrigation water is a useful method of supplying carefully regulated amounts of nitrogen to the soil. The process is called nitrogation.

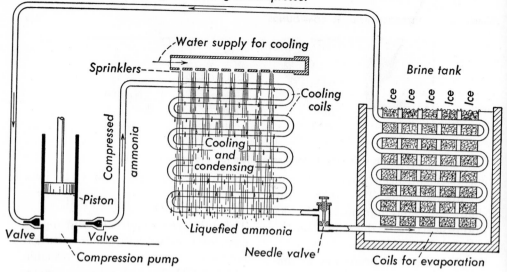

Fig. 30–11. The absorption of the heat needed to evaporate and expand the liquid ammonia lowers the temperature of the fresh water until it freezes to ice.

cannot be isolated as NH_4^+. All attempts to separate ammonium from ammonium compounds have resulted in the decomposition of the compound into ammonia and other products.

15. The uses of ammonia and ammonium compounds. *1. As fertilizers.* Ammonium compounds have long been used to supply nitrogen to the soil for growing plants. Recently, techniques have been worked out whereby ammonia can be used directly as a fertilizer. On irrigated land, carefully controlled amounts of ammonia are dissolved in the irrigation ditches. Ammonia dissolved in the irrigation water finally reaches the roots of the plants. Another method of adding ammonia gas to the soil employs a special plow with a hollow stem through which the ammonia passes into the bottom of the furrow. Blades attached to the back of the plow cover the furrow immediately, and the ammonia is buried beneath the surface.

2. As a cleaning agent. Ammonia-water solution makes a satisfactory cleaning agent because it is weakly

basic, emulsifies grease, and leaves no residue to be wiped up. The water and ammonia simply evaporate. Ammonia-water solution is used for cleaning windows and the surface of porcelain tile.

3. As a refrigerant. Ammonia is used in factories which make ice. A small compressor is used to liquefy ammonia gas, as shown in Fig. 30-11. The heat liberated during the compression of the gas is absorbed by water which flows down over the cooling and condensing coils. At this high pressure and lowered temperature, the ammonia liquefies. The cold, liquid ammonia then flows to a tank of brine in which are suspended the cans of fresh water to be frozen. As the liquid ammonia passes through a needle valve into coils of pipe immersed in the brine where reduced pressure is maintained, it evaporates and expands. This cools the brine to a temperature of about $-10°$ C, well below the freezing point of fresh water.

16. The operation of cold storage plants. In the operation of cold storage rooms, frozen food locker plants, or ice cream plants, brine is cooled by the evaporation of liquid ammonia, as in the making of ice. Then the cold brine is pumped through coils of pipes to the freezing and storage rooms. Just as hot water flowing through coils of pipe may warm a room, so cold brine flowing through a similar set of coils may cool a room.

17. Ammonia is used in gas refrigerators. In the gas-type refrigerator, a flame is used to heat a solution of ammonia in water so strongly that the ammonia gas is expelled from the solution. Since the ammonia gas is confined

in the apparatus, enough pressure develops to cause some of it to liquefy as it flows through coils where the heat of compression is absorbed. The liquid ammonia is then evaporated in a second set of coils which surrounds the freezing compartment. Finally it is redissolved in water and returned to be heated again.

18. Hydrazine is another compound of nitrogen and hydrogen. Hydrazine, N_2H_4, is produced by oxidizing ammonia-water solution with sodium hypochlorite. It burns readily, and finds considerable use as a fuel for rockets.

3. NITRIC ACID

19. The preparation of nitric acid. Two methods are commonly used to prepare this important acid.

1. From nitrates. Small amounts of nitric acid may be prepared in the laboratory by heating a nitrate with sulfuric acid. The reaction is carried out in a glass-stoppered retort because of the corrosive action of nitric acid on apparatus with rubber stoppers or rubber connectors. The equation for the reaction, using sodium nitrate, is

$$NaNO_3 + H_2SO_4 \rightarrow NaHSO_4 + HNO_3\uparrow$$

The nitric acid vapor is condensed in the side arm of the retort and collected in the receiver. Any nitrate may be used. We select sodium nitrate because it is an inexpensive one.

2. From ammonia. Wilhelm Ostwald (1853–1933), a German chemist, learned how to oxidize ammonia to nitric acid with the aid of a catalyst. This occurred about the same time that Haber developed the process for the synthesis of ammonia. These two processes fit together perfectly. Ammonia is made by synthesis from nitrogen and

hydrogen. The ammonia is then oxidized to nitric acid in another part of the same plant.

In the Ostwald process, a mixture of ammonia and air is heated to a temperature of 600° C. It is then passed through a tube containing platinum gauze, which serves as the contact catalyst. On the surface of the platinum, the ammonia is oxidized by the oxygen of the air to nitric oxide, NO.

$$4\,NH_3 + 5\,O_2 \rightarrow 4\,NO + 6\,H_2O$$

This reaction is exothermic and raises the temperature of the mixture of gases to about 1000° C. Now more air is mixed with the nitric oxide to oxidize it to nitrogen dioxide, NO_2.

$$2\,NO + O_2 \rightarrow 2\,NO_2$$

The nitrogen dioxide is cooled and absorbed in water, forming nitric acid.

$$3\,NO_2 + H_2O \rightarrow 2\,HNO_3 + NO\uparrow$$

The nitric oxide produced in this reaction is also oxidized to nitrogen dioxide and absorbed in water.

Today almost all of the nitric acid

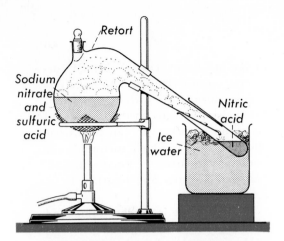

Fig. 30–12. Nitric acid may be prepared in the laboratory by the action of sulfuric acid on sodium nitrate.

used in industry is made by the oxidation of ammonia.

20. The physical properties of nitric acid. Pure HNO_3 is a colorless liquid, about 1.5 times as dense as water. It fumes in moist air and boils at 86° C. The 100% HNO_3 is unstable, and for that reason, the concentrated nitric acid of commerce is a 68% solution of HNO_3 in water. Such a solution boils at 120° C. A more dilute solution boils at a lower temperature, losing water, and becoming more concentrated.

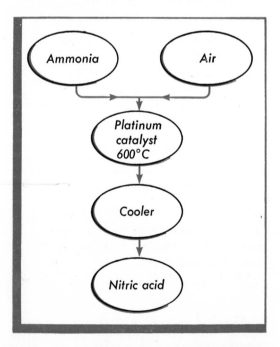

21. The chemical properties of nitric acid. *1. Stability.* Nitric acid is not very stable. When boiled, or even when exposed to sunlight, it decomposes to some extent. Water and nitrogen dioxide, NO_2, are two products of its decomposition. The deep yellow color of laboratory bottles of nitric acid is caused by small amounts of dissolved nitrogen dioxide which are formed when the acid is exposed to light. In water solution the acid is more stable. *Fuming nitric acid,* a very corrosive liquid, has a red color due to considerable amounts of dissolved nitrogen dioxide. It fumes in moist air and burns the skin painfully.

2. Acid properties. When *dilute,* nitric acid has the usual properties of acids. It reacts with metals and the oxides of metals. It reacts with hydroxides, forming salts known as *nitrates.*

Nitric acid stains the skin yellow, forming xanthoproteic (zan-thoh-proh-*tee*-ick) acid. It produces the same effect with any protein, and for that reason is used as a *test for proteins.* A drop of nitric acid added to a slice of hard-boiled egg white will show the test perfectly. The color deepens to a bright orange when ammonia-water solution is added.

3. As an oxidizing agent. The decomposition of nitric acid molecules furnishes oxygen which unites with various materials that may be in contact with the acid. Nitric acid is a powerful oxidizing agent. To illustrate, let us put 5 ml of fuming nitric acid in a test tube. Clamp the tube in a slightly inclined position. Now, with forceps, slide a loose plug of excelsior down into the

Fig. 30–13. Flow diagram of the Ostwald process for the oxidation of ammonia into nitric acid.

tube until it comes within an inch of touching the surface of the acid. When the acid is boiled, the excelsior is oxidized by the acid vapors. It burns within the tube with a brilliant glow.

CAUTION: *Be sure that the open end of the test tube is not directed toward anyone.*

Nitric acid may break up in a variety of ways. The concentration of the acid, the activity of the reducing agent that is mixed with it, and the temperature at which the reaction is carried out determine the products which will be formed. Under ordinary conditions, moderately dilute nitric acid is reduced to NO, nitric oxide. If concentrated nitric acid is reduced, NO_2, nitrogen dioxide, is the product. With other reducing agents and different conditions for the reaction, such other reduction products as N_2O, nitrous oxide, N_2, and NH_3 may be formed by the decomposition of nitric acid.

4. Action with metals. Nitric acid is such a vigorous oxidizing agent that hydrogen gas is *not usually* set free when we add this acid to common metals. If we use such active metals as sodium, calcium, or magnesium, *very dilute nitric acid* will react with them forming a nitrate and setting hydrogen free.

$$Mg + 2 HNO_3 \rightarrow Mg(NO_3)_2 + H_2\uparrow$$

With less active metals, such as zinc and copper, the hydrogen is oxidized to water. Copper reacts with cold, dilute nitric acid according to the following equation:

$$3 Cu + 8 HNO_3 \rightarrow$$
$$3 Cu(NO_3)_2 + 2 NO\uparrow + 4 H_2O$$

With concentrated nitric acid, copper reacts as follows:

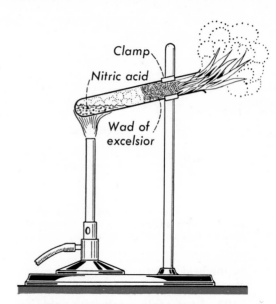

Fig. 30–14. Excelsior is oxidized very rapidly by boiling concentrated nitric acid.

$$Cu + 4 HNO_3 \rightarrow$$
$$Cu(NO_3)_2 + 2 NO_2\uparrow + 2 H_2O$$

Nitric acid does not react with gold or platinum because of the stability of these metals. It reacts with aluminum and iron very slowly, probably because of the formation of semi-protective surface coatings. When nitric acid reacts with a metal, the nitrate of that metal is usually formed. The nitrates of the various metals are crystalline compounds which are readily soluble in water.

22. The test for a nitrate. First, add 5 ml of the solution to be tested to a test tube. Then add an equal volume of a solution of ferrous sulfate, $FeSO_4$. Now, holding the test tube in an inclined position, add a few milliliters of concentrated sulfuric acid. You must add the acid so slowly that it will run down the inclined wall of the test tube very gradually and settle to the bottom, but not mix with the other mixture in the tube. If the solution being tested does contain a nitrate, a *brown layer* containing nitrosyl ferrous sulfate, $Fe(NO)SO_4$, will form at the junction

423

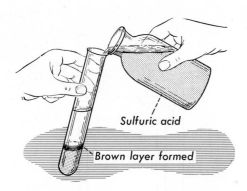

Sulfuric acid

Brown layer formed

Fig. 30–15. The brown layer formed when sulfuric acid is added slowly to a solution of ferrous sulfate containing nitrate ions, serves as a test for the nitrate ions.

of the acid and the other mixture (see Fig. 30-15).

23. Aqua regia reacts with gold. No single acid reacts with gold or platinum, but a mixture of nitric acid and hydrochloric acid will. Such a mixture of acids was named *aqua regia,* which means "royal water," by the early chemists because it reacts with gold, the king of metals.

The most common mixture of acids used for this purpose contains one part of concentrated nitric acid mixed with three parts of concentrated hydrochloric acid.

24. The uses of nitric acid. *1. For making nitrates.* These salts of nitric acid are made by treating either a metal or a metallic oxide with nitric acid.

2. For making dyes. There are several products obtained from coal tar with which nitric acid reacts to form *nitro compounds.* One of these is benzene with which nitric acid reacts to form nitrobenzene, $C_6H_5NO_2$. Aniline, $C_6H_5NH_2$, a compound used in making different dyes, is made by reducing nitrobenzene with hydrogen.

3. For making plastics. Cotton consisting mainly of cellulose, $(C_6H_{10}O_5)_n$, is treated with a mixture of nitric acid and sulfuric acid to make nitrocellulose plastics. A variety of products is formed, depending on the amount of nitric acid used, the temperature, and the length of time the acid is allowed to act on the cellulose. Manufacturers use sulfuric acid to absorb the water that is formed in the reaction. Celluloid, pyroxylins, and photographic film are made from such nitrocellulose plastics.

4. For making explosives. Practically all modern explosives are made directly or indirectly from nitric acid. The acid itself is not an explosive, but many of the compounds derived from it form the most violent explosives known. Among these are nitroglycerin, smokeless powder, and TNT.

4. EXPLOSIVES

25. Characteristics of explosives. *Explosives are compounds or mixtures which decompose suddenly and produce large volumes of gases.* Most explosives are nitrogen compounds which may be set off by: *1.* ignition; *2.* slight shock; and *3.* severe shock. Explosives are useful for blasting rock, digging ditches and tunnels, and many other uses. Their military value is well known. Terrible accidents have oc-

curred through the unintentional discharge of explosives. *It is never wise for inexperienced persons to handle them. And **under no conditions should an amateur ever try to make an explosive.***

26. Black gunpowder. Gunpowder is a mixture of 75 parts of potassium nitrate with 15 parts of charcoal and 10 parts of sulfur. Black gunpowder is set off by ignition. This explosive is used today in fireworks, for loosening coal in underground seams, and for making the ammunition used in hunting game.

27. Nitroglycerin and dynamite. Nitroglycerin is made by treating glycerol (glycerin) with a mixture of nitric and sulfuric acids. It is a dense, oily liquid that is extremely sensitive to shock. The slightest jarring may be sufficient to cause it to decompose with enormous force.

Dynamite is a solid mixture made by absorbing nitroglycerin in wood flour mixed with sodium nitrate. The dynamite is usually encased in cardboard cylinders to form "sticks." In this way the hazardous property of nitroglycerin is lessened, while its usefulness is retained. Dynamite is especially useful for blasting rock.

28. Smokeless powder. Smokeless powder, or nitrocellulose, is made by treating cellulose with nitric and sulfuric acids. It differs from nitrocellulose plastics in that the cellulose is more thoroughly nitrated.

When smokeless powder burns, the colorless products, carbon dioxide, carbon monoxide, water vapor, and nitrogen, are formed. Almost no smoke is produced. Hence the name "smokeless" powder.

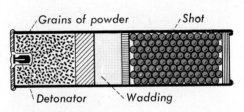

Fig. 30–16. Cross section of a shotgun shell such as is used for hunting game.

29. Shell-fillers and detonators. The explosive used inside an artillery shell must be able to stand the shock of the propellant which starts it on its course. It must also be capable of exploding with great force when it reaches its target. Explosives of this type, requiring severe shock to set them off, are called *shell-fillers.* Trinitrotoluene (try-ny-troh-*tol*-you-een), usually abbreviated TNT, is the most commonly used shell-filler for military purposes. Picric acid is also used as a shell-filler.

Detonators are extremely sensitive explosives which are set off by a shock and which decompose with almost incredible rapidity. They are used in small amounts in cartridges and shells to start the main explosion. Mercury fulminate is a well-known detonator. It is a very treacherous explosive that may be set off by heat, friction, or shock.

5. THE OXIDES OF NITROGEN

30. Five different oxides of nitrogen are known. Nitrous oxide has the formula N_2O; nitric oxide has the formula NO; dinitrogen trioxide, which is the anhydride of nitrous acid, is written N_2O_3; nitrogen dioxide has the formula NO_2; and dinitrogen pentoxide, which is the anhydride of nitric acid, has the formula N_2O_5.

31. The preparation of nitrous oxide. Nitrous oxide is prepared by gently heating ammonium nitrate, which decomposes into water and nitrous oxide.

$$NH_4NO_3 \rightarrow N_2O\uparrow + 2 H_2O$$

Nitrous oxide was formerly called "laughing gas" because of the mild hysteria it induces. Today it is mixed with oxygen and administered by dentists and surgeons as an anesthetic during brief operations. By mixing it with

Fig. 30-17. Small scale dynamite explosions such as the one shown here enable petroleum prospectors to map the underlying rock formations.

oxygen there are only slight aftereffects.

32. The properties of nitrous oxide. Nitrous oxide is a colorless gas which has a somewhat sweet odor and taste. It is about 1.5 times as dense as air and moderately soluble in cold water. It is easily liquefied, and is usually sold as a liquid compressed in steel containers.

At ordinary temperatures, nitrous oxide is stable, but it decomposes into oxygen and nitrogen when heated slightly. Even a glowing splint is likely to be hot enough to decompose the gas. Then the splint continues to burn almost as well as it does in oxygen. This is because the mixture of gases formed by decomposing nitrous oxide contains 1 part of oxygen to 2 parts of nitrogen and this is twice as rich as the proportion of oxygen to nitrogen in air, 1 to 4. We can distinguish nitrous oxide from oxygen because barely ignited, feebly burning sulfur is extinguished in nitrous oxide, although it burns more vigorously when thrust into oxygen. Vigorously burning sulfur continues to burn in either gas.

33. The preparation and properties of nitric oxide. Nitric oxide is produced naturally during a thunderstorm. We may prepare it for laboratory use by the reaction of dilute nitric acid on copper (see Section 21).

Nitric oxide is a colorless gas which is only slightly denser than air, and almost insoluble in water. Its most important chemical property is its ability to unite directly with the oxygen of the

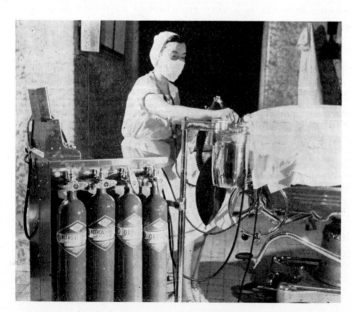

Fig. 30-18. Nitrous oxide is mixed with oxygen and administered as an anesthetic during minor surgical operations.

Fig. 30–19. The jar at the left contains colorless nitric oxide. When this gas is exposed to air, as at the right, it combines with oxygen to form reddish-brown nitrogen dioxide.

air to form nitrogen dioxide.

$$2 \, NO + O_2 \rightarrow 2 \, NO_2\uparrow$$

34. The uses of nitric oxide. Nitric oxide readily combines with oxygen from the air. The nitrogen dioxide that is formed will then give up oxygen in the presence of a reducing agent. Thus nitric oxide acts as a *carrier of oxygen*. It is used to convert sulfur dioxide to sulfur trioxide in the manufacture of sulfuric acid by the chamber process (see Chapter 28, Section 7).

35. Nitrogen dioxide. At ordinary temperatures the color of this gas is reddish-brown. Its density indicates a molecular formula, NO_2. It has a disagreeable, suffocating odor, and it is very poisonous. When cooled to lower temperatures, its color almost disap-

pears and its density increases markedly, showing that two NO_2 molecules have associated to form a molecule with the formula N_2O_4.

$$2 \, NO_2 \rightleftarrows N_2O_4$$

Nitrogen dioxide dissolves in water. It reacts with water, forming a mixture of nitrous and nitric acids. Nitrogen dioxide is one of the decomposition products of nitric acid. Because it gives up its oxygen readily to other substances, it is a vigorous oxidizing agent.

Summary

Nitrogen can be obtained from the air by fractional distillation, or by removing the oxygen with phosphorus or hot metals. Pure nitrogen is obtained by heating a mixture of ammonium chloride and sodium nitrite. Nitrogen is slightly less dense than air and only slightly soluble in water. Elementary nitrogen is rather inert. Nitrogen does not burn. It is difficult to make nitrogen unite with other elements and its compounds are not very stable. Under proper conditions, nitrogen can be combined with hydrogen to make ammonia. Nitrogen is nonpoisonous, but animals suffocate in it because of a lack of oxygen. The conversion of free nitrogen into nitrogen compounds is called nitrogen fixation. The nitrogen cycle occurs in nature over and over again.

Ammonia is formed by the decay of animal and vegetable matter. It is prepared by heating calcium hydroxide with an ammonium compound. It is obtained as a by-product in the destructive distillation of bituminous coal, or is made synthetically by the Haber process from nitrogen and hydrogen.

Ammonia is a colorless gas with a penetrating odor. It is less dense than air and is extremely soluble in water. Ammonia-water solution is weakly basic. The ammonium ion acts like a metallic ion and combines with negative ions to form salts.

Ammonia is used as a refrigerant. Ammonia-water solution is used as a cleaning agent. Ammonia and ammonium compounds are used as fertilizers.

Nitric acid is prepared in the laboratory by heating a mixture of sodium nitrate and sulfuric acid. Commercially, it is prepared by the oxidation of ammonia in the presence of a catalyst. It is a dense, colorless liquid. The pure acid is unstable, but a solution containing about 68% nitric acid is fairly stable. The concentrated acid is a vigorous oxidizing agent. It attacks metals, reacts with hydroxides, and forms salts called nitrates. Nitric acid is used for making nitrates, in the dye industry, for making nitrocellulose plastics, and for making explosives.

Explosives are compounds or mixtures which decompose suddenly and produce large volumes of gases.

Five oxides of nitrogen are known. Nitrous oxide is mixed with oxygen and used as an anesthetic during minor operations. Nitric oxide is used as a carrier of oxygen in the manufacture of sulfuric acid by the chamber process. Nitrogen dioxide is a good oxidizing agent.

Test yourself on these terms

ammonia	fixed nitrogen	nitrogen fixation
ammonium	fractional distillation	nitrogen-fixing bacteria
aqua regia	Haber process	nitroglycerin
azote	hydrazine	nodule
black gunpowder	hydrogen bond	Ostwald process
calcium cyanamid	laughing gas	protein
destructive distillation	niter	shell-filler
detonator	nitride	smokeless powder
dynamite	nitrocellulose	test for nitrate
explosive	nitrogen cycle	test for proteins

Questions

Group A

1. (a) Where do we find large quantities of elementary nitrogen? (b) In what kinds of compounds do we find combined nitrogen occurring naturally?

2. (a) Who first isolated relatively pure nitrogen? (b) Why was the gas given the name nitrogen?

3. (a) Write the balanced equation for the production of nitrogen from ammonium chloride and sodium nitrite. (b) Of what type of reaction is this an example?

4. What is meant by *nitrogen fixation*?

5. (a) What are two natural methods of nitrogen fixation? (b) Name two artificial methods.

6. Write a balanced equation for the reaction between calcium hydroxide and ammonium nitrate for producing ammonia.

7. (a) What is the purpose of high pressure in the Haber process? (b) What is the function of the catalyst?

8. Why is *ammonia-water solution* a better name for the solution of ammonia in water than *ammonium hydroxide*?

9. Why is a glass-stoppered retort used for the laboratory preparation of nitric acid?

10. Why may zinc be used with either hydrochloric or sulfuric acids for producing hydrogen, but not with nitric acid?

11. You are given a colorless solution of a salt. Tell how you would test it to determine whether the salt is a nitrate or not.

12. What is the difference between a detonator and a shell-filler?

13. (a) How is nitrous oxide prepared? (b) How is it administered as an anesthetic?

14. How could you prove that a metal is gold and not yellow brass?

Group B

15. What structural feature of the nitrogen molecule accounts for its stability?

16. How can you test a bottle of colorless gas to determine whether or not it is nitrogen?

17. Give two reasons why ammonia-water solution makes a good window cleaner.

18. What condition must be met for the reaction between sodium nitrate and sulfuric acid to run to completion?

19. Why can we remove oxygen from air by means of phosphorus without contaminating the air?

20. What must be the condition of the soil for nitrogen-fixing bacteria to be most effective?

21. What is the xanthoproteic test for proteins?

22. Why does concentrated nitric acid turn yellow in the laboratory?

23. Why might a farmer alternate crops of corn and lima beans on one of his fields in successive years?

24. Write three equations to show the steps in the production of nitric acid from ammonia.

25. The equation for the reaction of copper and dilute nitric acid indicates that nitric oxide is one of the products. Yet when we carry out this reaction in an evaporating dish, a dense reddish-brown gas billows over the rim of the dish. Explain.

★ 26. What is the oxidation number of nitrogen in: (a) NH_3; (b) N_2H_4; (c) N_2; (d) HNO_2; (e) HNO_3?

Problems

Group A

1. How many grams of ammonia will be produced by the reaction of steam on 160 g of calcium cyanamid?

2. What volumes of nitrogen and hydrogen are required for the preparation of 200 liters of ammonia?

3. If 15 g of HNO_3 is needed for a laboratory experiment, what weight of sodium nitrate is required for its preparation?

4. How many liters of nitrous oxide may be prepared by heating 400 g of ammonium nitrate?

Group B

5. What volume of nitrogen at S.T.P. can be prepared from a mixture of 10 g of NH_4Cl and 10 g of $NaNO_2$?

6. How many grams of nitric acid can be prepared from 50 g of potassium nitrate of 80% purity?

7. (*a*) What weight of cupric nitrate may be prepared from 254 g of copper by reaction with nitric acid? (*b*) What volume of nitric oxide is also produced?

Some things for you to do

1. Examine the roots of a clover plant and see if you can find the nodules that contain the nitrogen-fixing bacteria.

2. Test a sample of "household ammonia" and find the percentage of ammonia in the sample. Different brands may give interesting results. Burettes and acid of known normality can be obtained from the instructor.

3. React a piece of copper with concentrated nitric acid (outdoors). Note the vigorous action of concentrated nitric acid. Do not breathe the brown fumes that are produced, and be careful not to get the nitric acid on your fingers or clothing.

4. Under the supervision of your instructor you may make up a small quantity of aqua regia. Put a crumpled piece of gold foil in the aqua regia and observe the action. CAUTION: Use a hood or perform the experiment outdoors because the fumes evolved are poisonous. Do not get the acid on your skin or clothing.

Chapter 31   PHOSPHORUS, ARSENIC, ANTIMONY, AND BISMUTH

1. The Nitrogen Family of elements is Group VA of the Periodic Table. In addition to nitrogen, which we have already studied, this group consists of phosphorus, arsenic, antimony, and bismuth. The table below lists certain properties of all the members of this family.

In a family of non-transition elements, the metallic properties of the elements increase as their atomic number, atomic weight, and atomic size increase. This is shown most clearly by the elements of Group VA. Nitrogen and phosphorus are typical nonmetals. They show nonmetallic properties such

ELEMENT	ATOMIC NUMBER	ATOMIC WEIGHT	ELECTRON CONFIGURA- TION	PRINCIPAL OXIDATION NUMBERS	MELTING POINT, ° C	BOILING POINT, ° C	DENSITY, 15° C
NITROGEN	7	14.008	2,5	−3,+3,+5	−209.9	−195.8	1.25 g/l
PHOSPHORUS	15	30.97	2,8,5	−3,+3,+5	44.1	280.	1.82 g/cm³ (white)
ARSENIC	33	74.91	2,8,18,5	−3,+3,+5	814. (36 atm)	615. (sublimes)	5.73 g/cm³
ANTIMONY	51	121.76	2,8,18,18,5	−3,+3,+5	630.5	1380.	6.69 g/cm³
BISMUTH	83	209.00	2,8,18,32,18,5	−3,+3,+5	271.3	1450.	9.75 g/cm³

VOCABULARY

Alloy. A material composed of two or more metals.

Antifriction alloy. An alloy which reduces friction.

Fusible alloy. An alloy which has a low melting temperature.

Mordant. A substance which, by combining with a dye, produces a fast color in a textile fiber.

as covalent bonding with other atoms and being in the negative ions of acids. Bismuth is a typical metal in its properties. Its bonding with other elements is more ionic, and in solution it forms hydrated positive ions. Arsenic and antimony are intermediate in character, sometimes showing metallic properties and sometimes showing the properties of nonmetals.

Each of these elements has five electrons in its outer shell. Two of these electrons fill the first orbital of the outer shell. If the other three electrons are shared, the element has an oxidation number of +3. If the two electrons which already complete an orbital are also shared with two other atoms (as they may be in all the ele-

ments of this family but nitrogen) the element has an oxidation number of +5. Nitrogen and the other members of this family also attain an oxidation number of +5 by forming a double bond and two single bonds with three atoms. For example, the nitrate ion has the structure

$$\left[\ddot{\text{O}} \colon\colon \text{N} \overset{\circ}{\text{O}} \colon \atop :\ddot{\text{O}}: \right]^{-}$$

Nitrogen, surprisingly, is the most stable member of the family. This is due to the strength of the triple bond between the two atoms in a molecule. Phosphorus is so active that one form of it will catch fire spontaneously in the air. The other elements in the family will burn when we heat them in air.

1. PHOSPHORUS

2. The occurrence and discovery of phosphorus. Because phosphorus is such an extremely active element, it is not found free in nature. Its most important mineral source is rock phosphate, which is composed mostly of calcium phosphate, $Ca_3(PO_4)_2$. Extensive areas of rock phosphate are found in Florida, Tennessee, and other southern states. Scientists think these deposits have been produced from the accumulation of bones of prehistoric animals. The areas have supplied phosphate rock for the manufacture of fertilizer for years. Other deposits of rock phosphate have been discovered in the northern Rocky Mountains near Yellowstone Park, and in northern Africa. The bones and teeth of vertebrate animals contain calcium phosphate. Phosphorus, in the form of phosphates, is also found in protoplasm and nerve tissues, as well as in seeds and egg yolks.

Phosphorus was discovered in 1669 by Hennig Brand, a German alchemist. The name *phosphorus,* from a Greek word meaning "light-giver," was given to the element because it has the property of glowing in the dark.

3. The preparation of phosphorus. Phosphorus is prepared by heating a mixture of calcium phosphate, sand, and coke in an electric furnace. The mixture is fed into the furnace by means of a worm conveyor. An electric arc between the two electrodes near the bottom of the furnace produces the heat energy needed for the reaction. The following equations represent the action:

$$2\ Ca_3(PO_4)_2 + 6\ SiO_2 \rightarrow P_4O_{10} + 6\ CaSiO_3$$
$$P_4O_{10} + 10\ C \rightarrow P_4\uparrow + 10\ CO\uparrow$$

or, combining these two equations:

$$2\ Ca_3(PO_4)_2 + 6\ SiO_2 + 10\ C \rightarrow$$
$$6\ CaSiO_3 + 10\ CO\uparrow + P_4\uparrow$$

Fig. 31–1. The mining of an extensive deposit of phosphate rock in Florida.

The sand is used to combine with the calcium and form a calcium silicate slag which can be drawn off from the bottom of the furnace. The P_4O_{10} which is thus produced is reduced to elementary phosphorus by the coke. The P_4 vapors are conducted from the furnace and condensed under water. The molten phosphorus is run into molds where it solidifies in the form of sticks.

Phosphorus vapor, as well as liquid phosphorus and one of the solid allotropes, exists in the form of P_4 molecules. Frequently in equations, however, we represent phosphorus merely by its symbol, P, rather than by its molecular formula, P_4.

4. The properties of phosphorus. There are two important allotropic forms of phosphorus, *white phosphorus,* and *red phosphorus.* Their properties are so different that we shall discuss them separately.

1. White phosphorus. When phosphorus vapor from the electric furnace is condensed into a liquid and the liquid solidified, white phosphorus is produced. This is a waxy, translucent solid, with a density about twice that of water. White phosphorus is not the most stable allotrope of phosphorus at room temperature, and on standing acquires a lemon-yellow color because of partial conversion to the more stable red allotrope. White phosphorus melts at 44° C. But since its kindling temperature is only about 35° C, the melting must be done under water to prevent its combustion by contact with oxygen in the air.

Phosphorus is soft enough to be easily cut with a knife. It must always be cut under water to prevent the heat due to friction from kindling it. Phosphorus is insoluble in water, but white phosphorus dissolves readily in carbon disulfide and in oils.

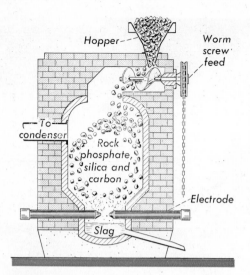

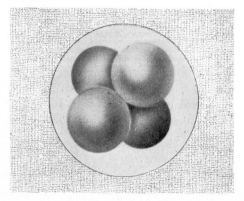

Fig. 31-2. Phosphorus is prepared from calcium phosphate in an arc-type electric furnace.

Phosphorus vapor and liquid and solid white phosphorus all consist of P_4 molecules. In these molecules each phosphorus atom forms covalent bonds with the other three atoms, as shown in Fig. 31-3.

White phosphorus oxidizes readily when exposed to the air, giving off dense fumes of P_4O_{10}. This compound is usually named diphosphorus pentoxide, corresponding to its empirical formula, P_2O_5, even though the molecules actually have the composition P_4O_{10}. If the oxidation of white phosphorus occurs in a dark room, a faint glow, or phosphorescence, can be seen. Phosphorus burns rapidly in air, and in oxygen with dazzling brilliancy.

Fig. 31-3. The structure of P_4 molecules of phosphorus.

White phosphorus can be changed to red phosphorus. To do this we heat it to a temperature of 250° C without access to air, and with a small amount of iodine as a catalyst.

CAUTION: *White phosphorus must never be handled with the fingers. It must be stored under water. It is exceedingly poisonous if taken internally.*

2. *Red phosphorus.* This allotropic form of phosphorus is a dark-red powder, believed to consist of molecules containing a large number of phosphorus atoms. It is slightly more than twice as dense as water, and insoluble in water or carbon disulfide. Pure red phosphorus is not poisonous, and it does not take fire when exposed to the air. If heated to its kindling temperature, about 250° C, it ignites and forms diphosphorus pentoxide as it burns. If heated without access to air to a temperature of about 290° C, it sublimes. White phosphorus is formed as it condenses.

5. The uses of phosphorus. Much phosphorus is converted into phosphoric acid, and its salts, the phosphates. Small quantities of phosphorus are used in making special alloys such as phosphor tin or phosphor bronze. The latter alloy is used for ship propellers, since it is not corroded by sea water. Most phosphorus, however, is used in two large industries: *1.* the match industry, and *2.* the fertilizer industry.

6. The manufacture of matches. Two types of matches are in common use: *1.* the friction match, which can be ignited on any rough surface; and *2.* the safety match, which can be ignited by rubbing it on a prepared surface.

1. The friction match. By the use of

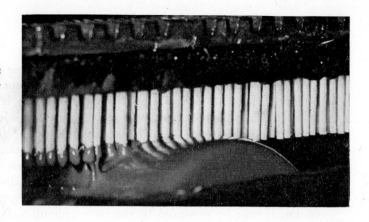

Fig. 31-4. A close-up view of safety match sticks passing over the composition dip roll.

continuous-operating machines, match sticks are first cut and then dipped into an ammonium phosphate solution. This prevents after-glow and lessens the danger of fire from careless handling of matches. The head end of the match is next dipped in melted paraffin. Then the first part of the head is applied. This consists of a paste containing glue, coloring matter, oxidizable matter such as sulfur, and an oxidizing agent such as potassium chlorate. The smaller portion of the head, called the tip, consists largely of phosphorus sesquisulfide, P_4S_3. When a match is struck, the heat produced by the friction ignites the tip. This, in turn, ignites the head, the paraffin, and finally the wood of the match itself. More than a million matches an hour can be made by one of the huge match-making machines.

2. *The safety match.* The head of a safety match contains antimony trisulfide, glue, and an oxidizing agent. The box upon which it is to be scratched is covered with a layer of red phosphorus, powdered glass, and glue. Such matches do not ignite easily unless rubbed against the preparation on the box itself.

7. The use of phosphorus in fertilizers. Calcium phosphate deposits are the main source of phosphorus for fertilizer. Rock phosphate itself is too insoluble to be of much value as a fertilizer, though it is being used to a small extent. Commonly, rock phosphate is treated with sulfuric acid to convert it to a more soluble material called *superphosphate*. Superphosphate contains an amount of available phosphorus equivalent to 18–20% diphosphorus pentoxide.

The demand for fertilizers richer in phosphorus has encouraged the production of enriched superphosphates (23–41% P_4O_{10}) and triple superphosphate (45–48% P_4O_{10}). These products are made by reacting rock phosphate with a mixture of phosphoric and sulfuric acids or with phosphoric acid alone.

Phosphorus in fertilizers is needed especially for raising seed crops such as corn.

8. The oxides and acids of phosphorus. If phosphorus burns in a limited supply of air, diphosphorus trioxide, P_4O_6, is formed. (Here again, the name given to the compound corresponds to its empirical formula, P_2O_3, even though the actual composition of the molecule is P_4O_6.) P_4O_6 is the anhydride of phosphorous acid. Diphosphorus pentoxide, P_4O_{10}, is a white solid formed by burning phosphorus in a plentiful supply of air or oxygen. It is

435

the anhydride of phosphoric acid. Its great affinity for water makes it useful for drying gases. It is also used in the manufacture of certain types of chemically resistant glassware.

Of the several acids formed by phosphorus, phosphoric acid, H_3PO_4, is the most important. It may be prepared by treating its anhydride, P_4O_{10}, with water. Or, it may be produced by the reaction of calcium phosphate and sulfuric acid.

$$Ca_3(PO_4)_2 + 3\,H_2SO_4 \rightarrow 3\,CaSO_4 + 2\,H_3PO_4$$

Phosphoric acid is used in the food, dyeing, pharmaceutical, and petroleum industries.

Phosphorous acid, H_3PO_3, metaphosphoric acid, HPO_3, and hypophosphorous acid, H_3PO_2, are best known through the usefulness of some of their salts.

9. Some useful salts of the acids of phosphorus. Since phosphoric acid is triprotic, it may form three different kinds of salts. For example, H_3PO_4 may ionize to furnish the $PO_4^{\equiv}$ ion, the $HPO_4^{=}$ ion, or the $H_2PO_4^{-}$ ion. It forms such salts as trisodium phosphate, Na_3PO_4; disodium hydrogen phosphate, Na_2HPO_4; or sodium dihydrogen phosphate, NaH_2PO_4.

Trisodium phosphate is used in washing powders as a water softener and detergent (cleansing agent). Ammonium phosphate is used for fireproofing. Monocalcium phosphate is used in one type of baking powder. Phosphates, as well as certain hypophosphites, are used in medicine. Sodium hexametaphosphate, $(NaPO_6)_6$, is used for softening hard waters. It has the advantage of softening hard water without leaving a precipitate in the water.

2. ARSENIC

10. The occurrence and preparation of arsenic. Some arsenic is found uncombined in nature. It is also found in ores containing arsenic and sulfur. It is prepared from these sulfide ores by roasting them to form oxides. These are then reduced with carbon to obtain metallic arsenic. Arsenic is also present as an impurity in many metallic ores. This arsenic is recovered from the chimney stacks of the smelters when these ores are processed. This is the most important source of arsenic in the United States.

11. The properties of arsenic. Metallic arsenic is a brittle, gray solid. When freshly cut, it has a bright metallic luster, but this rapidly tarnishes in moist air. It exists in three allotropic forms. Chemically it may act as a metal

and form oxides and chlorides. It may also act as a nonmetal and form acids which are analogous to those of phosphorus. When heated, arsenic sublimes and forms a yellow vapor, As_4, which has the odor of garlic.

When ignited, arsenic burns with a pale-blue flame and forms diarsenic trioxide, As_4O_6. (As was the case with the oxides of phosphorus, the name corresponds to the empirical formula, even though the actual formula is As_4O_6.) Arsenic unites indirectly with hydrogen to form arsine, AsH_3, a compound analogous to ammonia. Arsine is a deadly poisonous gas.

12. The uses of arsenic and its compounds. Metallic arsenic is little used. A small amount is added to lead used for making shot. It tends to harden the

Fig. 31-5. Dusting a field of cotton with calcium arsenate to reduce insect damage.

shot and make it more nearly spherical.

Diarsenic trioxide is used in making other compounds of arsenic. It is also used in making some kinds of glass. A third use is as a preservative of animal skins that are to be mounted. Some medicines contain small quantities of arsenic compounds.

CAUTION: *While very small amounts of arsenic have medicinal value, larger quantities are deadly.*

Arsenic compounds make excellent insecticides. Paris green, a compound of copper and arsenic, is used to destroy certain beetles and many other insect pests. However, it is now being replaced by the arsenates of lead and calcium. Enormous quantities of lead arsenate, $Pb_3(AsO_4)_2$, are used every year for spraying fruit trees and other plants. Calcium arsenate, $Ca_3(AsO_4)_2$, is also used as an insecticide.

3. ANTIMONY

13. The occurrence and preparation of antimony. Some antimony is found free in nature. Its most important ore is *stibnite,* a sulfide of antimony, Sb_2S_3. Antimony is usually prepared from stibnite by reduction with iron. While China has been the chief source of antimony, deposits in Bolivia and Mexico are now being developed. Very little antimony is found in the United States. Since the demand exceeds the supply,

most of the antimony used is imported.

14. The properties of antimony. Antimony is a dense, brittle, silver-white metal with a bright metallic luster. It is less active than arsenic, and exists in several allotropic forms. When strongly heated in air, antimony forms a white oxide, diantimony trioxide, Sb_4O_6. (Again the name corresponds to the empirical formula, not the actual one.) This compound is amphiprotic. It re-

Fig. 31–6. This slug of type metal contains antimony, tin, and lead.

acts with hydroxides to form antimonites, and with acids to form antimonous salts. Pure antimony is not affected by hydrochloric acid, but will react readily in aqua regia and form antimony pentachloride, $SbCl_5$. Antimonates, which are compounds analogous to the phosphates and arsenates, are also known.

15. The nature of an alloy. If two or more metals are melted together, an alloy may be formed. In some cases, the alloy seems to be a mixture of the metals. In a few cases, the proportion is definite, and a compound appears to have been formed. In still other cases, alloys contain interlocking crystals of the pure elements. In the majority of cases, the alloy is a solid solution of one or more metals in another metal.

An alloy may have properties unlike those of any of its constituents. Its properties may also be intermediate, somewhat like each constituent. Usually the melting point of the alloy is lower than the average melting point of its constituents. In many cases it is lower than the melting point of any one of them. This is easily explained when we remember that the melting point of a solution is lower than that of the pure solvent.

16. The uses of antimony. The metal from which the type used in this book was made contains antimony, tin, and lead. The antimony is important for type metal because it causes this alloy to expand when it solidifies. The edges of the type thus are sharp and distinct.

An antifriction alloy of lead and antimony is packed between the bearing surfaces of the moving parts of machinery. The friction of steel sliding over this antifriction alloy is much less than the friction of steel sliding over steel.

An alloy of lead and antimony is used for the plates in storage batteries. The addition of the antimony makes an alloy which is stronger and more resistant to acids than is lead alone.

17. Some compounds of antimony. Only a few of the compounds of antimony are used extensively. The sulfides are used in matches, and as pigments. Red rubber contains diantimony trisulfide. Tartar emetic, potassium antimonyl tartrate, $KSbOC_4H_4O_6$, is used to make a mordant in the dyeing of cotton goods. A mordant is generally

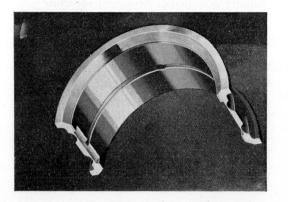

Fig. 31–7. An antifriction alloy is packed in a bearing to help reduce the friction produced when the shaft turns in the bearing.

an insoluble gelatinous material which fastens itself to the fibers of a fabric. When this mordanted cloth is later dyed, the dye in some way, perhaps by adsorption, unites with the mordant. Thus the mordant helps to make the dye fast.

CAUTION: *The soluble compounds of antimony are nearly as poisonous as the compounds of arsenic. Tartar emetic, $KSbOC_4H_4O_6$, containing antimony, must not be confused with cream of tartar, $KHC_4H_4O_6$, which is used in baking powder.*

4. BISMUTH

18. The sources, preparation, and properties of bismuth. Bismuth, which is found in certain regions of Bolivia and Canada, generally resembles antimony. However, it is denser and has a pinkish tinge. In the United States it is obtained principally as a by-product in the smelting of copper, lead, and zinc ores. Its acid-forming properties are less marked than those of antimony. It forms bases more readily. It exists in two allotropic forms.

19. The uses of bismuth. The chief use of bismuth is in the manufacture of fusible alloys. Two such alloys, Wood's metal and Rose's metal, melt at temperatures below that of boiling water. We have all seen the automatic valves used in sprinkler systems in factories, stores, and warehouses. If a fire starts, the fusible plug in the valve melts and releases the water automatically (see Fig. 31-8).

20. Some compounds of bismuth. If water is added to bismuth nitrate, $Bi(NO_3)_3$, hydrolysis occurs and $BiONO_3$ is formed. This compound is bismuthyl nitrate. It is used medicinally for relieving digestive disturbances. Bismuthyl carbonate is used for similar purposes. Other compounds of bismuth are used in paints and pottery glazes.

Fig. 31–8. These three photographs show how an automatic sprinkler system operates. Left: A fire starts in a rubbish can. The heat of the flames melts the fusible plug in the sprinkler system valve near the ceiling. Center: The water is released and sprays down over the burning rubbish, extinguishing the fire. Right: After the fire is extinguished, the master valve is shut off to stop the flow of water. Then the sprinkler valve is replaced, and the master valve reopened. Operation of an automatic sprinkler system prevents a serious fire and greatly reduces the damage from water which might result.

Summary

The Nitrogen Family consists of nitrogen, phosphorus, arsenic, antimony, and bismuth. As the elements of this family increase in atomic number, atomic weight, and atomic size, their properties undergo a transition from nonmetallic to metallic nature.

Phosphorus occurs in nature as calcium phosphate. It is extracted by heating the calcium phosphate with sand and coke in an arc-type electric furnace. Of the allotropic forms of phosphorus, white phosphorus and red phosphorus are most common. White phosphorus is active, even at room temperature. It burns with a hot flame, forming diphosphorus pentoxide. Red phosphorus is inactive at low temperatures. Phosphorus is used in making alloys, in the match industry, and as phosphates in fertilizers.

Arsenic is used for hardening shot. Its compounds are used in medicines and as insecticides.

Antimony is used in alloys. Its compounds are used in matches, as pigments, and to form mordants in dyeing.

Bismuth is used in the manufacture of fusible alloys. Its salts are used in medicine.

Test yourself on these terms

alloy	Paris green	safety match
antifriction alloy	phosphor bronze	stibnite
friction match	phosphor tin	tartar emetic
fusible alloy	red phosphorus	type metal
mordant	rock phosphate	white phosphorus

Questions

Group A

1. What is the principal mineral source of phosphorus?
2. What foods are important sources of phosphorus?
3. What precautions must always be observed when handling white phosphorus?
4. Why does white phosphorus become lemon-yellow on standing?
5. (a) How is white phosphorus converted to red phosphorus? (b) How can red phosphorus be changed to white phosphorus?
6. What are the two most important uses for phosphorus?
7. Give two uses for diphosphorus pentoxide.
8. Should the preparation of arsenic be classed as a product or a by-product of smelting operations?
9. Why must extreme care be exercised in handling arsenic and arsenic compounds?
10. Explain how fusible alloys are used in automatic sprinkling devices.
11. What is the function of a mordant in dyeing?
12. What bismuth compounds are used in medicine?

Group B

13. Describe the commercial production of phosphorus from rock phosphate.
14. (a) What is the formula for a molecule of solid white phosphorus? (b) Why do we usually not use this formula in equation writing?
15. Explain what happens when a friction match is struck.
16. Why are "safety" matches given this name?
17. Give the formulas and names of the three possible potassium salts of phosphoric acid.
18. (a) In what ways do metals form alloys? (b) How do the properties of an alloy compare with those of the metals of which it is composed?
19. Diphosphorus pentoxide is usually stored in glass, plastic-capped bottles, which have been sealed with wax. Why is this so?
20. How do the nonmetallic and metallic properties vary in the members of the nitrogen family?

roblems

Group A

1. How many pounds of phosphorus may be prepared from 620 lb of $Ca_3(PO_4)_2$ in an electric furnace?
2. What weight of calcium phosphate must be heated with sulfuric acid to produce 49 g of H_3PO_4?
3. Calculate the percentage composition of calcium arsenate.

Group B

4. How many grams of $SbCl_3$ can be prepared by the reaction of 10 g of antimony with chlorine?
5. Assume that P_4O_{10}, when used as a dehydrating agent, forms H_3PO_4 according to the following equation: $P_4O_{10} + 6 H_2O \rightarrow 4 H_3PO_4$. What weight of water can be combined with 50 g of P_4O_{10}?
6. A compound contains 96.15% arsenic and 3.85% hydrogen. Its vapor has a specific gravity, air standard, of 2.695. What is the formula of the compound?

ome things for you to do

1. Under the direction of your instructor, you may dissolve a piece of white phosphorus no bigger than a small match head in 5 ml of carbon disulfide. Lay a sheet of filter paper on an asbestos board, pour enough of the solution over it to moisten the paper, and stand back to await results. CAU-TION: *Keep flames away from carbon disulfide. Do not save any of the solution of phosphorus in carbon disulfide.*
2. Pour a small amount of a 5% solution of $CuSO_4$ over a small piece of burning phosphorus. Note that the phosphorus becomes incased in copper, which prevents further combustion. This technique is used in treating phosphorus burns.

Check your progress in chemistry

1. What are the principal chemical properties of the members of the Sodium Family?
2. What are the main differences in chemical properties between the elements of the Calcium Family and those of the Sodium Family?
3. What are the principal chemical properties of the members of the Halogen Family?
4. How do the reactions of oxygen and sulfur with metals compare with the reactions of the halogens with metals?
5. What property of the inert gases constitutes their chemistry?
6. In what important ways does the Nitrogen Family differ from both the Sodium Family and the Halogen Family?
7. What unusual property does carbon have that is not shown by any other element we have yet studied?
8. (a) In what way is hydrogen like the members of the Sodium Family? (b) Give several ways in which its behavior differs.
9. (a) What are the important gases of the air? (b) What is the percentage of each by volume in air?
10. Give several examples of striking changes in properties shown by common materials when chilled in liquid air.
11. What four conditions of the air are controlled by a complete air-conditioning unit?
12. Does the usefulness of the inert gases depend upon their physical properties or their chemical properties? Explain.
13. You are given some white crystals which the flame test shows is a sodium compound. How could you tell whether it is sodium chloride, sodium carbonate, sodium sulfite, or sodium nitrate?
14. For what purposes is elementary nitrogen used?
15. Describe the sequence of the various nitrogen compounds involved in the nitrogen cycle.
16. Draw electron-dot formulas for ammonia and ammonium ion.

Challenging your knowledge

1. Measure the length, width, and height of your chemistry laboratory in meters. Read and record the barometric pressure and the temperature. Calculate the weight of the air in the laboratory under your recorded conditions.
2. Why do you think Faraday failed to liquefy oxygen, hydrogen, and nitrogen, yet he was successful in liquefying chlorine and sulfur dioxide?
3. Why do steel companies often market ammonium sulfate for use as a fertilizer?
4. Why would you expect anhydrous ammonia to be a very poor conductor of electricity?
5. A laboratory bottle contains many small pieces of white phosphorus. How can you mold them into a single chunk?

UNIT
10

THE COLLOIDAL STATE

The term *colloid* was first used about a century ago to distinguish a group of substances which were observed to form suspensions rather than true solutions when placed in water. Today we know that particle size determines whether we have a colloidal suspension or a true solution. Thus we speak of the *colloidal state* of matter.

In the picture above you see a method of sorting solids with bubbles. Most of the energy foods we consume are colloidal. The living cell is colloidal in nature. The blue appearance of the sky, the white petals of flowers, and gray hair are due to colloidal dispersions.

Two chapters are included in this unit: *Colloidal Suspensions;* and *Suspensoids and Emulsoids.* A knowledge of the basic concepts of the colloidal state of matter will enable you to appreciate many of the processes of chemistry.

443

Chapter 32 COLLOIDAL SUSPENSIONS

1. THE COLLOIDAL STATE

1. What are colloidal suspensions? In 1861 a Scottish scientist, Thomas Graham (1805–1869), performed a series of experiments with starch, glue, and sugar in water. He enclosed these materials in parchment bags which he suspended in water, as in Fig. 32-1. He observed that substances that crystallize easily passed through the parchment readily. He called these materials *crystalloids.* Sticky substances, on the other hand (starch and glue in water), passed through the membrane hardly at all. He called these materials *colloids,* from the Greek word for glue. Sugar and salt form *true solutions* when added to water, because they are dispersed through the liquid as molecules or ions. Colloids only *appear* to go into solution when added to water. Actually, they are dispersed as particles larger than ordinary molecules, and are too large to pass through the parchment. Since Graham's time *the word* **colloid** *has been broadened to include any dispersion of particles of very small*

VOCABULARY

Adsorption. The concentration of a gas, liquid, or solid on the surface of a solid or liquid.

Colloidal state. A state of subdivision of matter ranging between the dimensions of ordinary molecules and microscopic particles.

Colloidal suspension. A two-phase system having dispersed particles suspended in a dispersing medium.

Dispersion. A scattering, or state of being scattered.

Emulsoid. A colloidal system in which there is a strong attraction between the dispersed substance and the dispersing liquid.

Suspensoid. A colloidal suspension in which there is little attraction between the dispersed substance and the dispersing liquid.

size that are larger than simple molecules. We still call such mixtures colloids, although they may not have anything to do with sticky substances such as those which Graham investigated.

Later investigations showed that some materials, under certain conditions, were nondiffusing and colloidal in behavior. Yet under different conditions, they were crystalline in nature. About 60 years ago enough evidence was available to prove that *the state of subdivision, rather than the chemical nature of a material, determined whether it formed a suspension or a true solution when dispersed in a second medium.* Sodium chloride may form a colloidal suspension if the sodium ions and chloride ions are brought together in a medium in which sodium chloride is not soluble.

A true solution is formed when a solute, as molecules or ions, diffuses throughout the solvent to form a homogeneous mixture. It consists of a *single phase*. The solute is said to be soluble in the solvent. *A **colloidal suspension**, on the other hand, is a two-phase system having dispersed particles rather than a solute, and a dispersing medium rather than a solvent.* The dispersed substance *(internal phase)* cannot be soluble in the dispersing medium *(external phase)*. It must consist of finely divided particles which remain suspended in the medium.

2. What is the range of colloidal size? The colloidal state has been called *the world of neglected dimensions*. It lies between true solutions which are homogeneous, and temporary mixtures which separate on standing. Colloidal size has no fixed limits. However, particles between molecular size and a size great enough to be seen

in the optical microscope are said to be colloidal. This includes particles with diameters ranging from 10 Å to 1000 Å. (The *Ångstrom* has been used in earlier chapters in describing the diameters of molecules; $1 \text{ Å} = 10^{-8}$ cm.) Ordinary simple molecules are only a few Ångstroms in diameter. The diameter of protein macromolecules may approach 100 Å and their molecular weights may be several hundred thousand. Viruses, known to be large protein molecules, may have molecular weights between one million and one billion. These macromolecular substances are well within the colloidal range.

If the size of the dispersed particles is at the lower limit of the colloidal range, a dispersion may begin to have the characteristics of a solution. As the size of the dispersed particles approaches the upper limit of the colloidal range, a dispersion may begin to show the properties of an ordinary suspension. Thus we see that there is no definite division between the true

Fig. 32–1. A colloidal dispersion is held back by the parchment membrane permitting it to be separated from substances in solution. The process is called dialysis.

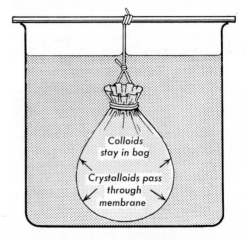

Colloids stay in bag

Crystalloids pass through membrane

COLLOIDAL DISPERSION	EXAMPLE
Liquid in gas	Fog, clouds
Solid in gas	Smoke
Gas in liquid	Whipped cream
Liquid in liquid	Cream, mayonnaise
Solid in liquid	Glue, India ink
Gas in solid	Floating soap, bread dough
Liquid in solid	Opal, jelly
Solid in solid	Ruby glass

solution and the colloidal state on one hand, and the colloidal state and the ordinary suspension on the other.

3. Types of colloidal suspensions. Since there are three (physical) states of matter—gas, liquid, and solid—we might assume that there are nine possible types of dispersions. But we know that all gases consist of simple molecules, and that molecules of one gas may mix completely in any proportion with the molecules of another gas. Therefore, disperse systems of *gas-in-gas* cannot occur. The eight possible types of colloidal systems are listed in the table above together with typical examples of each.

The properties of most colloidal systems fall into two general patterns of behavior. These depend primarily upon the relationship which exists between the internal and external phases.

1. Lyophobic (ly-oh-*foh*-bik) *systems.* Suppose we have a dispersion of

diarsenic trisulfide, As_2S_3, in water. Since water can disperse only a small amount of diarsenic trisulfide, *the concentration of the internal phase (the diarsenic trisulfide) is low.* The dispersed particles have negligible attraction for the water. Consequently this dispersion *has the same fluidity (viscosity) as pure water.* The particles of diarsenic trisulfide become negatively charged due to adsorption of hydroxide ions. If we add a solution of an electrolyte such as hydrochloric acid, *the dispersion coagulates and precipitates due to the loss of the charge.* The behavior of this diarsenic trisulfide dispersion is typical of *lyophobic colloids,* or **suspensoids.**

2. Lyophilic (ly-oh-*fih*-lik) *systems.* If we mix a relatively large amount of powdered gelatin in water and allow the dispersion to stand, it *"sets"* to form a firm *gel* or *jelly.* The dispersed particles of gelatin have a strong attrac-

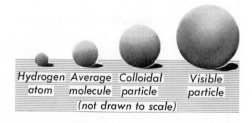

Hydrogen atom   Average molecule   Colloidal particle   Visible particle
(not drawn to scale)

Fig. 32-2. The colloidal range of particle size lies between that of simple molecules and visible particles.

tion for the dispersing medium (the water) and become thoroughly hydrated. This traps the water in such a way that *the viscosity of the system increases.* The relative concentration of gelatin is high and *small additions of solutions of electrolytes have little effect on the jelly.* The behavior of gelatin in water is typical of *lyophilic colloids,* or **emulsoids.**

Because of this significant difference between lyophobic colloids and lyophilic colloids, their characteristics and properties will be considered separately in Chapter 33.

Since the dispersed phase of colloidal systems consists of extremely finely divided particles, the surface area of this phase is enormous. Under such circumstances actions peculiar to "surface" will be most important. Therefore we must study some of the characteristics of surface behavior before we learn about specific colloidal suspensions. *This study of surface properties is called* **surface chemistry.**

2. SURFACE CHEMISTRY

4. The effect of subdivision on the properties of substances. Colloidal particles have a tremendous *specific surface.* **Specific surface** *is the ratio of the surface area of the particles to their volume.* If we divide a one-inch cube of soft clay across the middle of each face, we shall make eight smaller cubes (see Fig. 32-3). The surface area of the one-inch cube was 6 in². But the total surface area of the eight smaller cubes is 12 in². We have doubled the total surface area by this division but the total volume of material has remained the same. *Thus we have doubled the specific surface.* If we divide each of the half-inch cubes as before, we again double the specific surface. If we proceed in this manner until the original volume of material has been reduced to colloidal dimensions, the surface area will be more than 200 acres!

Fig. 32–3. The specific surface of a substance is increased when the surface area is increased and the volume remains constant.

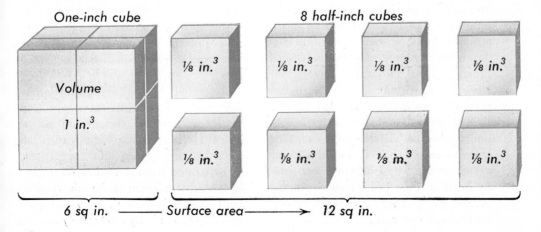

One-inch cube   8 half-inch cubes

Volume

1 in.³   ⅛ in.³   ⅛ in.³   ⅛ in.³   ⅛ in.³
           ⅛ in.³   ⅛ in.³   ⅛ in.³   ⅛ in.³

6 sq in. ——— Surface area ——→ 12 sq in.

When we produce this great increase in surface, we also produce a corresponding increase in the number of surface molecules, or ions, or atoms, as the case may be. Surface molecules are those which are no longer surrounded on all sides by molecules similar to themselves. This increase in the number of surface molecules is always accompanied by changes in physical properties and the appearance of new properties.

It is the appearance of these new properties with the subdivision of matter that truly defines the colloidal state. Changes may occur in solubility, melting point, heat of solution, and color of the subdivided material. With this vast increase in surface there appears a peculiar phenomenon called *adsorption.*

5. What is the nature of adsorption? *Adsorption* may be defined as the concentration of a gas, liquid, or solid on the surface of a liquid or solid with which it is in contact. The adsorption of a gas on a solid is sometimes referred to as *occlusion.* The material providing the surface upon which adsorption occurs is known as the **adsorbent.** The material adsorbed is called the **adsorbate.** Because of the tremendous surface of particles of colloidal dimensions, a remarkable amount of adsorption may occur. One volume of palladium black (finely divided palladium metal) will adsorb nearly 1000 volumes of hydrogen. A gas cylinder, first filled with activated charcoal and then with nitrogen under pressure, will discharge over 65% more nitrogen than it would without the charcoal. An adsorbent is *activated* by heating it to free its surface of adsorbed gases. Two aspects of adsorption must be stressed.

1. Adsorption is selective. This means that a given adsorbent will show a preference for one adsorbate over another. Activated coconut charcoal used in gas mask canisters will selectively adsorb most toxic gases in preference to oxygen and nitrogen even though the poisons may be present in the atmosphere in relatively minor proportions. In general, *gases of low volatility are adsorbed more readily than those of higher volatility.*

2. Adsorption is specific. The extent to which any substance is adsorbed under any given set of conditions depends on the physical and chemical natures of the adsorbent and adsorbate. We may, however, list two general rules which apply to cases of adsorption of gases on solids.

a. Effect of pressure. The adsorption of a gas on a solid will *increase* with *increase* in pressure.

b. Effect of temperature. Adsorption is *increased* as the temperature of a system is *decreased.*

6. Some practical applications of adsorption. We have already mentioned the use of activated charcoal in gas cylinders to store nitrogen, and in gas masks. Several different *adsorbents* may be used together with selected *absorbents* in gas mask canisters to provide protection against various combinations of gases which may be irritating or toxic.

Activated charcoal is used in liquefying gases, to obtain extremely high vacuums, and in the separation of gases. Helium is the least readily absorbed of any known substance. It may be separated from the other inert gases by permitting them to be adsorbed on cold activated charcoal. Activated alumina, Al_2O_3, made by moderately heating aluminum hydroxide, is an effective adsorbent for water vapor. It is useful for removing water vapor from various gases. Activated alumina is often used in the chemistry laboratory as a desiccant. A considerable saving in fuel is realized by passing air through silica gel prior to being forced into blast furnaces.

You have probably seen evidence of the adsorption of gases from the atmosphere on glass. Two pieces of glass tubing may be welded together by bringing them into contact in the flame of a Bunsen burner. The rise in temperature causes the gas molecules to be released from the glass surfaces. This enables the surfaces of the two tubes to make contact and cohere.

A liquid adsorbed on the surface of a solid is said to *wet* the solid. Water will wet clean glass but mercury will not. It is possible to float powders on water because of the slowness with which the particles adsorb water. This is the basis for *flotation processes* used in the concentration of ores. Diamonds are separated from *blue earth* by passing it over greased tables.

Exhausted oil sands have been made productive again by the addition of water or sodium carbonate solution. These are strongly adsorbed on the surface of the sand and displace more oil. Formations of glazes on pottery and of baked enamels on metals depend on the molten *frit* being adsorbed on the surface and remaining there after it cools.

The relative sizes of two solids seems to determine which is adsorbed on the other. If one is much finer than the other the finer will be adsorbed on the coarser. If the two solids are of different colors, the mixture will have the

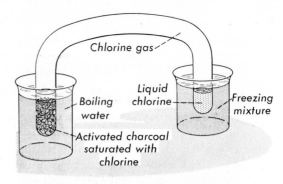

Fig. 32–4. Liquefaction of chlorine. Adsorbed chlorine is released as the temperature of the charcoal is raised; the pressure of the chlorine gas increases and the liquid chlorine forms in the upper end of the tube.

color of the one adsorbed. This fact is taken into account in the manufacture of paints.

Slow-setting cement consists of finely powdered gypsum which is adsorbed on the coarser cement particles. Manufacturers of chewing gum have made use of the fact that the first taste of a mixture of sugar and paprika is very sweet

Fig. 32–5. Hydrogen electrode, the standard reference electrode for the electrochemical series.

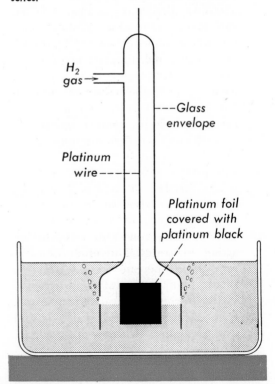

if the sugar in the mixture is very finely powdered.

★ *A hydrogen electrode* may be used as a reference electrode in an electrochemical cell. A layer of platinum so finely divided that it will not reflect light, and thus is *black,* is deposited on a platinum wire or foil by electrolysis. The electrode is then placed in the solution and hydrogen gas is passed over it. Hydrogen is adsorbed on the relatively great surface of the platinum black. Thus, in effect, the electrode presents a surface of hydrogen to the solution and acts as a "metallic" hydrogen electrode. The hydrogen electrode provides chemists with a direct method of determining the pH of solutions. An electrochemical series such as that shown in Chapter 23, Section 6, is compiled using the hydrogen electrode as a reference.

7. Contact catalysts are important in industry. Many reactions are brought about, or speeded, by contact with the surface of certain solids. As these solids are not permanently altered by the reactions in which they are involved we may consider them to be catalytic agents. Due to the nature of the catalytic action they are known as *contact catalysts* or simply **contact agents.**

If we subdivide even a minute quantity of the catalyst to colloidal size, it will present a very great surface area to the reacting substances. The reactants are then adsorbed on the surface of the contact agent. Thus we effect an increase in the concentration of the reacting substances. This produces a corresponding increase in the reaction speed. Many chemical industries are vitally interested in catalytic research. Consequently, catalytic agents, as well as the way in which they are used, are sometimes closely guarded trade secrets.

In the Haber process for the synthesis of ammonia, a contact agent, usually iron with the oxides of aluminum and potassium, is necessary to make the process economically feasible. Platinum gauze is employed as a contact agent in the synthesis of nitric acid by the Ostwald process. Finely divided vanadium pentoxide, or platinum, is similarly used in the contact process for manufacturing sulfuric acid.

The hydrogenation of vegetable oils to form solid fats is accomplished by using colloidal nickel. The semisolid vegetable shortenings used in many American homes are partially hydrogenated products from such liquid fats as cottonseed oil. The complete hydrogenation forms hard, brittle fats. Methanol is sometimes referred to as wood alcohol because it was originally produced by the destructive distillation of wood. Methanol is now made commercially by synthesis from carbon monoxide and hydrogen in the presence of zinc chromite.

8. How may catalytic poisoning occur? Chemical reactions involving the use of contact catalysts must be very carefully controlled. The presence of even slight amounts of certain foreign substances may seriously retard, or even stop, the chemical action. Chemists believe that these materials are preferentially adsorbed on the surface of the contact agent. Thus they prevent the molecules or ions of the reactants from reaching the surface of the catalyst. Such substances are known as *catalytic poisons.* Partial poisoning of a catalyst may be deliberately induced as a means of controlling the activity of a contact agent.

Summary

A colloidal suspension is a two-phase system consisting of a dispersed phase and a dispersing medium. The dispersed substance is known as the internal phase, and the dispersing medium is known as the external phase. Colloidal systems are characterized by insolubility rather than solubility as in true solutions. The colloidal state is one of subdivision rather than chemical nature.

Colloids fall into an intermediate position between molecular size and visible size, and range in diameters from 10 to 1000 Ångstroms. There is no fine line of demarcation between solutions and colloidal suspensions, and between colloidal suspensions and temporary suspensions.

Colloidal suspensions may be grouped into two general systems depending on the relationship between the internal and external phases. These are called lyophobic colloids, or suspensoids, and lyophilic colloids, or emulsoids.

The subdivision of materials results in a great increase in specific surface. Adsorption is a surface phenomenon of prime significance in the realm of colloids. Adsorption is both selective and specific. The adsorption of a gas on a solid is known as occlusion. Occlusion is influenced by both temperature and pressure. There are many practical applications of adsorption throughout the chemical industry.

Contact catalysts may be colloidal in nature. By occlusion, the concentration of gaseous reactants may be increased, resulting in a corresponding increase in reaction speed. Catalytic poisoning may result from the presence of slight amounts of impurities. Poisoning of a catalyst may be deliberately induced to retard or stop a reaction.

Test yourself on these terms

activated	colloidal suspension	internal phase
adsorbate	contact agent	lyophilic colloid
adsorbent	dispersed particles	lyophobic colloid
adsorption	dispersing medium	occlusion
catalytic poison	dispersion	specific surface
colloid	emulsoid	surface chemistry
colloidal state	external phase	suspensoid

Questions

Group A

1. What is the colloidal range of particle size?
2. Name eight possible types of colloidal suspensions.
3. Why is it not possible to have a colloidal suspension of a gas in a gas?
4. List three characteristics which are typical of lyophobic colloids.
5. List three characteristics typical of lyophilic colloids.
6. Distinguish between a true solution and a colloidal suspension.

7. Distinguish between the *internal* phase and the *external* phase of a colloidal system.

8. (*a*) What is the meaning of *specific surface?* (*b*) What is the relationship between the specific surface and the extent of subdivision of a substance?

9. Distinguish between *adsorption* and *absorption*.

10. How is an adsorbent activated?

Group B

11. What distinction did Graham make between *crystalloids* and *colloids?*

12. Explain why we now consider the colloidal state to depend on the subdivision rather than the chemical nature of a substance.

13. How can you account for the changes in physical properties and the appearance of new properties which accompany the subdivision of a substance to colloidal dimensions?

14. What conditions of temperature and pressure would you maintain if you were interested in causing a large volume of a gas to be adsorbed on a solid?

15. How would you treat a lump of charcoal in preparing it to act as an adsorbent for a gas?

16. Explain why an army gas mask is effective in removing poison gases from the air breathed by the soldier wearing it.

17. A solid which is more dense than water may be floated on the surface of the water if it is first reduced to a fine powder. Explain.

18. Given two solids each capable of adsorbing the other, what determines which will be adsorbed on the surface of the other when they are mixed?

19. Explain how a contact catalyst may act to bring about or speed up a chemical reaction.

★ 20. Explain how a hydrogen electrode is formed.

Some things for you to do

1. Prepare a demonstration illustrating different types of colloidal suspensions. Improvise from materials which are readily available. Your instructor may be able to provide you with some tested demonstrations.

2. Prepare a colloidal suspension of ferric hydroxide in water by adding dropwise a small amount of ferric chloride solution to boiling water. Place in a cellophane bag suspended in a beaker of water. Place a solution of cupric sulfate in a second bag similarly suspended in a beaker of water. Observe over a period of several days. How can you account for the difference in behavior you observe?

Chapter 33 SUSPENSOIDS
AND EMULSOIDS

1. SUSPENSOIDS

1. The characteristics of suspensoids. *Lyophobic colloidal systems* are distinguished by the negligible attraction of the dispersed particles for the dispersing medium. The internal phase (dispersed particles) adsorbs very little of the external phase (dispersing medium). Thus the viscosity of the system remains about the same as that of the dispersing medium. Such systems are called *suspensoids.*

Several different media are used for suspending the colloidal particles. When water is the suspending medium the term *hydrosol* is used. Thus a colloidal dispersion of metallic gold in water is called a gold hydrosol. *Organosol* indicates that an organic liquid

VOCABULARY

Aerosol (*a*-er-oh-sol). A suspensoid in which gas is the dispersing medium.

Biocolloid. Lyophilic colloidal systems existing within plant and animal organisms.

Gangue (gang). Worthless rock or vein matter in which valuable minerals occur.

Gel (jel). A jelly-like mass consisting of a colloidal suspension of a liquid in a solid.

Hydrosol (*hy*-droh-sol). A suspensoid in which water is the dispersing medium.

Organosol (or-*gan*-oh-sol). A suspensoid in which an organic liquid is the dispersing medium.

Protective agent. A colloidal substance which when adsorbed on suspended particles stabilizes the system.

Scattering. The deflection of rays of light sidewise by particles of suspended matter.

Solvation (sol-*vay*-shun). The adsorption of molecules of the dispersing liquid by dispersed particles.

Ultramicroscope. A microscope in which the object is illuminated at right angles to the optical axis of the microscope.

Fig. 33–1. A suspensoid is produced in which air is the dispersing medium when we use an aerosol bomb. The propellent is "Freon."

makes up the external phase. *Aerosol* is the term applied to suspensoids in which a gas is the dispersing medium. This type of suspensoid is produced when we release insect killer from a spray bomb.

2. The properties of suspensoids. We have already learned that the particle sizes range between the molecular or ionic dimensions of true solutions and the visible size of coarse suspensions. The size of the colloidal particles, together with the resulting vast specific surface, is responsible for the unusual properties of colloidal dispersions. Some of these properties are:

1. Brownian movement. In 1827 Robert Brown, an English botanist, observed the haphazard motion of pollen dust in water while viewing the suspen-

sion through his microscope. He suspected that the motion was in some way associated with the life process. But when he examined other suspended materials, which could in no way be related to living matter, he observed similar motion.

With the invention of the *ultramicroscope* about 1900 by the German chemist Richard Zsigmondy (1865–1929), the colloidal range could be studied directly. Brownian movement was rediscovered by Zsigmondy in a gold hydrosol, a suspension of colloidal gold in water. He described the astonishing motion of the tiny gold particles as "a swarm of dancing gnats in a sunbeam." Careful investigations have eliminated all possible outside factors as the cause of these random motions. *Thus we may conclude that the forces which act upon the dispersed particles are the result of collisions between these particles and the molecules of the dispersing medium.* This offers an excellent proof of the kinetic theory of matter.

We see here the *first* of three general reasons why colloidal suspensions do not settle. *The influence of gravity is not great enough to overcome the collision forces of the dispersing medium on particles which show Brownian movement.* Consequently they do not settle. A gold hydrosol prepared by Michael Faraday over one hundred years ago still exists as a colloidal suspension. We shall learn about the two remaining reasons for the stabilization of colloidal suspension later in this chapter.

2. Tyndall effect. If we shine a beam of light into a darkened room we see that there is a surprising amount of dust suspended in the air of the room. Rays of light are deflected sidewise, or

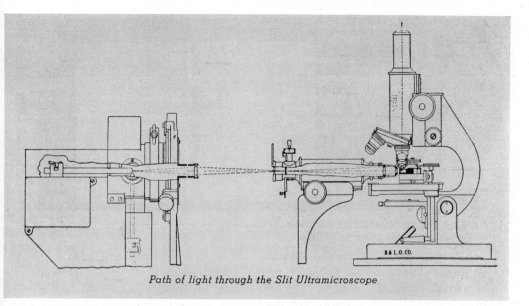

Path of light through the Slit Ultramicroscope

Fig. 33–2. The ultramicroscope enables us to observe the light scattered by colloidal particles too small to be seen with the ordinary microscope.

are *scattered*, from the surfaces of the dust particles. If the particles responsible for the scattering are extremely small, the scattered light will be somewhat bluish. Smoke suspended in air sometimes appears blue. Distant haze usually has a bluish tint. The blue sky and, in certain instances, the blue color of bodies of water are due to the scattering of light.

Let us direct a strong beam of light through a true solution, or through pure water, in a darkened room. We see little evidence of scattering. The beam is practically invisible. When we pass the light through a colloidal dispersion, however, the beam is plainly visible. The scattering is caused by the colloidal particles. This diffusion of light by colloidal particles is known as the **Tyndall effect,** after the English physicist John Tyndall (1820–1893). It may be used to detect the presence of suspended particles.

Fig. 33–3. The Tyndall effect produced by searchlights at night over Hollywood, California.

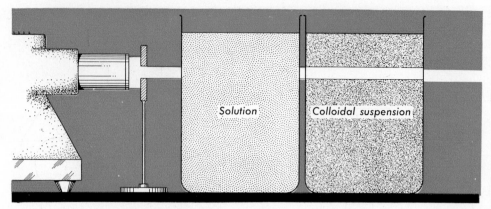

Fig. 33–4. The Tyndall effect is quite evident in the colloidal suspension on the right. The true solution on the left shows little scattering of light.

3. Structural colors. A physical chemist might classify all colors under two headings: *pigment* colors and *structural* colors. Pigment colors are due to the absorption by the pigment of some portions of the white light illuminating a substance. The color we observe is the complement of that absorbed. Colored inorganic substances generally contain elements found in the central region of the Periodic Table. The halides of the Sodium and Calcium Families are colorless. Anhydrous cupric sulfate is not colored. But water solutions prepared from anhydrous cupric sulfate or from the crystalline hydrate, $CuSO_4 \cdot 5\,H_2O$, are blue. Observe that it is the $Cu(H_2O)_4^{++}$ ion that is colored. Scientists believe that pigment colors are associated with the electronic arrangement of particles.

Structural colors, on the other hand, are due to the physical structure of the mass. They are not dependent upon the electronic configuration of the substance. The color of colloidal suspensions is usually structural. There is no blue pigment in the blue feathers of birds. Tiny air bubbles dispersed throughout the solid matter of the feathers are responsible for the scattering of light. There are no pigments present in the irises of blue eyes. Green

and gray eyes result from the combined effect of structural blue color, and yellow and brown pigments. The eye of the albino lacks both structural and pigment colors.

A very dilute solution of $FeCl_3$ possesses a faint yellow pigment color due to the hydrated ferric ion. If such a solution is boiled, colloidal $Fe(OH)_3$ is formed, resulting in a rich deep-red structural color. The quantity of iron present remains the same.

4. Electrical charge. Scientists have learned that the dispersed particles of lyophobic colloids are electrically charged while in a stable system. Some types possess positive charge and others negative charge. However, within a system all suspended particles have the same kind of electrical charge. Since particles with like charge repel each other, their mutual repulsion prevents them from joining together and finally settling out. Thus the system tends to remain stable. Here we have our *second* reason why colloidal suspensions do not settle: *The accumulation of similar charges on the suspended particles holds them apart thus stabilizing the system.*

How do the suspended particles acquire their charge? The charge is generally acquired by adsorbing positive or negative ions from the dispersing medium. The external phase will have the charge opposite to that on the dispersed particles. The system as a whole will be neutral. Most colloidal metals, sulfides, and acid dyestuffs acquire a *negative* charge. Most colloidal oxides and hydroxides of metals and basic dyestuffs become *positively* charged. Proteins appear to gain either a positive or a negative charge with equal ease.

We should expect such colloidal dispersions to be *precipitated* by the addition of solutions having a high concentration of ions of charge opposite to those which are adsorbed. An interesting result of this action is the formation of deltas at the mouths of large rivers. Colloidal sediment suspended in the river water flowing into the sea is precipitated by ions of the salt water. Fresh water is less dense than sea water. Thus, when fresh water first encounters the sea water, it fans out over the sea water in a surface layer. The deposition of the precipitated silt and clay eventually produces a fan-shaped delta. The large delta at the mouth of the Mississippi River is the result, in part at least, of this action.

3. How may suspensoids be prepared? The colloidal state is dependent upon the size of the suspended particles. There are two general methods by which particles may be brought to colloidal size: *1. The size of solute particles, which is below the colloidal range, may be increased.* This is known as **condensation.** *2. The size of visible particles, which is above the colloidal range, may be reduced.* This is known as **dispersion.**

1. Condensation of solute particles to colloidal size may be accomplished by hydrolysis, oxidation, or reduction reactions. Very rapid precipitation or crystallization in an insoluble environment may produce colloidally suspended microcrystals of the solute. Colloidal ferric hydroxide is prepared by the hydrolysis of ferric chloride in hot water.

$$Fe^{+++} + 3 H_2O \rightarrow Fe(OH)_3 + 3 H^+$$

Colloidal gold may be prepared by adding a reducing agent such as stannous chloride or ferrous sulfate to a dilute solution of gold chloride.

$$2 Au^{+++} + 3 Sn^{++} \rightarrow 2 Au^0 + 3 Sn^{++++}$$

The color of the gold hydrosol which results depends on the size of the gold particles but is usually purple.

If we add hydrogen peroxide, an oxidizing agent, to a water solution of hydrogen sulfide, sulfur is precipitated according to the following reaction:

$$H_2S + H_2O_2 \rightarrow S + 2 H_2O$$

We find, however, that the particles of sulfur are colloidal when we attempt to filter the suspension. The sulfur particles pass through the filter paper along with the water. Frequently, colloidal suspensions formed by condensation methods interfere with analysis procedures since ordinary filtration does not remove the precipitated material.

2. The *dispersion* method of producing colloidal particles may involve the use of an electric arc, purely mechanical methods such as grinding, shaking,

Fig. 33–5. Bredig arc. Less active metals may be used to form hydrosols. More active metals may be used to form organosols.

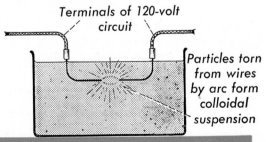

Terminals of 120-volt circuit

Particles torn from wires by arc form colloidal suspension

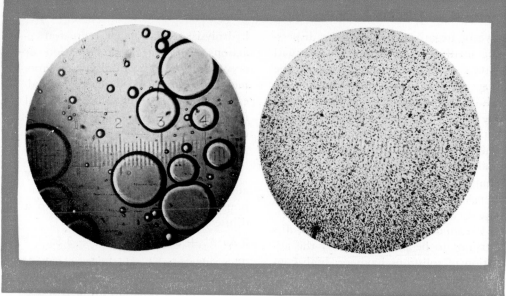

Fig. 33–6. Left, an emulsion of oil in water produced by an ordinary mixer. Right, the same emulsion after passing through a colloid mill.

or homogenizing, or the addition of a third substance. We may produce an electric arc under water by momentarily placing two energized conductors together and then separating them slightly so as to maintain the arc. If the conductors are made of gold, a purple gold dispersion will result from the disintegration of the ends of the electrodes within the arc. In a similar manner platinum electrodes will yield a brownish-black dispersion, and silver a brownish-green dispersion.

Many grinding and powdering operations are carried out in the chemistry laboratory with a mortar and pestle. Coarse particles may be reduced in size to such an extent that some colloidal suspensions may be prepared in this way. In commercial operations, large grinding and shearing machines are used to break down coarse particles to the desired colloidal size. Such machines are known as **colloid mills.**

Cement manufacturers know that the final hardness of concrete will depend largely on the fineness of the cement particles used. Thus they employ colloid mills to reduce cement particles to colloidal size. Colloidal dispersions may be produced by introducing the coarse particles and the dispersing medium into the colloid mill together.

Suppose we shake a few drops of oil with water in a test tube. The oil will be broken down into tiny droplets which remain suspended for a short time in the water before coalescing and rising to the surface. If these oil droplets are made much smaller, we can delay their separation from the water considerably. Milk is *homogenized* by breaking down the fat globules into particles of such small dimensions that they do not readily join together. Thus they do not rise to the surface as cream.

Colloidal dispersions are sometimes prepared by adding a third substance to the system. This substance acts upon the particles and reduces them to colloidal dimensions. Such a substance is called a *peptizing agent* and the process is known as **peptization**. Certain of the pre-digestive processes involve peptization.

4. Precipitation of suspensoids. The formation of river deltas by the introduction of an opposite electrical charge into a colloidal dispersion has already been mentioned. In the manufacture of soap, the product is formed in the colloidal state. The soap is precipitated, or *"salted out,"* by adding sodium chloride to the suspension. The salting-out process is frequently used in the precipitation of proteins. The opposite charge of ferric hydroxide and diarsenic trisulfide suspensions results in the precipitation of both when they are mixed.

Acids are sometimes used as coagulating agents. The milky colloid called *latex*, which is obtained from the rubber tree, is coagulated by the addition of acetic acid. Ammonia water, on the other hand, will act to prevent coagulation of the latex.

Heat will coagulate some colloids. If we boil the colloidal dispersions produced during chemical analysis we may cause the internal phase to coagulate. Then we can remove it by ordinary filtration. We coagulate egg albumin, a lyophilic colloid, by hot water or hot grease when we poach or fry eggs.

5. What is the Cottrell precipitator? In various manufacturing processes large volumes of smoke, dust, and mist were formerly expelled into the air. These waste products were a nuisance to people who lived near the factories. Certain smelters (plants for extracting metals from their ores) gave off chimney dust containing diarsenic trioxide, a poisonous compound. This dust was scattered by the wind, and some eventually settled on pas-

ture lands. Cattle were poisoned. The smelter operators were confronted with a serious problem which they solved by using the Cottrell precipitator.

Dr. Frederick G. Cottrell (1877–1948), an American chemist, devised a means of precipitating colloidal dust using high voltage electricity. The dispersed particles in the waste gases are passed into a high potential electrostatic field before reaching the flue or smoke stack. Here they acquire an electrical charge. As charged particles they are attracted to a collecting electrode. They are discharged and deposited as dust in the bottom of the precipitator.

In some cases the precipitated dusts contain valuable by-products. Thus the diarsenic trioxide from flue dust is used in making insecticides. Potassium salts are removed from the dust of cement kilns, and acid mists are recovered from sulfuric acid plants.

Fig. 33–7. The Cottrell precipitator is used to recover suspended particles from stack gases.

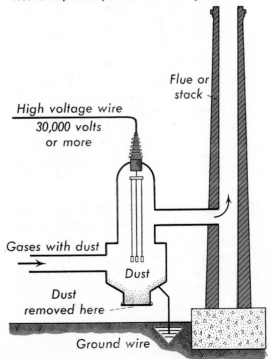

These are just a few examples of the economic importance of Cottrell precipitators. Today there is little excuse for air pollution in industrial areas because of the discharge of dust, smoke, or mists from factory chimneys.

Precipitators operating on the same general principle are available for home use. Dust, pollen, and other objectionable suspended particles may be removed from the air in the home. This helps reduce house cleaning. It also provides relief to those who suffer from allergies caused by pollen in the air. Dust filters, made of spun polyethylene are now available which acquire an electrostatic charge as a result of the passage of air through them. They are more effective in removing suspended particles than the disposable filters normally used in air conditioners and heating systems.

6. Protective colloids. In some colloidal systems the precipitation of the internal phase may be prevented by the addition of a second colloid known as a *protective agent*. When a pharmacist prepares an emulsion he triturates the oil and the dispersing medium with gum arabic or gum tragacanth. The protective agent is adsorbed on the surface of the dispersed particles. This coats them and prevents actual contact and subsequent coagulation. Here we have the *third* reason why colloidal suspensions do not settle: *a protective layer of adsorbed material stabilizes the suspended particles.*

Gelatin added to milk tends to prevent curdling. When we add it to an ice cream mix, it prevents the formation of objectionable ice crystals. This produces a smoother product. A protective colloid such as glue is added to electroplating baths to secure a smooth-

er surface. Glue or starch added to boiler water acts to prevent the deposition of scale.

Detergents (cleaning agents) are used to stabilize grease and water emulsions. A detergent molecule has a long hydrocarbon portion and an ionic portion. The hydrocarbon part of the molecule is insoluble in water but is soluble in oils. The ionic part is insoluble in oils but is soluble in water. A small amount of soap added to water forms a colloidal suspension. The hydrocarbon ends of groups of detergent molecules cluster together leaving the ionic ends in contact with the water. If grease or oil is introduced, and the system is agitated, the oil droplets are stabilized by the detergent as a colloidal suspension of oil in water. In this condition the grease or oil is easily floated away.

Mayonnaise is salad oil colloidally dispersed in vinegar. Egg is added as an

Fig. 33–8. A detergent will stabilize an oil-in-water emulsion.

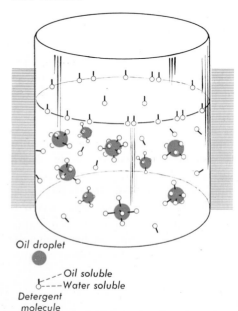

Oil droplet

--- Oil soluble
--- Water soluble
Detergent
molecule

emulsifying agent. The egg stabilizes the oil droplets by forming a protective coating around them. This prevents their coalescence.

7. The flotation process. *Foam* is a colloidal dispersion of a gas in a liquid. A very small quantity of an oil may act as a foam stabilizer, particularly in the presence of finely divided solids. Many metallic ores are found in nature in low concentrations. These are usually sulfides mixed with earthy materials known as **gangue.** Before the metal in such an ore may be extracted profitably the ore must be concentrated by separating it from the gangue.

This concentration is often accomplished by a process called **flotation.** Flotation depends on the fact that the gangue will be preferentially wetted by water while the unwetted ore particles will become attached to the oil-covered air bubbles. The low grade ore is ground very fine, then mixed with water, oil, and air to form a foamy, frothy mixture. The water-wetted particles of rock and earth settle to the bottom. The unwetted ore particles are carried to the surface in the frothy suspension of air bubbles where they are skimmed off.

In our present day economy the demand for minerals and metals steadily increases. Consequently our reserve of high grade minerals and ores steadily declines. This situation has stimulated the development of new flotation techniques. Chemists are able to change the composition of the flotation solution so that various substances are made floatable. Specific chemical additives, called *collectors,* may be introduced. These are selectively adsorbed by the particles to be floated. The collector provides the proper kind of surface for these

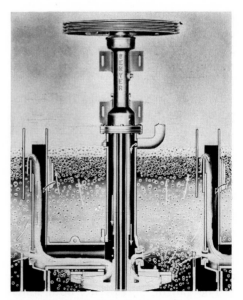

Fig. 33–9. Diagram of a flotation cell.

particles and enables them to adhere to air bubbles in the froth.

Now it is even possible to control the surface wetting of mixtures of desirable minerals. The minerals may be floated, one at a time, and thus concentrated and separated in the same operation. A low grade copper ore, *chalcopyrite,*

Fig. 33–10. Flotation cell. The ore is carried to the surface by air bubbles in the froth.

containing copper, iron, and sulfur, is often found together with *pyrite*, a sulfide of iron. Suppose we wish to separate the two ores and recover them in concentrated form.

The raw ore is first pulverized to fine particles with water in colloid mills to make a thick *slurry*. This slurry is pumped into a flotation cell along with water and very small quantities of certain chemicals. One chemical substance acts as a collector for the chalcopyrite, another causes the pyrite to be wetted. As air is blown through the cell only the copper ore particles stick to the air bubbles. They float to the surface and are skimmed off.

The gangue and pyrite, both water wetted, are pumped over to a second cell. Here the mixture is treated with another collector chemical. This displaces the water from the pyrite surfaces and makes them water-repellent. The frothing action is repeated and the pyrite particles are separated from the gangue.

Chemists have found flotation procedures for concentrating all solid mineral substances. Flotation techniques are employed in sewage disposal and in many areas in the chemical industry. The rapid strides made recently in flotation chemistry are largely the result of radioactive tracer studies concerning the behavior of the chemicals used as collectors.

2. EMULSOIDS

8. The characteristics of emulsoids. The internal phase of *lyophilic colloidal systems*, known as *emulsoids*, shows a marked attraction for the external phase. The intermingling of internal and external phases increases the viscosity of the system over that of the external phase alone. The system *sets* to form a gelatinous mass called a **gel**. Gels may become sufficiently rigid to retain the shape of the container in which the setting occurs.

In general, we find those substances which naturally form colloidal suspensions in this class. They are usually organic materials, while most suspensoids are inorganic. Some emulsoids are reversible. That is, they will redisperse in a liquid after having been separated from it. Brownian movement and

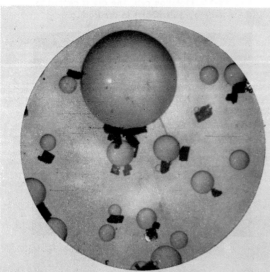

Fig. 33–11. Ore particles stick to the air bubbles in the flotation cell as shown by this photomicrograph.

the Tyndall effect are much less noticeable in the case of emulsoids. The dispersed particles of emulsoid systems carry an electric charge, usually negative. However, they are not easily precipitated by electrolytes, as are suspensoids.

A second factor, known as **solvation,** contributes to the stability of emulsoids. The internal phase becomes *solvated* in the presence of the dispersing liquid. The dispersed particles adsorb molecules of the dispersing liquid and thus become surrounded by a protective layer. Solvation is a general term which may be applied regardless of the identity of the dispersing liquid. If the liquid is water, the more specific term *hydration* may be used.

Solvation accounts for the change in viscosity of emulsoids. It is the basic distinction between lyophilic and lyophobic colloidal systems. The setting, or formation of gels, is due to proper conditions of concentration, temperature, and hydrogen-ion concentration.

9. Some common gels. Gelatin desserts are gels consisting of hydrated suspensions of gelatin, a protein, to which certain flavors have been added.

Fruit jellies consist of fruit acids, sugar, and *pectin*. Pectin, in the presence of fruit acids, produces the gel. During setting, the colloidal particles are thought to link together. They form a network of fibrils that entrap the liquid medium in which they are suspended (see Fig. 33-12). Enough pectin is present in some fruits such as apples and grapes. However, the pectin content of berry juices is usually insufficient to cause a jelly to set. Consequently, apple juice or a commercial pectin product is generally added in the preparation of berry jellies.

Let us add 15 ml of a saturated solution of calcium acetate to 85 ml of denatured alcohol. A jelly-like mass forms which is known as *solid alcohol*. Unless stabilized, however, the gel breaks down on standing. For this reason it is sometimes referred to as a *false gel*. Solid alcohol is commonly known as canned heat since it may be stored in small cans which can be opened and the alcohol ignited on appropriate occasions.

Gelatin dynamite and photographic film are gels. Silica gel is formed by dehydrating gelatinous silicic acid. It has remarkable capacity for the adsorption of many gases and vapors.

10. What are biocolloids? Lyophilic colloidal systems are of great importance in physiology and biology. Life processes largely involve actions dealing with natural colloidal substances existing within plant and animal organisms. These are known as **biocolloids.**

The biocolloids include nearly all of the energy foods: starches (insoluble carbohydrates), proteins, and fats. Together with water they are the chief constituents of living matter. Included also are the biocatalysts: enzymes,

Fig. 33-12. A gel forms a network of fibrils that entrap the liquid.

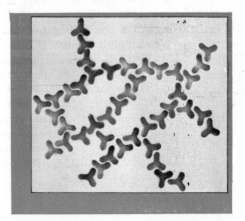

hormones, and vitamins. These stimulate and control the various chemical reactions involving the biocolloids. Thus the reactions of living organisms take place in matter that is colloidal in nature.

The biocolloids are the stable parts of the body, while the soluble substances are the migrating parts. The colloidal starches, proteins, and fats cannot pass through the tissue membranes but their soluble components do so freely.

Sugar circulates in the vein system of the plant. However, on entering the cells it is either utilized or converted, by catalytic action, to starch for storing. Similarly, in the animal body the blood sugar is converted to *glycogen* (animal starch) in the liver. The process is reversed, again by catalytic action, whenever this stored food is required.

The digestive process primarily prepares food substances for passage through the membranous walls of the intestine into the blood stream. Colloidal starches are acted upon by enzymes to produce water-soluble simple sugar.

Colloidal proteins, during digestion, are broken down to soluble *amino acids*. Colloidal fat substances are reduced to soluble *fatty acids* and *glycerin*. Upon entering the blood stream these soluble food substances are converted back into the colloidal state. This prevents their passage in the reverse direction.

Much of food-cooking involves the colloidal state. Bread becomes stale largely because of the adsorption of moisture by the colloidal materials of the ruptured cells. Thus bread should be stored in the refrigerator.

The tone of the body tissues may be associated with the degree of dispersion of the colloidal proteins composing them. Salts dissolved in the watery fluids of the body constitute the electrolytes which maintain the proper degree of dispersion of these colloidal systems. Certain functional mental disorders and diseases involving tissue swelling have been considered by some investigators to be directly related to the degree of dispersion of the colloidal proteins composing the nervous system and the body tissues.

Summary

Suspensoids are lyophobic colloidal systems which show no strong attracting forces between the internal and external phases. The haphazard Brownian motion observed in colloidal dispersions of very small particles is due to the molecular bombardment of the suspending medium. The Tyndall effect offers a means of distinguishing between colloidal suspensions and true solutions.

Pigment colors result from removal of portions of white light by absorption. Structural colors are due to the physical structure of the mass. Structural colors may vary with the size of the dispersed particles.

Colloidal suspensions are stabilized by: 1. Brownian movement; 2. the acquisition of an electrical charge; or 3. the addition of a protective agent. Suspensoids are prepared by: 1. condensation methods; and 2. dispersion methods. They may be precipitated by the introduction of: 1. the opposite electrical charge; 2. coagulating agents; or 3. heat. The Cottrell precipitator is useful in removing suspended matter from the air by discharging the particles as they pass through a high potential electric field.

The flotation process is an important means of concentrating many low grade ores and minerals. It depends on the fact that the gangue is readily wettable and the mineral fraction can be made water-repellent. Chemical additives, called collectors, make it possible to control the wettability of ores practically at will.

Emulsoids differ from suspensoids in that the internal phase becomes solvated by the adsorption of molecules of the dispersing liquid. Such systems form gels by entrapping the liquid medium in which they are suspended.

The life processes involve many natural emulsoids. These lyophilic colloids are known as biocolloids. They are very important in the areas of biology and physiology.

 est yourself on these terms

aerosol	fatty acid	protective agent
amino acid	flotation	salting out
biocolloid	gangue	scattering
Brownian movement	gel	slurry
colloid mill	hydrosol	solvation
condensation method	organosol	structural color
Cottrell precipitator	peptization	Tyndall effect
dispersion method	pigment color	ultramicroscope

Questions

Group A

1. What do we mean by Brownian movement?
2. Describe the Tyndall effect.
3. Distinguish between pigment colors and structural colors.
4. State three general reasons why colloidal suspensions do not settle on standing.
5. (a) What dispersions acquire a negative electrical charge? (b) A positive charge?
6. What are four common properties of suspensoids?
7. What are the two general methods by which suspensoids may be prepared?
8. What are three different methods by which suspensoids may be precipitated?
9. Why has the Cottrell precipitator been of great value to operators of smelters?
10. Organic materials usually form what kind of colloidal suspensions?

Group B

11. (a) Explain how a colloidal suspension of diarsenic trisulfide in water may acquire a negative charge. (b) What would be the result of adding hydrochloric acid to the suspensoid?

12. (a) Define peptization. (b) The fact that a peptizing agent is involved in certain pre-digestive processes suggests what concerning the nature of these processes?

13. Explain how soap can act as a protective colloid to stabilize oil in water.

14. On what basic fact does the ore-flotation process depend?

15. Explain the function of collectors in the flotation process.

16. Suggest a possible reason why Brownian movement is less noticeable in emulsoids than in suspensoids.

17. Why do colloidal suspensions sometimes cause difficulties in chemical analysis procedures?

18. How can you account for the formation of deltas at the mouths of large rivers?

19. What would you expect to occur as a result of mixing colloidal suspensions of ferric hydroxide and diarsenic trisulfide? Explain.

20. Would you consider the study of colloid chemistry important in the training of a physician? Give a reason for your answer.

Some things for you to do

1. Prepare colloidal gold by adding a reducing agent, such as stannous chloride solution, to a dilute solution of auric chloride. (If auric chloride is not available, it may be prepared by adding gold leaf to a few drops of aqua regia.) The colloidal gold suspension varies in color (why?), but is usually purple.

2. Coagulate rubber from latex by adding dilute acetic acid. Half fill a small beaker with latex, and then add a convenient amount of dilute acetic acid. Stir the mixture with a glass rod. The rubber coagulates and collects in a ball on the end of the glass rod.

3. Prepare some "canned heat." Add 15 ml of saturated solution of calcium acetate to 85 ml of denatured alcohol in a beaker. Stir the mixture, and note how it jells to a solid mass. Scoop out some of the "solid alcohol," place it on an asbestos square, and ignite it.

Check your progress in chemistry

1. The velocity of light is approximately 300,000 kilometers per second. Express this velocity in centimeters per second using the scientific notation form for large and small numbers.

2. (a) State the Law of Definite Proportions; (b) the Law of Multiple Proportions.

3. What is the empirical formula of potassium iodide which is found to contain 76.5% iodine?

4. What is the percentage composition of water of hydration in sodium carbonate, $Na_2CO_3 \cdot 10 H_2O$?

5. Write the balanced equation for each of the following reactions:
(a) copper + silver nitrate $\rightarrow$

    (b) ferric oxide + carbon monoxide →

    (c) calcium carbonate + hydrochloric acid →

    (d) potassium chlorate →

    (e) ammonium nitrate + potassium hydroxide →

6. How many moles of barium sulfate can be produced by a reaction between an excess of sodium sulfate and 100 g of barium chloride?

7. We wish to produce 100 g of carbon dioxide using limestone, which is 80.5% pure, and hydrochloric acid. (a) What weight of limestone is required? (b) What volume of concentrated hydrochloric acid must be measured out if it is 36% HCl by weight and has a specific gravity of 1.18?

8. Find the specific gravity (air standard) of carbon dioxide.

9. What is the volume of a gas at S.T.P. if 112 ml was collected at a temperature of 25° C and a pressure of 730 mm?

10. A gas is found to be 75% carbon and 25% hydrogen. It has a density of 0.715 g/l. What is the correct formula?

11. How many liters of oxygen are required to produce 50 liters of carbon dioxide during the combustion of coke?

★ 12. How many grams of zinc are required in a reaction with sulfuric acid to yield 2 liters of hydrogen collected over water at 740 mm pressure and 23° C? (The vapor pressure of water at 23° C may be taken as 21 mm.)

13. Calculate: (a) the freezing point; and (b) the boiling point of water in which 50 g of cane sugar, $C_{12}H_{22}O_{11}$, is dissolved per 100 g of water.

★ 14. It is found that 27 ml of 0.2-N HCl is required to neutralize 40 ml of NaOH solution. What is the normality of the basic solution?

★ 15. What is the pH of a 0.02-M HCl solution assuming complete ionization?

★ 16. List three conditions under which double replacement reactions may go to completion.

★ 17. Describe a practical application of the principle of Le Chatelier.

★ 18. Zinc reacts with dilute nitric acid to form zinc nitrate, water, and ammonium nitrate. Balance the equation for this oxidation-reduction reaction.

19. How can you account for the appearance of new properties and changes in the common physical properties as a result of a substance being subdivided to colloidal dimensions?

20. Explain the operation of the Cottrell precipitator.

Challenging your knowledge

1. Black drawing ink is a colloidal suspension of carbon in water. Suggest a way of preventing the carbon from settling out as a precipitate.

2. Why is peanut butter sometimes homogenized? Suggest how this might be accomplished.

3. How does the licorice used in foam-type extinguishers stabilize the foam?

4. When doing accurate work, why should a beaker containing a suspension of silver chloride be heated to boiling before it is filtered?

UNIT 11

THE LIGHT METALS

The four elements which are included in this unit are all light structural metals. Aluminum is probably most familiar to you in pots and pans for cooking, in porch furniture, and in the fuselage of an airplane. But magnesium is now being used in increasing quantities where lightness and strength are needed. Titanium has high resistance to the weakening effects of long periods at red heat. And beryllium is useful in controlling nuclear reactors. It is very likely that these metals will replace the heavier metals such as iron and copper in some of their applications, as well as be adapted to uses not before possible because of the unavailability of their properties.

There is only one chapter in this unit: *Beryllium, Magnesium, Aluminum, and Titanium.* You will be interested in the chemistry of these light structural metals.

Chapter 34 BERYLLIUM, MAGNESIUM, ALUMINUM, TITANIUM

1. The four metals we shall study here have low atomic numbers. Beryllium, atomic number 4, and magnesium, atomic number 12, are the first two members of Group IIA of the Periodic Table (see Chapter 25). Aluminum, atomic number 13, is a member of Group IIIA, and titanium, atomic number 22, is the first member of Group IVB, a group of transition elements. See the table at the top of page 471.

We have grouped the elements we have already studied on the basis of similar chemical properties. But the four elements we are going to study now are not grouped together for that reason. They are grouped together because all four are commercially important low density metals. Each of them is used structurally: *1.* as the pure metal; *2.* as an alloy with another light metal; or *3.* as an alloy with such heavy metals as copper and iron.

★ You will remember that the first member of a group of elements in the Periodic Table often exhibits properties somewhat different from those of the rest of the family. We have found that lithium has a far higher melting point and boiling point than would be expected from a study of these properties of the other elements of Group IA. Nitrogen, oxygen, and fluorine likewise differ in important ways from the other members of their respective groups. In this chapter we shall learn that beryllium and magnesium, though in the same family, possess somewhat different properties.

★ Chemists have discovered that even though a difference in valence exists be-

VOCABULARY

Self-protective metal. A metal which forms a nonporous, nonscaling coat of tarnish.

Thermite reaction. The reaction by which a metal is prepared from its oxide by reduction with aluminum.

ELEMENT	ATOMIC NUM— BER	ATOMIC WEIGHT	ELECTRON CONFIGURA— TION	OXI— DATION NUM— BER	MELT— ING POINT, ° C	BOIL— ING POINT, ° C	DEN— SITY g/cm³
BERYLLIUM	4	9.013	2,2	+2	1300	1500 (5 mm)	1.85
MAGNESIUM	12	24.32	2,8,2	+2	650	1100	1.74
ALUMINUM	13	26.98	2,8,3	+3	660	1800	2.70
TITANIUM	22	47.90	2,8,10,2	+2,+4	1800	over 3000	4.5

tween such diagonally arranged pairs of elements on the Periodic Table as lithium and magnesium, and beryllium and aluminum, their similar atomic and ionic radii gave them quite similar properties under certain circumstances.

1. BERYLLIUM

2. The preparation, properties, and uses of beryllium. Beryllium is not a common element. It occurs in the mineral beryl, $Be_3Al_2Si_6O_{18}$. The aquamarine and emerald are varieties of beryl which are prized as gems. Beryllium can be isolated by the electrolysis of a fused mixture of sodium and beryllium chlorides. Beryllium has a specific gravity of 1.85, is silvery-white, and very hard.

Beryllium forms nonsparking alloys with copper that are used for electric switches and for tools. Beryllium-copper springs can be bent almost innumerable times without danger of breaking the metal. Beryllium is used for making windows for X-ray tubes. X rays readily pass through elements with low atomic numbers. Of the low atomic number elements, beryllium can be best fabricated for this purpose. The addition of beryllium to light-metal alloys makes them easier to work.

Beryllium compounds are somewhat covalent. This is an important difference between beryllium compounds and the compounds of the other members of Group IIA. Furthermore, beryllium salts are extensively hydrolyzed in water. These characteristics show that nonmetallic properties begin to appear in the Period 2 elements even near the extreme left of the Periodic Table. Beryllium and its compounds are exceedingly poisonous.

2. MAGNESIUM

3. The occurrence of magnesium. Magnesium compounds are widely distributed on land and in the sea. Magnesium sulfate is found in the ground in many places, notably British Columbia and the state of Washington. A double chloride of potassium and magnesium is mined from the potash deposits of Texas and New Mexico. Sea water contains a significant quantity of magnesium compounds in solution.

Dolomite, $CaCO_3 \cdot MgCO_3$, is a double carbonate of magnesium and calcium which is often found in the United States and Europe. It is an excellent building stone, and it is useful for lining steel furnaces. Pulverized dolomite neutralizes soil acids and also supplies magnesium for the growth of plants.

Talc and asbestos are silicates of magnesium. Asbestos, which is mined in Ontario and Quebec, Canada, is a remarkable mineral. It has a high melting point, is nonflammable, and is a good heat insulator. Its fibrous structure permits the mineral to be spun into threads and woven into cloth. It is mixed with cement for making asbestos shingles. With magnesium oxide it is used for covering steam pipes and furnaces. Asbestos is also used for making automobile brake linings, fireproof curtains and clothing, and as an insulator for electric heating appliances.

Elementary magnesium was first prepared by Davy in 1807, in the series of experiments which resulted in the isolation of sodium, calcium, and similar active metals.

4. The extraction of magnesium. Two processes are used for preparing elementary magnesium.

1. From magnesium chloride. The sea provides an inexhaustible supply of magnesium. The first step in obtaining magnesium from sea water is to treat it with lime. The lime used in this process is made from oyster shells, since they are inexpensive and readily available. Treating sea water with lime causes the magnesium ions to be precipitated as magnesium hydroxide.

$$Mg^{++} + 2\ OH^- \rightarrow Mg(OH)_2\downarrow$$

The magnesium hydroxide is separated from the water by filtration. The addition of hydrochloric acid converts the magnesium hydroxide to magnesium chloride.

$$Mg(OH)_2 + 2\ HCl \rightarrow MgCl_2 + 2\ H_2O$$

Magnesium is liberated when the fused magnesium chloride is electrolyzed (see Fig. 34-3).

$$MgCl_2 \rightarrow Mg + Cl_2\uparrow$$

Magnesium is also prepared by electrolyzing fused magnesium chloride obtained from natural underground brine.

2. From magnesium oxide. In the United States some magnesium is prepared from magnesium oxide by reducing it with ferrosilicon. Ferrosilicon is an alloy of iron and silicon. The reduction is carried out at a temperature

Fig. 34-1. A thin disc of beryllium serves as a window in this X-ray tube. X rays readily pass through elements of low atomic number.

Fig. 34-2. An aerial view of an open pit asbestos mine in the province of Ontario, Canada.

of about 1150° C in a vacuum. At this high temperature and low pressure, the magnesium evaporates. The magnesium vapor is condensed to a liquid and cast into molds.

5. Magnesium has interesting properties. Magnesium is a silver-white metal that has a density only 1.74 times that of water. When heated, magnesium becomes ductile and malleable. Its tensile strength is not quite as great as that of aluminum.

Magnesium is not acted upon by dry air, but in moist air a coating of basic magnesium carbonate forms on the surface. Because this coating is not porous like iron rust, it protects the metal underneath from further tarnishing. *A metal which forms a nonporous, nonscaling coat of tarnish is said to be a self-protective metal.*

When heated in air to the kindling point, magnesium burns with an intensely hot flame and gives off a dazzling light. The products of the combustion are magnesium oxide, MgO, and magnesium nitride, Mg_3N_2. Magnesium is one of the few metals which combines directly with nitrogen. Water

Fig. 34-3. Flow diagram showing the main steps in the extraction of magnesium from sea water.

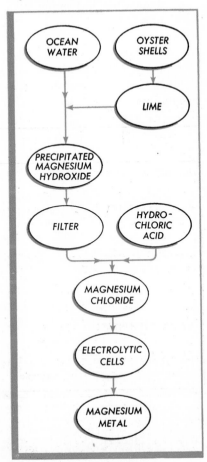

Fig. 34–4. This experimental model of the F–80 jet fighter plane was made entirely of magnesium.

at its boiling point reacts with magnesium slowly, and hydrogen is set free. All the common acids react with it, producing hydrogen and salts.

6. Magnesium has many uses. The brilliant white light which is produced when magnesium burns makes it useful for flares and fireworks. Magnesium forms alloys with aluminum which are light and strong. Two such alloys are magnalium and Dowmetal. These alloys are used for making many novelty articles, for tools and fixtures, for the beams of delicate chemical balances, and for automobile and airplane parts. The growth of the airplane industry has produced a much greater demand for magnesium. An experimental jet fighter with an all-magnesium body has been built and tested. The table below lists a few of the more common magnesium compounds.

CHEMICAL NAME	COMMON NAME	FORMULA	APPEARANCE	USES
MAGNESIUM CARBONATE	None	$MgCO_3$	White, usually fluffy	For lining furnaces; in making the oxide
BASIC MAGNESIUM CARBONATE	Magnesia alba	$Mg_4(OH)_2(CO_3)_3 \cdot 3\ H_2O$	Soft, white powder 85% pores	In tooth cleansers; "85% magnesia" for pipe coverings
MAGNESIUM OXIDE	Magnesia	MgO	White powder	As refractory; for lining furnaces
MAGNESIUM CHLORIDE	None	$MgCl_2$	White, crystalline solid	With asbestos for stone flooring
MAGNESIUM SULFATE	Epsom salts	$MgSO_4 \cdot 7\ H_2O$	White, crystalline solid	In laxatives, cathartics; in dye industry
MAGNESIUM HYDROXIDE	Milk of magnesia	$Mg(OH)_2$	White, milky suspension	As antacid; in laxatives

3. ALUMINUM

7. The occurrence of aluminum. Aluminum is the most abundant metal in the earth's crust, ranking next below oxygen and silicon. Its abundance is accounted for by the fact that aluminum is found in many clays, rocks, and other mineral materials. While the aluminum industry is working on processes by which aluminum may be economically extracted from clay, none has yet proved to be successful. Such a process would make the United States less dependent on foreign sources of aluminum ore. At the present time bauxite, an impure aluminum oxide which serves as an ore of aluminum, is imported from Jamaica, Surinam, and British Guiana, even though it is also mined in certain areas in Georgia, Alabama, Tennessee, and Arkansas. The occurrence of aluminum in other minerals of economic importance will be described later in this chapter.

8. The story of a famous discovery. In 1828 Frank F. Jewett, former Professor of Chemistry at Oberlin College, studied under Friedrich Wöhler, the German chemist who first isolated aluminum. As late as 1855 aluminum sold at $90 per pound; but by 1870 the price had fallen to $12 per pound. In 1886 Hamilton Castner learned how to prepare sodium cheaply enough so that it could be used to reduce aluminum from its compounds. This lowered the price of aluminum to about $2 per pound, but this was still prohibitive for industrial use.

Jewett was always interested in aluminum. In one of his lectures he said, "Any person who discovers a process by which aluminum can be made on a commercial scale will bless humanity and make a fortune for himself." As he left the laboratory, one of his students, Charles Martin Hall, told a classmate, "I'm going for that metal." Hall borrowed all the voltaic cells he could from the college laboratories and set up a workshop in his father's woodshed. Two years later, when Hall was only twenty-three years old, he rushed into Jewett's office, crying, "I've got it." He laid upon Jewett's desk some lumps of aluminum he had extracted by electrolysis! The Hall process for extracting aluminum was commercialized in 1889. It was so successful that the cost of aluminum was reduced to about 20¢ per pound. If you count the many uses of aluminum, from cooking utensils to airplanes, you will agree that Hall conferred a blessing on mankind. When

Fig. 34–5. Charles Martin Hall, the young American who discovered the electrolytic process for producing aluminum.

Fig. 34–6. The "crown jewels" of Oberlin College. The first nuggets of aluminum prepared by Charles Martin Hall.

Hall died in 1914, he left a bequest of several million dollars (a part of the wealth he had acquired) to Oberlin College. The nuggets of aluminum which Hall handed to Jewett are displayed today as the "crown jewels" of Oberlin. At a class reunion at Yale, Professor Jewett was asked what he had done since his graduation. His reply was, "I discovered a man."

9. The preparation of aluminum. In 1886, as we have just learned, Charles Martin Hall (1863–1914) discovered that aluminum can be liberated from purified aluminum oxide by means of an electric current. Aluminum oxide, Al_2O_3, is an infusible substance. However, Hall, after long experimentation, discovered that aluminum oxide would dissolve readily in fused cryolite. Cryolite is a double fluoride of sodium and aluminum, $AlF_3 \cdot 3 NaF$. It is mined in Greenland or is prepared synthetically. The electric current liberates the aluminum ions thus produced, and the aluminum is deposited on the cathode.

The electrolysis is carried out in an iron box lined with carbon. The box is connected with the negative terminal of a direct current generator, and thus becomes the cathode. Rows of carbon rods are used as the anodes. When current is passed through the liquid, the aluminum ions migrate to the cathode where they receive electrons and become atoms of aluminum.

$$Al^{+++} + 3\ e^- \rightarrow Al^0$$

Molten aluminum collects at the bottom of the tank and is tapped off periodically. Oxygen gas is discharged at the carbon anodes. Some of the oxygen combines with the carbon anodes, consequently the carbon rods must be replaced frequently. Aluminum oxide is added from time to time to make the process continuous. Because much electrical energy is needed to produce one pound of aluminum metal, plants for producing it are located near hydroelectric projects where electricity can be generated at a very reasonable cost.

10. The physical properties of aluminum. Aluminum is silver-white in color and has a density 2.7 times as great as water. It is ductile and malleable, but is not so tenacious as brass, copper, or steel. It ranks with the best conductors of electricity, being surpassed only by silver, copper, and gold. Aluminum can be welded, cast, or spun, but it can be soldered only with difficulty, and then only by the use of a special solder.

11. The chemical properties of aluminum. Aluminum takes a high polish, but soon becomes covered with a thin layer of aluminum oxide. This gives it a slight bluish tint. The color of the oxide resembles that of the metal itself so much that many people have the idea that aluminum does not tarnish at

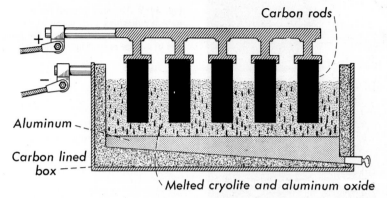

Fig. 34–7. Aluminum is produced by electrolysis. Purified aluminum oxide is dissolved in melted cryolite, sodium aluminum fluoride.

all. The oxide layer which forms is adherent and impervious; hence aluminum is a self-protective metal. Hydrochloric acid and sulfuric acid attack aluminum readily and form salts of the respective acids. Nitric acid hardly affects aluminum at all. Salt water corrodes it rapidly, especially when it is hot. Such a strong alkali as sodium hydroxide reacts with aluminum forming sodium aluminate and liberating hydrogen.

$$2\,Al + 6\,NaOH \rightarrow 2\,Na_3AlO_3 + 3\,H_2\uparrow$$

12. Aluminum is a very useful metal.
To some extent aluminum is used in place of copper for electrical conductors. It is only about 0.6 as good a conductor as copper, but is less than one-third as dense. Hence wires may be made larger to increase conductivity and still put less strain on the supporting poles or towers.

Flash bulbs used when taking photographs contain fine aluminum wire and enough oxygen to burn the wire completely. The wire burns with an intensely brilliant flash when ignited by the hot filament.

Powdered aluminum is used in paint, particularly to protect the surface of iron, in the "silvering" of radiators. Aluminum foil is used for wrapping candy bars, cheese, soap, and many other products, and as a heat insulator. Aluminum is also used for making various novelty articles, and for certain parts of airplanes and automobiles.

Aluminum is very popular for cooking utensils. It is light and durable, a good conductor of heat, does not tarnish noticeably, and is rather easily kept clean. Aluminum cooking utensils are easily bent or dented and will melt in a gas flame if the utensil boils dry.

Fig. 34–8. Corrugated aluminum sheet is one of the many building materials fabricated from aluminum.

Fig. 34–9. Thermite is used for repairing breaks in heavy machine parts made of steel. Here two crucibles are used in repairing the cracked steel arm of a large press. The reaction has just begun.

ies with the relative proportions of the metals used. One of them resembles silver, another resembles gold, and both take a high polish.

Duralumin is an alloy that contains about 95% aluminum, 4% copper, 0.5% manganese, and 0.5% magnesium. It is less than half as dense as steel, yet is nearly as strong. This alloy is extensively used for airplane parts where a strong, light alloy is required.

14. The thermite reaction. A mixture of coarsely powdered aluminum and iron oxide will react if it is raised to a high enough temperature to start the chemical change. A tremendous amount of heat is set free when the reaction occurs. Such a reaction between aluminum and the oxide of a less active metal is called the *thermite reaction.*

13. The alloys of aluminum. Magnalium, an alloy of aluminum and magnesium, has already been mentioned under magnesium. Several other alloys of aluminum and copper are known under the name of aluminum bronze. The color of such bronzes varies

Fig. 34–10. The thermite demonstration makes a striking spectacle. Dry sand should be used to protect the table top. Spectators must keep a safe distance away, as the sparks travel several feet.

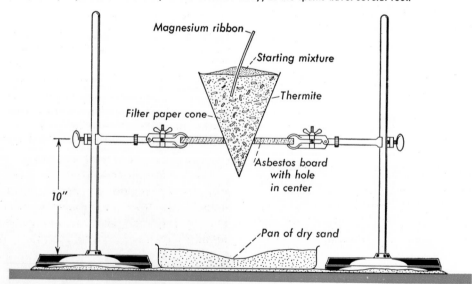

Fig. 34–11. This is a photograph of the demonstration shown in Fig. 34–10. The contrasting black and white indicates the brilliance of the light from the molten iron.

From Table 6 in the Appendix, we find that 390 kilocalories of heat are set free during the formation of one mole of aluminum oxide. The heat of formation of ferric oxide is 191 kilocalories. When the thermite reaction occurs, an amount of heat equal to the difference between these values is set free for each mole of aluminum oxide formed. The equation is:

$$2 \text{ Al} + \text{Fe}_2\text{O}_3 \rightarrow$$
$$\text{Al}_2\text{O}_3 + 2 \text{ Fe} + 199 \text{ kilocalories}$$

The liberation of such a large amount of heat so suddenly produces a very high temperature. The temperature of the thermite reaction is estimated at 3500° C. Reactions of this type are sometimes called *aluminothermy* or *aluminothermics*.

15. Some metals are reduced by the thermite reaction. It is not practical to use aluminum to reduce metals which are less expensive than aluminum. But this reaction may be used when it is desirable to produce a small quantity of carbon free metal. A more important use of the thermite reaction is to reduce metallic oxides which are not readily reduced with carbon. Chromium, manganese, titanium, tungsten, and molybdenum may be extracted from their oxides by the thermite reaction. The oxide of the desired metal is mixed with powdered aluminum to make a thermite mixture. All of these metals are used in making alloy steels of high quality. Uranium, which is used for producing nuclear energy, may also be reduced by the thermite reaction.

16. Thermite is also used in welding. The high temperature produced by the thermite reaction makes it possible to use such a mixture for welding. Massive steel parts, such as propeller shafts and rudder posts on a ship, or crankshafts of heavy machinery, can be repaired quickly by means of thermite. A mixture of powdered aluminum and an oxide of iron, either Fe_2O_3 or Fe_3O_4, is placed in a cone-shaped crucible above the metals to be welded. A little starting mixture consisting of barium peroxide and powdered magnesium is placed in a slight depression in the top of the mixture. Within a few seconds after the starting mixture is ignited, the white-hot molten iron flows out through the bottom of the cone and surrounds the broken ends that are to be welded.

Fig. 34-12. These crucibles are made of Alundum, an artificial oxide of aluminum.

17. The uses of aluminum oxide. We have learned that bauxite, the chief ore of aluminum, is an oxide of aluminum. Corundum and emery are also natural oxides of this metal, and are used as abrasives. Emery is used in the form of emery paper, emery cloth, or emery grinding wheels.

Rubies and sapphires are pure specimens of aluminum oxide colored by traces of metallic oxides. Many synthetic rubies and sapphires are now made by fusing pure aluminum oxide in the flame of an oxyhydrogen blow torch. In making clear sapphires, no coloring matter is added. To form blue sapphires, a trace of titanium oxide is added. Synthetic rubies are colored by the addition of a tiny quantity of chromium.

Alundum is an artificial oxide of aluminum which is made by fusing bauxite. It is used for making grinding wheels and other abrasives. It is also made into crucibles, funnels, tubing, and other pieces of laboratory apparatus.

18. The chemical behavior of aluminum hydroxide. If we add a little sodium hydroxide solution to a solution of an aluminum salt, such as aluminum chloride, a white gelatinous precipitate of aluminum hydroxide is formed (see Chapter 21, Section 11).

$$AlCl_3 + 3\ NaOH \rightarrow Al(OH)_3\downarrow + 3\ NaCl$$

Aluminum hydroxide is insoluble in water, but if we add an excess of sodium hydroxide, soluble sodium aluminate is formed. In this reaction aluminum hydroxide acts as an acid, H_3AlO_3.

$$H_3AlO_3 + 3\ NaOH \rightarrow Na_3AlO_3 + 3\ H_2O$$

If, on the other hand, we add hydrochloric acid to aluminum hydroxide, the aluminum hydroxide acts as a hydroxide, $Al(OH)_3$.

$$Al(OH)_3 + 3\ HCl \rightarrow AlCl_3 + 3\ H_2O$$

These reactions show the amphiprotic nature of aluminum hydroxide.

Aluminum hydroxide is so weakly basic that its salts with weak acids are almost completely hydrolyzed. If we add sodium carbonate to a solution of aluminum chloride, we might expect to have aluminum carbonate precipitated. It is possible that aluminum carbonate may be first formed, but, if so, it immediately hydrolyzes and forms aluminum hydroxide. A precipitate of aluminum hydroxide is always formed when a soluble carbonate, or even a soluble sulfide is added to a solution of an aluminum salt.

19. The uses of aluminum hydroxide. In our study of water purification, we learned that aluminum hydroxide may be used to remove suspended matter from drinking water (see Chapter 10, Section 12). It also finds use as a mordant. As a rule, aluminum hydroxide is precipitated on the fibers before they are dipped into the dye bath (see Chapter 44, Section 17).

Colored pigments for use in the paint industry are sometimes made by precipitating a dye of some kind with aluminum hydroxide in a large vat. The insoluble compound, which contains the dye, is then filtered off. Such pigments are known as lakes.

Aluminum hydroxide is used medicinally as an antacid.

20. Aluminum forms double salts known as alums. If we mix solutions of potassium sulfate and aluminum sulfate, and then evaporate some of the liquid, a double salt crystallizes. The formula of the double salt is

$$KAl(SO_4)_2 \cdot 12 \, H_2O$$

Any double sulfate formed in such a manner and having similar properties is called an *alum*.

Instead of potassium sulfate, either ammonium sulfate or sodium sulfate may be used. The sulfates of such trivalent metals as chromium or iron may be used instead of aluminum sulfate. The general formula,

$$M^+M^{+++}(SO_4)_2 \cdot 12 \, H_2O$$

in which M^+ is some univalent element or radical, and M^{+++} is some trivalent metal, is used to represent the alums. The different alums are used to form mordants.

21. Some silicates of aluminum are useful. Fuller's earth is a silicate of aluminum which is a good adsorbent. It is used for clarifying oils by filtration and for removing spots from textile fabrics.

Mica is a potassium aluminum silicate which is translucent and infusible. Mica is also used for the translucent tops of fuse plugs. As an electrical insulator, it is used in the commutators of motors and dynamos.

Fig. 34–13. A sheet of mica $\frac{1}{16}$ inch thick, partially separated to show its layered structure. Sheets of mica are used as insulation in electrical equipment.

The feldspars are complex silicates which usually contain aluminum silicate with the silicates of either sodium or potassium. They fuse rather easily. When water or carbon dioxide brings about the weathering of the feldspars, the alkalies are leached out as the soluble silicates or carbonates. Hence the disintegration of a feldspar may add potassium to the soil. The insoluble portion is a fine white clay, or hydrated aluminum silicate, which is known as

Fig. 34–14. Clay is used in making pottery. Here a potter is shaping the clay into a vase on a potter's wheel.

Fig. 34–15. Bricks being removed from a kiln in a large brickyard.

kaolin. The colored clays found in soils usually owe their color to the presence of iron compounds as impurities.

22. Clay is used to make pottery. Clay becomes plastic when it is mixed with water and can then be molded into any desired shape. When the plastic mass is dried and baked at a high temperature it does not melt, but shrinks and forms a hard, porous mass capable of resisting considerable pressure. These properties of clay make it suitable for use in the pottery industry. The particular use to which the clay is put depends on its purity.

In making bricks, an impure clay is used. Field tile is made from the same material. The red color is due to the presence of iron compounds in the clay. In making vitrified brick the tem-

Fig. 34–16. The porous bisque of a large funnel is being sprayed with a suspension of powdered feldspar and kaolin in water before receiving the second firing.

perature used is high enough to start the fusion of the clay at the surface. The glaze thus produced fills the pores at the surface. Firebricks contain both clay and sand.

Earthenware and tile are made from coarse clays, and a low temperature is used in firing them, in order to keep the mass porous. Flowerpots are examples of such ware. If such clays are heated hot enough so they become vitrified throughout the mass, they form stoneware. The cheaper kinds of stoneware and crockery are glazed by throwing salt into the furnace. The product of sodium and aluminum silicate which forms at the surface has a rather low melting point. It fuses and closes the pores.

Porcelain or china (dinnerware) is made from a very pure white clay mixed with powdered feldspar. It is usually fired twice. After the first firing the porous bisque or biscuit is dipped into water containing in suspension a mixture of powdered feldspar and kaolin. During the second firing the feldspar melts and fills the pores to make the porcelain impervious to liquids.

Ohio and New Jersey produce the most pottery. New York, California, and Pennsylvania are also large producers. Fine chemical laboratory porcelain is produced in Colorado.

4. TITANIUM

23. The occurrence of titanium. Titanium is the ninth most abundant element, comprising an estimated 0.6% of the earth's crust. It is found as rutile, TiO_2, and in titanates, such as ilmenite, $FeTiO_3$. Traces of titanium are almost always found in sand, clay, soil, mineral waters, and plant and animal tissue.

24. The preparation of titanium. Metallic titanium is prepared commercially by the reduction of titanium tetrachloride with magnesium or sodium at 750° to 900° in an atmosphere of argon or helium. The powder thus formed, titanium sponge, is carefully melted to form a mass of metallic titanium. Some titanium is prepared as an alloy with iron for use in the production of certain special steels.

25. The properties of titanium. Titanium can be purified and treated to produce a strong, ductile metal which can be forged, drawn, and fabricated. It is stable in air, but when heated to

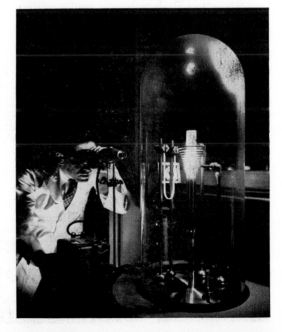

Fig. 34-17. This bar of titanium is being purified by the zone refining method. The interior of the top of the bar is heated electrically by induction until it melts. Then the bar is moved up through the heating coil gradually so the interior of the bar melts successively throughout its entire length. Since the impurities tend to dissolve in the melted portion, they are thus moved along to the bottom of the bar, leaving the rest of the bar highly purified.

Fig. 34–18. Rotary filters used in one step of the production of titanium dioxide pigment for paint, paper, rubber, and plastics.

600° C it takes fire and burns with a brilliant light.

Titanium is the first transition metal we have studied in any detail. Titanium has the electronic configuration 2, 8, 10, 2. While titanium does lose the 2 N-shell electrons and form Ti++ ions, its most common valence is +4. Notice that to form this ion the 2 N-shell electrons and 2 M-shell electrons are lost. The Ti+4 ion has an octet for its outermost shell. Titanium also is found in the negative titanate ion, $TiO_3^=$.

26. The uses of titanium and its compounds. Titanium is used as an alloying metal with iron in making alloy steels which must have resistance to shock and corrosion. Titanium also alloys with copper and bronzes. An alloy of nickel, chromium, and titanium has been used in constructing the combustion chambers of jet aircraft engines. Titanium also shows promise of being used in alloys with very great strengths per unit of weight. These are being made into parts for new types of military aircraft.

Titanium dioxide, TiO_2, is used in the manufacture of enamels, glazes, white rubber, paper, and face powders. Its most important use is as a paint base. It possesses great covering power, lightness, permanence, a nonpoisonous nature, and is easily mixed with oil.

Titanium tetrachloride is used with ammonia in skywriting. When released to the air, titanium tetrachloride hydrolyzes with the moisture of the air to form hydrochloric acid which then reacts with the ammonia present to form clouds of white ammonium chloride.

Summary

Beryllium, magnesium, aluminum, and titanium are four commercially important low density metals. Each of them is used for structural purposes.

Beryllium is not a common element. It is used for making nonsparking alloys with copper. Its compounds are somewhat covalent.

Magnesium compounds are widely distributed. Sea water contains magnesium compounds in solution. Dolomite, a double carbonate of calcium and magnesium, is used as a building stone, and for neutralizing soil acids. Talc and asbestos are silicates of magnesium.

Magnesium metal is obtained by the electrolysis of fused magnesium chloride, and by the reduction of magnesium oxide with ferrosilicon. It is a silver-white metal with a density less than twice that of water. Magnesium forms a self-protective coating of tarnish. It is used for making alloys of low specific gravity, and for making flares and fireworks.

Aluminum is a silver-white metal with a density 2.7 times as great as water. It is ductile and malleable and a good conductor of electricity. Aluminum forms a self-protective coating of tarnish. Aluminum is attacked by hydrochloric and sulfuric acids, but nitric acid hardly affects it. Strong alkalies react with aluminum.

Aluminum is used for making electrical transmission cables and cooking utensils. Powdered aluminum is used to make "silver" paint for metallic surfaces. Flash bulbs contain very fine aluminum wire. Duralumin is an aluminum alloy that is used for making airplane parts. Aluminum is used as a reducing agent with the oxides of less active metals.

Aluminum oxide in the form of corundum or emery is used as an abrasive. Synthetic rubies and sapphires are made from fused aluminum oxide. Aluminum hydroxide is used in water purification, in mordant dyeing, and in the preparation of lakes.

Feldspars are complex silicate rocks. Water and carbon dioxide bring about the weathering of feldspars to form clay. Bricks, earthenware, tile, and stoneware are made from clay. Porcelain or china is made from pure white clay mixed with powdered feldspar.

Titanium is prepared by the reduction of titanium tetrachloride with magnesium or sodium in an inert atmosphere. It is used in alloys which resist shock and corrosion. Titanium dioxide is used in paints.

Test yourself on these terms

alum	corundum	magnalium
aluminothermy	cryolite	mica
alundum	dolomite	nonsparking alloy
amphiprotic	Dowmetal	porcelain
anode	duralumin	rutile
asbestos	feldspar	self-protective metal
bauxite	fuller's earth	thermite reaction
beryl	kaolin	tile
cathode	lake	titanium sponge

Questions

Group A

1. Why are beryllium, magnesium, aluminum, and titanium grouped together for study?
2. What useful alloy is made from beryllium and a heavy metal?
3. List some of the common uses for asbestos.
4. (a) What is dolomite? (b) For what purposes is it used?
5. Since magnesium is an active metal, why do objects made from it not corrode to a mass of rust as iron does?
6. What are the uses for magnesium metal?
7. In what materials does aluminum occur in nature?
8. What are the physical properties of aluminum?
9. Why is aluminum so popular for cooking utensils?
10. What are two important alloys of aluminum and magnesium?
11. What is the difference between *vitrified brick, stoneware,* and *earthenware?*
12. For what purposes is titanium used?

Group B

13. Write three balanced chemical equations to show the steps in the preparation of magnesium from sea water.
14. What is the chemical nature of corundum and emery?
15. Why must aluminum oxide be dissolved in fused cryolite before it can be decomposed by electricity?
16. Why are certain metallic oxides reduced with aluminum rather than with carbon?
17. Write the chemical formulas for four different alums.
18. In terms of atomic structure, describe how titanium attains an oxidation number of $+4$.
19. Why must the reduction of magnesium oxide by ferrosilicon be carried out in a vacuum?
20. What reaction occurs when aluminum is placed in: (a) hydrochloric acid solution; (b) sodium hydroxide solution?
21. How do beryllium compounds differ from those of other Group IIA elements?
22. Write equations to show the anode and cathode reactions during the electrolysis of aluminum oxide.
23. Write balanced formula equations to show the amphiprotic nature of aluminum hydroxide.
★ 24. What similarity of structure exists between lithium and magnesium, and beryllium and aluminum?

Problems

Group A

1. Calculate the percentage of beryllium in beryl, $Be_3Al_2Si_6O_{18}$.
2. What weight of magnesium can be prepared from a ton of magnesium oxide, MgO?
3. A cubic mile of sea water contains in solution enough minerals to form about 35 million pounds of magnesium chloride. How much metallic magnesium could be obtained from this?
4. How many pounds of aluminum granules and how many pounds of ferric oxide flakes must be used in a thermite mixture to produce 10 lb of iron for a welding job?

Group B

5. If dolomite is 95% a double carbonate of calcium and magnesium, together with 5% of impurities such as iron and silica, what is the percentage of magnesium in the sample?
6. What is the percentage of aluminum in sodium alum which crystallizes with 12 molecules of water of hydration?
7. How many liters of hydrogen can be prepared by the reaction of 50 g of aluminum and 100 g of sodium hydroxide in solution?

Some things for you to do

1. Make a batch of "Milk of Magnesia." Add 100 ml of 10% sodium hydroxide solution to a large flask. Add 10% magnesium sulfate solution, a little at a time, as long as a precipitate is formed. Shake the mixture and allow it to settle. Pour off the clear solution above the white precipitate. Fill the flask with water, shake, and allow it to settle again. Now pour off the clear liquid to wash away excess of either magnesium sulfate or sodium hydroxide. Repeat the washing process several times. The milky precipitate left is a suspension of magnesium hydroxide which is called "milk of magnesia." It is not advisable to use this milk of magnesia because it may still contain harmful alkali.
2. Clean some silverware by the aluminum process. Use an old aluminum pan. Put the silverware in the pan and cover with water. Now add a teaspoonful of baking soda for each quart of water. Boil the liquid for twenty minutes. Remove the silver. Rinse thoroughly under hot and cold water. Dry with a clean, soft cloth.
3. Prepare insoluble pigments called lakes. Add 50 ml of 2% alizarin solution to an equal volume of saturated solution of aluminum sulfate. Then add the same amount of 10% ammonium hydroxide solution. The precipitate which forms is colored and is known as a lake. Filter off the precipitate and dry it in a warm oven. Grind the residue that results to a fine powder in a mortar. Cochineal solution may be used instead of alizarin. Salts of chromium and tin yield different colored lakes from those produced by aluminum salts.

4. Prepare a report on the life and work of Charles Martin Hall and present it before the class.
5. Consult recent scientific magazines to learn about new uses for titanium.

Check your progress in chemistry

(Write balanced formula equations for the following reactions.)

1. Priestley's discovery of oxygen.
2. The reaction between sodium and water.
3. The reduction of cupric oxide by hydrogen.
4. The reaction between aluminum sulfate and calcium hydroxide in a sedimentation basin.
5. The production of carbonic acid from its acid anhydride.
6. The preparation of oxygen from potassium chlorate.
7. The reaction between marble chips and hydrochloric acid.
8. The synthesis of methanol.
9. The laboratory preparation of acetylene using calcium carbide.
10. The production of 1,2-dibromoethane from ethylene.
11. The loss of water of hydration on heating $BaCl_2 \cdot 2 H_2O$.
12. The ionization of hydrogen chloride producing hydronium ions and chloride ions.
13. The anode and cathode reactions during the electrolysis of water.
14. The reaction between zinc and hydrochloric acid.
15. The hydrolysis of hydrated cupric ion, $Cu(H_2O)_4^{++}$.
16. The reaction between sodium chloride and ammonium bicarbonate.
17. The laboratory preparation of plaster of Paris from gypsum.
18. The laboratory preparation of chlorine from chloride of lime.
19. The over-all reaction for the production of sulfuric acid by the contact process from sulfur, oxygen, and water.
20. The reaction between copper and dilute nitric acid.

Challenging your knowledge

1. Explain why magnesium is a self-protective metal.
2. What double function does pulverized dolomite perform for the farmer?
3. Why do we import bauxite from the West Indies and South America when almost any clay bank in the United States contains aluminum?
4. Write the equation for the reaction which occurs when a flash bulb is set off.
5. What geographic conditions affect the location of plants for the production of aluminum from purified bauxite?

THE HEAVY METALS

The very inactive heavy metals occur free in nature. Others are recovered from their compounds which are mined as ores. Some are abundant, easily extracted, and relatively inexpensive. Others, because they are scarce, or difficult to recover, command high prices.

In the picture above you see one of the spectacular reactions in the manufacture of steel, the "blowing off" of a Bessemer converter. While it does not account for a large portion of the steel manufactured today, the Bessemer process ushered in the Age of Steel. Steel is undoubtedly the most useful of all metals.

Three chapters are included in this unit: *The Iron Family; The Copper Family;* and *Zinc, Cadmium, Mercury, Tin, and Lead.* Knowledge of the metallurgy, properties, and uses of these heavy metals will enable you to appreciate their importance in modern life.

Chapter 35 THE

IRON FAMILY

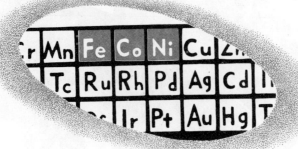

1. The metals of Group VIIIB occupy the central region of the Periodic Table. This group consists of a unique arrangement of nine transition elements in three vertical columns. *Iron, cobalt,* and *nickel,* the Group VIIIB elements in the fourth period, have very similar properties. In fact, they show greater similarity to one another than any of them does to the element lying below it. These three well-known metals compose the *Iron Family.* Iron is by far the most important member of the family. Alloys of iron, cobalt, and nickel are important structural metals.

The remaining six metals of Group VIIIB are *ruthenium, rhodium,* and *palladium,* in the fifth period, and *osmium, iridium,* and *platinum,* in the sixth period. All have properties similar to platinum and may be considered to be members of the *Platinum Family.* They are noble metals—rare and expensive. Important properties of the metals of the Iron Family are listed in the table on next page.

The three metals of the Iron Family show oxidation states of +2 and +3. The ferric state of iron is generally more stable than the ferrous state. This

VOCABULARY

Alnico (*al*-nih-ko). A strongly ferromagnetic alloy of iron, nickel, aluminum, and cobalt.

Carboloy (*kar*-bol-oy). An extremely hard alloy of cobalt and tungsten carbide.

Flux. A material used to promote the fusion of minerals.

Nitralloy (*nye*-tral-oy). An alloy steel that has been treated with ammonia.

Permalloy (*per*-mal-oy). A high nickel alloy of steel that is easily magnetized.

Stellite. A hard alloy of cobalt and chromium.

Trunnion (*trun*-yun). One of a pair of opposite protruding pivots that provide a means of turning a heavy vessel.

ELEMENT	ATOMIC NUM-BER	ATOMIC WEIGHT	ELECTRON CONFIGURA-TION	OXIDA-TION NUM-BERS	MELT-ING POINT, ° C	BOIL-ING POINT, ° C	DEN-SITY (g/cm³)
IRON	26	55.85	2,8,14,2	+2,+3	1535	3000	7.86
COBALT	27	58.94	2,8,15,2	+2,+3	1495	2900	8.90
NICKEL	28	58.71	2,8,16,2	+2,+3	1455	2900	8.90

tendency decreases through cobalt to nickel. Nickel occurs only rarely in the oxidation state of +3. The Iron Family is located in the midst of the transition elements. Atoms of these elements have less than the maximum number of electrons in the level just beneath the valence shell. An electron can be removed from this shell almost as easily as the electrons from the valence shell. This is particularly true of iron and explains why iron attains the +3 oxidation state so easily.

All three metals of the Iron Family have magnetic properties. Cobalt is strongly magnetic, nickel is the least magnetic of the group. The magnetic nature of iron, cobalt, and nickel is related to peculiarities in the incomplete electron shell just beneath the valence electrons.

Electrons revolving about the nucleus of an atom are thought to spin on their own axes. Physicists believe that magnetism in metals is associated with this electron spin. Each spinning electron is a tiny magnet. Electron pairs are formed by two electrons spinning in opposite directions. The electronic magnetisms of such a pair of electrons neutralize each other. The members of the Iron Family have incomplete M shells containing unpaired electrons giving the atoms a net magnetic effect. Groups of such atoms may be so aligned as to form a small magnetized region, called a *domain.* Ordinarily magnetic domains within the metallic crystals point in every possible direction and cancel one another so that the net magnetism is zero. A piece of iron becomes magnetized when an outside force lines up the domains in the same direction.

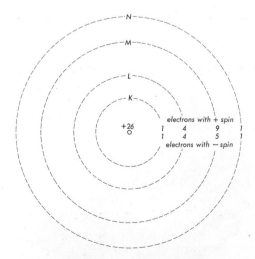

Fig. 35-1. The atom of iron is magnetic because the electron spins in the M shell are not all counterbalanced.

1. IRON

2. The occurrence of iron. Iron is the fourth element in abundance by weight in the earth's crust. Nearly 5% of this crust consists of iron. It is the second most abundant metal, being surpassed only by aluminum. We know that meteors contain iron. This fact, together with the knowledge of the magnetic nature of the earth itself, has led scientists to believe that the core of the earth may be composed mainly of iron.

Unfortunately, we cannot profitably remove much of the iron in the crust of the earth. Only those iron-bearing minerals from which we can recover the iron by a practical and profitable method are considered to be *iron ores.*

The most abundant ore is *hematite,* Fe_2O_3, a reddish-brown substance. *Limonite,* $2 Fe_2O_3 \cdot 3 H_2O$, is a hydrated oxide which yields a yellow powder when it is crushed. *Magnetite,* Fe_3O_4, is a magnetic ore which is rich in iron. Pieces of magnetite will attract iron filings like an ordinary magnet. These were the lodestones of ancient times. *Siderite,* $FeCO_3$, is a carbonate of iron that is also mined as an ore. *Pyrite,* FeS_2, called fool's gold, is an abundant

iron mineral used in the production of sulfuric acid. It is of minor importance as an iron ore.

If iron ore occurs at the surface of the ground, it is broken up and then loaded on cars by power shovels. In northern Minnesota where the ore is abundant, it is covered with loose, earthy material which is stripped away by power shovels to get at the ore underneath. Sometimes this ore occurs at a depth of as much as 2000 feet below the surface of the ground. For such deposits, a shaft is sunk. From the bottom of the shaft, tunnels branch off in all directions.

Iron ore is mined in nearly half of the states of the United States. Minnesota and Michigan produce many millions of tons each year. Alabama has a thriving iron and steel industry which is favored by the fact that iron ore, coal for making coke, and limestone are all located within a few miles of each other. New York, Pennsylvania, West Virginia, Ohio, and Missouri also produce considerable amounts of iron ore. Blast furnaces have been constructed in Utah and California to supply the needs of our western states.

The largest deposits of iron ore in the world are those of hematite in the Lake Superior region of the United States. Over 90 million tons of ore are shipped through the Great Lakes from this area each year. It is estimated that, at the present rate of consumption, these reserves of high grade hematite will be exhausted by 1970.

New fields in Labrador and Quebec are expected to yield 10 million tons of rich ore by 1960. A veritable mountain of high grade hematite, the Cerro

Fig. 35–2. Magnetite is rich in iron and has magnetic properties. Pieces of this ore were once used in magnetic compasses.

Fig. 35–3. An iron ore storage yard at a lake front steel mill. Ore from the Lake Superior region must be stockpiled during the summer to supply the blast furnaces through the winter months.

Bolivar of Venezuela, was discovered in 1947 by American geologists. It contains more than 400 million tons of ore of about 58% iron. When developed it is expected to yield 10 million tons annually. A 30-million-ton mountain of perhaps the richest iron ore on earth is being developed for mining in the Liberian jungle of Africa by American and Dutch interests.

In addition to the high grade hematite deposits of the Lake Superior region, there is an abundance of low grade ore, *taconite,* which is a mixture of hematite and magnetite in a matrix of rock. The proportions are two parts magnetite to one part hematite. The magnetite is recovered by magnetic separation; the hematite and rock are discarded as tailings.

3. Iron is extracted from its ores by reduction. Coke is the reducing agent. About one ton of coke is required to produce one ton of iron. Limestone is ordinarily used as a *flux* in the reaction. The flux unites with impurities in the ore to form an easily melted *slag.*

Fig. 35–4. Cerro Bolivar, a mountain in southeastern Venezuela, is capped with a thick deposit of high grade iron ore.

Prior to reduction, some ores are improved by a process called **beneficiation.** This is a general term applied to any process, physical or chemical, which renders the ore more suitable for reduction. The magnetic separation of magnetite from low grade ores is an example of *physical beneficiation.* By roasting a low grade of hematite in a reducing atmosphere, it may be converted to magnetite. This is an example of *chemical beneficiation,* the equation for which is:

$$6 \; Fe_2O_3 + C \rightarrow 4 \; Fe_3O_4 + CO_2\uparrow$$

4. The operation of the blast furnace. Iron oxide is reduced to iron in a giant structure called a **blast furnace.** The furnace is about 100 ft high and has an internal diameter of about 25 ft, which makes it about as tall as a 7- or 8-story building. It has a steel shell that is lined with firebrick. A blast of hot air, sometimes enriched with oxygen in the most modern furnaces, is forced into the base of the furnace through blowpipes called **tuyères** (twee-*yair*). This is why it is called a blast furnace.

Hoisting engines raise many tons of raw materials to the top of the furnace each day. The charge consists of iron oxide, coke, and a flux, in the proper proportions as calculated from an analysis of the raw materials. Usually the flux is limestone, because silica or sand is the most common impurity in the iron ore. Some iron ores contain limestone as an impurity. In such cases, the flux that is added is sand.

For a large furnace, during every 24 hours, about 2000 tons of raw materials are dumped into the bell-shaped hopper at the top of the furnace. Once started, a blast furnace is kept in operation night and day, week after week, until the lining of the furnace is worn out. A double hopper is used at the top of the furnace to permit additional materials to be supplied without disturbing the operation.

A single blast furnace may produce 1500 tons of iron, 500 tons of slag, and 2000 tons of flue gas daily. The United States now produces approximately 80 million tons of iron each year. This is being increased constantly by improving blast furnace technology and by the construction of additional furnaces.

A large blast furnace requires about 50,000 cubic feet of hot air every min-

Fig. 35–5. In this typical beneficiation process, heavy waterborne ore particles are separated from lighter impurities by centrifugal force.

Fig. 35–6. A battery of seven stoves serves these two blast furnaces.

ute for the air blast. This air is heated in gigantic stoves that are almost as tall as the furnace itself. Usually there are four stoves so that two can be used for heating the air blast while the other two are being heated. The gas, which comes through the *downcomer* near the top of the furnace, contains carbon monoxide and is combustible. It is this gas which is burned at the base of the stoves that are being warmed. The stoves are filled with a checkerwork of firebrick which becomes white-hot from the combustion of the gas. When the air blast is forced up through the checkerwork of a hot stove, it is heated to 800° C before it is admitted to the base of the blast furnace. When one pair of stoves cools, the air blast is shifted to the other pair, while the cool stoves are reheated.

5. Chemical reactions within the blast furnace. The blast furnace serves two functions: *1.* to reduce the iron ore to iron; and *2.* to remove the earthy gangue as slag. The coke is required for the first function and the limestone for the second. The products of the blast furnace are *pig iron, slag,* and *flue gas.*

The chemical changes which occur are complex. The coke is ignited by the blast of hot air and some of it burns forming carbon dioxide:

$$C + O_2 \rightarrow CO_2\uparrow$$

But as the carbon dioxide which is formed just above the tuyères rises through the furnace, it comes in contact with more coke and is reduced to

Fig. 35–7. Tapping the blast furnace.

Fig. 35–8. Molten pig iron is hauled from the blast furnace to the steel furnace in a refractory-lined railroad car.

carbon monoxide, as in this equation:

$$CO_2 + C \rightarrow 2\ CO\uparrow$$

The carbon monoxide thus formed is actually the reducing agent that reduces the iron oxide to metallic iron.

$$Fe_2O_3 + 3\ CO \rightarrow 2\ Fe + 3\ CO_2\uparrow$$

To prevent the possibility of any reversal of the reactions, the operation is so controlled that there will be a large excess of carbon monoxide. For that reason, the gases that leave the furnace through the downcomer contain from 20 to 30% carbon monoxide.

The white-hot liquid iron flows to the bottom of the furnace as it is reduced. Every 4 or 5 hours it is tapped off. It may be cast into molds to form *pig iron,* or it may go directly to a furnace or converter where it is made into steel.

In the middle region of the furnace, the limestone decomposes into calcium oxide and carbon dioxide.

$$CaCO_3 \rightarrow CaO + CO_2\uparrow$$

The calcium oxide then combines with silica to form a calcium silicate slag which is more readily fused than silica.

$$CaO + SiO_2 \rightarrow CaSiO_3$$

This glassy slag, which consists mostly of calcium silicate, also collects in a pool at the bottom of the furnace. Since it has a much lower density than liquid iron, it floats on top of the melted iron. This is an advantage because it prevents the reoxidation of the iron. The melted slag is tapped off every few hours. Usually the slag is thrown away, although it is sometimes used for making Portland cement.

6. Impurities in cast iron. Not all of the impurities in the iron ore find their way into the slag. Manganese, phosphorus, silicon, and sulfur are usually present in minute quantities in the reduced iron. Pig iron may contain from 2 to 5% carbon, and as much as 1% manganese, 0.1% phosphorus, 3% silicon, and 0.3% sulfur. The carbon may be present either as free carbon in the form of graphite, or as a compound, iron carbide, Fe_3C. This compound, which is called *cementite,* is very hard. *White cast iron* has been cooled quickly and contains much cementite. *Gray cast iron* has been cooled slowly and has more graphite.

7. The properties of wrought iron.
Wrought iron is the purest form of iron which is used commercially. It is made by heating cast iron in a reverberatory furnace which is lined with iron oxide (see Fig. 35-9). The oxygen from the iron oxide lining unites with the excess carbon in the cast iron, and the oxides of carbon escape. Other impurities in the cast iron are similarly oxidized and form a slag. As the purity of the iron increases, the melting point rises, and the iron is collected as a pasty mass. Most of the slag is removed by hammering the iron while it is still plastic.

8. The uses of the different kinds of iron. Several varieties of iron are prepared for different commercial uses by separate types of heat treatment and purification processes. Steel contains more carbon than wrought iron, as a rule, and less carbon than cast iron. Steel varies decidedly in its carbon content, ranging from 0.05% to 1.7% carbon. In fact, steel which contains from 0.05 to 0.4% carbon is often spoken of as *low-carbon steel*. *Medium-carbon steel* contains from 0.4 to 0.8% carbon. Steel which contains from 0.8 to 1.7% carbon is called *high-carbon steel.*

As one would infer from its name, cast iron is used for making castings.

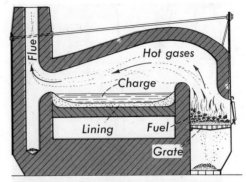

Fig. 35–9. In the reverberatory furnace the hot gases are deflected down on the charge in the bed of the furnace.

The molten iron is poured into sand molds and allowed to cool. Over 75% of the cast iron produced is used every year in making steel.

Wrought iron is used to some extent for making high-grade steel. It is used for blacksmith iron, chains, ornamental furniture, and wire, although the cheaper low-carbon steel has replaced it for many purposes. Wrought iron water pipes resist corrosion better than those of steel or cast iron.

Steel is used for many purposes that require a metal of great tensile strength, such as railroad rails, structural steel for buildings, bridges, automobiles, and ships.

2. THE PRODUCTION OF STEEL

9. The processes for making steel.
Cast iron is a crystalline form of a metallic solution of iron and iron carbide with small amounts of graphite, manganese, phosphorus, silicon, and sulfur present. The relatively high carbon content makes it very hard and brittle. It is very brittle at low temperatures due to the presence of phosphorus. It is also very brittle at high temperatures due to the sulfur.

The conversion of cast iron to steel is essentially a purification process in which the impurities are removed by oxidation. Near the end of the process the proper amounts of carbon and selected alloying substances are added to give the desired properties to the steel.

Three important methods of producing steel are in use today. *1. The Bessemer process* accounts for about 5% of the steel produced in the United

Fig. 35–10. A Bessemer converter "blowing off."

States. Air, or oxygen, is used as the oxidizing agent. *2. The open-hearth process* accounts for about 85% of the steel produced in this country. Ferric oxide is used as the oxidizing agent. *3. The electric-furnace process* accounts for about 10% of the total steel production. Electric-furnace steel is very high in quality. Ferric oxide is used as the oxidizing agent.

Nearly 130 million tons of steel were produced by these processes in the

Fig. 35–11. A charge of molten pig iron being poured into an open hearth furnace.

United States in 1956, and the demand for steel is increasing yearly.

The modern Age of Steel began with the development of the *Bessemer process* a century ago. The great advantage of this process is that tons of steel can be made in approximately 20 minutes from pig iron. The *open-hearth process,* which was developed later, produces even larger batches, but 6 to 12 hours are required for converting the iron into steel. The *electric-furnace process* is a still more recent development that is growing in importance, especially for steels of high quality.

10. The Bessemer process. In this process, the cast iron is poured into an egg-shaped *converter* which is big enough to hold from 15 to 20 tons. The converter is mounted on *trunnions,* which permit it to be turned down on its side to receive the charge of cast iron. The air blast is then turned on, and the converter is turned almost to a vertical position, as you see in Fig. 35-10. The oxygen unites with the carbon and the other impurities present, forming products which either escape as gases or unite with the lining of the converter.

In about 15 or 20 minutes the process is complete. The converter is then turned down on its side, and a measured amount of *spiegeleisen* (*spee*-g'l-eye-zun) , or *ferromanganese,* is added to the iron in the converter. These alloys are rich in carbon and manganese. The carbon thus added to the purified iron gives a steel having the proper carbon content. The manganese unites with the oxygen left in the steel from the blast of air and prevents the formation of blowholes.

Sir Henry Bessemer (1813–1898) , who developed this process, found it hard to tell just when to turn off the air blast so as to leave exactly the right amount of carbon in the finished steel. The problem was solved by burning out all of the carbon, and then adding a small quantity of iron alloy that is rich in carbon. This explains why ferromanganese is added in making steel by the Bessemer process.

Another problem that confronted Bessemer was how to get rid of phosphorus. Phosphorus, present as an impurity in some iron ores, makes steel brittle when it is cold. Sulfur is another undesirable impurity because it makes hot steel brittle. Sulfur is burned out of the steel and escapes as a volatile gas, sulfur dioxide. But phosphorus forms a solid oxide, diphosphorus pentoxide, which is not eliminated so easily. Finally, two English chemists, Thomas and Gilchrist, suggested lining the converter with dolomite, $CaCO_3 \cdot MgCO_3$. When dolomite is heated, it yields the basic anhydrides, CaO and MgO. These compounds react with diphosphorus pentoxide, an acid anhydride, as shown in the following equations:

$$6\ CaO + P_4O_{10} \rightarrow 2\ Ca_3(PO_4)_2$$
$$6\ MgO + P_4O_{10} \rightarrow 2\ Mg_3(PO_4)_2$$

The slag that is formed contains phosphates which are poured off from the converter. Ground to a fine powder, this slag is used as a phosphate fertilizer.

One of the faults of Bessemer steel is the speed by which it is made. "Twenty tons in twenty minutes" yields a tremendous tonnage in 24 hours, but it is hard to control the composition of the steel with precision. All the steel in one batch must be homogeneous, and all gases must be expelled completely, otherwise weak spots would be present as blowholes in the finished steel. These faults have caused the Bessemer process to be superseded largely by the *open-hearth process* today. This more leisurely process allows frequent testing of the steel while it is in process, which insures a more reliable quality in the finished product.

11. The open-hearth process. We shall consider this process under three headings: *1.* the furnace; *2.* the heating system; and *3.* the charge.

1. The furnace. The open-hearth furnace is a monster. It holds a pool of molten steel that is 30 to 80 feet in length, 12 to 15 feet in width, and about

Fig. 35-12. Sectional diagram of an open-hearth furnace for the manufacture of steel.

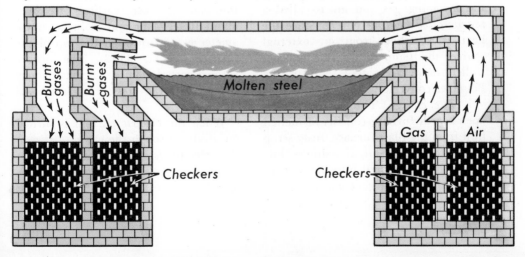

2 feet in depth. From 50 to 200 tons are made in one batch. The furnace is built of steel plates which are covered with a thick lining of either limestone or silica. The choice of the lining depends on whether the cast iron has acid or basic impurities that are to be removed. At the end of the process, the melted steel is poured out into a large ladle.

2. The heating system. A high temperature is necessary to burn out the impurities from the cast iron, and to melt the steel scrap which forms part of the charge. Producer gas is used as the fuel. Both the gas and the air needed for its combustion are preheated before they enter the furnace by passing them over a checkerwork of hot firebrick. As the gas burns inside the furnace, the heat from the flames is reflected down on the charge. The hot waste products of combustion pass out of the furnace through a second checkerwork of firebrick, heating it to a high temperature.

At intervals of about twenty minutes, the valves are reversed to direct the incoming gas and air through the checkerwork just heated. Thus a very hot flame is supplied continuously by the burning of the preheated gas in preheated air. Such a method of utilizing the heat from waste gases to preheat the incoming gas and air is called a *regenerative heating system.* Since the heat is supplied from an external source, the temperature can be controlled more accurately than in the Bessemer converter.

3. The charge. The charge for an open-hearth furnace consists of melted iron from the blast furnace, rusty scrap steel, iron ore, and limestone. The melted iron is poured into the furnace from ladles. A charging machine picks up scrap steel, iron ore, and limestone, and dumps them into the furnace. The iron ore supplies oxygen to unite with the carbon present in the liquid iron from the blast furnace. The limestone unites with impurities to form a slag which is drained off. Scrap steel, shipped from junk yards everywhere, may form as much as 50% of the charge. Thus relatively fewer blast furnaces are required to produce steel in the open-hearth process.

The impurities in the pig iron are oxidized in the following way:

$$3 \ C + Fe_2O_3 \rightarrow 3 \ CO\uparrow + 2 \ Fe$$
$$3 \ Mn + Fe_2O_3 \rightarrow 3 \ MnO + 2 \ Fe$$
$$12 \ P + 10 \ Fe_2O_3 \rightarrow 3 \ P_4O_{10} + 20 \ Fe$$
$$3 \ Si + 2 \ Fe_2O_3 \rightarrow 3 \ SiO_2 + 4 \ Fe$$
$$3 \ S + 2 \ Fe_2O_3 \rightarrow 3 \ SO_2\uparrow + 4 \ Fe$$

The limestone flux decomposes as in the blast furnace:

$$CaCO_3 \rightarrow CaO + CO_2\uparrow$$

Calcium oxide and the oxides of the impurities, except those of carbon and sulfur which escape as gases, react to form the slag:

$$P_4O_{10} + 6 \ CaO \rightarrow 2 \ Ca_3(PO_4)_2$$
$$SiO_2 + CaO \rightarrow CaSiO_3$$
$$MnO + SiO_2 \rightarrow MnSiO_3$$

12. The electric-furnace process. In one common type of electric furnace for making steel, carbon electrodes about 10 feet long and 15 inches in diameter extend through the top of the furnace (see Fig. 35-13). The furnace is lined with dolomite. The charge may consist of scrap steel, cast iron, and iron ore.

When the electric current is turned on, it arcs through the charge between the electrodes, producing the heat necessary to carry out the process. There is no electrolysis. This process

Fig. 35–13. The electric furnace pictured here is tilted while a heat of high grade steel is being tapped. These furnaces may draw 12,000 amperes at 40 volts to produce the heat required to make stainless steel and other alloy steels.

makes high grade steel because: *1.* there is an opportunity to test the steel at various intervals before it is finished; *2.* usually, purer raw materials are used for the charge; and *3.* the operation is carried on in a reducing atmosphere, which prevents oxidation of the steel.

Sometimes a duplex process of making steel is used. Because of its speed, the Bessemer process is first used. Before the reaction is complete, the charge is transferred to either an open-hearth furnace or an electric furnace where it is finished more slowly.

13. How is steel worked? As the steel comes from the furnace, it is usually drawn off into a huge ladle from which it is poured into ingot molds. Such molds are hollow shells in which the steel is permitted to cool until it solidifies. Then the molds are stripped from the ingots of white-hot steel and the ingots are placed in *soaking pits* where they are kept at a uniform high temperature until removed to be worked.

The ingots, at the proper temperature, may be put through a series of rolls. They may be *rolled* into any desired thickness, shape, or length.

Sometimes steel is treated by *drop-forging*. In this treatment, the steel is placed on a block and hammered with a powerful mechanical hammer.

Steel is often shaped in a hydraulic press. Some of the huge presses used

for *stamping* out automobile bodies, or armor plate, are capable of exerting a force of from 12,000 to 14,000 tons.

A *hot extrusion* process has recently been perfected which enables hot billets of steel to be extruded into long seamless tubes. This is a development of great importance for atomic power plants, jet engines, and petroleum refineries. In these industries tough steel

Fig. 35–14. A steel ingot heated to 1300° C is removed from the soaking pit to be worked.

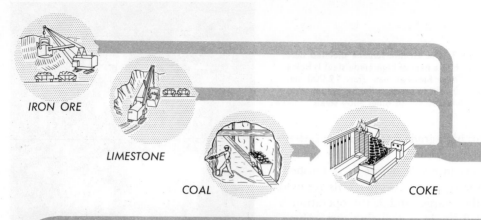

IRON ORE

LIMESTONE

COAL

COKE

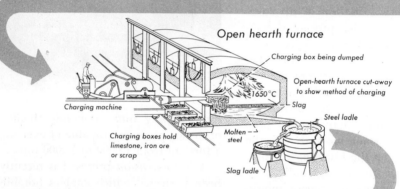

Open hearth furnace

Charging box being dumped

Open-hearth furnace cut-away
to show method of charging

1650°C

Slag

Steel ladle

Charging machine

Charging boxes hold
limestone, iron ore
or scrap

Molten
steel

Slag ladle

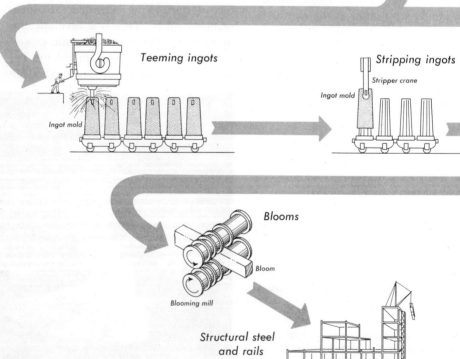

Teeming ingots

Stripping ingots

Stripper crane

Ingot mold

Ingot mold

Blooms

Bloom

Blooming mill

Structural steel
and rails

Fig. 35–15. A flow chart showing the various processes in the manufacture of steel.

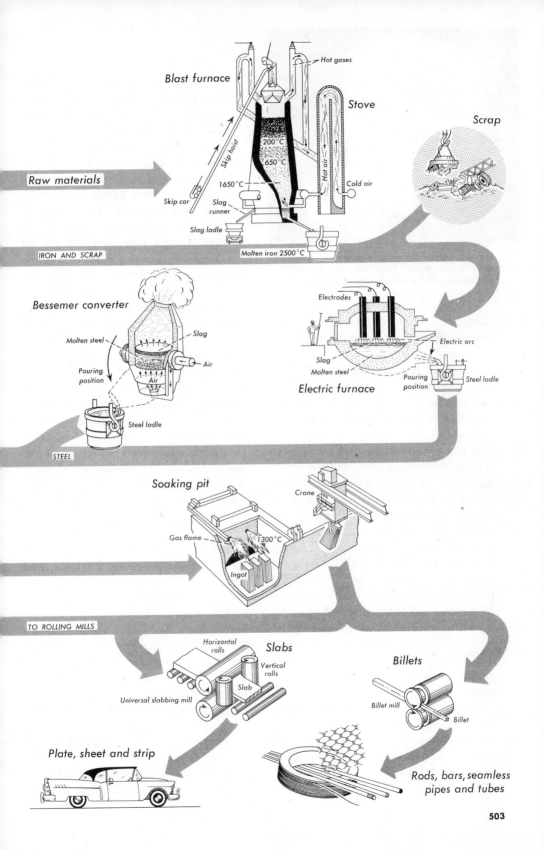

Blast furnace

Hot gases

Stove

Scrap

Skip hoist

200°C

650°C

1650°C

Hot air

Cold air

Raw materials

Skip car

Slag runner

Slag ladle

Molten iron 2500°C

IRON AND SCRAP

Bessemer converter

Electrodes

Molten steel

Slag

Electric arc

Pouring position

Air

Slag

Air

Molten steel

Pouring position

Steel ladle

Electric furnace

Steel ladle

STEEL

Soaking pit

Crane

Gas flame

1300°C

Ingot

TO ROLLING MILLS

Horizontal rolls

Slabs

Billets

Vertical rolls

Universal slabbing mill

Slab

Billet mill

Billet

Plate, sheet and strip

Rods, bars, seamless pipes and tubes

503

Fig. 35–16. Stainless steel contains chromium as an alloying metal. Here we see a lump of chromium and a pitcher made of stainless steel.

tubes are needed to contain liquids and gases under very high temperatures and pressures.

14. How is steel tempered? The properties of steel depend not only on the percentage of carbon it contains, but also on the manner in which the carbon is held.

When a high-carbon steel is heated to a bright cherry-red heat, about 670° C, iron carbide, Fe_3C, is formed. It dissolves in the iron that is present. If such a solution is cooled quickly by plunging it into water, oil, or some other tempering medium, the carbide does not decompose, and a very hard steel is formed, although it is decidedly brittle. If the solution of iron carbide in the iron is cooled slowly, by letting it cool in air, for example, some of the iron carbide decomposes and the product contains iron carbide, iron, and graphite. Such a product is soft and tough.

All grades of hardness between these extremes may be obtained by reheating hardened steel to a definite temperature and then cooling it quickly. For example, suppose we have a piece of hard, brittle steel. If it is reheated to a temperature of 220° C, and then cooled quickly, it will not be quite so hard or quite so brittle. Such a process is called **tempering**. Such a steel will be hard enough for razor blades. If we had reheated the piece of steel to 280° C, and then cooled it quickly, we would have had a product which is still more flexible, but not so hard. It might be suitable for use in making watch springs. To get a product suitable for making handsaws and other woodworking tools, we would need to reheat to a temperature of 300° C to 350° C.

15. Alloy steels have special properties. Ordinary carbon steel is really an alloy, but the name **alloy steel** is traditionally given to steels to which certain metals, or nonmetals, have been added. Just before the steel is drawn from the furnace, a number of metals may be added to the batch to produce special properties in the finished product. Such alloy steels are in great demand by the manufacturers of tools, machines, automobiles, and airplanes. Some of the common alloy steels are listed in the following paragraphs.

1. Nickel steel. A small percentage of nickel added to steel makes an alloy steel that is not easily corroded and combines toughness with hardness. Such a strong, elastic steel is used for making automobile parts, bridges, and armor plate. *Invar* is a nickel-steel alloy that contains about 36% nickel. It expands and contracts very little with temperature changes. It is used for making surveyor's tapes and clock pendulums. *Permalloy* is another nickel-iron alloy which contains about 80% nickel. It is very easily magnetized and is used for transformer cores.

2. Chrome steel. When chromium is added to steel, a hard, tough product is formed. It is useful for making ball bearings, roller bearings, automobile parts, and the jaws of rock-crushing machinery. *Stainless steel* contains about 14% chromium. It resists corrosion very well and is popular for making cutlery, surgical instruments, and nontarnishing metal trim.

3. *Chrome-nickel steel.* Steel that contains about 4% chromium and 4% nickel is exceedingly hard and tough. It is used for making plowshares, crankshafts, files, and gear teeth. Alloy steel, known as "18–8" in the trade, contains 18% chromium and 8% nickel. It does not tarnish.

4. *Chrome-vanadium steel.* Alloy steel that contains both chromium and vanadium withstands severe strains and shocks without breaking. For this reason it is used for making some automobile parts and wrenches.

5. *Manganese steel.* Steel containing considerable amounts of manganese is exceedingly hard. Such manganese steel is used for making burglar-proof safes, and the teeth of the scoops on

power shovels and dredging equipment.

6. *Silicon steel.* Silicon, a nonmetal, is also added to make a special kind of alloy steel. Silicon steel is easily magnetized and demagnetized. Hence it is used for making the cores of transformers and electromagnets.

7. *Tungsten steel.* The addition of considerable tungsten to steel produces an alloy that can be heated red-hot and still retain a hard cutting edge. It is used for making cutting tools for lathes, and for making hacksaw blades.

8. *Molybdenum steels.* Molybdenum alloy steel is very strong. Usually molybdenum is added in small amounts to other alloying metals to produce a strong, tough steel that will resist strains without breaking. Such alloys are used for making automobile parts.

9. *Nitralloy steels.* Nitralloy steels are made by treating a special steel that contains some aluminum with ammonia gas at a temperature of about 500° C. Nitralloy steel is extremely hard and is used on motor parts that are subjected to heavy wear.

3. IRON AND ITS COMPOUNDS

16. Pure iron is seldom seen. Really pure iron is a metal that is seldom seen. It is silver-white, soft, ductile, tough, and does not tarnish readily. It melts at 1535° C. Commercial iron contains carbon and other impurities that alter its properties. Cast iron melts at about 1150° C. All forms of iron corrode, or rust, in moist air, so it is not a self-protective metal. The rust that forms is brittle, and it scales off, leaving the metal underneath exposed to corrosion.

In many cases the corrosion of iron seems to be an electrochemical process.

A carbon particle in contact with a piece of moist iron will cause the iron to rust rapidly. The carbon acts as the positive element of a miniature electrochemical cell, and the iron becomes the negative element (see Fig. 35-17). Rain water containing dissolved carbon dioxide enhances the action.

Merely a difference in the amount of oxygen over the surface of wet iron will result in rusting. A single drop of rain containing dissolved carbon dioxide sets up a tiny cell between the iron at the center of the drop and the iron around the edge. Ferrous hydroxide is

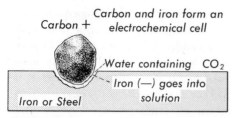

Carbon + Carbon and iron form an electrochemical cell

Water containing CO_2

Iron (—) goes into solution

Iron or Steel

Fig. 35–17. Iron or steel contains impurities and corrodes readily unless covered by a protective coating.

formed and is readily converted to ferric hydroxide. By loss of water the familiar red rust, $Fe_2O_3 \cdot x\ H_2O$ is formed.

Dilute acids generally act readily on iron, but alkalies do not react with it. Concentrated nitric acid does not react with iron. In fact, dipping iron into concentrated nitric acid renders the iron *passive*, or *inactive*, with respect to its behavior toward other chemicals. Concentrated sulfuric acid has little effect upon iron.

17. How can iron be protected? There are several ways of protecting iron:

1. By coating it with other metals. In the galvanizing process, iron is coated with zinc. In some cases cadmium is used. In making tinware, sheet iron is covered with a thin layer of tin.

2. By coating it with metallic compounds and lacquers. Some kinds of paint, such as red lead or zinc chromate, protect iron against corrosion. Lacquers and varnishes are also used to prevent the corrosion of iron.

3. By alloying the iron with other metals. Silicon alloys and stainless steel which contains chromium are alloys of iron or steel which do not tarnish.

4. By using chemicals to form a surface coating. By treating red-hot iron with steam, a thin coating of magnetic iron oxide, Fe_3O_4, is formed on the surface. This coating is adherent and non-

porous. It protects the metal underneath from corrosion. The product, which is called *Russia iron,* is used for making stovepipes. The blue-black oxide on handsaws is similar in its nature.

Iron is "Parkerized" by dipping it into a hot alkaline solution of sodium phosphate. The phosphate forms a thin coating of basic phosphate of iron.

5. By attaching a more active metal. Iron pipes lying in acid soil may be attached to blocks of magnesium. Magnesium is a more active metal than iron as it stands higher on the electrochemical series. As the magnesium corrodes, the attached iron is maintained at a negative potential and does not corrode. Magnesium rods are sometimes placed in hot-water heaters where electrochemical action between iron and copper or brass fittings would cause the iron to corrode.

18. There are three oxides of iron. Of the three oxides of iron, *ferrous oxide,* FeO, is of little importance since it changes rapidly, when exposed to the air, into *ferric oxide,* Fe_2O_3. This oxide is the most important ore of iron, and it is used as a cheap red paint pigment known as red ocher, Venetian red, or Indian red. It is used for grinding and polishing glass under the name of *rouge.*

Limonite is a natural *hydrated ferric oxide* which is pulverized and used as a pigment called yellow ocher. When it is heated or roasted, it forms pigments known as *siennas* and *umbers.* *Magnetic iron oxide,* Fe_3O_4, is an important ore of iron. It is composed of Fe_2O_3 and FeO, and may be considered to be a *ferrous ferrite,* $Fe(FeO_2)_2$.

19. Reactions of the ferrous ion. Hydrated ferrous sulfate, $FeSO_4 \cdot 7\ H_2O$ is the most important compound of iron in the +2 oxidation state. It is commonly called *green vitriol* or *copperas*. It is used to form a mordant, and for making blue-black inks. Ferrous sulfate may be prepared by the action of dilute sulfuric acid on iron. The crystalline hydrate, on exposure to air, loses water of hydration and turns brown due to oxidation. Ferrous sulfate in solution is gradually oxidized to the ferric state. Dissolved oxygen is the oxidizing agent. The formation of a brown precipitate of basic ferric sulfate is evidence of this change.

$$4\ FeSO_4 + O_2 + 2\ H_2O \rightarrow 4\ Fe(OH)SO_4\downarrow$$

By making the solution acidic with sulfuric acid and adding a small amount of metallic iron, the ferrous ion may be maintained in the reduced state. Hydrated ferrous ammonium sulfate, $Fe(NH_4)_2(SO_4)_2 \cdot 6\ H_2O$ is a better source of Fe^{++} ions in the laboratory because it is stable in contact with air.

Ferrous salts are readily oxidized to ferric salts by use of the corresponding acid and an oxidizing agent. In the case of the nitrate, nitric acid meets both requirements.

$$3\ Fe(NO_3)_2 + 4\ HNO_3 \rightarrow$$
$$3\ Fe(NO_3)_3 + NO\uparrow + 2\ H_2O$$

Crystals of hydrated ferrous chloride, $FeCl_2 \cdot 4\ H_2O$, are blue as long as the reduced state is maintained. Gradual oxidation to the ferric state is evident as a green color develops. Ferrous chloride may be prepared by the action of hydrochloric acid on iron.

Ferrous hydroxide is formed as a white precipitate when sodium hydroxide is added to a solution of a ferrous salt. The precipitate is first green, in the presence of air, and finally brown as the ferric hydroxide is formed.

We may show the oxidation of the Fe^{++} ion in the use of an iron ink (ordinary blue-black ink). If a freshly prepared solution of ferrous sulfate is added to a solution of tannic acid, the nearly colorless compound, *ferrous tannate,* is formed. It slowly oxidizes to form the black compound, *ferric tannate.* Usually a blue dye is added to an iron ink, which also contains dextrin to make it wet the pen and the paper, and some poison to prevent the growth of mold. Such an ink writes blue, but soon turns black.

Iron inks are easily removed by the use of a reducing agent, such as oxalic acid, or salt and lemon juice. Skimmed milk applied at once to fresh ink stains, and then followed by cold water, will usually remove nearly all the stain.

Stains made from fountain pen ink (usually a solution of a dye) can generally be removed by adding first a solution of citric acid or tartaric acid, and then following with a solution of sodium hypochlorite. Hydrogen peroxide may then be used also.

20. Reactions of the ferric ion. Ferric chloride, $FeCl_3 \cdot 6\ H_2O$, is the most important compound of iron in the +3 oxidation state. The anhydrous salt may be recovered as black crystals in the composition reaction between iron and chlorine. The hydrated ferric ion, $Fe(H_2O)_6^{+++}$, imparts a pale violet color which usually is not seen because of hydrolysis. Hydrated ferric chloride has a yellow-brown color.

The ferric ion undergoes hydrolysis in water solutions of ferric salts. The solutions are acidic.

$$Fe^{+++} + H_2O \rightleftarrows FeOH^{++} + H^+$$
$$FeOH^{++} + H_2O \rightleftarrows Fe(OH)_2^+ + H^+$$
$$Fe(OH)_2^+ + H_2O \rightleftarrows Fe(OH)_3 + H^+$$

The hydrolysis is extensive when it occurs in boiling water and the blood-red colloidal suspension of ferric hydroxide is formed.

Ferric ions are removed from solution by the addition of a solution containing hydroxide ions. A red-brown gelatinous precipitate of ferric hydroxide is formed. By evaporating the water, red Fe_2O_3 remains. It is the pigment, Venetian red, or the polishing powder, rouge, referred to in Section 18.

$$Fe^{+++} + 3\ OH^- \rightarrow Fe(OH)_3\downarrow$$

21. Tests for the iron ions. Potassium *ferrocyanide*, $K_4Fe(CN)_6$, is a light yellow crystalline salt containing the complex ferrocyanide ion, $Fe(CN)_6^{\equiv}$. The iron is in the ferrous (+2) oxidation state as indicated by the name *ferro(us)*. It may be formed by adding an excess of cyanide ions to a solution of a ferrous salt. CAUTION: *Solutions containing the cyanide ion are deadly poisons and should never be handled by inexperienced chemistry students.*

$$6\ KCN + FeCl_2 \rightarrow K_4Fe(CN)_6 + 2\ KCl$$

The *ferro*cyanide ion may be oxidized by chlorine to the *ferricyanide* ion, $Fe(CN)_6^{\equiv}$.

$$2\ K_4Fe(CN)_6 + Cl_2 \rightarrow 2\ K_3Fe(CN)_6 + 2\ KCl$$

Observe that iron has been oxidized from the +2 ferrous state to the +3 ferric state. Chlorine has been reduced from the 0 to the −1 oxidation state. Potassium *ferri*cyanide, $K_3Fe(CN)_6$, is a dark red crystalline salt.

When *ferrous*, Fe^{++}, ions and *ferri*cyanide, $Fe(CN)_6^{\equiv}$, ions are brought together a deep blue precipitate forms. *The pigment color is due to the presence of iron in two different oxidation states.* This insoluble substance is called Turnbull's blue, and is now considered to have this composition: $KFeFe(CN)_6 \cdot H_2O$.

$$FeSO_4 + K_3Fe(CN)_6 + H_2O \rightarrow$$
$$KFeFe(CN)_6 \cdot H_2O\downarrow + K_2SO_4$$

or simply

$$Fe^{++} + K^+ + Fe(CN)_6^{\equiv} + H_2O \rightarrow$$
$$KFeFe(CN)_6 \cdot H_2O\downarrow$$

Similarly, *ferric*, Fe^{+++}, ions and *ferrocyanide*, $Fe(CN)_6^{\equiv}$, ions form a deep blue precipitate. Again the color is a pigment color and is due to the presence of *two different* oxidation states of iron. The precipitate is called Prussian blue, and is now recognized as having the same composition as Turnbull's blue, $KFeFe(CN)_6 \cdot H_2O$.

$$Fe^{+++} + K^+ + Fe(CN)_6^{\equiv} + H_2O \rightarrow$$
$$KFeFe(CN)_6 \cdot H_2O\downarrow$$

Ferrous, Fe^{++}, ions and *ferrocyanide*, $Fe(CN)_6^{\equiv}$, ions form a white precipitate of $K_2FeFe(CN)_6$, if precautions have been taken to prevent the oxidation of any ferrous ions. Of course, on exposure to air, it begins to turn blue due to oxidation. *Ferric*, Fe^{+++}, ions and *ferricyanide*, $Fe(CN)_6^{\equiv}$, ions give only a brown solution. We can see from these reactions that we have a means of detecting the presence of the two oxidation states of iron.

1. Test for the Fe^{++} ion. Let us add a few drops of potassium *ferricyanide* solution to a solution of ferrous sulfate (or ferrous ammonium sulfate). The characteristic dark blue precipitate, $KFeFe(CN)_6 \cdot H_2O$ forms.

$$Fe^{++} + SO_4^= + 3\ K^+ + Fe(CN)_6^{\equiv} + H_2O \rightarrow$$
$$KFeFe(CN)_6 \cdot H_2O\downarrow + 2\ K^+ + SO_4^=$$

You will recognize that two potassium ions and the sulfate ion are merely spectator ions in this reaction. The *formation of a blue precipitate when potassium ferricyanide is added to a solution suspected of containing the ferrous ion serves as a test for the ferrous, Fe++, ion.*

2. Test for the Fe+++ ion. If we add a few drops of potassium *ferrocyanide* solution to a solution of ferric chloride, the characteristic dark blue precipitate, $KFeFe(CN)_6 \cdot H_2O$, forms.

$$Fe^{+++} + 3\,Cl^- + 4\,K^+ + Fe(CN)_6^{\equiv} + H_2O \rightarrow$$
$$KFeFe(CN)_6 \cdot H_2O\downarrow + 3\,K^+ + 3\,Cl^-$$

Three potassium ions and three chloride ions are spectators in this reaction. *The formation of a blue precipitate when potassium ferrocyanide is added to a solution suspected of containing ferric ions serves as a test for the ferric, Fe+++, ion.*

Potassium thiocyanate, KCNS, provides another excellent test for the ferric ion. It is often used to confirm the ferrocyanide test. A blood-red solution results from the formation of the complex *ferrithiocyanate* ion.

22. The blueprint process. In making blueprints, a solution of *ferric ammonium citrate* is mixed with *potassium ferricyanide*. This forms a brown solution, with which a well-sized paper is coated, and then permitted to dry. All of this is done in a dark room.

When the paper is placed under a negative and exposed to light, reduction occurs and a *ferrous* salt is formed wherever the light strikes the sensitive paper. The print is then developed by dipping it in water. Any ferrous salt formed during the reduction reacts with the potassium ferricyanide and forms an intense blue color.

At those places where no light strikes the paper, no reduction occurs and the water washes away the mixture of unchanged iron compounds, thus fixing the print. The exposed portions are blue in color, and the unexposed portions are white.

4. COBALT AND ITS COMPOUNDS

23. Occurrence and uses of cobalt. Cobalt is found in nature in numerous minerals, together with iron, nickel, copper, silver, and arsenic. It is ordinarily recovered as a by-product of the smelting of various ores. Both cobalt and nickel often remain as oxides after the roasting and reduction processes have been carried out. Cobalt is usually found combined with arsenic and sulfur. The principle ores are *cobaltite*, CoAsS; *smaltite*, $CoAs_2$; and *linnalite*, Co_3S_4. Metallic cobalt may be produced by the reduction of its oxide with aluminum.

This metal so closely resembles nickel that the two metals are often spoken of as "twins." Cobalt has been used to plate iron, but its most important uses are in the making of alloys, three of which are well known.

1. Stellite. A very hard alloy of cobalt and chromium, known as stellite, is used for making metal-cutting tools for use in lathes.

2. Carboloy. This alloy is made by combining cobalt with a carbide of tungsten. It is one of the hardest materials manufactured for use in making cutting tools. It is hard enough to bore holes through glass or porcelain, or to cut threads on glass. It is a tough alloy, not easily broken. Hence it can be used for high-speed cutting tools.

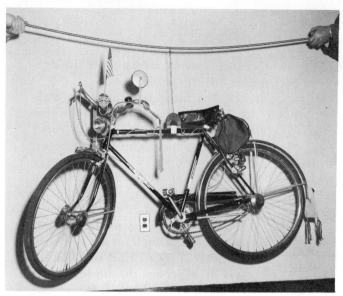

3. Alnico. Alnico is a very strongly ferromagnetic alloy composed of aluminum, cobalt, iron, and nickel. It is used extensively for making small permanent magnets used in loudspeakers, telephones, and hearing aids.

24. Compounds of cobalt. Cobalt forms *cobaltous* and *cobaltic* compounds, in which the oxidation numbers are +2 and +3, respectively. The cobaltous compounds, which exist as red crystals and form pink-colored solutions, are more common than cobaltic compounds.

Cobaltous chloride, $CoCl_2 \cdot 6\,H_2O$, is red when it exists as the hydrate, but turns blue when dehydrated. Paper flowers or doll dresses may be used as a crude *hygrometer* to tell how much moisture the air contains. Such materials are covered with a solution of cobaltous chloride. In moist, damp weather, the flowers or dresses appear pink, changing to violet, and then to blue, as the air becomes less moist. Since the blue color is more intense than the pink, a solution of cobaltous chloride may be used as an invisible ink. When you write on a paper with such a dilute solution, the pink line can hardly be seen. If the paper is heated, the intense blue appears. This color change is frequently used in conjunction with silica gel to indicate when the gel is spent as a desiccant.

Cobaltous nitrate, $Co(NO_3)_2$, is used to some extent in analytical work. It forms a test for zinc, magnesium, or aluminum. Cobalt compounds impart a blue color to glass. Cobalt can be made radioactive and has recently been used successfully in treating the victims of certain types of cancer (see Chapter 39, Section 9).

25. Cobalt nitrate tests. Cobaltous nitrate provides a simple test for the identification of aluminum, magnesium, and zinc by a method of blowpipe analysis. This test is based on the fact that the nitrate, when heated strongly, decomposes to the oxide and combines with the oxides of these metals to form distinctly-colored complexes. A compound of the metal in question is first heated in the oxidizing flame of the blowpipe on charcoal or plaster of Paris. A drop of cobaltous nitrate is then added and the mass is heated again. If *aluminum* is present, a blue coloration develops. *Magnesium* yields a pink-colored mass. *Zinc* produces a green color.

5. NICKEL AND ITS COMPOUNDS

26. The occurrence and properties of nickel. Very little nickel is found in the United States. Almost our entire supply comes from Ontario, Canada, although New Caledonia also produces considerable quantities of the metal.

Nickel is a hard, silver-white metal, capable of taking a high polish. It does not tarnish easily. Its chemical properties resemble those of iron, although it is less active.

27. Some uses of nickel. The uses of nickel for toughening steel, for nickel-plating, and as a catalyst for hardening oils have all been mentioned. Nickel is used in several alloys.

1. Coin nickel. Nickel coinage in the United States is composed of 25% nickel and 75% copper.

2. Monel metal. Attempts to extract nickel from a complex ore of nickel and copper were not very successful, but it was found possible to make the alloy directly from the ore itself. It contains about 67% nickel, 28% copper, and small quantities of iron and manganese. This alloy is strong and tough, and it resists the action of air, sea water, and acids. Monel metal is used in making valves for steam engines, decorative trimmings in cafeterias, and for other purposes requiring a metal that does not tarnish easily.

3. Nichrome. This alloy of nickel, chromium, iron, and manganese melts at a high temperature, and it has a high resistance to the passage of an electric current. It is used in making the heating units for electric irons, toasters, and other heating appliances.

28. Compounds of nickel. Nickel forms *nickelous* and (rarely) *nickelic* salts, in which the oxidation numbers are +2 and +3, respectively. Nickelous salts, which are more common, usually crystallize as beautiful green crystals. The most common nickelous salts are nickelous chloride, nickelous nitrate, and nickelous sulfate. Nickelous sulfide, when prepared by precipitation, is a black, amorphous powder. Nickel flake and nickelous oxide are used for making the active mixture inside the positive plates of the Edison storage battery. When such a battery is charged, *the nickelous compound is oxidized to the nickelic,* being reduced again as the battery is discharged. Nickelous ammonium sulfate, a double salt, is used as the electrolyte for nickel plating. A piece of pure nickel is used as the anode of the plating cell, and the object to be plated is the cathode.

Fig. 35–19. Monel metal is a nonferrous alloy that is both decorative and functional.

Summary

Iron, cobalt, and nickel have many similarities and compose the Iron Family of metals. Iron exists in both the +2 and +3 oxidation states. Hematite is the most abundant iron ore.

Iron ore is reduced in the blast furnace. Coke is the reducing agent. Calcium carbonate (limestone) is added as a flux to remove the gangue. The products of the blast furnace are pig iron, slag, and flue gas. Wrought iron is the purest form of iron used commercially.

The conversion of cast iron to steel is essentially a purification process in which the impurities are removed by oxidation. There are three important methods in use today: *1.* the Bessemer process, in which oxygen is the oxidizing agent; *2.* the open-hearth process, in which ferric oxide is the oxidizing agent; and *3.* the electric-furnace process, in which ferric oxide is the oxidizing agent. The open-hearth accounts for about 85% of the steel produced in the United States. By using different alloying metals, steel alloys of many special varieties can be produced.

Ferrous sulfate is the most important ferrous compound. Ferric chloride is the most important ferric compound. The ferrous ion may be identified by using a solution of potassium ferricyanide. The ferric ion may be similarly identified by using a solution of potassium ferrocyanide.

Cobalt is used in producing several very hard alloys used as cutting tools. Cobaltous compounds, in which cobalt is in the +2 oxidation state, are more common than cobaltic (+3) compounds.

Nickel is used in producing alloys which are highly resistant to corrosion. Nickelous (+2 oxidation state) compounds are common. Nickelic compounds, in which nickel has the oxidation number of +3, are rarely encountered.

Test yourself on these terms

alloy steel	dropforging	Parkerized
beneficiation	flux	pig iron
Bessemer process	high-carbon steel	regenerative heating process
blast furnace	ingots	reverberatory furnace
blueprints	invar	slag
carboloy	low-carbon steel	spiegeleisen
cast iron	monel metal	stellite
cementation process	nichrome	tempering
copperas	nitralloy	trunnions
domain	open-hearth process	wrought iron

Questions

Group A

1. Name four common iron ores.
2. What is the difference between *white cast iron* and *gray cast iron*?
3. Which process is most used for making steel in this country? Explain.

4. What are five methods of protecting the surface of iron against rusting?
5. What is monel metal, and what are some of its properties?
6. What is an advantage and a disadvantage of the Bessemer steel process?
7. How is wrought iron made?
8. Explain how a steel knife blade is tempered.
9. (a) What is nichrome? (b) Why is it used in electric toasters?
10. What was the old cementation process for making steel?
11. Explain why iron inks write blue and dry black.
12. What fortunate situation favors the iron and steel industry in Alabama?

Group B

13. Why does impure iron rust more rapidly than pure iron?
14. Name four advantages of the open-hearth process for steelmaking over the Bessemer process.
15. Give the common names of two oxides of iron that are used as pigments.
16. What steel process would probably be used for making a batch of steel for the blades of kitchen knives?
17. (a) How can "sympathetic ink" be made from a cobalt compound? (b) Why does it turn blue when the paper is heated?
18. What are the advantages of the duplex process for making steel?
19. How do the percentages of carbon in *low-carbon, medium-carbon,* and *high-carbon* steel compare?
20. Mention a use for which each of the following is particularly suitable: (a) permalloy; (b) invar; (c) silicon steel; (d) stainless steel; (e) manganese steel; (f) chrome-nickel steel; (g) tungsten steel.
21. (a) What chemical change occurs when blueprint paper is exposed to the light? (b) What is the chemical formula for the blue compound that is formed on the blueprint paper?
22. Explain the regenerative heating system that is employed in the open-hearth steel process.
23. How can phosphorus be removed from steel that is made by the Bessemer process?
24. How can you detect a *ferrous* and a *ferric* compound, if both are present in the same solution?

Problems

Group A

1. How much ferrous chloride can be made by adding 100 g of iron to an excess of hydrochloric acid?
2. How much ferric chloride can be prepared from the ferrous chloride in the preceding problem if more hydrochloric acid is added and air is blown through the solution?

Group B

3. A sample of hematite ore contains Fe_2O_3 87%, silica 8%, moisture 4%, other impurities 1%. What is the percentage of iron in the ore?
4. What will be the loss in weight when a million tons of the ore in the preceding problem is heated to 200° C?

5. How much limestone will be needed to combine with the silica in a million tons of the ore of Problem 3?

6. (*a*) How many tons of carbon monoxide are required to reduce 1 million tons of the ore of Problem 3? (*b*) How many tons of coke must be supplied to meet this requirement? (Assume the coke to be 100% carbon.)

7. Ferrous sulfate is oxidized to ferric sulfate in the presence of sulfuric acid using nitric acid as the oxidizing agent. Nitric oxide and water are also formed. Balance the equation.

Some things for you to do

1. Collect samples of different kinds of steel from a machine shop. Low-carbon steel, medium-carbon steel, high-carbon steel, tool steel, and various alloy steels should be available. Note the difference in appearance, hardness, resistance to corrosion, etc. of the samples.

2. Prepare some iron tannate ink. To a solution of freshly reduced ferrous sulfate, add a solution of tannic acid. If the ferrous salt is not contaminated by ferric salt, the ferrous tannate that results will be nearly colorless. Separate the ferrous tannate solution into three parts. Use one portion to write a message on paper. Note that the result is nearly colorless writing. Add a few drops of a blue dye solution to the second portion and write with this liquid. Note that the solution "writes blue." To the third solution add a few drops of hydrogen peroxide solution to serve as an oxidizing agent. Note that the ferrous tannate is immediately changed to ferric tannate, a black, insoluble substance. The writing with ferrous tannate solution will gradually turn black as the ferrous compound is oxidized by the air. The blue writing of the second portion will change to black, also, as the ferrous tannate oxidizes.

Chapter 36 THE
COPPER FAMILY

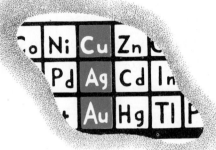

1. The Copper Family is composed of the three inactive metals, copper, silver, and gold. Together they compose Group IB in the Periodic Table of the elements. All three metals appear below hydrogen in the electrochemical series.

They are not easily oxidized and may occur free in nature.

Copper, silver, and gold resemble the Group IA metals, the Sodium Family, only to the extent that they each have one electron in their outer shells. They form compounds in which they show the oxidation number of +1. The Cop-

per Family is characterized by a shell of 18 electrons just beneath the valence shell. One or two electrons may be easily removed from this shell. Thus copper and gold more often exhibit the oxidation numbers of +2 and +3, respectively.

The members of the Copper Family are very dense, ductile, and malleable. They are classed as heavy metals along with the other transition metals of the central region of the Periodic Table. Some important properties of each metal are shown in the table at the top of page 516.

VOCABULARY

Amalgam (a-*mal*-gam). An alloy of mercury with another metal or metals.

Calcine (*kal*-syne). A partially roasted copper ore.

Cupel (*koo*-pel). A porous crucible or dish of bone ash.

Matte (*mat*). A crude mixture of sulfides produced in a partially refined ore.

Poling. The use of green wood to prevent oxidation in the production of crude copper.

Riffle (*rif*-'l). A strip laid crosswise in a sluice for retaining gold particles.

Sluice (*sloos*). A trough for washing out gold from gold-bearing gravel.

ELEMENT	ATOMIC NUMBER	ATOMIC WEIGHT	ELECTRON CONFIGURA-TION	OXIDA-TION NUM-BERS	MELT-ING POINT, °C	BOIL-ING POINT, °C	DEN-SITY g/cm³
COPPER	29	63.54	2,8,18,1	+1,+2	1083	2336	8.9
SILVER	47	107.880	2,8,18,18,1	+1	960.8	1950	10.5
GOLD	79	197.0	2,8,18,32,18,1	+1,+3	1063	2600	19.3

1. COPPER AND ITS COMPOUNDS

2. The occurrence of copper. Copper, alloyed with tin in the form of bronze, has been in use over 5000 years. The first copper mines were probably located in northern Africa. The Romans obtained copper from Cyprus and Spain.

Today the United States produces more than one-quarter of the world's output. Chile, Canada, the Belgian Congo, and Northern Rhodesia are other large producers of copper. Prior to 1940, the United States exported copper. In 1956 over 1 million tons of copper were produced from domestic ores; however, American industries consumed nearly 1.5 million tons.

For many years Michigan was the leading copper-producing state. Native copper, mixed with rock, or present in

Fig. 36–1. This mass of native copper, weighing over 600 pounds, was found in northern Michigan in 1766.

large masses, is found there. Now the deposits lie deep underground, which increases the cost of the mining. The shaft in the famous Calumet and Hecla mine leads underground more than 8500 feet in vertical depth. Arizona, Utah, Montana, New Mexico, and Nevada are today the five largest copper-producing states.

Sulfide ores of copper yield most of our supplies of this metal. *Chalcocite*, Cu_2S, *chalcopyrite*, $CuFeS_2$, and *bornite*, Cu_3FeS_3, are the principal sulfide ores. *Malachite*, $Cu_2(OH)_2CO_3$, and *azurite*, $Cu_3(OH)_2(CO_3)_2$, are beautiful minerals that are basic carbonates of copper. Malachite is a rich green, and azurite is a deep blue. Besides serving as ores of copper, extra fine specimens of these minerals are sometimes polished for ornamental purposes or used in making jewelry.

3. The extraction of copper. The native ore is crushed in a stamp mill, which is like a huge mortar and pestle, and the rock is washed away by a stream of water. The remaining metal is then melted with a flux to remove any gangue that was not washed away, and is cast into large plates.

The carbonate ores of copper are leached with dilute sulfuric acid forming a solution of cupric sulfate. The copper is then recovered by electrolysis. High grade carbonate ores may be roasted to convert them into cupric oxide. The oxide is then reduced with coke to yield the metal.

The sulfide ores, particularly when iron is present as well as copper, present a more difficult refining problem. These are usually low-grade in quality and require concentrating before they can be smelted profitably. The concentration is accomplished by oil-flotation. Earthy gangue is wetted by water and the ore is wetted by oil. A froth is produced and the oil-wetted ore is floated to the surface of the flotation cell in the froth (see Chapter 33, Section 7, for a detailed description of the flotation process). Approximately two-thirds of the gangue is removed in this way. The concentrated ore may be nearly 10% copper.

The concentrated ore is partially roasted to form a mixture of Cu_2S, FeS, FeO, and SiO_2. This mixture is known as *calcine*. The calcine is then fused with limestone as a flux in a reverberatory furnace. Part of the iron is removed as a silicate slag, while the rest

of the iron, together with the copper, forms a mixture of sulfides known as *matte*. Copper matte contains approximately 40% copper. The melted matte is then poured into a converter much like that used in the Bessemer steel process. A blast of air is blown through the converter for about five hours. Sulfur from the sulfides, as well as arsenic and antimony which are present as impurities, are oxidized and escape as volatile oxides. Iron forms a slag which is poured off at intervals. The blast of air converts some of the cuprous sulfide into cuprous oxide. The cuprous oxide then reacts with more cuprous sulfide and forms metallic copper and sulfur dioxide. The equations follow:

$$2\ Cu_2S + 3\ O_2 \rightarrow 2\ Cu_2O + 2\ SO_2\uparrow$$
$$2\ Cu_2O + Cu_2S \rightarrow 6\ Cu + SO_2\uparrow$$

At the end of the operation, the copper is poured into a reverberatory furnace for further treatment. Sticks of green wood are thrust into the melted metal. The products of the decomposition of the green wood reduce any cuprous oxide present. This operation is known as **poling**. The copper is then cast in

Fig. 36–2. Low grade copper ores are concentrated in froth-flotation cells.

Fig. 36–3. A copper converter in action. Molten metal is being withdrawn for further treatment in a reverberatory furnace.

molds. As it cools, dissolved gases escape, forming blisters, hence the name *blister copper* for the crude metal obtained. Blister copper is about 99% pure. It contains about 1% iron, silver, gold, and perhaps zinc.

4. The refining of blister copper. Crude copper is usually refined before it is marketed for two reasons: *1. The crude copper contains appreciable amounts of silver and gold.* The value of these metals when recovered is enough to pay the cost of refining. *2. Copper is largely used for making electrical conductors,* and very small amounts of impurities increase the electrical resistance decidedly.

In the refining process, sheets of pure copper are used as the cathodes in electrolytic cells, and large plates of blister copper are used as the anodes. The electrolyte is a solution of cupric sulfate in sulfuric acid. A direct current at low

voltage is used to operate the cell. During the electrolysis, copper and other metals above it in the electrochemical series, which compose the anode, are oxidized and enter the solution as ions.

$$Cu^0 - 2 e^- \rightarrow Cu^{++}$$
$$Fe^0 - 2 e^- \rightarrow Fe^{++}$$
$$Zn^0 - 2 e^- \rightarrow Zn^{++}$$

Higher voltages than that used would be required to oxidize the less active silver and gold. These metals do not go into solution. As the anode is used up they fall to the bottom of the cell as a sludge from which they are easily recovered.

We might expect the various positive ions of the electrolyte to be reduced at the cathode. However, hydrogen ions (as H_3O^+), Fe^{++} ions, and Zn^{++} ions all require higher voltages than Cu^{++} ions to be discharged. At the low potential maintained across the cell, only Cu^{++} ions are reduced at the cathode.

$$Cu^{++} + 2 e^- \rightarrow Cu^0$$

Thus of all the metals present, only

Fig. 36–4. The principle of electrolytic refining of copper is illustrated by the action in this simple electroplating cell.

Fig. 36–5. Copper is refined to a high degree of purity in these small electrolytic tanks.

copper plates out on the cathode. Electrolytic copper is over 99.9% pure.

5. The properties of copper. Copper is a soft, red metal which is ductile, malleable, and has a density of 8.9 g/cm³. Next to silver, it is the best conductor of electricity.

Heated in air, copper forms a black coating of cupric oxide, CuO. A copper wire, and most copper compounds, color a Bunsen flame green. The copper halides produce a blue flame as do other copper compounds when moistened with hydrochloric acid.

Copper forms cupric salts which dissociate in water to form blue solutions. The color is characteristic of the hydrated cupric ion, $Cu(H_2O)_4^{++}$. The addition of an excess of ammonia to solutions containing this ion produces the deeper blue $Cu(NH_3)_4^{++}$ ion.

Sulfur vapor forms a blue-black coating of cupric sulfide on copper. In moist air, copper tarnishes and forms a protective coating of a green basic carbonate, $Cu_2(OH)_2CO_3$. Sulfur dioxide in the air may also combine with copper to produce a green basic sulfate, $Cu_4(OH)_6SO_4$. The green color seen on copper roofs is due to the formation of these compounds.

Both *cuprous* and *cupric* compounds are known, although cupric compounds are much more common. Cupric oxide is used in current rectifiers to change alternating current to direct current. It is also used as an oxidizing agent in chemical laboratories.

Hydrated cupric sulfate, formula, $CuSO_4 \cdot 5 H_2O$, commonly called *blue vitriol,* is the most important copper compound. It is used to kill algae in reservoirs, for making the agricultural spray known as Bordeaux mixture, for electroplating, and for making other copper compounds.

As copper stands below hydrogen on the replacement series, it does not replace hydrogen from acids. Thus it is not acted on by non-oxidizing acids such as hydrochloric and dilute sulfuric except very slowly when oxygen is present. The oxidizing acids, nitric and hot concentrated sulfuric, react vigorously with copper to produce the corresponding cupric salts. These are typical oxidation-reduction reactions.

CAUTION: *All the soluble compounds of copper are poisonous.*

★ **6. Tests for the cupric ion.** A dilute solution of a cupric salt changes to a very deep-blue color when ammonia

is added. This is caused by the formation of the complex cupric-ammonia, $Cu(NH_3)_4^{++}$, ion. The addition of potassium ferrocyanide to a solution containing the cupric ion produces a red precipitate of cupric ferrocyanide, $Cu_2Fe(CN)_6$. If copper is present in a borax bead formed in the *oxidizing* flame, a clear blue color appears on cooling. The hot bead is green. A bead formed in the *reducing* flame is colorless while hot and an opaque red when cool.

7. Copper is a very useful metal. More electrical conductors are made from copper than from any other metal. Copper is also used for sheathing the bottoms of ships, for making electrotypes used in printing, for making water pipes, tanks, and hot water coils. Large quantities are used for making alloys, especially brass. Sheet copper is used for a permanent roofing material. Flashings around chimneys, gutters, and rain conductors are made from copper because it lasts indefinitely.

8. Many common alloys contain copper. *Brass* is an alloy of copper and zinc. *Bronze* contains copper and tin, and sometimes zinc. *German silver* contains copper, zinc, and nickel. All our coins contain copper, the penny having as high as 95%. Both silver and gold coins contain 10% copper to increase the hardness. Some silver and gold jewelry also contains copper for the same reason.

Fig. 36–7. Brass, an alloy of copper and zinc, has excellent working properties for cutting and machining.

2. SILVER AND ITS COMPOUNDS

9. The occurrence of silver. Utah, Montana, Idaho, Arizona, Nevada, and Colorado have valuable silver mines. Mexico is the largest silver-producing country, followed by the United States and Canada. Peru and Bolivia also produce considerable amounts.

Much silver is obtained as a by-product in the refining of silver-bearing lead and copper ores. Silver is also found free in nature. Silver sulfide, Ag_2S, and silver chloride, $AgCl$, are compounds from some silver mines.

10. How is silver extracted? Three methods are used for extracting silver. *1. By-product silver.* The residue that falls to the bottom of the electrolytic tank in which copper is refined is treated with dilute sulfuric acid to remove impurities more active than silver. By treating the residue with concentrated sulfuric acid, the silver is separated from the gold as silver sulfate. Scrap copper is then added to the silver sulfate solution to precipitate the silver.

$$Ag_2SO_4 + Cu \rightarrow CuSO_4 + 2 Ag\downarrow$$

2. Cyanide process. Crushed silver ore is roasted with common salt to convert the silver to silver chloride. It is added to a huge wooden tank with a large volume of water. Sodium cyanide, $NaCN$, is then added, and the mixture is allowed to stand for two weeks. The cyanide ions form complex argenticyanide, $Ag(CN)_2^-$, ions which are soluble.

$$AgCl + 2 NaCN \rightarrow NaAg(CN)_2 + NaCl$$

Silver is precipitated from the filtered sodium argenticyanide solution by adding metallic zinc:

$$2 NaAg(CN)_2 + Zn \rightarrow Na_2Zn(CN)_4 + 2 Ag\downarrow$$

3. Parkes process. Crude lead which contains silver and gold as impurities is melted in a large kettle. Pieces of zinc are then added, and the mixture is stirred. Both silver and gold are much more soluble in molten zinc than in lead. The zinc rises to the surface, carrying with it almost all of the silver and gold. The zinc alloy is scraped off, and the zinc is vaporized in a retort. The residue which is left consists of silver, gold, and a little lead. It is heated in a bone ash container called a *cupel*. The lead oxidizes, and the lead oxide is absorbed by the cupel, leaving a button of silver and gold. Nitric acid

Fig. 36–8. Ancient silver coins.

Fig. 36–9. Silver and gold are recovered from crude lead by the Parkes process.

reacts with silver but does not react with gold. In this way, the silver is separated from the gold.

11. What are the properties of silver? Silver is a soft, white, lustrous metal. Its specific gravity is 10.5, and it is the best conductor of heat and electricity known.

Silver is an inactive metal. It does not unite with oxygen in the air, even at elevated temperatures. Traces of hydrogen sulfide in the air cause a brownish-black coating of silver sulfide to form on the surface of silver. The sulfur compounds present in such foods as mustard and eggs will cause silverware to tarnish readily.

Tarnished silverware may be cleaned easily by putting it in an aluminum pan, covering it with water, adding a teaspoonful of baking soda (sodium hydrogen carbonate) per quart of water, and boiling the solution. This arrangement forms an electrochemical cell in which the aluminum pan is the cathode and the silverware is the anode. The silver sulfide is reduced by hydrogen which forms at the anode. The silverware should be thoroughly rinsed in hot and then cold water after the process.

Silver reacts readily with oxidizing acids such as nitric acid and hot concentrated sulfuric acid. Hydrochloric acid does not react with it, nor does fused sodium hydroxide or potassium hydroxide.

12. The uses for silver. Much silver is used in making coins and jewelry. The United States coins contain 90% silver and 10% copper. Sterling silver contains 92.5% silver and 7.5% copper. Silver plate tableware and other silver plate articles are widely used. In the silvering of mirrors, a solution of a silver compound mixed with a reducing agent such as formaldehyde is poured on the clean glass. A film of metallic silver is deposited on the glass as the reduction occurs. Next to coinage, the principal use for silver is in photography.

13. Some silver compounds are useful. *Silver nitrate,* $AgNO_3$, crystallizes in colorless scales. It is sometimes used, under the name *lunar caustic,* for cauterizing wounds and bites. *Argyrol* is a compound of silver with a protein, silver vitellin, that is used in medicine as an antiseptic.

The halogen compounds of silver, *silver chloride,* AgCl, *silver bromide,* AgBr, and *silver iodide,* AgI, are sensitive to light, especially if organic matter is present. The chemical action which occurs is one of reduction. Finely divided silver, which is black in color, is formed. Silver bromide is the most sensitive to light, although all three are used in photography.

14. The principal steps in photography. There are three main steps in the chemistry of photography. *1. Making the film or plate.* A film of cellulose acetate, or a glass plate, is coated with a light-sensitive emulsion. This consists of finely divided silver bromide colloidally dispersed in gelatin. The process is carried out in a dark room. Light must not fall on the film or plate until it is ready for exposure.

2. Making the negative. This consists of four steps. (*a*) *Exposure.* The film (or plate) is exposed to light, which is focused on it by the camera lens, just long enough to start the reduction of the sensitive silver salt. (*b*) *Developing.* The exposed film is developed in a dark room by immersing it in a solution of an alkaline reducing agent. Hydroquinone, pyrogallol, and other organic compounds are used as developers. The developing does not readily start the reduction of any unchanged silver salt, but it continues the reduction started by the exposure to light. (*c*) *Fixing.* After the developing has continued long enough to bring out the picture, the film must be fixed. Fixing consists of immersing the film (still in the dark room) in a solution of sodium thiosulfate, called *hypo.* The sodium thiosulfate dissolves any unchanged silver salts leaving metallic silver wherever the light struck the silver salt. (*d*) *Washing.* The film must then be thoroughly washed in water to remove excess chemicals. Light and

Fig. 36–10. Left, a photographic negative. Right, a positive print made from the same negative.

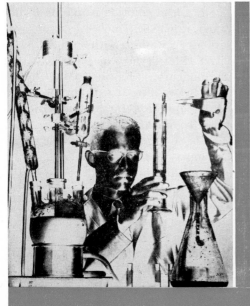

Fig. 36–11. Many chemistry students find photography a fascinating hobby.

dark shades of the original object are reversed now on the film, and it is called a *negative.*

3. *Making the print. A* **positive print** is made by placing the negative over a sheet of paper that has been sensitized in the same manner as the film or plate. The paper with the negative superposed is exposed to light for a brief interval. The paper is then developed, fixed, and washed in a dark room just as the negative was.

★ **15. Test for the silver ion.** Certain solubility characteristics of the silver, Ag^+, ion enable us to recognize its presence in solutions. The chlorides of silver, mercury (ous), and lead are very slightly soluble. If we add a soluble chloride to a test solution containing silver ions, silver chloride will form as a white precipitate. If lead and mercurous ions are present they too will

precipitate as chlorides. Certain other metallic oxy-chloride complexes, which otherwise might precipitate, may be prevented from doing so by first making the test solution acid with HNO_3.

Since lead chloride is soluble in hot water, it may be removed from our precipitate by washing with hot water. The silver chloride may be separated from the mercurous chloride in the precipitate by washing it with an ammonia-water solution. This produces the soluble complex, the $Ag(NH_3)_2{}^+$ ion. The basic filtrate contains these silver-ammonia ions and chloride ions. By neutralizing the hydroxide ions of the basic filtrate with nitric acid, silver chloride will again precipitate. *The formation of a white precipitate when this filtrate is made acidic in the manner described indicates the presence of silver.*

3. GOLD—THE YELLOW METAL

16. The occurrence of gold. Gold was probably the first metal known to man, being found free in nature. Primitive people collected gold for its ornamental value before any metallurgical processes were known.

California, South Dakota, and Alaska have valuable gold mines. Gold is also mined in a number of other states. Much of the metal produced in the United States is obtained as a by-product from copper and lead mining. The Union of South Africa, the Soviet Union, Canada, and the United States, in that order, are the greatest gold-producing countries. Australia produces a considerable amount.

Gold occurs in *alluvial* deposits as fine particles mixed with sand. It is also found in veins mixed with quartz. While it is usually found as the native metal, compounds of gold with tellurium sometimes occur. Sea water contains 0.1 mg to 0.2 mg per metric ton, but it would cost many times its value to extract it.

17. How is gold extracted? When the gold is in alluvial sand deposits, *hydraulic mining* is used. Powerful streams of water wash the sand into inclined troughs, called *sluices*. The dense particles of gold fall to the bottom, where they are retained by crosswise strips known as *riffles*.

Gold-bearing quartz ores are crushed to a fine powder in a stamp mill. As the powdered ore is carried away by running water it comes in contact with mercury, which forms an amalgam with the gold. The gold amalgam is then distilled to get the gold, and to recover the mercury. This is called the **amalgamation process.**

Low-grade gold ores are pulverized and mixed with a large volume of water in a tank. Sodium cyanide is added and, in the presence of air, a soluble *sodium aurocyanide,* $NaAu(CN)_2$, is formed. Metallic zinc is used to precipitate the gold from the aurocyanide.

$$2\,NaAu(CN)_2 + Zn \rightarrow Na_2Zn(CN)_4 + 2\,Au\downarrow$$

This method, known as the *cyanide process,* has made it possible to extract gold profitably from ores that contain very little gold per ton.

Gold is sometimes extracted from pulverized ore with moist chlorine gas. It unites with the chlorine to form *auric chloride,* $AuCl_3$, which is soluble in water. The solution of auric chloride is reduced by ferrous sulfate to metallic gold, which precipitates.

18. The properties of gold. Gold is a soft, yellow metal that is very ductile. It is so malleable that it can be hammered into sheets so thin that 250 of them would be required to equal the thickness of this page. Gold is an excellent conductor of heat and electricity. It is very dense and has a specific gravity of 19.3.

Gold does not tarnish when exposed to the air, even at elevated tempera-

Fig. 36-12. A nugget of native gold.

Fig. 36–13. Gold is extracted from low grade ores by the cyanide process.

tures. Hydrofluoric acid reacts with it slowly. Such strong acids as hydrochloric, nitric, and sulfuric do not react with it, if used singly, but *aqua regia* ($HNO_3 + 3 HCl$) does react with it readily forming auric chloride.

19. The uses of gold. Gold is used in coins and jewelry. Pure gold is too soft to wear well, hence copper is almost always alloyed with it. Its purity is expressed in *carats,* pure gold being 24 carats fine. Jewelry that is 18 carat is stamped 18K, and contains 18 parts by weight of gold mixed with 6 parts by weight of copper. Less expensive, but more durable jewelry is made from 14-carat gold. Rings made of 10-carat gold are still less expensive.

Considerable quantities of gold are used in dentistry in the form of fillings, inlays, crowns, and bridges. Gold leaf is used for lettering and window decorating. Some gold is used for decorating expensive china tableware and in gold plating.

20. Gold forms two series of compounds. Both *aurous* and *auric* compounds of gold are known. In aurous compounds, the gold has the oxidation number of +1. In auric compounds, which are more common, the gold has the oxidation number of +3. *Auric chloride* is used in photography to give the prints a more pleasing shade. *Sodium aurocyanide* is used for gold-plating.

Colloidal gold may be produced by the electric arc method (see Chapter 33, Section 3) or by the reduction of auric chloride. If a solution of stannous chloride and stannic acid is added to a dilute solution of auric chloride, the gold is reduced to the free metal. Stannous chloride is the reducing agent. Colloidal stannic acid may be formed by heating the mixture, and the gold particles are adsorbed on the stannic acid dispersion. A purple structural color results which is known as *purple of Cassius.*

Summary

Native copper is mined in certain areas; however, the principal ores are sulfides. Crude copper is usually refined by electrolysis, as most of the uses of the metal require a very high degree of purity. Copper is a red metal that ranks next to silver as a conductor of electricity. In combined form it may display an oxidation number of +1 or +2, the latter being more common. In moist air copper forms a protective coating of a basic carbonate or sulfate.

Silver is a white, lustrous metal found in the native state, as silver sulfide, and as silver chloride. It is recovered as a by-product in the refining of lead and copper ores. Silver does not unite with oxygen, but forms black silver sulfide readily. Silver halides are sensitive to light, a property that is the basis for the photographic process.

Gold usually occurs as the native metal. It is a soft, lustrous metal and is almost always alloyed with copper to increase its hardness. Gold reacts readily with aqua regia to form auric chloride.

Test yourself on these terms

alluvial	calcine	matte
amalgam	cupel	Parkes process
amalgamation process	cyanide process	poling
blister copper	18K	purple of Cassius
blue vitriol	electrolytic copper	riffles
brass	hypo	sluices
bronze	lunar caustic	sterling

Questions

Group A

1. What are the uses of blue vitriol?
2. What are five points of similarity between copper, silver, and gold?
3. What are the two most important uses for silver?
4. What type of copper ores provides the bulk of the copper produced in the United States today?
5. A gold ring is stamped 14K. What does this mean?
6. What are the uses for copper?
7. (a) What is blister copper? (b) How did it get its name?
8. What are four uses for gold?
9. How is copper obtained from the native metal?
10. (a) Have you ever seen any silver oxide? (b) What is the tarnish on a piece of old silverware?
11. Describe the aluminum process for cleaning silverware.
12. What happens to the halogen compounds of silver when they are exposed to light?
13. Why does the copper trim on roofs frequently acquire a surface that is green?
14. How is crude copper refined?

Group B

15. How can silver be obtained from the *anode mud* that collects in a tank used for the electrolysis of copper?
16. Explain the process of making photographic film.
17. German silver is an alloy of what metals?
18. How is photographic film developed?
19. How may lead chloride be separated from silver chloride?
20. How is a piece of glass silvered to make a mirror?
21. Why is a developed film placed in a fixing bath?
22. How is gold obtained by hydraulic mining?
23. What are the formulas for *aurous* and *auric* chlorides?
24. Why does it usually pay to refine copper by electrolysis?
25. How is the silver, present as an impurity in crude lead, extracted?
26. What is the cyanide process of extracting gold?
27. Describe the cyanide process of extracting silver from silver ore.
28. How is crude copper obtained from chalcopyrite ore?

Problems

Group A

1. What is the percentage of copper in $CuSO_4 \cdot 5 H_2O$?
2. How many grams of silver nitrate can be obtained by adding 100 g of pure silver to an excess of nitric acid?

Group B

3. Silver reacts with dilute nitric acid to form silver nitrate, water, and nitric oxide. Balance the equation.
4. Copper reacts with hot concentrated sulfuric acid to form cupric sulfate, sulfur dioxide, and water. Balance the equation.

Some things for you to do

1. Plate some copper from solution by electrolysis. Use a solution of cupric sulfate, to which a little sulfuric acid has been added, as the electrolyte. The anode can be a piece of scrap copper. The cathode should be a piece of sheet copper. Use a direct current.
2. Make a "silver tree" from sheet zinc and silver nitrate solution. Cut a piece of sheet zinc into a more or less triangular shape, like an evergreen tree. Cut horizontal slits in the zinc toward the center and bend the zinc so as to give it a three-dimensional effect. Immerse the zinc in a solution of silver nitrate (about 1%).
3. Dissolve gold leaf in aqua regia. Mix one volume of concentrated nitric acid with three volumes of concentrated hydrochloric acid. Add a bit of gold leaf to the mixed acids, and stir. Gold reacts with the aqua regia, forming auric chloride. Try to prepare a gold hydrosol from this solution.

Chapter 37

ZINC, CADMIUM, MERCURY, TIN, AND LEAD

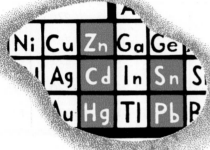

1. Zinc, cadmium, and mercury make up Group IIB of the Periodic Table. Each metal has 2 electrons in the outermost shell and forms ions with an oxidation number of +2. Like several other elements of the B-Groups, these metals have 18 electrons in the shell immediately beneath the valence shell. Mercury also exhibits the oxidation number +1. The *mercurous* ion is known to have the $(Hg \cdot \quad)^{++}$ structure rather than Hg^+ as it is commonly written in empirical formulas. The Hg^+ ion has a single electron remaining in the valence shell. Two such ions share their odd electrons to form a covalent bond and attain greater stability, hence the structure, Hg_2^{++}.

Ions of mercury are much more difficult to form than those of zinc and cadmium. In fact, mercury has a strong tendency to form covalent bonds. In some respects it resembles metals of the Copper Family more closely than zinc and cadmium.

Tin and *lead* occupy the last two positions in Group IVA of the Periodic Table. Together with *germanium* they constitute the metals of this group. The properties of tin and lead are similar to those of the metals of Group IIB and thus are studied along with zinc, cadmium, and mercury. All have low melting points, that of mercury being below room temperature. Both tin and lead have 4 electrons in their

VOCABULARY

Diluent (*dil*-yoo-ent). A diluting agent.

Dross. A powdery scum that floats on top of molten metals.

Lithopone. A white paint base composed of barium sulfate and zinc sulfide.

Sacrificial metal. The metallic electrode of an electrochemical cell that is oxidized.

Sherardize (*sher*-ar-dize). To galvanize by the condensation of zinc vapor on a ferrous metal surface.

Spelter. Commercial zinc.

ELEMENT	ATOMIC NUM- BER	ATOMIC WEIGHT	ELECTRON CONFIGURA- TION	OXIDA- TION NUM- BERS	MELT- ING POINT, °C	BOIL- ING POINT, °C	DEN- SITY g/cm³
ZINC	30	65.38	2,8,18,2	+2	419.5	970	7.14
CADMIUM	48	112.41	2,8,18,18,2	+2	320.9	767	8.64
MERCURY	80	200.61	2,8,18,32,18,2	+1,+2	−38.87	356.6	13.55
TIN	50	118.70	2,8,18,18,4	+2,+4	231.9	2270	7.28
LEAD	82	207.21	2,8,18,32,18,4	+2,+4	327.4	1620	11.34

outer shells and exhibit the oxidation number +4. However, the oxidation state of +2 is more common for these metals. Each has the characteristic shell of 18 electrons just under the valence shell.

The properties of these five metals are listed in the table above.

1. ZINC AND ITS COMPOUNDS

2. The occurrence of zinc. Zinc ores were used for making brass for centuries before the discovery of zinc as a metal. It is thought to have been produced first in 1746 from a silicate ore by heating the ore with charcoal.

The United States produces more zinc than any other nation, nearly one half of the world production being extracted from ores in this country. British Columbia, in Canada, is also an important zinc-producing area. Missouri, Kansas, and Oklahoma have large mineral deposits in the region where these three states join. Zinc sulfide is found there mixed with *galena,* a lead ore. New Jersey is also an important zinc-producing state. Montana, Colorado, and Arkansas produce considerable amounts of this metal.

Fig. 37–1. Zinc of high purity is now recovered by the electrolytic process. Here we see cathodes being lifted from a cell in the tank house of a zinc recovery plant.

Zinc does not occur as the native metal because of its chemical activity. The principal ore of zinc is *sphalerite,* ZnS, which is also called *zinc blende. Zincite,* ZnO, and *smithsonite,* ZnCO$_3$, are also important ores. *Willemite,* Zn$_2$SiO$_4$, and *calamine,* Zn$_2$SiO$_4 \cdot$ H$_2$O, are silicate ores of zinc. At Franklin, New Jersey, the mineral *franklinite,* a complex mixture of oxides of zinc, iron, and manganese, is found. Franklinite is mined as a zinc ore.

3. The metallurgy of zinc. Zinc is extracted by two processes, the older *reduction* method, and the newer *electrolytic* process.

1. By reduction with coal. The zinc ores are first roasted to convert them into oxides, for example:

$$2\ ZnS + 3\ O_2 \rightarrow 2\ ZnO + 2\ SO_2\uparrow$$

The oxides are mixed with powdered coal and heated in earthenware retorts:

$$ZnO + C \rightarrow Zn + CO\uparrow$$

Because of the low boiling point of zinc (907° C) it is distilled from the retorts as a vapor. It is then condensed in iron or earthenware receivers. Some of the zinc is deposited as *zinc dust* in the upper part of the receivers. Liquid zinc collects at the bottom of the receivers. It is drawn off and cast in molds. Such *spelter,* as it is called, may contain arsenic, cadmium, and carbon as impurities, but may be purified by redistillation.

2. By electrolysis. In the newer electrolytic process, the ore is first roasted, and then extracted with sulfuric acid. This produces a solution of zinc sulfate. Iron and manganese are removed as impurities by adding lime and blowing air through the solution. Sheets of aluminum are used as cathodes in the electrolytic cells. By passing an electric current through the cell, zinc ions are reduced at the cathode and metallic zinc plates out on the aluminum. Zinc that is 99.9% pure is then stripped off the cathodes. Electrolytic zinc is now preferred for making brass and other alloys because of its higher purity.

4. The properties of zinc. Metallic zinc is bluish-white in color. At room temperature it is somewhat brittle, but above 100° C it becomes malleable and ductile. It can be rolled into sheets or drawn into wire at this higher temperature, after which it does not become brittle again when it cools. It is a moderately hard metal with a density slightly less than that of iron.

Zinc burns in air with a bluish-white flame and forms white clouds of zinc oxide. At room temperature dry air does not affect zinc, but moist air attacks it and forms a coating of basic zinc carbonate, Zn$_2$(OH)$_2$CO$_3$. The tarnish which forms is adherent and somewhat impervious. Hence zinc is a self-protective metal.

Zinc stands well above hydrogen in the electrochemical series (see Chapter 23, Section 6) and may be expected to react readily with acids replacing the hydrogen. *Mossy* zinc, produced by pouring molten zinc dropwise into water, is commonly used in the laboratory to displace hydrogen from nonoxidizing acids. It is found, however, that pure zinc reacts only very slowly with acids. Thus spelter, rather than electrolytic zinc, is used in preparing mossy zinc for ordinary laboratory use.

The active hydroxides, such as sodium hydroxide, react with zinc and set free hydrogen gas. Soluble zincates, which may be considered as the salts of zincic acid, are formed.

$$Zn + 2\,NaOH \rightarrow Na_2ZnO_2 + H_2\uparrow$$

From this behavior, we see that the hydroxide of zinc is amphiprotic, acting as a hydroxide, $Zn(OH)_2$, in the presence of a strong acid, but acting as an acid, H_2ZnO_2, in the presence of a strong hydroxide. Thus:

$$2\,HCl + Zn(OH)_2 \rightarrow ZnCl_2 + 2\,H_2O$$
$$2\,NaOH + H_2ZnO_2 \rightarrow Na_2ZnO_2 + 2\,H_2O$$

5. Zinc is a very useful metal. Large quantities are used for making *galvanized* iron. To keep iron from rusting, it is thoroughly cleaned by pickling it in an acid bath to remove any scale or tarnish. Then it is coated with zinc by one of three methods.

1. By dipping. The iron utensil is dipped beneath the surface of a vat of molten zinc. Wire is galvanized by pulling the wire through molten zinc.

2. By plating. In some cases galvanizing is done by electro-plating the zinc on the surface of the metal to be protected.

3. By sherardizing. In this process the zinc is heated to vaporize it. Then the zinc vapor is permitted to condense on the surface of the metallic object which is to be coated.

CAUTION: *All soluble salts of zinc are poisonous. Acid foods must not be stored in galvanized iron containers.*

Again, from the electrochemical series, we see that zinc is a strong reducing agent and is well suited for use as the negative electrode in an electrochemical cell. Here electrolytic zinc is used, because particles of impurities in the cathode, such as carbon, would cause local electrochemical action between the impurities and the zinc. The

Fig. 37-2. Control station for one of the galvanizing lines in a large mill. In the left background is the galvanizing pot containing the molten zinc into which sheets are fed and conducted through the bath by suitable mechanisms. Emerging from the pot, the zinc-coated sheets are deposited on the wire-mesh conveyor, where they cool. The molten zinc solidifies to produce the spangled surface which is characteristic of this product. Succeeding units then wash, dry, and flatten the sheets which are then ready for inspection and shipment.

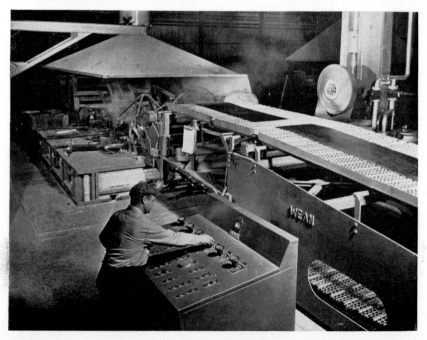

metal cylinder, or can, of the dry cell is made of electrolytic zinc which acts as the cathode. The anode is made of carbon (see Fig. 23-4).

6. Zinc is used to make alloys. The most important alloy of zinc is *brass,* which contains zinc and copper. The proportions vary, but ordinary brass contains about 60% copper and 40% zinc. *Bronze* contains copper and tin; usually some zinc is added.

German silver, sometimes called *nickel silver,* is an alloy containing copper, nickel, and zinc. The name *silver* is a misnomer, since there is no silver in the alloy.

7. The cobalt nitrate test for zinc. Some metals form a distinct color when their compounds are heated with cobalt nitrate. To test for zinc, for example, we make a slight depression in a charcoal block or in a block made of plaster of Paris. The metal, or its compound, is then placed in this depression and heated strongly with the oxidizing flame of a blowpipe. If zinc is present, its oxide will be canary yellow when hot, and white when cold. The residue is then moistened with a drop or two of cobalt nitrate solution, and again heated. If the residue is *dark green,* we know that zinc is present. When tested in the same manner, magnesium and its compounds give a *rose* color; aluminum and its compounds give a *blue* color.

8. Important compounds of zinc. Enormous quantities of zinc are burned to form zinc oxide. This compound is a white solid which is much used as a paint base, as a filler in rubber for automobile tires, in oilcloth, in linoleum, and for glazes and enamels. Zinc ointment contains zinc oxide and zinc stearate in an ointment base. It is used for treating various skin eruptions.

Zinc chloride, a white, deliquescent solid, is used in preserving wood which comes into contact with the earth, such as railroad ties and fence posts. It may be used alone or with creosote. Such doubly treated wood is very resistant to decay. A solution of zinc chloride is sometimes used as a soldering flux. The fluxing action is produced by the hydrolysis of the zinc chloride to form hydrochloric acid. The acid converts the metallic oxides to soluble chlorides, and thus leaves a clean, metallic surface.

Zinc chloride attacks wood fiber and converts it into cellulose hydrate, a product which can be pressed into any desired shape and then dried. This strong, tough product, which is called *fiberboard,* or *vulcanized fiber,* is used for making boxes, trunks, washers, pails, wastebaskets, and insulating materials.

Hydrated zinc sulfate, $ZnSO_4 \cdot 7\,H_2O$, is a white, crystalline solid used in making *lithopone,* a white paint base. Zinc sulfate is used in preserving hides, and to form a mordant in calico printing.

The sulfide of zinc is the only ordinary sulfide which is white in color. It is present in lithopone, which is made by mixing solutions of barium sulfide and zinc sulfate. In this reaction, represented by the equation,

$$BaS + ZnSO_4 \rightarrow BaSO_4\downarrow + ZnS\downarrow$$

barium sulfate and zinc sulfide are precipitated together. If this mixture of precipitates is heated and then plunged into cold water, the product which is formed may be ground with linseed oil to make lithopone. Lithopone does not darken on exposure to air containing hydrogen sulfide as does white lead.

Fig. 37-3. After small parts are electroplated with cadmium, they are dipped in an acid solution of hydrogen peroxide to increase their brightness.

2. CADMIUM AND ITS COMPOUNDS

9. The occurrence and uses of cadmium. Cadmium was discovered in 1817 as an impurity in zinc carbonate. It is usually found in nature associated with zinc. It also occurs as the sulfide, CdS, in the rather rare mineral known as *greenockite*. It is a bluish-white metal which resembles zinc and magnesium in its chemical properties. Cadmium is used as one ingredient of an amalgam for filling teeth, and in the making of some fusible alloys. It forms a more durable coating for iron and steel than zinc does. For that reason, a considerable amount of cadmium is used for plating screws, nuts, bolts, and other objects made of iron or steel. Cadmium metal is used for making the negative plates of the *nickel-cadmium storage battery*. Cadmium sulfide is a fine yellow pigment which is used as an artist's color, called cadmium yellow. *The soluble salts of cadmium are poisonous.*

Cadmium is becoming increasingly important industrially. Because of its low coefficient of friction and resistance to fatigue, it is used in bearing alloys. Production of cadmium in the United States has been stimulated by its use in control rods for nuclear reactors.

3. MERCURY AND ITS COMPOUNDS

10. The occurrence of mercury. Mercury was known in ancient China and India. It has been found in the tombs of Egypt built nearly 3500 years ago.

The bulk of the world's supply of mercury comes from California and Texas in the United States, and from Spain and Italy as foreign sources. It may occur as tiny globules scattered through rock, although the chief ore of mercury is a red mineral known as *cinnabar*, which is mercuric sulfide, HgS. The metal can be obtained by simply heating the ore:

$$HgS + O_2 \rightarrow Hg + SO_2\uparrow$$

11. Mercury is an unusual metal. Mercury is the only metal that is a liquid at ordinary temperatures. It is often called *quicksilver*. It is silver-white, lustrous, and about 13.6 times as dense as water. It freezes to a hard, brittle solid at approximately −39° C, and boils at a temperature of nearly 357° C.

12. Chemical properties of mercury. Neither dry nor moist air will react with mercury at ordinary temperatures. If heated in air, it slowly changes to a red oxide, HgO. Hydrochloric acid does not react with mercury since hydrogen is above mercury in the replacement series. Nitric and hot concentrated sulfuric acids, however, react with it to form mercuric nitrate and mercuric sulfate, respectively, in typical oxidation-reduction reactions.

Mercury is found far down on the electrochemical series. Thus most of the metals replace it from its compounds. It is a poor reducing agent, which accounts for its reluctance to combine with oxygen and its inability to displace hydrogen from nonoxidizing acids.

13. The uses of mercury. Mercury is used for making thermometers, barometers, and other pieces of scientific equipment. It is used in mercury-vapor lamps and also in arc rectifiers for changing alternating current into direct current.

14. What are amalgams? An alloy of mercury with one or more other metals is known as an amalgam. Mercury forms amalgams with most metals, although platinum and iron are exceptions. Mercury is sometimes used to extract gold and silver from ores by an amalgamation process. The mercury is distilled from the gold or silver amalgam and condensed for use over again. The gold or silver remains as a residue.

An amalgam consisting of silver, tin, cadmium, and mercury is used for fillings in teeth. When freshly prepared, it is soft enough to be pressed into the cavity of a tooth, but it hardens in a very short time.

15. Important compounds of mercury. Mercury forms two series of compounds, *mercurous,* oxidation number +1, and *mercuric,* oxidation number +2.

1. Mercurous chloride. This white solid has the molecular formula, Hg_2Cl_2, and is insoluble in water. It is used in medicine as a laxative under the name

Fig. 37–4. The action of hot springs has deposited large amounts of mercury at Sulfur Bank, California.

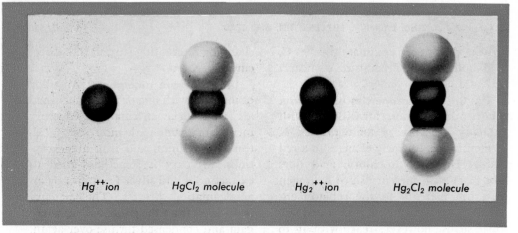

Fig. 37–5. Mercuric chloride and mercurous chloride are formed as covalent molecules. The mercurous ion is also a covalent structure.

of *calomel.* Exposure to sunlight causes mercurous chloride to change slowly to mercury and mercuric chloride:

$$Hg_2Cl_2 \rightarrow Hg + HgCl_2$$

Mercurous nitrate is fairly soluble in water. Mercurous chloride is precipitated when chloride ions are added to a solution of $Hg_2(NO_3)_2$. Ammonia reacts with this precipitate forming insoluble white *mercuric aminochloride* and metallic mercury as a black dispersion. *The mixture of these two products gives a gray residue which serves as a test for the mercurous ion.*

$$Hg_2Cl_2 + 2\,NH_3 \rightarrow$$
$$\underset{\text{white}}{HgNH_2Cl\downarrow} + \underset{\text{black}}{Hg\downarrow} + NH_4Cl$$

CAUTION: *All the soluble salts of mercury are extremely poisonous.* The white of eggs, or milk, may be used as an antidote because the albumin in egg whites or milk forms an insoluble mercury albuminate. The use of Hg_2Cl_2 (calomel) in medicine is safe even though the Hg_2^{++} ion is very poisonous, because the compound is only very slightly soluble.

2. *Mercuric chloride.* This compound is usually called *bichloride of mercury* or *corrosive sublimate.* It is essentially covalent and has the molecular formula $HgCl_2$. It forms white crystals that can be purified by sublimation. One part of mercuric chloride added to 1000 parts of water forms an antiseptic solution that is sometimes used in hospitals. Great care should be exercised in handling bichloride of mercury because it is extremely poisonous.

Mercuric oxide, HgO, is used as an antiseptic under the name *red precipitate.* Priestley obtained oxygen by heating this compound. Sublimed *mercuric sulfide,* HgS, forms a red pigment known as vermilion. It is used as a paint to prevent the growth of barnacles on the bottoms of ships.

4. TIN AND ITS COMPOUNDS

16. The occurrence of tin. The Malay States, Indonesia, Thailand (Siam), together with Bolivia in South America, and Nigeria in Africa, supply almost all of the tin mined in the world.

For many centuries, tin ore was mined at Cornwall, England, but these deposits have now become almost exhausted. A little tin has been mined in the Black Hills of South Dakota, and

Fig. 37–6. Pigs of tin on the dock in the Federated Malay States consigned to customers in the United States.

some has been discovered in Alaska. The United States, which uses more tin than any other nation, is almost entirely dependent on foreign sources for this useful metal.

The principal ore of tin is *cassiterite,* SnO_2, which is also called *tinstone.*

17. The metallurgy of tin. Tin ore is usually concentrated by the froth-flotation process to get rid of silica and other impurities. Tin ore concentrates from the mountains of Bolivia are carried by pack animals to the seacoast. Ships then transport the ore to a large smelter in Texas. Much refined tin metal is imported from Great Britain. New Jersey is a center of the tin industry in the United States.

The tin ore is sintered, mixed with carbon, and reduced in a reverberatory furnace:

$$SnO_2 + 2\ C \rightarrow Sn + 2\ CO\uparrow$$

The crude metal is purified by heating it cautiously on a sloping hearth. The tin, which has a melting point of approximately 232° C, melts and drains away from the less easily melted impurities. It may be still further purified by electrolysis.

18. The properties of tin. Tin is a soft, white metal that is not quite so dense as iron. It is so malleable that it can be rolled into very thin sheets known as *tin foil.* The pure metal is called *block tin.*

Tin exists in three allotropic forms. At low temperatures it changes to a gray powder with a cubic crystal structure. This is the stable form below 18° C. At ordinary temperatures it forms a tetragonal crystal structure, while at temperatures just under the melting point it forms rhombic crystals. The crumbling of tin to a gray powder in very cold climates is sometimes called "tin disease."

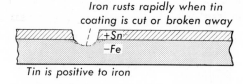

Iron rusts rapidly when tin coating is cut or broken away

+Sn
−Fe

Tin is positive to iron

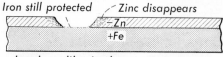

Iron still protected   Zinc disappears

−Zn
+Fe

Iron is positive to zinc

Fig. 37–7. Tin accelerates the corrosion of iron when the tin coating is broken. Zinc continues to offer some protection to iron after the zinc coating is broken.

Air and water do not react with tin at ordinary temperatures. When heated strongly, the metal burns to form stannic oxide, SnO_2. Carbonated water has no effect on it, hence the use of block tin pipes in soda fountains.

Tin reacts slowly with dilute acids to replace hydrogen. If dilute hydrochloric acid is used, stannous chloride and hydrogen are the products.

$$Sn + 2\ HCl \rightarrow SnCl_2 + H_2\uparrow$$

With *dilute* nitric acid, stannous nitrate is formed and nitrogen is reduced to ammonia which forms ammonium nitrate.

$$4\ Sn + 10\ HNO_3 \rightarrow$$
$$4\ Sn(NO_3)_2 + NH_4NO_3 + 3\ H_2O$$

The reaction with concentrated acids is quite vigorous. Tin and hot concentrated sulfuric acid produce stannous sulfate, sulfur dioxide, and water.

$$Sn + 2\ H_2SO_4 \rightarrow SnSO_4 + SO_2\uparrow + 2\ H_2O$$

Concentrated nitric acid reacts with tin to form a hydrated stannic oxide, $SnO_2 \cdot H_2O$, which is usually called metastannic acid, with the formula written as H_2SnO_3.

Hot alkali hydroxides react readily with tin to release hydrogen and form the corresponding *stannites*.

$$2\ NaOH + Sn \rightarrow Na_2SnO_2 + H_2\uparrow$$

This action is similar to that of zinc and aluminum. We would expect stannous hydroxide to be amphiprotic.

19. Tin is a very useful metal. Tin foil has long been used for wrapping chocolate and other foods. It is rapidly being replaced by aluminum foil for such purposes. Block tin pipes are used as conduits for slightly acid liquids.

More tin is used for making tinware or tin plate than any other use. "Tin cans" are made from sheet iron that has been cleaned in acid, and then dipped in molten tin. If the coating is thick enough, it protects the iron very well. However, if the tin is scratched through at any place, the iron underneath rusts much more readily than would unprotected iron. In such a case, the tin and iron form an electrochemical cell in which the tin is the anode, the iron is the cathode, and the moist air acts as the electrolyte. Iron becomes the "sacrificial metal" since it is more active than tin, and is oxidized rapidly. (The metal which is attacked in such a cell is often called the "sacrificial metal.") With galvanized iron, zinc is the sacrificial metal because iron is less active electrochemically than zinc. Even so, foods are packed in tin cans because tin does not affect the quality of the foods. Galvanized iron should never be used for holding foods because zinc compounds are poisonous.

20. Tin forms many alloys. Alloys that contain tin are very common. Type metal, antifriction metals, bronze, and fusible alloys have been mentioned previously. *Solder* is an alloy of tin and lead. Soft solder contains 50% tin and 50% lead, but other solders may contain these metals in other proportions. Plumbers use a solder containing 67% lead for *wiping* the joints of lead waste pipes because it becomes plastic before it hardens to a rigid solid. *Terne plate* is sheet iron coated with an alloy of tin and lead that is used for roofing. *Pewter* is an alloy of variable composition but often contains 80% tin and 20% lead.

21. Tin may form stannous or stannic compounds. If tin and hydrochloric acid react, *stannous chloride* is formed. It is used in mordant dyeing and produces brilliant colors with some dyestuffs. It is also used for weighting silk.

Stannous chloride is a good reducing agent. If we add stannous chloride to a solution of mercuric chloride, we have an interesting example of an oxidation-reduction reaction. By varying the amount used, we can reduce the mercuric chloride to mercurous chloride, or even to metallic mercury, as in the following equations:

$$SnCl_2 + 2\,HgCl_2 \rightarrow SnCl_4 + Hg_2Cl_2$$
$$SnCl_2 + HgCl_2 \rightarrow SnCl_4 + Hg$$

In each case the mercuric chloride acts as an oxidizing agent, and the stannous chloride as a reducing agent. The tin, which has an oxidation number of $+2$ in *stannous* chloride, is oxidized to the $+4$ state as *stannic* chloride. At the same time, the *mercuric* chloride is reduced from the $+2$ oxidation state to the $+1$ state or to the 0 oxidation state in metallic *mercury*. The electronic changes may be expressed as follows:

$$Sn^{++} - 2\,e^- \rightarrow Sn^{++++}$$
$$2\,Hg^{++} + 2\,e^- \rightarrow Hg_2^{++}$$
or $$Hg^{++} + 2\,e^- \rightarrow Hg^0$$

Stannic sulfide, SnS_2, is used as a yellow pigment under the name of *mosaic gold*. Metastannic acid is used sometimes to make cotton cloth nonflammable. Stannic chloride, like stannous chloride, is also used for weighting silk and in mordant dyeing.

Fig. 37–8. When a sheet of steel is plated with tin by electrolysis it is heated by high frequency coils as it passes through this machine. The tin melts and flows to form a lustrous coat.

5. LEAD AND ITS COMPOUNDS

22. The occurrence of lead. Lead was known to the ancients. It is mentioned in the book of Exodus. Lead pipes bearing the insignia of Roman emperors are still in use in Rome.

The principal ore of lead is *galena*, PbS, which occurs as grayish-black, cubical crystals. It is widely distributed, both in this country and in other parts of the world. Missouri, Colorado, Utah, Idaho, Montana, and Oklahoma are our most important lead-producing states. British Columbia and Mexico also produce large amounts of lead.

★ **23. The metallurgy of lead.** Lead ore is first concentrated by the froth-flotation process. This operation not only concentrates the ore, but also separates it from zinc sulfide which commonly occurs mixed with it. Concentrated ore is then carefully roasted to convert the lead sulfide into *lead oxide* and *lead sulfate*.

$$2\ PbS + 3\ O_2 \rightarrow 2\ PbO + 2\ SO_2\uparrow$$
$$PbS + 2\ O_2 \rightarrow PbSO_4$$

The roasted ore is then mixed with unroasted ore, coke, and limestone. A blast furnace is used to smelt the lead from this mixture. The lead sulfide in the unroasted ore acts as a reducing agent on the lead oxide and lead sulfate of the roasted ore.

$$2\ PbO + PbS \rightarrow 3\ Pb + SO_2\uparrow$$
$$PbSO_4 + PbS \rightarrow 2\ Pb + 2\ SO_2\uparrow$$

The coke provides necessary fuel, and may also assist in the reduction. The limestone of the charge reacts with silica, present as an impurity, and forms a calcium silicate slag.

The crude lead contains arsenic, antimony, bismuth, and copper as impurities, as well as the precious metals, silver and gold. It is heated and stirred. The impurities, except the precious metals, form oxides which rise to the surface of the melted lead. These oxides are skimmed off as *dross*. The precious metals are removed from the lead by the Parkes process, which is described in Chapter 36, Section 10.

24. The properties of lead. Lead is a soft, bluish-white metal that has a specific gravity of 11.3, and a melting point of approximately 327° C. It is malleable, but not ductile. Lead wire may be made by *extruding* the heated metal through a die. Lead pipe is made in a similar manner by forcing the lead through a ring-shaped opening.

Lead oxidizes rapidly, but the coating of oxide which forms on the surface is adherent and protects the metal underneath from further oxidation. Hydrochloric acid and sulfuric acid have little effect on lead, but nitric acid reacts with it vigorously. Acetic acid and some other organic acids react with lead, and water which contains carbon dioxide in solution reacts slowly with this metal.

CAUTION: *All soluble lead compounds are very poisonous.* They are particularly dangerous because they are not excreted, but tend to accumulate in the body. Painters and others who handle lead compounds should use great care so as not to contract lead poisoning.

25. The uses of lead. *Sheet lead* is used for making the lead chambers of sulfuric acid plants, and has other uses for which its chemical inactivity makes it suitable. It is sometimes used as a roofing material. *Lead foil* is used for lining tea chests, and as a substitute for tin foil. *Lead shot* usually has 1% arsenic added to make the lead harder. *Lead pipe* is used for waste pipes and sink traps. It is easily cut, and it can be bent into any desired shape. Telephone cables are protected by a lead covering in underground wire systems. Large quantities of lead are used to make lead compounds, such as white lead, litharge, and red lead. About 30% of all the lead consumed in the United States is used in lead storage batteries.

The accompanying table summarizes the properties and uses of some of the more important lead compounds.

★ **26. The lead storage battery.** Automobile storage batteries account for a considerable portion of the lead consumed annually in the United States. The six-volt battery consists of three

cells connected in series. Twelve-volt batteries are made up of six cells. As the name implies, the *storage* battery is a *storehouse* of energy. As the battery is charged, electrical energy is converted to chemical energy by an oxidation-reduction reaction in which each cell acts as an *electrolytic cell*. While the battery is being discharged, the reverse oxidation-reduction reaction occurs. Chemical energy is converted to electrical energy and the cells behave as *electrochemical cells*.

A fully-charged lead storage cell consists of an anode of lead dioxide, a cathode of spongy lead, and an electrolyte of moderately dilute sulfuric acid. During the *discharging cycle*, the lead at the cathode is oxidized to Pb^{++} ions which then form lead sulfate, $PbSO_4$, as a precipitate on the cathode:

CHEMICAL NAME	COMMON NAME	CHEMICAL FORMULA	COLOR	IMPORTANT USES
LEAD SUBOXIDE	None	Pb_2O	Gray	Forms a coating on lead
LEAD MONOXIDE	Litharge	PbO	Yellow	In making glass; in the paint and varnish industries
LEAD DIOXIDE	Lead peroxide (a misnomer)	PbO_2	Brown	It forms the active material of the positive plate of storage batteries
LEAD PLUMBATE	Red lead	Pb_3O_4	Red	To make a protective paint for iron and steel
LEAD ACETATE	Sugar of lead	$Pb(C_2H_3O_2)_2$	White, crystalline	For making white lead; as a mordant; to treat ivy poisoning
LEAD CHROMATE	Chrome yellow	$PbCrO_4$	Yellow	As a yellow pigment
LEAD ARSENATE	Arsenate of lead	$Pb_3(AsO_4)_2$	White	As an insecticide
BASIC LEAD CARBONATE	White lead	$Pb_3(OH)_2(CO_3)_2$	White	As a paint base

$$Pb^0 - 2\ e^- \rightarrow Pb^{++}$$
$$Pb^{++} + SO_4^= \rightarrow PbSO_4\downarrow$$

This cathode oxidation may be summarized as follows:

$$Pb^0 - 2\ e^- + SO_4^= \rightarrow PbSO_4\downarrow$$

Simultaneously at the anode, hydrogen ions (as H_3O^+) may be reduced and may then, in turn, reduce the PbO_2 to PbO forming water in the process. A double replacement reaction with sulfuric acid will then produce lead sulfate and water. Lead sulfate precipitates on the anode.

$$2\ H^+ + 2\ e^- \rightarrow 2\ H^0$$
$$2\ H^0 + PbO_2 \rightarrow PbO + H_2O$$
$$PbO + H_2SO_4 \rightarrow PbSO_4\downarrow + H_2O$$

The anode reduction is not fully understood, so the above reactions may be an over-simplification of the actual process. The action may be summarized as follows:

$$2\ H^+ + 2\ e^- + PbO_2 + H_2SO_4 \rightarrow$$
$$PbSO_4\downarrow + 2\ H_2O$$

The overall oxidation-reduction reaction of the cell during discharge is shown in the series of equations below.

During the discharging process, electrons released by oxidation at the cathode flow through the external circuit of the battery to the anode, where the reduction occurs. This constitutes an electric current which operates the devices connected to the battery circuit.

In the discharged condition, both electrodes consist of lead sulfate, and the electrolyte is a more dilute solution of sulfuric acid. The cell may be made electrochemically active again by re-

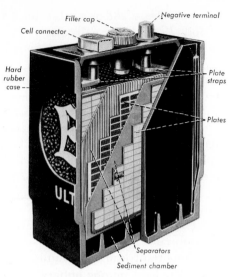

Fig. 37–9. A cutaway view of one cell of an automobile storage battery.

charging. This is accomplished by applying a direct current from an external source so as to flow through the circuit in the opposite direction to the discharging current. The action at the electrodes is reversed and the cell is restored to its charged condition.

During the *charging cycle,* lead sulfate at the cathode is reduced to the element, lead.

$$PbSO_4 + 2\ e^- \rightarrow Pb^0 + SO_4^=$$

Simultaneously at the anode, lead sulfate is oxidized forming lead dioxide.

$$PbSO_4 - 2\ e^- + 2\ H_2O \rightarrow$$
$$PbO_2 + H_2SO_4 + 2\ H^+$$

The overall oxidation-reduction reaction of the cell during charge is shown in the series of equations at the top of page 543.

(cathode)	$Pb^0 - 2\ e^- + SO_4^= \rightarrow PbSO_4\downarrow$
(anode)	$2\ H^+ + 2\ e^- + PbO_2 + H_2SO_4 \rightarrow PbSO_4\downarrow + 2\ H_2O$
(cell)	$Pb + 2\ H_2SO_4 + PbO_2 \rightarrow 2\ PbSO_4\downarrow + 2\ H_2O$

(cathode) $PbSO_4 + 2 e^- \rightarrow Pb^0 + SO_4^=$
(anode) $PbSO_4 + 2 H_2O - 2 e^- \rightarrow PbO_2 + H_2SO_4 + 2 H^+$
(cell) $\overline{2 PbSO_4 + 2 H_2O \rightarrow Pb + PbO_2 + 2 H_2SO_4}$

During the charging process, electrons are supplied to the cathode, and are removed from the anode, by the external source of electrical energy. Electrical energy is thus stored as chemical energy in the cell through the mechanism of the oxidation-reduction action.

Observe that our last equation is the reverse of the overall equation for the discharging action.

$$\xrightarrow{\text{charging}}$$
$$2 PbSO_4 + 2 H_2O \underset{\text{discharging}}{\overset{}{\rightleftarrows}} Pb + PbO_2 + 2 H_2SO_4$$
$$\xleftarrow{\hspace{1cm}}$$

Fig. 37–10. Diagrams illustrating the essential action in a storage cell.

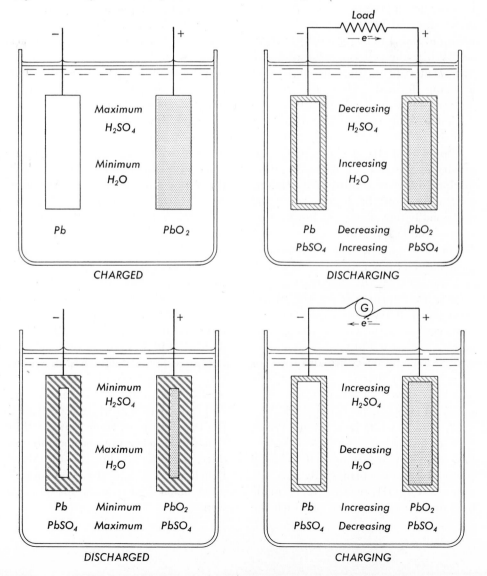

You will note that during charging, sulfuric acid is being formed and water is being decomposed. The specific gravity of the acid increases during charging up to about 1.300 for a fully-charged cell. While the cell is discharging, sulfuric acid is being used up and water is being formed. Thus the specific gravity of the acid is lowered during discharge. The specific gravity of the acid in a completely discharged cell is about 1.100. By testing the specific gravity of the cell, we can gain information as to its condition of charge. Pure water must be added to the cell occasionally to replace that lost by electrolysis and evaporation.

The principal use of storage batteries is in automobiles to provide ignition, and to operate the headlights, self-starter, and equipment on the instrument panel. A direct-current generator connected with the engine charges the battery while the automobile is in motion. Storage batteries are also used for other purposes that require a portable source of power, or where a source of power in emergencies is required.

27. How is white lead made? White lead, an important paint base, is a basic lead carbonate of somewhat variable composition, but principally has the formula $Pb_3(OH)_2(CO_3)_2$. It is made by a number of processes, of which the Dutch process and the Carter process are best known.

1. Dutch process. In this process, perforated discs or *buckles* are stamped out of sheet lead. The lower portions of earthenware pots contain acetic acid, and the upper portions are filled with the lead buckles. The pots are then placed in rows and covered with spent tanbark or stable manure. Other tiers of pots are stacked on top of the first ones until the room is completely filled. The chamber is then sealed and left for about four months.

The organic matter in the bark or manure soon begins to ferment and gives off carbon dioxide. The heat from the fermentation vaporizes the acetic acid which acts upon the lead and forms *basic lead acetate.* Then the carbon dioxide converts the acetate into *basic lead carbonate.* The resulting product is broken up, and ground with linseed oil to make the *white lead* used in paint.

2. Carter process. Melted lead is atomized by blasts of steam. The finely divided lead is then treated with carbon dioxide and acetic acid in a slowly rotating, sealed cylinder for about two weeks. The product has the same general composition as white lead made by the Dutch process. Some painters think that this quicker process does not produce particles as fine as the slower Dutch process, and that consequently paint made from it does not spread as well.

6. THE PAINT INDUSTRY

28. The composition of paint. Paint is a mixture of: *1. a paint base; 2. a vehicle; 3. a pigment* for colored paint; *4. a drier;* and usually *5. a thinner.* The paint manufacturer has a choice of different materials to serve as each of these components.

A good paint should have four qualities. First, it should be opaque in thin layers, and have good covering power to conceal the surface beneath. Second, it should not rub off or become excessively chalky, and should not crack and peel. (Any paint is likely to peel if it is applied to a moist surface.) Third, it should work well under the brush without too much pull or drag. Fourth, it should be impervious and durable.

29. Important paint bases. Of the various paint bases in use, the following are the most important:

1. White lead. For centuries, white lead has been used as a paint base, and it is still popular with most painters. It makes a good paint base, although paint made from this base alone tends to become chalky in time. White lead is poisonous. It has caused many cases of *painter's colic,* or lead poisoning, especially when painters have been habitually careless about washing their hands before eating. White lead is not suitable for inside use because traces of hydrogen sulfide in the air will cause it to darken. The salt air along the seashore causes white lead to deteriorate rather quickly.

2. Zinc oxide. This paint base, used alone, tends to crack and peel. It is whiter than the lead base, and it does not turn dark in the presence of hydrogen sulfide. It makes an excellent base for inside use. A paint that is made of white lead and zinc oxide, mixed in the proper proportions, will wear better than a paint made from either one alone for outside use.

3. Lithopone. This product is made by *calcining* a mixture of barium sulfate and zinc sulfide. It is a very white paint base and has excellent covering power. It is suitable for inside use, particularly as an undercoat for enamels.

4. Titanium dioxide. Titanium dioxide, TiO_2, is a newer paint base. It has excellent covering power, and it is durable. It is becoming increasingly popular as a base for outside paint.

30. Common paint vehicles. A vehicle for oil paint is an oil that absorbs oxygen when exposed to air, forming an elastic solid that holds the paint firmly in place.

Linseed oil is the most common vehicle. It is obtained from flaxseed. When linseed oil is exposed to air, it reacts with oxygen, and changes to a solid. The paint is said to "dry," but actually the drying is a case of oxidation. Both raw and boiled linseed oil are used, often a mixture of both. The boiled oil has been heated with oxides of lead and manganese, which makes the oil "dry" more quickly.

Tung oil, or Chinese wood oil, is pressed from the nuts of the tung tree, which is a native of China. It makes an excellent vehicle for use in paints or enamels which must be subjected to severe weather conditions. It forms a harder film than linseed oil does. Groves of tung trees are now producing tung oil in Florida and some other southern states.

Rosin oil is sometimes used to adulterate linseed oil. It has some drying

Fig. 37–12. Paint products are tested and evaluated under all weather conditions.

qualities. *Fish oils* are used, after treatment, as a paint vehicle. *Soybean oil,* with proper treatment, may also be used in paint.

31. Thinners are diluents. Such substances as turpentine, alcohol, and certain mineral spirits are used as paint thinners. They dry by evaporation, but do not form a film to hold the base in place. Thus they are distinguished from vehicles. Thinners, or *diluents,* make the paint easier to spread. Excessive amounts of a thinner should be avoided for obvious reasons.

32. Driers are catalysts. Driers are made by boiling the oxides of lead and manganese in linseed oil. A little drier added to mixed paint acts as a catalyst to promote the oxidation of the oil vehicle. Too much drier injures the elastic film.

33. Colored paints contain pigments. The paint bases are all white in color. They form the bulk of all paints, because it takes only a small amount of pigment to color a large volume of paint. The pigment is an insoluble substance which has a high coloring pow-er. Pigments include certain lakes, the oxides and sulfides of certain metals, complex cyanides, and other compounds. Some of the substances used as pigments include: *1. Red pigments.* Red lead, red ocher, vermilion, carmine, and some lakes; *2. Blue pigments.* Prussian blue, ultramarine, and cobalt blue; *3. Yellow pigments.* Chrome yellow, yellow ocher, and litharge; and *4. Gray pigment.* Lampblack is used to produce a gray or black coloration.

Various shades of color are produced by mixing the pigments listed above with one another, or with still other pigments. It is essential that pigments selected to color a paint do not react with the compounds used in the paint base. Otherwise, undesirable shades are produced by the chemical action of the ingredients.

34. Latex emulsion paints. Interior flat wall paints consisting of latex emulsions in water have grown steadily in popularity in the United States since their introduction in 1949. Today they account for approximately 10% of the total paint production in this country. Most of the latex paints in use have a *styrene-butadiene* base. However, *vinyl acetate* and *acrylic* emulsions are rapidly becoming important bases for water-emulsion paints.

Latex emulsion paints are easy to apply, comparatively durable, and fast drying. They are odorless because they do not have petroleum and lacquer solvents. Latex paints are dry to the touch in less than an hour after being applied.

Summary

Zinc is extracted from sulfide, carbonate, silicate, and oxide ores. It is a bluish-white metal that becomes malleable above 100° C and burns with a bluish-white flame forming zinc oxide. Pure zinc reacts slowly with acids, but impure zinc is attacked readily.

Zinc is used to coat iron, forming galvanized iron, and to make alloys, such as brass. Zinc oxide is used as a paint base, as a filler for rubber to make automobile tires, and for making glazes and enamels. Zinc chloride is used for preserving wood against decay. Zinc sulfate is used in making lithopone, a paint base.

Cadmium is used for coating iron and steel, for making the negative plates of the nickel-cadmium storage battery, and for making fusible alloys. Cadmium sulfide is used as a yellow paint pigment.

Mercury is a very dense metal and is liquid at ordinary temperatures. It is used for various scientific instruments. Alloys of mercury are called amalgams. Mercury forms two series of compounds: mercurous and mercuric.

Tin oxide is easily reduced with carbon. Metallic tin is soft, white, very malleable, and has a low-melting point. In very cold climates it is sometimes changed to a powdered allotropic form. Tin foil is used for wrapping foods. Block tin is used for piping. Some tin compounds are used in mordant dyeing and for weighting silk.

The principal ore of lead is lead sulfide. The concentrated ore is carefully roasted and then reduced in a blast furnace. Lead is a soft, bluish-white metal that is very dense and has a low melting point. All soluble lead compounds are poisonous. Storage batteries use much lead. Lead compounds are components of many paints.

Test yourself on these terms

amalgam	Dutch process	self-protective
block tin	foil	sherardizing
brass	galvanized iron	solder
bronze	lithopone	spelter
Carter process	paint base	storage battery
cinnabar	pewter	terne plate
diluent	pigment	tinstone
drier	red lead	vehicle
dross	sacrificial metal	white lead

uestions

Group A

1. What are three methods of protecting sheet iron with zinc?
2. Why is so much zinc metal burned to form zinc oxide?
3. What are some uses for the metal cadmium?
4. Starting with zinc sulfide, how is metallic zinc obtained?
5. Where are the most important deposits of tin located throughout the world?
6. What are the uses of tin?
7. What five ingredients does a mixed house paint usually have?
8. (*a*) Why does paint "dry"? (*b*) What oils are used as vehicles in paint?
9. What is meant by "tin disease"?
10. What are the physical properties of tin?
11. What are the uses for lead?
12. What is the difference between *tin plate, block tin,* and *tin foil?*
13. Why do house painters sometimes contract lead poisoning?
14. Suggest two objections to the use of sheet lead for a roofing material.
15. Why are pipes for conducting distilled water often made of block tin?
16. What is an amalgam?
17. A mixture of what metals is used for *silver* fillings in teeth?
18. How is the mercury recovered from the amalgam formed in the amalgamation process?

Group B

19. How is *spelter* purified?
20. Would galvanized iron containers be suitable for holding milk and other dairy products? Explain.
21. Artists speak of "cadmium yellow." What is it?
22. How can the brittleness of zinc be overcome so that it can be rolled into sheets?
23. Mention three uses for zinc chloride.
24. What is meant when we say that zinc hydroxide is amphiprotic?
25. What is the general composition of these substances: (*a*) zinc blende; (*b*) sphalerite; (*c*) zincite; (*d*) smithsonite; (*e*) calcimine?
★ 26. Explain why the term *storage battery* is appropriate in reference to an automobile battery.
★ 27. What constitutes the anode, cathode, and electrolyte of a fully-charged lead storage cell?
★ 28. (*a*) What action occurs at the cathode of a lead storage cell during the discharge cycle? (*b*) Write the equation for this cathode action.
★ 29. (*a*) What action occurs at the anode of a storage cell during the discharge cycle? (*b*) Write the equation for this anode action.
★ 30. (*a*) What is the action at the cathode of a lead storage cell during the charging cycle? (*b*) What action occurs at the anode? (*c*) Write the equation for the reversible oxidation-reduction reaction which occurs in the lead storage battery during its normal use.

Some things for you to do

1. Galvanize a piece of clean sheet iron. First melt some zinc in an iron dish. Dip the sheet iron that is to be galvanized in dilute hydrochloric acid to remove any coating of oxide. Then dip the sheet iron in the melted zinc. Observe the coating of zinc that forms on the iron.
2. Prepare some test strips of different kinds of house paint, both white and colored. The pieces of wood used should have as nearly the same grain characteristics as possible. Plan a series of controlled tests which will enable you to compare the paints used as to the four qualities of a good paint. See if you can show any correlation between the paint constituents and these four qualities.

Check your progress in chemistry

(Write the equations for reactions 1–12.)

1. The roasting of zinc sulfide ore.
2. The reaction between limestone and silica in a blast furnace.
3. The reduction of ferric oxide with carbon monoxide.
4. The thermite reaction with aluminum and ferric oxide.
5. The reaction which occurs when dry sodium hydrogen carbonate is heated.
6. The reduction of zinc oxide with carbon.
7. Sodium hydroxide solution and zinc metal.
8. Zinc hydroxide and hydrochloric acid.
9. Zinc hydroxide (zincic acid) and sodium hydroxide solution.
10. Barium sulfide and zinc sulfate.
11. Hydrogen sulfide and a solution of cadmium nitrate.
12. The discharge of a lead storage cell.
13. What is the weight of 1 mole of Prussian blue?
14. What is the percentage of iron in a sample of limonite, $2 Fe_2O_3 \cdot 3 H_2O$?
15. What is the weight of a liter of carbon monoxide at S.T.P.?
16. How would you make a molal solution of methanol, CH_3OH?
17. When 46 g of a certain organic compound is added to 500 g of water, the boiling point is raised 0.52 C°. What is the molecular weight of the compound?
18. A certain hydrocarbon has the following composition: $C = 92.3\%$, $H = 7.7\%$. The weight of 224 ml of the gas is 0.26 g. (*a*) What is the empirical formula? (*b*) What is the molecular weight of the gas? (*c*) What is the correct formula?
19. How much basic lead carbonate, $Pb_3(OH)_2(CO_3)_2$, can be made from 621 kg of lead?
20. When 239 g of lead sulfide is roasted, how many grams of lead monoxide, PbO, will be produced?
21. When 150.7 kg of tin oxide, SnO_2, is reduced with carbon, what weight of tin is produced?

22. One molecule of nitrogen unites with three molecules of hydrogen in the *Haber* process. If one million liters of nitrogen is used, what volume of ammonia is produced?

23. How much barium hydroxide, $Ba(OH)_2$, is needed to make one liter of 0.01-N solution?

24. By titration, 8.3 ml of 0.1-N hydrochloric acid neutralized 17.4 ml of an unknown basic solution. What is the normality of the hydroxide?

25. If the basic solution in the previous problem is potassium hydroxide, how many grams of potassium hydroxide are dissolved in 100 ml of the solution?

Challenging your knowledge

1. Why is it necessary to devise a special treatment for each different kind of ore in order to extract the metal from it?

2. Why did man have some metals in very early times, yet many metals have been obtained only within the last century?

3. Explain the chemistry of the process for making blueprints.

4. Why do all three steel processes, the *open-hearth*, the *Bessemer*, and the *electric furnace*, continue to be used for producing steel in this country?

5. Suppose you had a powdered mixture that contained 90% gold and 10% silver. How could you obtain pure gold from such a mixture?

6. How would you plate a small silver ornament with gold? What would you use as the electrodes in the cell, and what would you use as the electrolyte?

UNIT 13

Nuclear reactions

One of man's first useful, large-scale applications of a nuclear reaction as a source of energy was in the atomic-powered submarine *Nautilus,* shown above. Other submarines, as well as surface craft, are now being built which will use nuclear fuels. Electricity is also being generated today by nuclear reactions. New developments in the study of healthy as well as diseased plant and animal tissues, are being brought about by applications of radioactive materials produced in huge nuclear reactors.

Radioactivity was discovered only about sixty years ago. In the time that has elapsed, man has used this discovery to improve health, to furnish an almost unlimited source of power, and to probe the structure and age of the world in which he lives.

The two chapters in this unit, *Natural Radioactivity* and *Artificial Radioactivity,* will tell you about natural as well as artificial nuclear changes.

Chapter 38 NATURAL RADIOACTIVITY

1. The discovery of radioactivity. In 1896 the French scientist Henri Becquerel (bek-*rel*) (1852–1908) was studying the properties of certain minerals. He was particularly interested in their ability to *fluoresce,* or give off visible light, after they had been exposed to sunlight. Among these minerals was a sample of uranium ore. By accident, Becquerel found that uranium ore gives off certain invisible rays without exposure to the sun. These invisible rays affect an unexposed photographic plate in the same way that light does when the plate is exposed. Substances which emit such invisible rays are *radioactive,* and the property is called *radioactivity.*

2. The discovery of radium. Becquerel was intensely interested in the source of radioactivity. At his suggestion, Pierre Curie (1859–1906) and his wife Marie (1867–1934) started to in-

VOCABULARY

α (alpha) particle. Particle identical with a helium nucleus emitted from the nucleus of a radioactive element.

β (beta) particle. Particle identical with an electron emitted from the nucleus of a radioactive element.

γ (gamma) ray. High energy X ray emitted from the nucleus of a radioactive element.

Half-life. The length of time required for the disintegration of one-half of the present number of atoms of a radioactive element.

Nuclear equation. An equation representing changes in the nuclei of atoms.

Radioactive. Having the property of radioactivity.

Radioactivity. The spontaneous, uncontrollable disintegration of the nucleus of an atom with the emission of particles and rays.

Transmutation reaction. A reaction in which the nucleus of an atom undergoes a change in its positive charge, and consequently in its identity.

vestigate the properties of uranium and its ores. They soon learned that uranium and uranium compounds are mildly radioactive. But one uranium ore had unexpected properties. It was four times more radioactive than the amount of uranium warranted. This ore was *pitchblende,* and was mined in Bohemia.

It was a tremendous task to process several tons of pitchblende. But in 1898 the Curies discovered in it two new radioactive elements, *polonium,* and *radium.* These accounted for the excess radioactivity of pitchblende. The Curies separated only a few milligrams of radium chloride, $RaCl_2$. But even this tiny amount involved more than 10,000 crystallizations and recrystallizations. Radium is about 1,000,000 times as radioactive as the same weight of uranium.

The metal radium was not isolated by Madame Curie until 1910. What is today marketed as radium usually consists of one of its salts, the bromide, the chloride, or the carbonate. Radium is radioactive either as the element or as a part of a compound. The Curies and Becquerel received the Nobel Prize for physics jointly in 1903 for their work on radioactivity.

3. The sources of radium. Radium is always found in uranium ores. However, it cannot occur in such ores in a greater proportion than 1 part of radium to 3,000,000 parts of uranium. The reason for these conditions will be explained in Section 8. The extraction of radium is a long, tedious, and costly procedure. Formerly, ores from Europe and the Belgian Congo were used. Now, however, ore deposits near Great Bear Lake in northern Canada are utilized for the production of radium.

Fig. 38-1. Mme. Marie Curie, a Polish scientist, who, together with her French husband, Pierre, discovered the elements polonium and radium.

4. The properties of radium. Radium is the element of highest atomic weight in Group IIA of the Periodic Table. Its physical properties were listed in the table at the beginning of Chapter 25. It is chemically the most active member of its group, with chemical properties which are similar to those of barium.

Radium is an important element not because of its physical or chemical

Fig. 38-2. A fragment of metallic uranium, one of the radioactive elements. See Fig. 38-3.

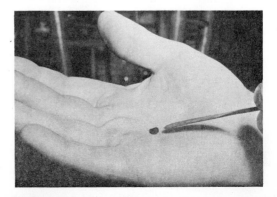

Fig. 38–3. Radiation from the fragment of uranium shown in Fig. 38–2 penetrated the light-tight wrappings of a photographic plate and produced this picture.

properties, but because of its radioactivity. It is one of the most highly radioactive elements known. Because of this radioactivity, radium and radium compounds have several unusual properties. These properties are true of other radioactive materials, too.

1. It affects the light-sensitive emulsion on a photographic plate. Even though a photographic plate is wrapped in opaque paper and kept in the dark, the invisible rays from radioactive materials will affect the plate in the same way that light does when the plate is

Fig. 38–4. An electroscope is used to measure the intensity of an electric charge.

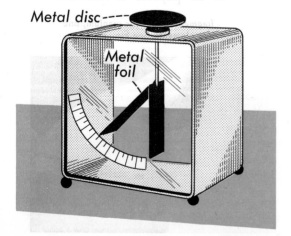

Metal disc

Metal foil

exposed. When the plate is developed, a black spot shows up on the negative where the invisible radiation struck it. The rays from radioactive materials penetrate paper, wood, flesh, and *thin* sheets of metal.

2. Radium and its compounds discharge an electroscope and affect a Geiger counter. The radiation from radium ionizes the molecules of the gases in the air. These ionized molecules conduct the electric charge away from the knob of an electroscope. The activity of a sample of a radium compound may be measured by the speed with which it discharges an electroscope. In a similar way, the rays given off by radium ionize the low pressure gas in the tube of a Geiger counter. Electricity can thus momentarily pass through the tube. The passage of electricity may be registered as a "click" by a loudspeaker.

3. Radium compounds produce fluorescence with certain other compounds. A small quantity of radium bromide added to zinc sulfide causes the zinc sulfide to glow in the dark. Such a mixture is used in making a luminous paint for coating the dials of airplane instruments. It may also be used for the hands and dials of clocks and watches.

4. The physiological effects of radium. The radiation from radium may destroy the germinating power of seeds, kill bacteria, or even small animals. Those who work with radium may be severely burned by the rays which it emits. Such frightful burns require a long time to heal, and may sometimes prove fatal. Because the radiations from radium destroy tissue, it is used in the treatment of cancer and certain skin diseases.

5. Radium salts emit energy continuously. Part of this energy is light energy

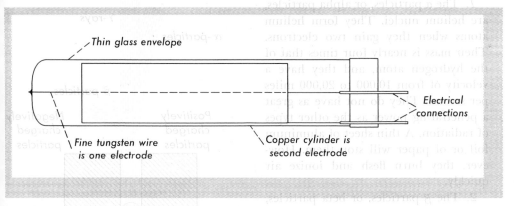

Fig. 38–5. This cutaway view shows the structure of a Geiger-Müller counter tube. Such tubes are used to detect radioactive materials.

which causes radium salts to glow in the dark with a pale phosphorescence. This glow is so pale, however, that in the daylight the salts resemble common table salt in their appearance. Radium salts also emit heat continuously. In one hour radium gives off enough heat to melt 1.5 times its own weight of ice. That means 120 calories of heat per hour per gram. The source of this energy is the transformation of matter into energy which occurs as a radium atom disintegrates into a slightly simpler atom and simultaneously emits radiation. One half of any number of radium atoms will disintegrate into simpler atoms in about 1600 years. One half of what remains, or one-fourth of the original atoms, will disintegrate in the next 1600 years. One half of what yet remains, or one-eighth of the original atoms, will disintegrate in the next 1600 years, and so on. This process continues until all the radium atoms have disintegrated. This period of 1600 years is called the *half-life of radium.* Each radioactive isotope has its own characteristic half-life.

5. Other natural radioactive ele-

ments. The radioactive elements known to Becquerel were uranium and thorium. We have already learned how the Curies discovered two more, polonium and radium. Since that time, several more natural radioactive elements have been discovered. All the elements beyond bismuth in the Periodic Table are radioactive. Several artificial radioactive elements have also been prepared, but a description of that work will be given in Chapter 39. One of the important natural radioactive elements is the inert gas *radon.* While it is chemically inert, it is quite radioactive. Radon is a gas which is given off by radium when radium atoms disintegrate. It is collected in tubes and used in place of radium for the treatment of disease.

6. The nature of radioactivity. The radiation emitted by such radioactive elements as uranium, thorium, and radium has been carefully studied. Sir Ernest Rutherford, an English scientist, discovered that such radiation is complex, consisting of two types of particles and one type of ray. These are named as follows:

1. The **α** particles, or alpha particles, are helium nuclei. They form helium atoms when they gain two electrons. Their mass is nearly four times that of the hydrogen atom, and they have a velocity of from 10,000 to 20,000 miles per second. They do not have as great a penetrating power as the other types of radiation. A thin sheet of aluminum foil or of paper will stop them. However, they burn flesh and ionize air quickly.

2. The **β** particles, or beta particles, are electrons. They are negatively-charged particles each $\frac{1}{1837}$ as heavy as the hydrogen atom. They travel at a velocity of from 60,000 to 160,000 miles per second. Their penetrating power is much greater than that of alpha particles.

3. The **γ** rays, or gamma rays, are high energy X rays. **X rays** are the same kind of radiation as light, but with much shorter wave length and higher frequency. Gamma rays are believed to be caused by transitions in energy levels in the nucleus. They are the most penetrating of the radiations given off by radioactive elements.

Fig. 38-6 shows the effect of a powerful magnetic field, perpendicular to the plane of the paper, on the complex radiation emitted from a small particle of radioactive material. Note that the north pole is above the paper and the south pole is below the paper. The heavier alpha particles are deflected slightly in one direction. The lighter beta particles are deflected more markedly in the opposite direction. The gamma rays are not affected by the magnet. By the use of such a magnetic field, Rutherford studied the radiations from radioactive material and learned their nature.

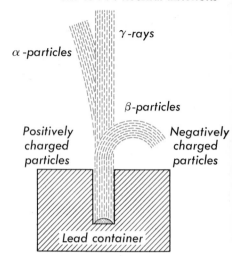

Fig. 38–6. How a magnet affects the different types of radiations. The north pole of the magnet is above the paper and the south pole is beneath the paper.

7. The disintegration of atoms of radioactive elements. We now know that radioactive atoms disintegrate spontaneously. They yield heat and light energy in so doing. At first they did not appear to lose mass and it was believed that they would give off heat and light forever. More careful investigation shows that radioactive materials do, however, lose mass slowly.

What is the source of so much energy? A long series of experiments has shown that the nuclei of radium and other radioactive elements are disintegrating. The alpha and beta particles are the products of such nuclear disintegration. Spontaneously, certain heavy nuclei break down into simpler and lighter nuclei. Enormous quantities of energy are released by this disintegration of matter.

8. A series of related radioactive elements. All naturally-occurring radioactive elements belong to one of three series of related elements. The heaviest or "parent" elements of these

The Uranium Disintegration Series

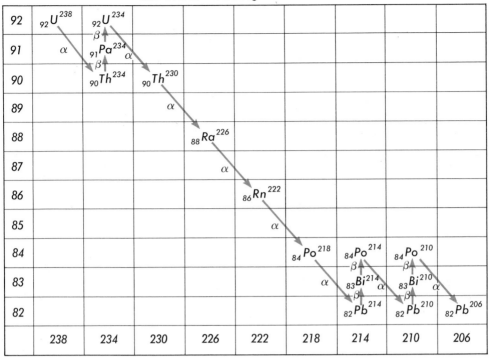

Fig. 38-7. The parent element of the Uranium Disintegration Series is $_{92}U^{238}$. The final stable element of the series is $_{82}Pb^{206}$.

three series are the uranium isotope with atomic weight 238, the uranium isotope with atomic weight 235, and the thorium isotope with atomic weight 232. Since radium is a member of the family which has the uranium isotope with atomic weight 238 as its parent, let us trace this series of disintegrations.

The nucleus of the parent atom contains 92 protons, since the atomic number of uranium is 92. The nucleus has an atomic weight of 238. As this nucleus disintegrates, it ejects an alpha particle. This becomes an atom of helium when its positive charge is neutralized. An alpha particle has an atomic weight of 4. Since it contains two protons, it has an atomic number of 2. The residue left from the uranium nu-

cleus will thus have an atomic number of 90 and an atomic weight of 234. It is an isotope of thorium, sometimes designated Uranium X_1. The *nuclear equation* for this transmutation reaction is:

$$_{92}U^{238} \rightarrow \, _{90}Th^{234} + \, _{2}He^{4}$$

A *transmutation* is the change in the identity of a nucleus because of a change in the number of protons it has. Since the above equation is a nuclear equation, only nuclei are represented. The superscript is the atomic weight. The subscript is the atomic number. Alpha particles are represented as helium nuclei, $_{2}He^{4}$. The total of the atomic weights on the left must equal the total of the atomic weights on the right. The total of the atomic numbers on the left must equal the total of the atomic numbers on the right.

The half-life of Uranium X_1 is about 24 days. It disintegrates by emitting a beta particle. The loss of a beta particle from the nucleus increases the number of positive charges in the nucleus, the atomic number, by one. The beta particle is believed to be formed by the transformation of a neutron into a proton and beta particle (electron). Since the weight of a beta particle is negligible, the atomic weight stays the same.

$$_{90}Th^{234} \rightarrow \, _{91}Pa^{234} + \, _{-1}e^0$$

The symbol $_{-1}e^0$ represents an electron with an atomic number of -1 and an atomic weight of 0. $_{91}Pa^{234}$ is an isotope of protactinium, sometimes designated Uranium X_2. This isotope disintegrates by emitting a beta particle and producing $_{92}U^{234}$, sometimes designated Uranium II.

$$_{91}Pa^{234} \rightarrow \, _{92}U^{234} + \, _{-1}e^0$$

The disintegration of Uranium II is by alpha particle emission.

$$_{92}U^{234} \rightarrow \, _{90}Th^{230} + \, _2He^4$$

The isotope of thorium produced also emits an alpha particle, forming radium.

$$_{90}Th^{230} \rightarrow \, _{88}Ra^{226} + \, _2He^4$$

Now we can see why ores of uranium must contain radium. Radium is one of the products of the disintegration of uranium atoms. The rates of disintegration of $_{92}U^{238}$, the intervening elements, and of radium itself, determine the proportion of uranium atoms to radium atoms which is found.

The disintegration of radium proceeds according to the chart shown in Fig. 38-7. You should be able to explain

the changes in atomic number and atomic weight in terms of the emitted particles. When Radium F, an isotope of polonium, loses an alpha particle, it forms an element with atomic number 82 and atomic weight 206. This is a stable, that is, non-radioactive, isotope of lead. These spontaneous transmutations, beginning with $_{92}U^{238}$, passing through $_{88}Ra^{226}$, on down to $_{82}Pb^{206}$, occur continuously at a rate which man has never been able to alter.

9. Applications of natural radioactivity. The age of minerals containing radioactive substances can be estimated. Since radioactive substances disintegrate at a known rate, an analysis of the mineral is made to determine the amount of long-lived "parent" element and the amounts of the "descendent" elements at present in the sample. Then by calculation, scientists can determine how long it must have taken for these amounts of "descendent" elements to be produced. This is assumed to be the age of the mineral. One of the oldest minerals whose age has been estimated is over two billion years old.

The carbon atoms involved in the oxygen-carbon dioxide cycle of living plants and animals are kept at a low but constant level of radioactivity because of the production of the radioactive $_6C^{14}$ isotope from $_7N^{14}$ atoms in the atmosphere by the action of cosmic rays. (Cosmic rays are protons of very high energy which come to the earth from outer space.) But when living things die, the oxygen-carbon dioxide cycle no longer operates in them. They no longer replace carbon atoms in their cells with other carbon atoms. Thus the radioactivity of the carbon atoms in nonliving materials slowly diminishes.

Carbon from a wooden beam taken

from the tomb of an Egyptian pharaoh has about half the radioactivity of wood in living trees. Since the half life of a $_6C^{14}$ atom is 5570 years, the age of wood with half the radioactivity of currently-living wood is about 5570 years. Objects up to 24,000 years old have been dated in this manner.

Summary

Substances which give off rays which affect photographic plates the same way light does are radioactive.

Radium was discovered by Pierre and Marie Curie in 1899. It is a very radioactive element which is always found in uranium ores. It resembles the element barium in its chemical properties. Because of its radioactivity, it has several unusual properties either as the element, or in compounds: *1.* it affects a photographic plate; *2.* it discharges an electroscope and affects a Geiger counter; *3.* it produces fluorescence with certain compounds; *4.* its radiation destroys tissue; *5.* it emits energy in the form of light and heat continuously.

The radiation from radioactive substances is of three types: *1.* alpha particles, or helium nuclei; *2.* beta particles, or electrons; and *3.* gamma rays, or high energy X rays. The discharge of these particles from the nuclei of radioactive elements causes them to disintegrate into simpler elements.

All naturally-occurring radioactive elements belong to one of three series of related elements. Uranium-238 is the parent element of the radioactive series which contains radium.

The age of certain minerals and of carbon-containing materials can be estimated by the radioactive isotopes they contain.

Test yourself on these terms

α particle	nuclear equation	radium
β particle	parent element	radon
electroscope	pitchblende	subscript
γ ray	polonium	superscript
Geiger counter	radioactive	transmutation reaction
half-life	radioactivity	uranium

Questions

Group A

1. (*a*) Who discovered radioactivity? (*b*) How was the discovery made?
2. What evidence led Pierre and Marie Curie to suspect that there were radioactive elements other than uranium in pitchblende?
3. How does the radioactivity of radium compare with that of uranium?
4. What are the sources of radium ore?
5. What practical use is made of the fluorescence produced in zinc sulfide by a radium compound?
6. What is meant by the *half-life* of a radioactive element?

7. What inert gas is radioactive?

8. How many kinds of radiation are given off by radioactive materials?

9. From what part of a radioactive atom do the alpha and beta particles come?

10. What change in identity and mass occurs when a radioactive atom gives off an alpha particle?

11. What change in identity and mass occurs when a radioactive atom gives off a beta particle?

12. How is the age of a radioactive mineral estimated?

Group B

13. Why is radium studied separately rather than with the other elements of Group IIA?

14. Is the radioactivity of an element affected by the other elements with which it may be chemically combined?

15. Why can the radiation from a radioactive material affect photographic film, even though the film is well wrapped in black paper?

16. How does a radioactive material affect the rate of discharge of an electroscope?

17. Where do we find most of the natural radioactive elements in the Periodic Table?

18. Give the mass, nature, and velocity range of: (a) alpha particles; (b) beta particles.

19. What do scientists believe gamma rays to be?

20. Write the nuclear equation for the emission of an alpha particle by $_{88}Ra^{226}$.

21. Write the nuclear equation for the emission of a beta particle by $_{82}Pb^{214}$.

22. Write nuclear equations for successive emissions of an alpha particle and a beta particle from $_{84}Po^{214}$.

Some things for you to do

1. Examine the luminous dial on a watch or clock in the dark with a magnifying glass. You will find that the glow is really a series of tiny flashes caused by the impact of alpha particles with zinc sulfide.

2. Determine the rate of discharge of an electroscope. Then bring some radioactive material, such as a uranium compound, close to the electroscope. How is the rate of discharge affected? Explain.

3. Read *Madame Curie,* written by Eve Curie. This is the biography of the famous woman scientist written by one of her daughters.

Chapter 39 ARTIFICIAL RADIOACTIVITY

1. The stability of a nucleus. We have already learned in Chapter 38 that the nuclei of certain naturally-occurring heavy atoms are unstable. They break down at a definite rate into somewhat simpler nuclei and simultaneous-ly emit particles and rays. Let us now learn what conditions promote such instability in the nuclei of atoms.

On the atomic mass scale, the isotope of oxygen with eight protons and eight neutrons in its nucleus is defined to

VOCABULARY

Binding energy. The energy which holds the protons and neutrons together in the nucleus of an atom.

Chain reaction. A reaction in which the material or energy which initiates the reaction is also one of the products.

Critical size. The amount of radioactive material required to sustain a chain reaction.

Cyclotron. An electromagnetic device for accelerating protons or deuterons in a spiral path.

Electron-volt. The energy required to move an electron across a potential difference of one volt.

Fission. The break-up of a nucleus into two medium-weight parts.

Fusion. The combination of two light-weight nuclei to form a heavier, more stable nucleus.

Nuclear disintegration. The emission of a proton or neutron from a nucleus as a result of bombarding the nucleus with alpha particles, protons, deuterons, or neutrons.

Nuclear reactor. A device in which the controlled fission of radioactive material produces new radioactive substances and energy.

Radioactive fall-out. The showering down of radioactive particles which were originally carried high into the air by a nuclear explosion.

Fig. 39–1. Albert Einstein, a theoretical physicist, was the first man to predict the interrelationship of matter and energy.

have an *atomic mass* of 16.0000 (see Chapter 4, Section 18). On this scale, a $_2He^4$ nucleus has a mass of 4.0028, while the mass of a proton is 1.00758 and the mass of a neutron is 1.00893. (In Chapter 4 we used only the "rounded-off" values of the atomic mass. They were sufficiently accurate for our purposes then. Now we must use more precise values for the masses since they are necessary to our understanding of the stability of atomic nuclei.) Since a $_2He^4$ nucleus contains two protons and two neutrons, we might expect its mass to be the combined mass of these four particles, 4.0330. [2 (1.00758) +2 (1.00893) = 4.0330]. But there is a difference of 0.0302 atomic mass unit between the actual mass, 4.0028, and the calculated mass, 4.0330, of a $_2He^4$ nucleus. *This difference in mass, converted to energy according to Einstein's equation, $E = mc^2$, (see Chapter 1, Section 11),*

holds *the protons and neutrons together in the helium nucleus.* This energy is called the **binding energy.**

If the binding energies of the atoms of the elements are calculated, it is found that the lightest and the heaviest elements have the smallest binding energies. The elements of intermediate atomic weights have the greatest binding energies. The elements with the greatest binding energies are the ones with the most stable nuclei. Therefore, we see that the nuclei of the lightest and heaviest atoms are less stable than the nuclei of the elements of intermediate atomic weight.

★ There seem to be factors other than weight that are associated with the stability of atomic nuclei. These are: 1. the ratio of neutrons to protons; and 2. the even-odd nature of the number of neutrons and the number of protons.

★ In the most stable nuclei, the ratio of neutrons to protons is 1:1; that is, there is an equal number of neutrons and protons. Nuclei with a greater number of neutrons than protons (and the ratio increases to 1.6 :1 in the heavier elements) have lower binding energies and are less stable. In nuclei with an equal number of protons and neutrons, these particles occupy what appear to be the lowest energy levels in the nucleus. Scientists believe that many properties of nuclear particles indicate that in a nucleus there are energy levels, just as there are electron energy levels in atoms. When there is an excess of neutrons over protons, the neutrons must occupy levels of greater energy. This lowers the binding energy, and consequently lowers the stability of the nucleus.

★ On the basis of frequency of occur-

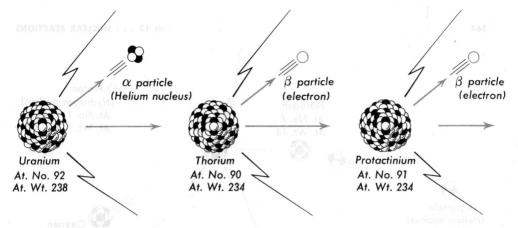

α particle
(Helium nucleus)

β particle
(electron)

β particle
(electron)

Uranium
At. No. 92
At. Wt. 238

Thorium
At. No. 90
At. Wt. 234

Protactinium
At. No. 91
At. Wt. 234

Fig. 39-2. These diagrams show successive alpha and beta particle emissions in the disintegration of $_{92}U^{238}$.

rence alone, the even-odd nature of the number of protons and of the number of neutrons must affect the stability of a nucleus. By far the greatest number of stable nuclei have an even number of protons and an even number of neutrons. Less frequent in occurrence are the nuclei with an even number of protons and an odd number of neutrons, or vice versa. Only a few stable nuclei with an odd number of protons and an odd number of neutrons are known.

Because of this difference in the stability of the different nuclei, there are four types of nuclear reactions in which nuclear energy is liberated. In each case a small amount of the mass of the reactants is converted into energy and yields products of greater stability.

1. A nucleus undergoes *radioactive decomposition,* forming a slightly lighter, more stable nucleus, and emitting an alpha particle or a beta particle, and gamma rays.

2. A nucleus is bombarded with alpha particles, protons, deuterons (deuterium, $_1H^2$, nuclei), or neutrons. The unstable nucleus that is formed emits a proton or a neutron and becomes more stable. This process is called *nuclear disintegration.*

3. A very heavy nucleus is split and forms two medium-weight nuclei. This process is known as *fission.*

4. Light-weight nuclei combine to form heavier, more stable nuclei. This process is known as *fusion.*

While we have already studied natural radioactivity, in this chapter we shall review radioactive changes in terms of nuclear stability. Then we shall go on to describe the other three types of nuclear reactions.

2. Radioactive changes produce more stable nuclei. The emission of an alpha particle from a radioactive nucleus decreases the mass of the nucleus. The nucleus of lower mass that is produced has a higher binding energy, and is for that reason more stable.

Alpha particle emission decreases the number of protons and neutrons in a nucleus equally and also by an even number. Beta particle emission, by transforming a neutron into a proton, brings the neutron-proton ratio nearer to 1:1. Both of these changes thus promote an increase in the stability of the nucleus undergoing such change.

3. Rutherford produced the first nuclear disintegration. When scientists discovered how uranium and radium

563

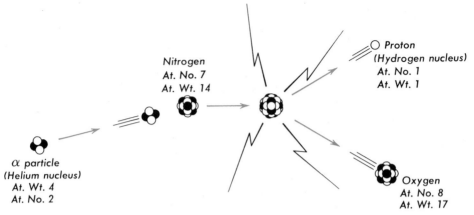

Fig. 39–3. These diagrams show the historic nuclear disintegration performed by Rutherford.

undergo natural disintegration and transmutation, they wondered if man-made transmutations could be produced. Could extra protons be added to the nucleus to make new elements? In 1919 Rutherford produced the first nuclear disintegration. He bombarded nitrogen with alpha particles from radium. He obtained protons (hydrogen nuclei) and an isotope of oxygen.

$$_7N^{14} + _2He^4 \rightarrow _8O^{17} + _1H^1$$

4. Experiments with another nuclear disintegration verified Einstein's equation. In 1932 two English scientists, J. D. Cockroft (1897–   ), and E. T. S. Walton (1903–   ), experimentally verified Einstein's equation, $E = mc^2$. They bombarded lithium with high speed protons. Alpha particles and a great amount of energy were produced.

$$_3Li^7 + _1H^1 \rightarrow _2He^4 + _2He^4 + \text{energy}$$

There is a loss of matter in this reaction. One atom of lithium, with an atomic mass of 7.0180, was hit by a proton with a mass of 1.0081. These formed two alpha particles (helium nuclei) each having a mass of 4.0039.

Simple arithmetic, $(7.0180 + 1.0081) - 2(4.0039)$, shows that there is a loss of 0.0183 atomic mass unit. Cockroft and Walton found that the energy emitted in the reaction agreed very well with that predicted by Einstein for such a loss in mass. Subsequent experiments have offered further proof for Einstein's equation for the conversion of matter into energy.

5. Neutrons are emitted in some nuclear disintegrations. We have already learned that neutrons were discovered by Chadwick in 1932. He first detected them during the bombardment of beryllium by alpha particles:

$$_4Be^9 + _2He^4 \rightarrow _6C^{12} + _0n^1$$

The symbol for a neutron is $_0n^1$, indicating a particle with zero atomic number (no protons) and an atomic weight of 1. This reaction offered proof that neutrons were the second type of particle in the nuclei of atoms.

6. The cyclotron and other "atom smashers." Radium, the natural source of alpha particles used in many early experiments, is rather inefficient in producing nuclear changes. As a result, scientists sought more efficient ways of producing high energy particles for nuclear bombardment. This search resulted in the development of the cyclotron and other devices for the acceleration of charged particles.

The *cyclotron* is the invention of Dr. E. O. Lawrence (1901–   ) of the University of California. It consists of a cylindrical box placed between the poles of a huge electromagnet and exhausted until a high vacuum is produced. The "bullets" used to bombard nuclei are usually protons or deuterons. They are introduced into the cylindrical box through its center.

Inside the box are two hollow, D-shaped electrodes called *dees*. These are connected to a source of very high voltage through an oscillator. When the cyclotron is in operation, the electrical charge on these dees is reversed very rapidly by the oscillator. The combination of the alternating high voltage and the action of the field of the electromagnet causes the protons or deuterons inside to take a spiral course. They move faster and faster as they near the outside of the box, acquiring more and more energy. When they reach the outer rim of the box, they are deflected toward the target. The energy of the particles accelerated in a

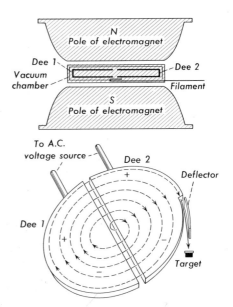

Fig. 39–4. A diagram of the cyclotron used to produce "atomic bullets" of very high energy.

cyclotron may reach 15,000,000 *electron-volts*. This is the energy an electron would have if it were accelerated across a potential difference of 15,000,000 volts. By studying the fragments of atoms formed by bombardment, scientists have learned a great deal about atomic structure. They also have discovered many things about the products formed by the disintegration of

(Text continues on page 569.)

Fig. 39–5. The 60-inch cyclotron of the Brookhaven National Laboratory.

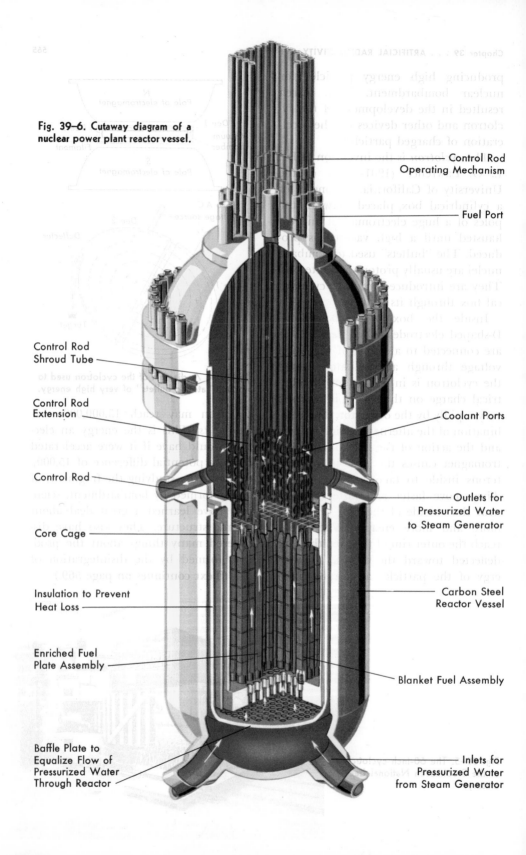

Fig. 39-6. Cutaway diagram of a nuclear power plant reactor vessel.

Control Rod
Operating Mechanism

Fuel Port

Control Rod
Shroud Tube

Control Rod
Extension

Coolant Ports

Control Rod

Core Cage

Outlets for
Pressurized Water
to Steam Generator

Insulation to Prevent
Heat Loss

Carbon Steel
Reactor Vessel

Enriched Fuel
Plate Assembly

Blanket Fuel Assembly

Baffle Plate to
Equalize Flow of
Pressurized Water
Through Reactor

Inlets for
Pressurized Water
from Steam Generator

The first large nuclear power plant in the United States is located near Pittsburgh, Pennsylvania. On pages 566–568 you will find diagrams which show the construction and operation of the nuclear reactor in this plant. Beginning opposite page 568 is a Trans-Vision insert which explains the nuclear reactions and shows how nuclear energy is used to generate electricity.

Fig. 39-6 is a cut-away diagram of the reactor vessel. The vessel is made of steel plates, and is about thirty feet high and about ten feet in diameter. At the top are the control rod operating mechanisms and the ports for inserting or removing fuel rods. Midway down the sides of the reactor vessel are the outlets for the heated pressurized water. At the bottom are the inlets for the pressurized water.

The fuel rods in the reactor vessel are supported in the core cage. There are two types of fuel rods: (1) seed fuel rod, and (2) blanket fuel rod.

The seed fuel rod assemblies are arranged in the reactor vessel in a hollow square. Each assembly consists of four boxes holding plates of enriched $_{92}U^{235}$ alloyed with zirconium, as shown in Fig. 39-7. The cross-shaped space between the boxes contains a hafnium control rod. The control rod may be raised or lowered in the seed fuel rod assembly to regulate the rate of the reactions taking place in it. Pressurized water is pumped up between the plates in the fuel rod assemblies to absorb the heat of the reaction.

The remainder of the core cage is filled with blanket fuel rod assemblies. A blanket fuel rod is a zirconium alloy tube filled with pellets of uranium oxide. These fuel rods are grouped into blanket bundles. These bundles are held together by end plates with coolant flow holes. Thus the pressurized water coolant may flow upward around each fuel rod. The blanket bundles are fastened together in blanket fuel rod assemblies. Both the blanket fuel rod assemblies and the seed fuel rod as-

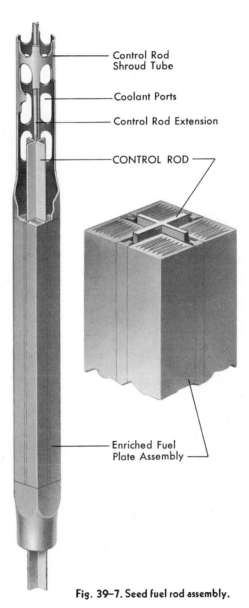

Control Rod
Shroud Tube

Coolant Ports

Control Rod Extension

CONTROL ROD

Enriched Fuel
Plate Assembly

Fig. 39–7. Seed fuel rod assembly.

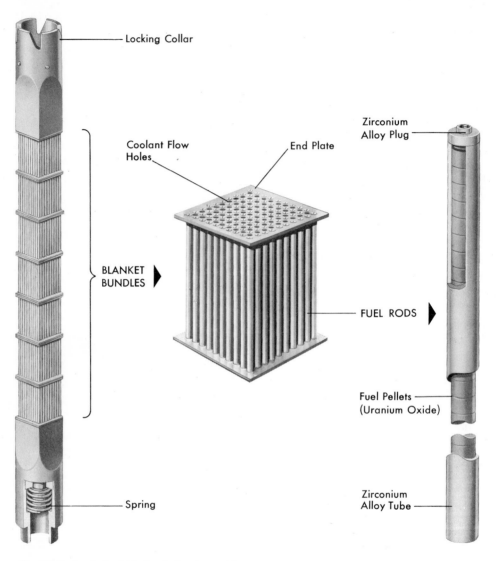

Locking Collar

Coolant Flow
Holes

End Plate

Zirconium
Alloy Plug

BLANKET
BUNDLES ▶

FUEL RODS ▶

Fuel Pellets
(Uranium Oxide)

Spring

Zirconium
Alloy Tube

Fig. 39–8. Analysis of blanket fuel rod assembly.

semblies are held in the core cage by a locking collar, which also provides a means by which the rod may be inserted or removed from the reactor vessel.

The fission of $_{92}U^{235}$ in the seed assemblies furnishes energy at the start of reactor operation. Neutrons from these reactions cause reactions in the uranium oxide in the blanket assemblies. They promote the fission of $_{92}U^{235}$ and the transmutation of $_{92}U^{238}$ to plutonium. This plutonium may then undergo fission and provide additional energy. Thus the operation of this reactor depends upon both fission and breeder reactions.

Power from Nuclear Energy
as seen by the "Trans-Vision" process

A nuclear power plant produces electricity from the energy within atomic nuclei. In this "Trans-Vision" insert, you will see the various types of energy-producing nuclear reactions which occur in the nuclear reactor—the source of heat energy for the power plant. You will see how this heat energy is absorbed in the moderator-coolant and transferred to steam in steam generators. The heat energy of the steam is transformed into mechanical energy as the steam spins the turbine blades. The turbine is connected directly to the electric generator, completing the steps in the energy transfer—nuclear energy to heat energy to mechanical energy to electrical energy.

The drawings showing the nuclear changes in the reactor are explained on the left-hand pages. Those indicating how this nuclear energy is utilized in generating electricity are explained at the bottom of this page, continuing on the back cover.

The drawings were done by Mr. F. R. Gruger, Jr. Those of the power plant are simplified from photographs and drawings of the Pressurized Water Reactor Power Plant at Shippingport, Pennsylvania, supplied by Bettis Atomic Power Division, Westinghouse Electric Corporation. This plant is sponsored by the United States Atomic Energy Commission. Duquesne Light Company, Pittsburgh, Pennsylvania, is participating in its development and construction and will operate and maintain the plant after it is completed.

Producing Electricity from Nuclear Energy

Steam Generation—Page I

Pressurized water at a temperature of 542° F and a pressure of 2000 lb/in^2 comes from the nuclear reactor through pipe (1). The pressurizer (2) is connected to this pipe and maintains 2000 lb/in^2 pressure in the primary circuit. The primary circuit is the pressurized water circuit between the reactor and the steam generator. The water in the pressurizer is electrically heated to 636° F. At this temperature water boils and produces steam which exerts a pressure of 2000 lb/in^2 on the water in the primary circuit.

In the steam generator (3), the heated water from the reactor produces steam from the preheated water in the secondary circuit. As the pressurized water from the reactor passes through the steam generator, its temperature drops to 508° F because of the transfer of heat to the steam in the secondary circuit. The pressurized water now enters the

(Continued on back cover)

This drawing shows sche-
matically a cross-section of
the nuclear reactor. Only
nuclei of the elements found
in each part are repre-
sented. The reactor is fueled
with enriched $_{92}U^{235}$ in seed
assemblies and natural uranium oxide in blanket as-
semblies. Pressurized water,
circulated around the fuel
assemblies, is used as the
moderator-coolant. The control rods are hafnium metal.
In the seed sub-assembly
at the left, a slow neutron
is about to strike a $_{92}U^{235}$
nucleus.

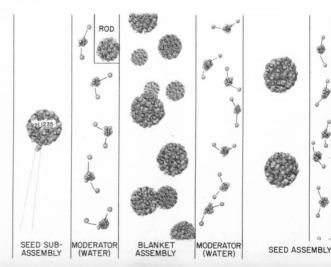

SEED SUB-   MODERATOR   BLANKET   MODERATOR   SEED ASSEMBLY
ASSEMBLY   (WATER)   ASSEMBLY   (WATER)

PRODUCTION OF ELECTRICITY

14 ELECTRIC GENERATOR.

15 TRANSFORMERS.

16 CIRCUIT BREAKERS.

17 HIGH VOLTAGE DISTRIBU-
   TION LINES.

18 High pressure side of turbine.

19 Low pressure side of turbine.

20 Cold water feed to condenser.

21 Condensate well.

coolant pump (4) which circulates the pressurized water in the primary circuit at the rate of approximately 18,300 gal/min. The coolant pump forces the pressurized water through pipe (5) back to the reactor for reheating. Pipe (6) is the secondary-circuit preheated water inlet pipe to the steam generator.

The elements of the primary circuit are isolated by the walls and ceiling of a concrete enclosure. This is to restrict the spread of radioactivity in the event of a break in the primary circuit. In actual practice the elements of the primary circuit are enclosed in steel containers as well.

Steam Utilization — Page 3

Steam is produced in the steam generator (3) when preheated secondary-circuit water drops over the hot tubes containing the primary-circuit water. Moisture is removed from the steam by the vaned devices in the steam separator at the top of the generator.

This dry steam at a pressure of 600 lb/in^2 passes through the steam line (7) to the turbine. It enters the turbine through a governor-controlled inlet valve (8). After passing through a portion of the turbine (9), some steam is diverted to serve as a source of heat for the feed-water heater (13). The remaining steam goes to a separator (10) which removes the moisture which has condensed. This moisture is drained off to the feed-water heater

(13). The steam from the separator (10) again enters the turbine (9). After this passage through the remainder of the turbine, the spent steam passes to the condenser (11), where it is condensed to water. This water now enters the feed-water pump (12) which forces it through the feed-water heater (13) and the feed-water pipe (6) back to the steam generator

Production of Electricity — Page 5

We can now see the direction of flow of steam through the turbine. Steam from the generator (3) first enters the high-pressure side of the turbine (18). After part of the steam's energy is expended by this passage, the condensed moisture is removed in the separator (10). The remaining steam now enters the low-pressure side of the turbine (19). The cooling water for the condenser flows in through the cold water feed (20). The condensed secondary-circuit water collects in the condensate well (21).

The force of the steam, pushing against the turbine blades, spins the turbine shaft at 1800 revolutions per minute. This shaft is connected directly to an electric generator (14) capable of producing 100,000 kilowatts of electric power. The voltage of the electricity produced by the generator is increased by the transformers (15). The electrical circuits are protected with circuit breakers (16). The high voltage distribution lines (17) conduct the electricity from the power station to the consumer.

(Text continued from page 565.)
atoms. Other recently-devised machines for bombarding atomic nuclei are the *betatron*, the *synchrotron*, and the *linear accelerator*.

The betatron is a device which accelerates electrons rather than positively-charged particles as does the cyclotron. The accelerated electrons may be used as "bullets" for bombardment, or for producing high-energy X rays. The synchrotron operates in principle like the cyclotron. But by varying both the oscillating voltage and the magnetic field, the particles can be accelerated in a circular path rather than in a spiral path. A synchrotron can impart an energy of several billion electron-volts to the protons which it accelerates. Still another type of particle accelerator is the linear accelerator. In this device the particles travel in a straight line through many stages of relatively small potential difference which act to accelerate the particles.

7. Neutrons make better "bullets." Prior to the discovery of neutrons in 1932, alpha particles and protons were used in studying atomic nuclei. However, alpha particles and protons are charged particles. It requires great quantities of energy, such as are imparted to these particles by cyclotrons and synchrotrons, to "fire" these charged "bullets" into a nucleus. Their positive charge causes them to be repelled by the positive nuclear charge.

Neutrons have no charge. They can easily penetrate the nucleus of an atom since there is no force of repulsion acting. Fast neutrons may go right through an atom without causing any change in it. Some fast neutrons, however, may produce the disintegration of a nucleus. Slow neutrons, on the other hand, are sometimes trapped by a nucleus. This nucleus then becomes unstable, and may disintegrate. Fast neutrons may be slowed down by passage through elements of low atomic weight such as those found in deuterium oxide and graphite. Neutrons are produced by an atom smasher when the accelerated positively-charged particles strike a target material, possibly beryllium.

8. Neutron bombardment may produce man-made elements. When $_{92}U^{238}$, the most plentiful isotope of uranium, is bombarded with slow neutrons, a $_{92}U^{238}$ nucleus may capture a neutron. An unstable isotope of uranium, $_{92}U^{239}$, is formed. This emits a beta particle

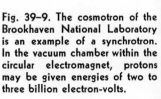
Fig. 39–9. The cosmotron of the Brookhaven National Laboratory is an example of a synchrotron. In the vacuum chamber within the circular electromagnet, protons may be given energies of two to three billion electron-volts.

Fig. 39–10. This photograph shows the interior of the heavy ion linear accelerator or "Hilac" at the University of California Radiation Laboratory. The Hilac is designed to accelerate the nuclei of atoms ranging up to argon in mass. It may thus be possible to add large fragments of matter to the nuclei of uranium atoms and produce elements with atomic numbers higher than nobelium, No. 102.

(electron) and forms a man-made radioactive element, neptunium. Neptunium has the atomic number 93.

$$_{92}U^{238} + _0n^1 \rightarrow _{92}U^{239}$$
$$_{92}U^{239} \rightarrow _{93}Np^{239} + _{-1}e^0$$

Neptunium is an unstable element, also. Its nucleus ejects a beta particle, forming still another man-made element, plutonium, atomic number 94.

$$_{93}Np^{239} \rightarrow _{94}Pu^{239} + _{-1}e^0$$

Neptunium and plutonium were the first man-made *transuranium* elements. ***Transuranium elements*** are those with more than 92 protons in their nuclei. Now there are ten artificially prepared transuranium elements. In addition to neptunium and plutonium, there are americium, curium, berkelium, californium, einsteinium, fermium, mendelevium, and nobelium. These have been prepared by bombardment of the nu-

Fig. 39–11. The patient has just swallowed a solution containing radioactive iodine. The scientist is adjusting the Geiger counter placed above the patient's thyroid gland to determine how quickly the iodine becomes concentrated in the gland.

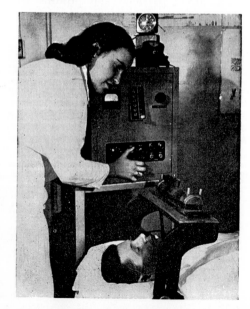

clei of uranium or more complex elements with neutrons, alpha particles, or other "nuclear bullets."

9. Radioactive atoms can be made artificially. In 1934 Madame Curie's daughter Irene (1897–1956), working with her husband, Frederic Joliot (1900–   ), discovered that stable atoms can be made artificially radioactive. This occurs when they are bombarded with deuterons or neutrons. Now radioactive isotopes of all the elements have been prepared. Many new radioactive isotopes are manufactured by slow-neutron bombardment in the nuclear reactor at Oak Ridge, Tennessee. The equation showing the formation of radioactive $_{27}Co^{60}$ from naturally-occurring non-radioactive $_{27}Co^{59}$ by slow-neutron bombardment is:

$$_{27}Co^{59} + _{0}n^{1} \rightarrow _{27}Co^{60}$$

The radiation from $_{27}Co^{60}$ consists of beta particles and gamma rays.

Radioactive $_{15}P^{32}$ is prepared by bombardment of $_{16}S^{32}$ with slow neutrons:

$$_{16}S^{32} + _{0}n^{1} \rightarrow _{15}P^{32} + _{1}H^{1}$$

The radiation from $_{15}P^{32}$ consists only of beta particles.

Radioactive phosphorus and radioactive cobalt are being used in the treatment of various forms of cancer. Radioactive iodine may be used as part of the treatment of persons suffering from thyroid gland disorders.

Radioactive cobalt, cesium, or iridium, in specially designed apparatus, produces an intense beam of radiation for the treatment of deepseated tumors. Radioactive arsenic is helpful in locating brain tumors, while neutron-irradiated boron may be used for treatment.

Radioactive cobalt may be added to a fluid flowing through a pipeline. When it is followed by means of a Geiger counter, it is possible to retrace the path of the pipeline or to determine the position of an obstruction in it. This is an example of the use of a radioactive isotope as a *tracer*.

Radioactive tracer materials are used to study the wear of machine parts. For example, a radioactive material may be applied to a bearing, and a shaft turned in the bearing. Then the radioactivity of the shaft is measured. In this way the amount of bearing metal rubbed off by the shaft can be accurately known. In a similar way the wear of automobile tires can be measured. A radioactive tracer may be included in the tire tread. Then, after the tire has been driven over a road surface, the radioactivity of the surface is measured and the amount of rubber rubbed off on it may be determined.

Manufacturers of detergents use radioactive "soil" to determine the efficiency of their products. Any trace of radioactivity in the washed clothes shows that all of the "soil" has not been removed.

One manufacturer of protective paint coatings has used a radioactive isotope to prove that his paint penetrates through several layers of rust down to the bare metal.

The utilization of fertilizer elements by plants is shown by using radioactive tracer elements. Possibly radioactive phosphorus compounds are added to the soil with the fertilizer. Then the amount taken up by the plants is measured to learn how well the plant is making use of the phosphorus added to the soil in the fertilizer.

Radioactive isotopes make it possible

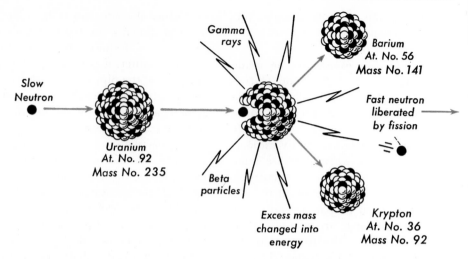

Fig. 39–12. Neutrons from the fission of $_{92}U^{235}$, when slowed down by a moderator, can cause fission in

to study the life processes of plants, particularly photosynthesis. The radiation of seeds and of plants is producing new, more desirable varieties.

10. $_{92}U^{235}$ undergoes fission. The element uranium exists as three naturally-occurring isotopes. These are $_{92}U^{238}$, $_{92}U^{235}$, and $_{92}U^{234}$. Most uranium is the isotope $_{92}U^{238}$. Only 0.7% of natural uranium is $_{92}U^{235}$. $_{92}U^{234}$ is found only in insignificant traces. We have already learned that man-made elements may be produced when $_{92}U^{238}$ is bombarded with slow neutrons. $_{92}U^{235}$ reacts differently when bombarded with slow neutrons. When $_{92}U^{235}$ is bombarded with slow neutrons, one may be captured by a $_{92}U^{235}$ nucleus. This additional neutron in the nucleus makes it very unstable. Instead of emitting an alpha particle, or beta particle, as in other radioactive changes, the nucleus splits into two parts of medium weight. *This break-up of a heavy nucleus into two medium-weight parts is called **fission**.* Neutrons are usually given out during this fission. There is a small loss of mass,

which appears as emission of a great amount of energy. One equation for the fission of $_{92}U^{235}$ is:

$$_{92}U^{235} + _{0}n^{1} \rightarrow$$
$$_{56}Ba^{141} + _{36}Kr^{92} + 3 \, _{0}n^{1} + \text{energy}$$

The atomic mass of $_{92}U^{235}$ is slightly greater than 235. The atomic masses of the unstable isotopes of barium and krypton are slightly less than 141 and 92. So instead of the masses of the reactants equalling the masses of the products, there is a conversion of about 0.2 atomic mass unit into energy.

11. A nuclear chain reaction. *A chain reaction is one in which the material or energy which initiates the reaction is also one of the products.* The fission of $_{92}U^{235}$ can produce a chain reaction. It requires a neutron to initiate the fission of one $_{92}U^{235}$ nucleus. Two or three neutrons are given out when this fission occurs. These neutrons can start the fission of other $_{92}U^{235}$ nuclei. Again neutrons are emitted. These can cause the fission of still other $_{92}U^{235}$ nuclei.

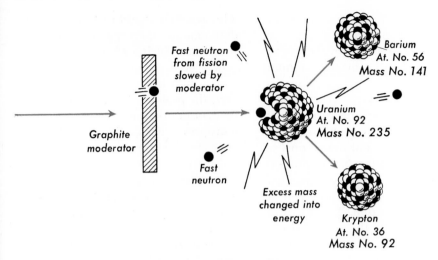

Fast neutron from fission slowed by moderator

Graphite moderator

Fast neutron

Barium
At. No. 56
Mass No. 141

Uranium
At. No. 92
Mass No. 235

Excess mass changed into energy

Krypton
At. No. 36
Mass No. 92

a second $_{92}U^{235}$ atom. This makes a chain reaction possible.

This is a chain reaction. It will continue until all the $_{92}U^{235}$ atoms have split or until the neutrons fail to strike $_{92}U^{235}$ nuclei.

12. The action in a nuclear reactor. A *nuclear reactor,* sometimes called an atomic pile, *is a device in which the controlled fission of radioactive material produces new radioactive substances and energy.* One of the earliest types built at Oak Ridge, Tennessee,

in 1943, contains natural uranium. It has a lattice-type construction. Blocks of graphite form the framework and act to slow down the neutrons. Spaced between the blocks of graphite, and encased in aluminum cans for protection, are rods of uranium. *Control rods* of neutron-absorbing boron steel are inserted into the lattice to regulate the number of free neutrons. This reactor is air cooled.

Fig. 39-13. This diagram shows a cutaway view of the Oak Ridge Reactor.

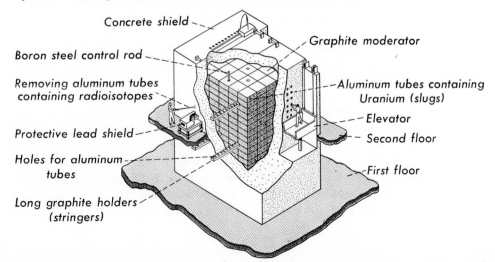

Concrete shield

Graphite moderator

Boron steel control rod

Removing aluminum tubes containing radioisotopes

Aluminum tubes containing Uranium (slugs)

Elevator

Protective lead shield

Second floor

Holes for aluminum tubes

First floor

Long graphite holders (stringers)

The rods of uranium or uranium oxide are the *nuclear fuel* for the reactor, since the energy released in the reactor comes from changes in the uranium nuclei. The blocks of graphite are called the *moderator*. A moderator slows down the fast neutrons produced by fission and makes them more effective for producing additional nuclear changes. The amount of uranium in such a reactor is important, too. Enough uranium must be present to sustain a chain reaction. This quantity of uranium is called the **critical size.**

Two types of reactions occur in the fuel in such a reactor. Neutrons cause the nuclei of $_{92}U^{235}$ to undergo fission. The fast neutrons from this fission are slowed down by passage through the graphite. Some strike other $_{92}U^{235}$ nuclei and continue the chain reaction. Other neutrons strike $_{92}U^{238}$ nuclei, and initiate the changes which finally produce plutonium. Great quantities of energy are liberated so the reactor has to be cooled continuously by blowing air through tubes in the lattice. The rate of the reaction is controlled by the insertion or removal of the neutron-absorbing control rods. This reactor is currently being used for producing radioactive isotopes by utilizing the neutrons in excess of those required to maintain the chain reaction. Other types of reactors are described in Sections 15, 16, and 17.

13. The separation of uranium isotopes. The intensity of the chain reaction in a nuclear reactor is controlled somewhat by the absorption of neutrons by $_{92}U^{238}$ nuclei. Control rods which absorb neutrons are also used. But if the critical size of $_{92}U^{235}$ could be obtained in *pure* form, a rapidly accelerating chain reaction would start.

This reaction would liberate a tremendous amount of energy in an incredibly short time. Such a liberation of energy would occur with explosive violence. This would be an atomic bomb. However, the problem of separating the isotopes of uranium to get pure $_{92}U^{235}$ presents great difficulty. Isotopes have the same chemical properties. Hence, chemical methods of separation are not possible. The only practical difference between isotopes is their mass. And in the case of $_{92}U^{235}$ and $_{92}U^{238}$, this amounts to only three atomic mass units.

Scientists working on atomic bomb research discovered several methods for separating uranium isotopes. One method involved gaseous diffusion. This depended on the slight difference in the rate of diffusion through a porous membrane of two hexafluorides of uranium $_{92}U^{235}F_6$ and $_{92}U^{238}F_6$. Another method was electromagnetic. The slight difference in mass caused the two nuclei to follow different paths when deflected by a strong electromagnetic field. This effected a separation.

14. The atomic bomb. $_{92}U^{235}$ undergoes fission when bombarded with neutrons. Plutonium also undergoes fission when bombarded with neutrons. These are the two active materials which have been used in atomic bombs.

We have already learned how $_{92}U^{235}$ is separated from $_{92}U^{238}$. Plutonium, being a new element with different properties, can be separated from the uranium by chemical means.

When sufficient quantities of either of these materials, that is, their critical sizes, are brought together to sustain a rapidly accelerating chain reaction, the atoms undergo fission almost instantaneously. They liberate tremendous energy. The explosive violence with

Fig. 39–14. A view of the destruction wrought by the atomic bomb dropped on Nagasaki, Japan, during World War II. This scene was 800 yards from the center of the target area.

which this reaction occurs produces terrible devastation.

Atomic bomb tests have been conducted by the United States to determine the destruction wrought by these bombs. The effect of the radioactivity produced in the target area has also been studied. These topics are discussed more fully in Section 20.

15. Other types of nuclear reactors.
1. Hanford Reactors. These reactors are located on the Columbia River at Hanford, Washington. They are primarily converter reactors, used for producing $_{94}Pu^{239}$ from $_{92}U^{238}$ by neutrons from the fission of $_{92}U^{235}$ in natural uranium. They are called *converter reactors* because they use one type of fissionable material to produce a nearly equal quantity of another fissionable material. The fuel is natural uranium. The moderator is graphite. Because of some difficulties in air cooling encountered in the construction of the Oak Ridge reactor, which was to serve as a model for the Hanford reactors, the Hanford reactors use water as the coolant. At Hanford are also located the facilities for remote control processing to recover the plutonium being produced in gram quantities, from tons of material including uranium and numerous fission products. The plutonium is being stockpiled for use in nuclear weapons.

Fig. 39–15. An aerial view of one of the Hanford reactors which produce $_{94}Pu^{239}$ from $_{92}U^{239}$. These reactors are cooled with water from the Columbia River.

2. Savannah River Reactor. The Savannah River reactor is a high-power reactor fueled with natural uranium, but using deuterium oxide (heavy water), D_2O, as a moderator. Deuterium oxide is a better moderator than either graphite or water because it absorbs fewer neutrons, and yet a small amount slows down neutrons effectively. Because of this, deuterium oxide moderated reactors require less uranium and may be made much smaller. However, the high cost of deuterium oxide limits its use in reactors.

3. Materials Testing Reactor. This reactor, located near Arco, Idaho, uses $_{92}U^{235}$ as fuel, and water as moderator and coolant. It is controlled by cadmium rods. It produces neutrons at a very high rate. This reactor is used for testing the behavior of various materials under very high radioactivity.

4. Experimental Breeder Reactor. This reactor is also located near Arco, Idaho. It contains a central core of $_{92}U^{235}$ surrounded by natural uranium metal. The coolant is a liquid alloy of sodium and potassium. No moderator is used. The purpose of a breeder reactor is to make fissionable material, $_{94}Pu^{239}$, for example, at a greater rate than the $_{92}U^{235}$ used as fuel is consumed. This can be done by cutting down the loss of neutrons by using fast neutrons and eliminating the moderator which would absorb some neutrons. Since only 2.5 neutrons, on an average, are released by the fission of one $_{92}U^{235}$ nucleus, and 1.0 of these neutrons is needed to carry on the chain reaction, only 1.5 neutrons, on an average, remain to produce plutonium. If there were no loss of neutrons, 1.5 $_{94}Pu^{239}$ atoms, on an average, would be formed from the fission of 1.0 $_{92}U^{235}$ nucleus —a production of fissionable material at a rate greater than the consumption of the fissionable $_{92}U^{235}$ fuel. It has been reported that such a breeder reaction is feasible, though not with this theoretical efficiency. The use of $_{94}Pu^{239}$ to produce more $_{94}Pu^{239}$ from $_{92}U^{238}$ is a more promising breeder reaction since each $_{94}Pu^{239}$ nucleus which undergoes fission produces, on an average, 3.0 neutrons. But, of course, $_{94}Pu^{239}$ can only be made at first by the bombardment of $_{92}U^{238}$ by slow neutrons that result from the fission of $_{92}U^{235}$ nuclei.

5. Raleigh Reactor. The Raleigh reactor at North Carolina State College is an example of a *homogeneous reactor*. In a homogeneous reactor, the fuel is dissolved in the moderator. The fuel for the reactor is UO_2SO_4, uranyl sulfate, in which all the uranium is the $_{92}U^{235}$ isotope. The uranyl sulfate is dissolved in water which acts as a moderator. Boron carbide rods are used to control the reactor, which is operated at about 80° C. It is cooled by circulation of water through stainless-steel coils placed in the uranyl sulfate solution. This reactor is used for research purposes.

16. Power production from nuclear reactors. A nuclear reactor can serve as a source of heat energy, just as a coal, oil, or gas fire does. Moreover, the relatively greater amount of energy available from the world supply of nuclear fuels as compared with the diminishing supply of coal and petroleum makes nuclear fuels worth developing for future use.

Several nuclear power plants for the generation of electricity are planned or in operation in the United States, as well as in Canada, Great Britain, Russia, and several other countries. The first large nuclear power plant in the United States is located at Shippingport, near Pittsburgh, Pennsylvania.

This power plant uses a reactor containing natural uranium enriched with $_{92}U^{235}$ as fuel. The fuel rods are surrounded by a blanket of rods of natural uranium oxide. The control rods are of hafnium metal. The moderator and heat transfer fluid is pressurized water. This pressurized water is circulated between the reactor core and the steam generators. The operating temperature of the reactor is approximately 525° F, with a pressure of about 2000 lb/in².

The hot pressurized water from the reactor is pumped through the steam generators. In the steam generators, the heat of the pressurized water converts other water to steam under pressure.

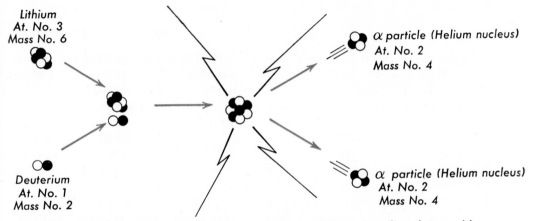

Lithium
At. No. 3
Mass No. 6

Deuterium
At. No. 1
Mass No. 2

α particle (Helium nucleus)
At. No. 2
Mass No. 4

α particle (Helium nucleus)
At. No. 2
Mass No. 4

Fig. 39–16. This diagram shows the reaction in which lithium and deuterium undergo fusion and form helium nuclei. This process yields large amounts of energy.

The pressurized water, cooled by the transfer of its heat to produce steam, is returned to the reactor for reheating. The steam formed in the heat exchangers is led to the turbines. The steam under pressure drives the turbines, which in turn, drive the generators. The steam, after passage through the turbines, is condensed, and returned to the steam generators to be converted to steam once again.

17. The atomic submarine. The first practical use of a reactor for power production was in the atomic submarine, U.S.S. *Nautilus*. The heat generated by this reactor is used to increase the temperature of water which is kept under pressure to prevent it from changing into steam. This superheated, pressurized water is pumped to a heat exchanger. In the heat exchanger, it gives up some of its heat to other water, which is thereby converted into steam. The pressurized water returns to the reactor for reheating. The steam produced in the outer jacket of the heat exchanger drives the steam turbine. The turbine then runs the propellers. The spent steam from the turbine is condensed and pumped back to the heat exchanger. Using atomic power, a

submarine may cruise rapidly for long distances without surfacing.

18. Fusion reactions—the sun. Earlier in the chapter (Section 1) we learned that increased nuclear stability could be produced by combining light-weight nuclei to form heavier nuclei. This process was defined as *fusion*.

Fusion reactions are undoubtedly the source of the sun's energy. There are probably two such reactions going on in the sun, one at the very hot central region of the sun's interior, and another in the larger portion of the sun which is at a slightly lower temperature. The net effect of these two reactions is the same, though they have a different sequence of intermediate reactions. The net effect is the combination of four hydrogen nuclei to form a helium nucleus, with a loss of mass and corresponding production of energy.

19. The hydrogen bomb. The thermonuclear bomb, sometimes called the hydrogen bomb, or H-bomb, produces energy by a fusion reaction. A hydrogen bomb can be made much more destructive than an atomic bomb because more energy is liberated in a fusion reaction than in a fission reaction, and the quantities of reacting materials may be made much larger, in fact they are theoretically unlimited.

One possible reaction in a hydrogen bomb is the formation of alpha particles and tremendous energy from a compound of lithium and hydrogen. This compound may be formed of the particular isotopes $_3Li^6$ and $_1H^2$. Such a fusion reaction can be started only by subjecting $_3Li^6_1H^2$ to extremely high temperature and pressure. These conditions are met by using an atomic bomb as the necessary detonator to set off the hydrogen bomb.

Research is currently being conducted which indicates that fusion reactions may be carried out at lower temperatures. If so, this may be another possible source of energy for power generation.

20. The destructive effects of nuclear weapons. The destructive effects of an atomic bomb may be roughly divided into four types. The extent of the damage produced by the explosion of an atomic bomb equivalent to 20,000 tons of T.N.T. in air at the height required to produce maximum damage is given for each type.

1. The shock wave, or blast effect. The shock wave produces virtually complete destruction over an area 0.5 mile in radius from the target zone. Severe damage extends for about 1 mile from the target, while partial damage is found up to about 2 miles from the target.

2. The thermal radiation, or flash effect. The thermal radiation (heat) will heat the surface of materials in the direct target area to about 3000° C.

Fig. 39–17. This drawing shows the radioactive fall-out pattern from a large nuclear weapon.

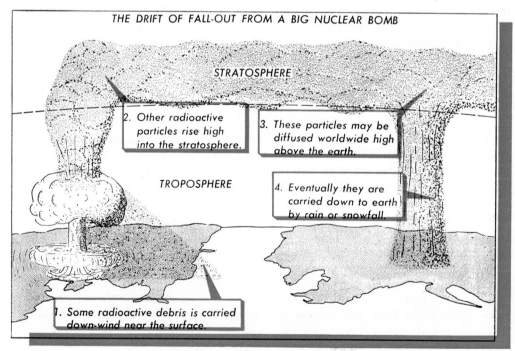

THE DRIFT OF FALL-OUT FROM A BIG NUCLEAR BOMB

STRATOSPHERE

2. Other radioactive particles rise high into the stratosphere.

3. These particles may be diffused worldwide high above the earth.

TROPOSPHERE

4. Eventually they are carried down to earth by rain or snowfall.

1. Some radioactive debris is carried down-wind near the surface.

Serious skin burns and fires will be found up to a radius of about 1 mile, while significant amounts of heat are received as far as 2 miles from the target. Even at 30 to 40 miles from the explosion, the light given out will temporarily blind a person if he looks directly at it.

3. The nuclear radiations. Nuclear radiations such as gamma rays and neutrons destroy living tissues. This type of damage is severe within a 0.5-mile radius of the target area, and significant out to a 1-mile radius of the target area.

4. The residual radioactivity. For a 20,000 ton T.N.T. equivalent bomb, detonated in the air, the residual radioactivity is negligible. However, for a surface detonation, this would be only a temporary hazard.

With more powerful hydrogen bombs, equivalent to between 10 and 20 million tons of T.N.T., these same types of destructive effects also occur. They are, however, more serious. The shock wave produces damage or partial damage to structures up to 10 miles from the target area. The thermal radiation from such a bomb extends up to 20 miles from the target area. The nuclear radiations from the blast itself will produce destructive effects a few miles from the blast scene. A much more serious threat to people far from the scene of the blast may be produced by a hydrogen bomb. This threat is *radioactive fall-out.*

A powerful hydrogen bomb explosion can blow radioactive particles high into the stratosphere, over 30,000 feet above the surface of the earth. Because of atmospheric conditions in the stratosphere, small particles of radioactive material may remain there for as long as ten years. During this time, the particles can become thoroughly mixed and be uniformly distributed in the stratosphere over all parts of the earth. Eventually they fall back to the earth's surface.

A shower of intensely radioactive particles may produce severe, or perhaps fatal, burns. If radioactive particles are eaten with food, internal damage may be produced in the body. Some of the most serious types of internal damage are those which prevent the production of blood corpuscles or of disease-fighting antibodies. Radiation damage may also affect the hereditary characteristics transmitted from one generation of living things to the next.

One of the radioactive isotopes which may be produced in a nuclear explosion is $_{38}Sr^{90}$, sometimes called strontium-90. This is a fairly long-lived radioactive isotope with a half-life of about 27 years. If it is showered down on the earth, even in very small concentrations, it is taken up from the soil by plants. Animals eating these plants collect more and more $_{38}Sr^{90}$ in their bodies. Then when a person drinks milk, eats meat, or uses other animal products, he may take into his body a much greater quantity of $_{38}Sr^{90}$ than would be showered down on him as an aftermath of a nuclear explosion. The $_{38}Sr^{90}$ accumulates in his bones because it is chemically similar to calcium, which is an important element in the materials forming the body skeleton. As it becomes more concentrated in the bones, $_{38}Sr^{90}$ can cause cancer, destroy tissues, and ultimately produce death. While estimates differ, many scientists believe that the amount of $_{38}Sr^{90}$ already produced by nuclear explosions is so small as not yet to become a serious hazard.

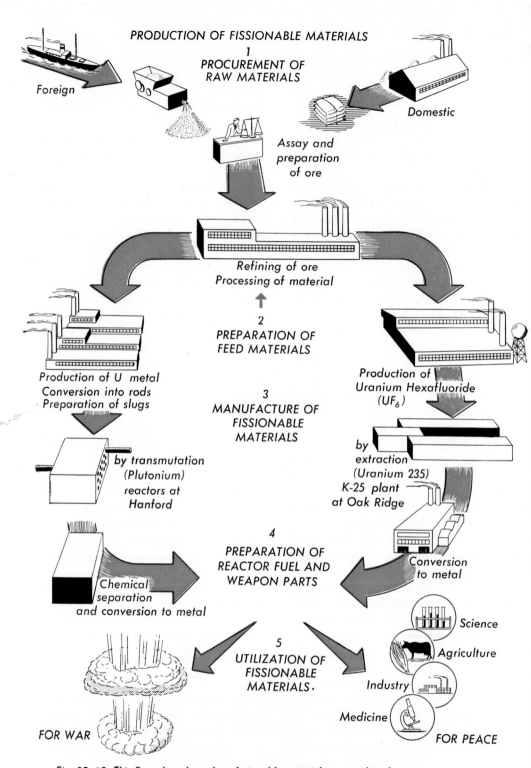

PRODUCTION OF FISSIONABLE MATERIALS

1
PROCUREMENT OF
RAW MATERIALS

Foreign

Domestic

Assay and
preparation
of ore

Refining of ore
Processing of material

2
PREPARATION OF
FEED MATERIALS

Production of U metal
Conversion into rods
Preparation of slugs

3
MANUFACTURE OF
FISSIONABLE
MATERIALS

Production of
Uranium Hexafluoride
(UF$_6$)

by transmutation
(Plutonium)
reactors at
Hanford

by
extraction
(Uranium 235)
K-25 plant
at Oak Ridge

4
PREPARATION OF
REACTOR FUEL AND
WEAPON PARTS

Conversion
to metal

Chemical
separation
and conversion to metal

Science

Agriculture

5
UTILIZATION OF
FISSIONABLE
MATERIALS.

Industry

Medicine

FOR WAR

FOR PEACE

Fig. 39–18. This flow chart shows how fissionable materials are produced.

Summary

The binding energy of a nucleus holds the protons and neutrons together in the nucleus. The lightest and heaviest elements have the smallest binding energies, and their nuclei are least stable. Elements of intermediate weight have larger binding energies, and their nuclei are more stable. There are four ways in which nuclei may become more stable: 1. by radioactive decomposition; 2. By nuclear disintegration; 3. by fission; and 4. by fusion.

The cyclotron is an electromagnetic device for accelerating protons and deuterons in a spiral path. Other particle accelerating devices are the betatron, the synchrotron, and the linear accelerator.

When bombarded with slow neutrons, a $_{92}U^{238}$ nucleus may capture a neutron, and ultimately be transformed into $_{94}Pu^{239}$. Stable atoms may be made artificially radioactive by bombardment with deuterons or neutrons. Artificial radioactive isotopes are used as tracers, in medicine, and in research.

When $_{92}U^{235}$ is bombarded with slow neutrons, it undergoes fission. Fission is the break-up of a heavy nucleus into two medium-weight parts. A chain reaction is one in which the material or energy which initiates the reaction is also one of the products. Uranium isotopes may be separated by gaseous diffusion and by electromagnetic methods.

A nuclear reactor is a device in which the controlled fission of radioactive material produces new radioactive substances and energy. Scientists have devised various types of reactors using different kinds of fuels, moderators, and cooling agents. Nuclear reactors furnish heat energy for power.

A fusion reaction is one in which two light nuclei combine to form a heavier, more stable nucleus. Fusion reactions produce the sun's heat and light, and produce the destructive effects of hydrogen bombs. The destructive effects of atomic bombs may be classed as due to the shock wave, to thermal radiation, to nuclear radiations, and to the residual radioactivity. Hydrogen bombs present the added hazard of radioactive fall-out because they blow radioactive materials high into the stratosphere. Radioactive fall-out is the showering down of radioactive particles which were carried high into the air by a nuclear explosion.

Test yourself on these terms

artificial radioactivity	electron-volt	nuclear reactor
atomic bomb	fission	radioactive decomposi-
atomic mass	fusion	tion
atomic submarine	homogeneous reactor	radioactive fall-out
betatron	hydrogen bomb	radioactive tracer
binding energy	linear accelerator	residual radioactivity
breeder reactor	materials testing reactor	shock wave
chain reaction	moderator	stability of a nucleus
control rod	nuclear disintegration	strontium-90
converter reactor	nuclear fuel	synchrotron
critical size	nuclear power plant	thermal radiation
cyclotron	nuclear radiations	transuranium element

Questions

Group A

1. Name the four types of nuclear reactions which produce more stable nuclei.
2. In what ways do natural radioactive decompositions produce more stable nuclei?
3. How were neutrons first detected as nuclear particles?
4. Why are neutrons better particles than protons or alpha particles for bombarding atomic nuclei?
5. What may happen to a neutron that is fired at the nucleus of an atom?
6. What are the names and atomic numbers of the transuranium elements?
7. For what purposes are radioactive isotopes used?
8. (a) What are the naturally-occurring isotopes of uranium? (b) What is their relative abundance?
9. (a) What is fission? (b) How is it produced in $_{92}U^{235}$?
10. What is meant by the *critical size* of a reactor?
11. Why must a nuclear reactor be continually cooled?
12. Why is it difficult to separate isotopes?
13. What is the principal difference between the action in a nuclear reactor and in an atomic bomb?
14. What is the distinguishing feature of a homogeneous reactor?
15. What reaction produces the sun's energy?
16. What is radioactive fall-out?

Group B

17. (a) Which kinds of elements have the smallest binding energy? (b) Which kind has the largest binding energy? (c) How does the binding energy affect the stability of a nucleus?
18. (a) Who produced the first nuclear disintegration? (b) Write the equation for this reaction.
19. How was Einstein's equation, $E = mc^2$, proved to be correct?
20. (a) Describe the path of the accelerated particles in a cyclotron. (b) What causes them to take this path?
21. Explain the changes by which $_{94}Pu^{239}$ is produced from $_{92}U^{238}$.
22. (a) How are artificially-radioactive isotopes prepared? (b) Write a nuclear equation to show the preparation of such an atom.
23. (a) Describe a chain reaction. (b) How does the fission of $_{92}U^{235}$ produce a chain reaction?
24. How is a uranium-graphite reactor constructed?
25. (a) What materials are used as coolants for nuclear reactors? (b) As moderators? (c) As control rods?
26. What ways have been devised for separating uranium isotopes?
27. Give two reasons why plutonium is a more desirable fissionable material than $_{92}U^{235}$.
28. (a) What is the function of a converter reactor? (b) Of a breeder reactor?

29. Describe the energy transformations and transfers which occur in a nuclear power plant.
30. Give two reasons why a hydrogen bomb may be more powerful than an atomic bomb.
31. Describe the types of destructive effects produced by atomic bombs.
32. In what way is $_{38}Sr^{90}$ a menace to civilization?
33. Why is the radiation from a nuclear weapon dangerous?
★ 34. What factors affect the stability of a nucleus?

Some things for you to do

1. Make a mousetrap model to show a chain reaction. You will need about 20 small mousetraps, and twice as many rubber stoppers. Set the mousetraps, and place two rubber stoppers over each trap wire, so they will be shot off when that trap is sprung. Start the chain reaction by setting off one trap. The rubber stoppers shot off from this trap should set off the other traps in ever increasing numbers until they are all sprung.
2. Prepare a report on new nuclear power developments.
3. From recent newspaper and magazine articles compile a list of uses of radioactive isotopes.

Check your progress in chemistry

1. What are five statements that summarize the atomic theory?
2. What do we mean when we say that barium has an atomic weight of 137?
3. Define the following terms: (a) protons; (b) electrons; (c) neutrons; (d) nucleus; (e) the L shell; (f) valence electrons; (g) isotopes.
4. Explain the difference between *electrovalence* and *covalence*.
5. How do the three isotopes of hydrogen differ?
6. Explain how $_{92}U^{235}$ can be separated from $_{92}U^{238}$ by the gaseous diffusion process.
7. Explain why calcium has an oxidation number of $+2$ and fluorine an oxidation number of -1.
8. What do we mean by a negative radical, such as sulfate?
9. How do the nuclei of elements above number 83 differ from most of the nuclei of lower atomic number?
10. What is the nature of the radiation emitted by radium?
11. What is the source of at least some of the atoms of lead in the ground?
12. Rutherford bombarded nitrogen with alpha particles and obtained protons and an isotope of oxygen. Write the equation for this transmutation.
13. Explain why it is impossible to find a chunk of pure radium compound in the ground.
14. What is the word equation for the relation between matter and energy?
15. Write three equations to show how plutonium is obtained from $_{92}U^{238}$.
16. Write the equation to show the fission of $_{92}U^{235}$ into barium and krypton.
17. Why is it unlikely that californium will ever be a common element?

18. Assuming that the seventh period of the Periodic Table, like the sixth, would be complete with 32 elements, how many elements would then be theoretically possible?
19. Why do the elements of the lanthanide series have very similar properties?
20. What do we mean by amphiprotic elements?

Challenging your knowledge

1. A sample of radium ore contained 1,000,000,000 atoms of radium 16,000 years ago. Assuming the half-life of radium to be 1600 years, how many of these atoms are still radium atoms today?
2. Why is there, at present, a poor prospect for using nuclear fission for providing the necessary power for driving our automobiles?
3. Do you think there is a possibility that the seventh period of elements in the Periodic Table was complete at some time in the history of the world? If so, why do we not usually find elements above number 92 now in the world?
4. Indicating the isotopes of hydrogen and oxygen as $_1H^1$, $_1H^2$, $_1H^3$, and $_8O^{16}$, $_8O^{17}$, $_8O^{18}$, write the formulas for the different kinds of water molecules theoretically possible.

BORON AND SILICON

How Priestley, Lavoisier, Berzelius, and the other great chemists of the past would have liked a set of laboratory glassware such as the one pictured above! Today, we have glass apparatus of improved design that is capable of withstanding shock and sudden changes in temperature. Great improvements have also been made in glass for household and industrial uses.

Glass is usually a mixture of silicates, which are compounds of the element silicon. Sand of high purity, silicon dioxide, is one of the most important raw materials for making glass.

Boron is a solid element that is seldom seen. Two compounds of boron, borax and boric acid, are familiar materials in many households.

There is only one chapter in this unit: *Boron, Silicon, and Glass.* Here you will discover the similarities of these two elements and learn about one of their common uses.

Chapter 40

BORON,
SILICON,
AND GLASS

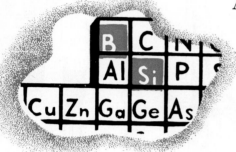

1. Boron and silicon have similar properties. The small size of the atoms of boron and silicon gives them similar properties even though boron is a member of Group IIIA of the Periodic Table and silicon belongs in Group IVA.

We found a situation similar to this in Chapter 34 when we studied beryllium and aluminum. However, boron has an oxidation number of +3, while silicon nearly always has an oxidation number of +4. They are essentially nonmetals.

1. BORON AND ITS COMPOUNDS

2. The occurrence and preparation of boron. Boron is not found as the free element. But it can be isolated as a nearly pure brown powder by reducing boron trioxide with metallic magnesium. It has little commercial value; hence chemists seldom separate it from its compounds.

Colemanite, a hydrated borate of calcium which is given the formula $Ca_2B_6O_{11} \cdot 5\,H_2O$, is found in the desert regions of California and Nevada. Sodium tetraborate, $Na_2B_4O_7 \cdot 4\,H_2O$, is found as the mineral *kernite* in California, also. The salt brines of Searles Lake, California, yield most of the com-

VOCABULARY

Annealing. The process of heating a material above a certain temperature and then slowly cooling it in order to decrease its hardness and brittleness.

Flux. A substance used to remove the oxide coating from a metallic surface prior to soldering or welding.

Glass. An amorphous material, usually transparent, consisting ordinarily of a mixture of silicates.

Silicone. A compound containing a chain of alternate silicon and oxygen atoms, with organic groups attached to the silicon atoms.

ELEMENT	ATOMIC NUMBER	ATOMIC WEIGHT	ELECTRON CONFIGURATION	OXIDATION NUMBERS	MELTING POINT, ° C	BOILING POINT, ° C	DENSITY g/cm³
BORON	5	10.82	2,3	+3	Sublimes at 1600	———	2.33
SILICON	14	28.09	2,8,4	+2,+4,−4	1420	2600	2.42

mercial supply of boron compounds today. When calcium borate is treated with sodium carbonate, sodium tetraborate, or *borax*, is produced. Some hot springs contain small amounts of boric acid, H_3BO_3, in solution.

3. Useful compounds of boron. Boron carbide, B_4C, known as Norbide, is an extremely hard abrasive that is made by combining boron with carbon in an electric furnace. The form of boron nitride called Borazon, made by combining boron and nitrogen under extreme heat and pressure, is the hardest synthetic material known. It is equal in hardness to the diamond.

Boric acid can be prepared by adding sulfuric acid to a concentrated solution of sodium tetraborate in water. The boric acid is only moderately soluble and separates as colorless, lustrous scales. It is such a weak acid that 4%

solutions of it may be introduced into the eye with safety. It is a mild antiseptic. A test for boric acid depends on the fact that boric acid colors an alcohol flame green (see Fig. 40-2).

Borax, or sodium tetraborate, has the formula $Na_2B_4O_7 \cdot 10\ H_2O$. It is used alone and in washing powders as a water softener. Because it dissolves metallic oxides leaving a clean metallic surface, it is also used as a *flux* for welding metals. The borates of certain metals are used in making glazes and enamels. Large amounts of boron compounds are used to make borosilicate glass of which Pyrex is an example.

Boron combines with hydrogen to form several boron hydrides such as B_2H_6, diborane, and B_4H_{10}, tetraborane. Methyl and ethyl groups may be substituted for the hydrogen atoms in these compounds. These boron com-

Fig. 40-1. A view of Searles Lake, California. This dry lake bed is 30 square miles in area. It is a source of borax, as well as many other chemical raw materials which are extracted from the brine pumped from deposits beneath.

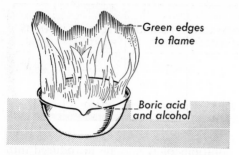

Fig. 40–2. An alcohol flame has green edges when boric acid is present. This serves as a test for boric acid.

pounds have negative heats of formation. Thus, when they are oxidized, they liberate unusually large amounts of energy. Some show great promise as fuels for jet airplanes and rockets.

4. Borax beads are used to identify some metals. First, dip a platinum wire with a loop on one end in powdered borax. Then hold it in a flame. The borax will swell and then fuse to a clear, glass-like bead. If such a bead is heated in an oxidizing blowpipe flame with a tiny speck of some metal, or compound of a metal, the oxide of the metal which is formed will react with the borax bead. It may impart to the bead a characteristic color. The color depends on the kind of metal used. For example, cobalt colors such a bead *blue;* chromium produces a *green* bead; and nickel yields a *brown* bead. This borax bead test is most useful in identifying certain metals.

2. SILICON AND ITS COMPOUNDS

5. The occurrence and preparation of silicon. Silicon ranks second in abundance by weight among the elements of the earth's crust. But, as in the case of boron, it does not occur free in nature. Silicon dioxide is reduced to elementary silicon by carbon in an electric furnace. The chief use for elementary silicon is in an alloy with iron, called *ferrosilicon,* for making silicon steel.

The compounds of silicon, such as sand, sandstone, quartz, and many different silicate rocks are widely distributed in nature. It is the abundance of these compounds that gives silicon its high rank among the elements of the earth's crust.

6. Silica is a common mineral compound. Silicon dioxide, SiO_2, commonly called *silica,* is one of the most widely distributed mineral compounds in the world. It is found in many forms, four of which are given below.

1. As sand. Ordinary sand is silicon dioxide. Layers of sand of varying thickness lie under the topsoil of a large portion of all the continents. Great quantities of sand are used in making glass. It is mixed with lime and water to make mortar. It is mixed with crushed stone and cement in making concrete. It is also used for lining molds into which molten iron is to be poured in making castings. It is especially useful for this purpose because it is infusible and easily removed from the finished casting.

In making *sandpaper,* a heavy paper is covered with glue, and sand is then sifted over the paper. A *sandblast,* which is used for cutting and polishing very hard surfaces, consists of a stream of sand driven at high velocity by means of compressed air. Brick and stone buildings are cleaned in this way.

Scouring soaps or powders usually contain powdered soap, washing soda,

Fig. 40–3. Quartz apparatus such as this can be heated red hot and then plunged into cold water without breaking.

and powdered silica, which is gritty enough for scouring purposes.

2. In the mineral sandstone. This mineral is a sedimentary rock formed under water by particles of sand which are bound together by a kind of natural cement. Sandstone is used as a building stone.

3. As quartz. The transparent crystalline variety of silica is known as quartz. Quartz plates of suitable thickness are used to control the frequency of radio transmitters. Pure *rock crystal* is colorless, but traces of impurities impart different colors to such forms of quartz as amethyst, smoky quartz, rose quartz, and milky quartz.

4. As amorphous silica. Such common substances as flint, jasper, chalcedony, sard, carnelian, onyx, and agate are minerals which consist largely of silica. Onyx and agate are made up of bands of different colors. Fine specimens of crystallized and amorphous silica are used as semiprecious gems.

7. The production of quartzware. Quartz may be softened in an oxyhydrogen blowtorch and fashioned into tubing, crucibles, and other laboratory apparatus. Quartz is also melted in a graphite crucible in an electric furnace and then extruded from the furnace under high pressure. Quartz trans-

mits ultraviolet rays much better than glass does. It is not so easily acted upon by acids and alkalies as ordinary glassware. Because it has a very low coefficient of expansion, about one-eighteenth that of glass, it is not likely to break if heated or cooled suddenly. In fact, a quartz crucible may be heated red-hot and then plunged into cold water without breaking.

8. The properties of silica. Silicon dioxide is a hard solid which can be fused with difficulty at a high temperature. It is insoluble in water and ordinary acids, but hydrofluoric acid reacts with it, as follows:

$$SiO_2 + 2 H_2F_2 \rightarrow SiF_4\uparrow + 2 H_2O$$

The silicon tetrafluoride, SiF_4, which is formed by the reaction, is volatile and escapes into the air. Sodium carbonate reacts with silica at high temperatures and forms sodium silicate.

$$Na_2CO_3 + SiO_2 \rightarrow Na_2SiO_3 + CO_2\uparrow$$

9. Silicic acid and silica gel. Many acids of silicon are known but none are important compounds. Many of the salts of the different silicic acids are found in natural minerals. The simplest silicic acid has the formula H_2SiO_3, or $SiO_2 \cdot H_2O$. It is formed as a jelly-like precipitate when an acid such as hydrochloric acid is added to a solution of sodium silicate, Na_2SiO_3. If this jelly-like precipitate is carefully heated, a porous solid, called *silica gel,* is produced. Silica gel is used for adsorbing various gases. When saturated, the adsorbed gases can be driven off by heating, and the silica gel is ready for use again. Silica gel is also used in the refining of petroleum. Although silicic acid yields silicon dioxide and water when it is heated, the reaction is not reversible. It is not possible to add water to silicon dioxide and form silicic acid.

10. What is water glass? Sodium silicate and potassium silicate are the only water-soluble silicates. A water solution of sodium silicate, Na_2SiO_3, is called *water glass.* As usually prepared for the market, water glass is a thick, syrupy solution about 1.3 times as dense as water. It is used as a filler in laundry soaps, as a binder in abrasive wheels and furnace linings, for fireproofing materials, and as an adhesive in the manufacture of wallboards and corrugated paper boards for cartons.

11. Many silicates are found in nature. These include such well-known minerals as: clay, asbestos, talc or soapstone, feldspar, granite, slate, shale, pumice, and many others. Most of these silicate minerals have rather complex formulas. Clay and feldspar are used in making pottery. Asbestos is used for insulation and for making fireproof fabrics. Soapstone is used for laboratory sinks and laundry tubs. Granite and slate are used for building materials. Pumice finds some use as a scouring material. Except for limestone, which is calcium carbonate, most of the common rocks are made up of either: *1.* silica; *2.* a silicate; or *3.* a mixture of both.

12. What are silicones? Silicon resembles carbon in the ability of its atoms to link together to form chains. A group of compounds, called **silicones,** has alternate silicon and oxygen atoms, with hydrocarbon groups attached to the silicon atoms. Thus the silicones are part organic and part inorganic. By using different hydrocarbon groups, a variety of silicones can be produced. One silicone chain has the structure

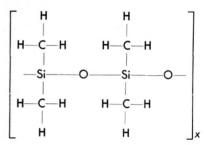

The silicones are not much affected by heat, have excellent electrical insulating properties, and are water repellents. Some silicones are oils or greases which may be used as lubricants. Silicone varnishes are used to coat wires for the windings of electric motors. The use of the silicone varnish permits the electric motor to operate at high temperatures without short circuits. Cloth that has been treated with a silicone will repel water. Silicones are used in automobile and furniture polishes.

13. Silicon carbide is very hard. This compound has the formula SiC. It is made by heating sand and coke in an electric furnace. Salt is usually added to the mixture to facilitate fusion, and sawdust is also used to make it more porous. The main reaction is:

$$SiO_2 + 3\ C \rightarrow SiC + 2\ CO\uparrow$$

The charge is heated for about 36

Fig. 40–4. A resistance electric furnace used for producing silicon carbide.

hours. Then the furnace is allowed to cool. Beautiful, iridescent crystals of silicon carbide are formed surrounding the central core. The crystals are crushed, graded to size by sifting through fine sieves, mixed with a binder, and manufactured into grinding wheels and sharpening stones. Silicon carbide is sold under the trade names of Carborundum and Crystolon.

Carborundum is a crystalline form of silicon carbide with extreme hardness. In fact, it is one of the hardest of the compounds made artificially. It is an excellent abrasive and is used for grinding and polishing metals.

Crystolon is a similar abrasive that is made in much the same manner. Crystolon is made into hones, polishing cloths, and grinding wheels.

3. GLASS MANUFACTURE

14. What is glass? Glass was made by the Egyptians many centuries before the Christian era. It is hard and very brittle when cold but softens when heated. In fact, it becomes so plastic when very hot that it can be blown, rolled, or pressed into any desired shape. It is transparent and almost entirely insoluble in water.

Ordinary glass is composed of the silicates of sodium and calcium. It is often spoken of as a mixture of these compounds, but it is probably a solid solution of these silicates in each other. In making the many different kinds of glass, potassium may be substituted for

sodium. Barium, lead, aluminum, boron, and even zinc may be substituted for all or part of the calcium or silicon.

15. The manufacture of glass. There are three separate stages in the process.

1. The raw materials. For making *ordinary glass,* the raw materials are sand, limestone, and sodium carbonate. A certain proportion of old, broken glass, known as *cullet,* is added to the batch when it is available. The cullet uses up what would otherwise be a waste material, and it also makes the whole batch melt more rapidly. The mixture is heated in a long, tank-like furnace to a temperature of about

Fig. 40–5. A sectional view of an electric furnace which is used for making Carborundum.

2500° F by the combustion of fuel gas. The process is continuous, raw materials being dumped in at one end and liquid glass being withdrawn from the farther end. Some of the sand reacts with the limestone as follows:

$$CaCO_3 + SiO_2 \rightarrow CaSiO_3 + CO_2\uparrow$$

The rest of the sand reacts with the sodium carbonate in this way:

$$Na_2CO_3 + SiO_2 \rightarrow Na_2SiO_3 + CO_2\uparrow$$

The material passes through the furnace very slowly. Several days elapse from the time the raw materials are added before the liquid glass is ready to be withdrawn. This insures the

Fig. 40–6. Crystals of silicon carbide.

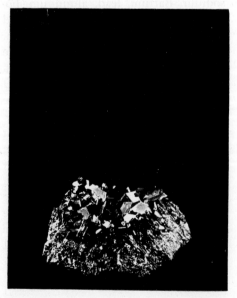

elimination of all bubbles of carbon dioxide which would make flaws.

Optical glass is made by heating sand, potassium carbonate, and lead oxide in pots made of fire clay. Such glass is made in small batches of a few hundred pounds each. Glass for cut glass tableware is made from the same raw materials in a fire-clay pot.

Pyrex glass is made in a tank furnace by fusing sand, borax, and aluminum oxide. It is a sodium aluminum borosilicate glass and has a coefficient of expansion only one-third that of ordinary, soda-lime glass.

2. The working of glass. In making hand-blown glass, the glass-blower inserts one end of a six-foot long blowpipe into a pot of molten glass. He rolls the blowpipe around until the required amount of glass has adhered to the end of the pipe. Then he blows a bubble in the glass and fashions it into the desired shape. Frequently he blows the bubble into a mold to give the object its finished form. However, the skill of the experienced glassblower in making water goblets and other objects, without the aid of a mold, is great. He uses a few simple tools, such as a paddle and a rounded rod, to shape the article. The surplus glass is cut off by shears while it is still plastic. Certain types of laboratory glassware and the better grades of table glass are still made by the hand-blown process.

The greatest tonnage of products in the glass industry is now machine made. Bottles are produced in large numbers by an intricate machine that duplicates hand-blowing in molds. Compressed air is used to blow the bubbles. Window glass is made by lowering a horizontal rod into the molten glass in the furnace. As the rod is drawn

Fig. 40-7. These workmen are using long steel bars to push sand, limestone, sodium carbonate, and cullet from the hoppers into the melting tank during the production of glass.

Fig. 40-8. Glassblowers are skilled craftsmen who fashion glass articles with great precision. They require only a few simple tools and are extremely accurate in their work.

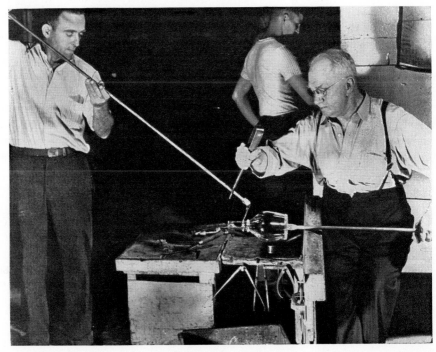

Fig. 40–9. The continuous strip of glass at the lower left moves between large pairs of grinding wheels. These simultaneously grind both surfaces smooth and parallel.

vertically upward, the glass clings to the rod and forms a sheet. The thickness of the sheet of glass can be regulated by controlling the rate at which the rod is elevated, and also by controlling the temperature of the molten glass in the furnace. Plate glass is made

by extruding a wide strip of glass directly from the furnace. In one continuous operation, the glass is cooled, cut, ground, and polished. The surfaces of plate glass are smooth and parallel.

3. *The annealing of glass.* After glass has been formed into a sheet or a finished article, it must be cooled very slowly. Otherwise the glass would be so brittle as to be worthless. The slow cooling of glass is called **annealing**, and is accomplished by passing the glass through a long, narrow chamber called a *lehr*. The temperature in the lehr is regulated carefully so that it is hot at one end and room temperature at the other end. Blown glass objects, for example, travel very slowly through the lehr on a moving belt. So slowly does the belt move through the lehr that several days elapse before the glass objects reach the unloading end.

16. There are many kinds of glass. Besides ordinary *soda-lime glass* which is used for window glass and bottles, *lead-potash glass* is used when a more lustrous product is desired. *Sodium aluminum borosilicate glass* is used for baking dishes and laboratory glassware which must stand wide changes in temperature. *Ultraviolet glass* is composed mostly of silica because glass of this composition transmits ultraviolet rays which cannot pass through ordinary glass. *Quartz glass* is made from pure silica and has such a low coefficient of expansion that it can be plunged red-hot into cold water without breaking.

Ordinary glass may be modified for special purposes. *Reinforced glass* has a network of wire that is embedded in

Fig. 40–10. Lenses for automobile headlamps being ejected from the molding machine.

the glass while it is still plastic. *Shatterproof glass,* which is used in automobiles, is made by cementing sheets of glass to both sides of a sheet of vinyl butyral, or other plastic. *Securite* is a type of glass that is so annealed that its surface is very hard. It is said not to splinter when broken, but rather to break up into rounded particles.

17. Metals impart colors to glass. Even a small quantity of iron compounds present as impurities in sand will impart a pale-green color to finished glass. Consequently, glassmakers try to secure as pure sand as possible. Manganese gives an amethyst or red color when added to glass, and small quantities of a manganese compound are sometimes added to a batch of glass to neutralize the pale-green color imparted by iron compounds. Chromium in glass gives it a deep-green color. Cobalt produces a deep blue. Silver is used to make yellow glass. Selenium is added to the batch to make the red taillights for automobiles. White, or opalescent glass is made by adding calcium fluoride to the raw materials. It takes only a small amount of a metallic compound to color a large batch of glass.

18. Glass blocks and glass fibers are useful products. Hollow glass blocks are a building material which allows sunlight to enter a room. The glass has a wavy construction that prevents clear vision, thus providing privacy. The "dead air" space inside the blocks is a good heat insulator. Glass blocks are rigid and strong.

Glass fibers are produced by forcing molten glass through tiny holes while a jet of high pressure steam is directed

Fig. 40–11. The use of glass blocks makes this kitchen bright and attractive.

against the glass as it emerges through the holes. Lustrous, silky fibers of glass are produced. These fibers can be spun into yarn and woven into fireproof cloth that is "all glass." Fluffy masses of the glass fibers are used for insulation of refrigerators. Large blankets of glass fibers are often used to insulate the walls of homes.

Fig. 40–12. This refrigerated truck body is being insulated with batts of glass wool.

Summary

The small size of boron and silicon atoms gives them many similar chemical properties.

Boron can be isolated as a brown powder, but it has little commercial value. Calcium borate occurs in California and Nevada. Sodium tetraborate (borax) and boric acid are the most important boron compounds. Borates are used for making glazes, enamels, and Pyrex glass. Boron carbide and boron nitride are extremely hard substances. Boron nitride equals a diamond in hardness. Boron hydrides show promise as jet and rocket fuels.

Elementary silicon is prepared in an electric furnace. Its chief use is in making silicon steel. Silicon compounds are found as sand and silicate rocks in great abundance in the earth's crust. Silica, SiO_2, occurs in nature as sand, sandstone, quartz, and in several amorphous varieties. Fused silica is used in making silica glass for laboratory glassware and ultraviolet lamps.

Silicic acid is a weak acid that is not an important compound. But its salts, the silicates, are abundant natural minerals. Talc, mica, asbestos, clay, granite, feldspar, and pumice stone are common silicates. Water glass is a concentrated solution of sodium silicate. Silicones are compounds that have hydrocarbon groups attached to the silicon atoms. Silicon carbide is used as an abrasive.

Glass may be considered to be a solid solution of two or more silicates. Ordinary glass is made from sand, limestone, and sodium carbonate. Optical glass and high grade glass for tableware may be made from sand, lead oxide, and potassium carbonate. Pyrex glass is a sodium aluminum borosilicate glass. It stands sudden changes in temperature without breaking better than ordinary glass. Small quantities of mineral compounds color glass green, blue, red, brown, and other colors.

Test yourself on these terms

annealing	ferrosilicon	rock crystal
borax	flux	silica
borax bead test	glass	silica gel
Borazon	lehr	silicate
boric acid	Norbide	silicon carbide
Carborundum	optical glass	silicone
Crystolon	Pyrex glass	soda-lime glass
cullet	quartz	water glass

Questions

Group A

1. What is the main source of boron compounds in the United States?
2. Why may borax be used as a flux in welding metals?
3. What is the chief use for elementary silicon?
4. Give some uses for sand.
5. Name some of the varieties of amorphous silica.

6. (a) How is silica gel prepared? (b) For what purpose is it used?

7. (a) How does silicon rank in abundance among the elements? (b) What accounts for this rank?

8. (a) From what raw materials is silicon carbide made? (b) Write the equation for the reaction by which it is prepared.

9. (a) Of what is ordinary glass composed? (b) How are these materials believed to be related in glass?

10. What are the raw materials used in making ordinary glass?

11. (a) How does Pyrex glass differ in composition from ordinary glass? (b) How does it differ in properties?

12. (a) How is window glass made? (b) How is plate glass made?

Group B

13. (a) How can elementary boron be prepared? (b) Why is it seldom seen in school laboratories?

14. Explain how the test for boric acid is performed.

15. For what purpose is quartz used as a radio transmitter?

16. Write the equation for the reaction of hydrofluoric acid on silica.

17. Why do you suppose *water glass* was given that name?

18. (a) What is a silicone? (b) What are some important uses for silicones?

19. Why is sand of very high purity desired by glass manufacturers?

20. What is a *lehr* and for what is it used?

21. How is shatterproof glass made?

22. How is glass of different colors obtained for use in "stained glass" windows in churches and public buildings?

23. Why is quartz not damaged by rapid temperature changes?

24. Write equations for the reactions of limestone and sodium carbonate with sand in glass manufacture.

25. When a red crystalline compound was tested by means of a borax bead, the bead turned blue. What metal was probably present in the compound?

26. Boron nitride and diamond have similar crystal structures. Is there any relationship between this fact and their similar hardness?

Problems

Group A

1. Calculate the percentage of boron in colemanite, $Ca_2B_6O_{11} \cdot 5 H_2O$.

2. How many grams of sodium silicate can be prepared from 1 kg of sodium carbonate by reacting it with an excess of silica?

3. What volume of carbon dioxide is liberated in Problem 2?

Group B

4. Boric acid, H_3BO_3, is produced when sulfuric acid is added to a water solution of borax, $Na_2B_4O_7$. How much boric acid can be prepared from 5 lb of borax?

5. What weight of silicon dioxide and what weight of carbon are needed in order to prepare one ton of silicon carbide?

Some things for you to do

1. Put some borax in an evaporating dish and moisten it with sulfuric acid. Then add a few teaspoonfuls of denatured alcohol and ignite it. Note the green flame that is characteristic of boric acid.
2. Make some borax beads in the loop on the end of a platinum wire, and color them with tiny traces of cobalt, chromium, and manganese compounds. Dip the hot wire in powdered borax and heat it. The borax will swell, then shrink to a glassy bead. Then dip the hot bead in the speck of mineral compound and reheat to produce the colored bead.
3. Make a "silica garden" in a tall glass cylinder. Add one volume of 40% water glass solution to seven volumes of water and mix well. Pour this diluted water glass in a tall glass cylinder. Drop in a tiny crystal of cobalt chloride, manganese sulfate, or nickel sulfate. Watch the crystals "grow." Pretty color effects can be obtained by using different colored salts.

Check your progress in chemistry

1. Give examples of each of the eight types of colloidal dispersions.
2. What are the four principal properties of suspensoids?
3. What two factors contribute to the stability of emulsoids?
4. Draw a labeled diagram of the apparatus used for preparing aluminum from purified bauxite.
5. Write an equation for the preparation of magnesium by electrolysis of fused magnesium chloride.
6. Describe the tests for the presence of Fe^{++} and Fe^{+++} ions.
7. Why is crude copper refined before being marketed?
8. Describe the Dutch process for making white lead.
9. (a) What do the subscripts in a nuclear equation represent? (b) What do the superscripts represent?
10. Why are neutrons more successful for nuclear bombardment than protons or electrons?
11. Describe the use of boric acid as an antiseptic.
12. For what purpose may borax be used in the laundry?
13. How is elementary silicon produced?
14. How is quartzware fashioned?

Challenging your knowledge

1. (a) In what form does boric acid principally exist in water solution, as molecules, or as hydronium and borate ions? (b) What experimental evidence supports your answer?
2. How does borax act as a water softener?
3. (a) Why isn't nearly pure silica glass used more frequently in school laboratories? (b) What advantage does such a glass have over aluminum borosilicate glass?
4. Why do we not usually classify silicon dioxide as an acid anhydride?
5. Why would you expect silicones to be water-repellant?

UNIT 15

COMMON ORGANIC COMPOUNDS

The fractionating towers and gas tank shown above symbolize one of today's important sources of organic compounds—petroleum. From petroleum we get not only gaseous and liquid fuels, but the starting materials for making alcohols, detergents, synthetic rubber, plastics, and many other products of the organic chemist.

To describe all the organic compounds known would require many volumes. Here we can learn briefly about only a few of the more important ones. Then, if you are interested in a particular type of compound you can study more about it as you continue with further courses in chemistry.

There are five chapters in this final unit: *Fuels, Petroleum, Hydrocarbon Substitution Products, Textiles and Paper,* and *Rubber and Plastics.* These chapters include some of the most recent developments in chemistry.

Chapter 41 FUELS

1. THE NATURE OF FUELS

1. What is a fuel? A fuel may be a solid, a liquid, or a gas. Almost without exception, our fuels come directly or indirectly from the plant kingdom. Either they are plants of the present, or are derived from plants that lived millions of years ago. *A fuel is any substance which is burned to provide heat.* The table in Fig 41-1 shows that nearly all our fuels contain a large percentage of carbon. This carbon may be present as the free element, or in the combined form as compounds of carbon and hydrogen.

2. The products of combustion of a fuel. The carbon in a fuel forms carbon dioxide when the fuel burns. The hydrogen in it burns to form water vapor. If the fuel contains a high percentage of carbon, there may be difficulty in supplying sufficient oxygen to burn it completely. In such a case, both carbon dioxide and carbon monoxide may be produced. Sometimes dense clouds of carbon, or soot, escape into the air. This not only pollutes the atmosphere, but also wastes tremendous quantities of fuel.

3. What should govern the choice of fuel? The ideal fuel should be cheap. It should kindle readily and should have a high heat content. There must be little or no ash, and no waste products that would become a nuisance. Few if any fuels meet all these conditions. Local conditions and personal tastes influence the consumer in his choice of a fuel.

4. Measuring the heat content of a fuel. Fig. 41-2 shows the amounts of heat produced by one-gram samples of various fuels that are widely used

VOCABULARY

Calorimeter. An apparatus for measuring quantities of heat.

Explosive range of gas. A pair of percentages, representing the proportions of a gas mixed with air, between which the mixture of the gas and air will explode if ignited.

Fuel. A material which is burned to provide heat.

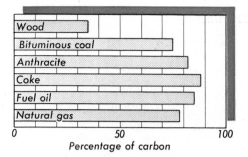

Fig. 41-1. The percentage of carbon in different fuels used by homes and industries.

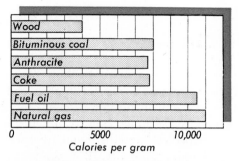

Fig. 41-2. The amount of heat in equal weights of different fuels shows considerable variation.

for home and industrial heating. The heat content of a fuel is determined by burning a weighed sample of the fuel and measuring how much it warms a weighed quantity of water. A sample of coal is powdered, dried, and weighed. Then it is mixed with some oxidizing agent, such as sodium peroxide, Na_2O_2. The oxidizing agent is added to insure complete combustion in a closed vessel called a *bomb*. The bomb is surrounded with a known weight of water in a cylindrical container called a *calorimeter* (see Fig. 41-3). The temperature of this water is carefully measured just before the burning begins. A loop of wire dips into the mixture in the bomb. When a switch is closed, an electric current passes through the loop and ignites the fuel. As the fuel burns, the bomb is rotated by means of an electric motor. Paddles fastened to the rotating bomb stir the water, causing it to be heated uniformly. The increase in temperature of the water is observed by reading a thermometer which is sensitive to a hundredth or thousandth of a degree.

If we know the weight of the sample of fuel, the weight of water used, and the increase in temperature of the water, the heat value of the fuel can be computed. A sample of high-grade coal may yield as much as 14,500 Btu per pound (see Chapter 10, Section 4).

The same method is used to determine the energy value of the foods that we eat.

Fig. 41-3. The bomb calorimeter is used by chemists to measure the amount of heat in a given weight of a sample of fuel.

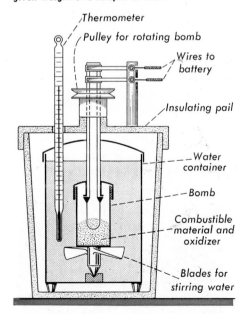

2. SOLID FUELS

5. The heat content of wood is not high. Probably no fuel is more widely distributed than wood. In those places where the cost is not too high, wood meets the demand for a good fuel. Where some other fuel is the main source of heat, wood is frequently used for kindling the fire. But compared with coal and some other fuels, the heat content per pound of wood is not very high.

6. What is peat? Extensive peat bogs are found in Pennsylvania, Michigan, Wisconsin, and other states. The bogs contain mosses, sedges, and other forms of vegetation which have undergone partial decomposition in swampy land. In some places such deposits are several feet thick. Sedge peat may be cut into blocks and dried for use as fuel. Even after being dried in the air, peat contains a considerable percentage of moisture. The heat content per pound of fuel is rather low, and peat burns with a smoky flame. This fuel may be con-

sidered as the first step in the evolution of coal.

7. What is lignite? Several million years ago, plants grew more luxuriantly than today. Possibly there was more carbon dioxide in the atmosphere and this may have caused the increased luxuriance of vegetation. In the *Carboniferous age,* tree ferns, giant club mosses, and other forms of vegetation supplied the material for our coal deposits. Peat bogs were probably formed first. Then upheavals of parts of the earth's crust buried thick masses of vegetable matter underground. Once buried, it was subjected to increased temperatures and pressures.

At a fairly early stage in these changes, *lignite* was formed. Lignite is sometimes called *brown coal* because of its brownish-black color, and is common in some of our western states. It burns with a smoky flame and yields less heat than bituminous coal. It disintegrates badly when stored, becoming powdery and losing heat value.

8. Bituminous coal is a widely used fuel. *Bituminous coal,* commonly called soft coal, was probably formed from the fossil remains of prehistoric plants. It appears to have been subjected to greater heat and pressure than that encountered in the formation of lignite. We may consider it a third step in the evolution of coal. Bituminous coal has a higher percentage of carbon and a higher heat content than lignite. The map in Fig. 41-5 shows that many states in the United States possess rather extensive coal fields.

9. Anthracite is hard coal. There seems to be little doubt of the vegetable origin of *anthracite.* We think

Fig. 41–4. Coal sometimes contains fossil remains of plants which indicate its origin.

that it has been subjected to still greater temperatures and pressures than the other forms of coal. Anthracite contains the least amount of volatile matter of all coals. It also has the highest percentage of carbon. The percentage of ash left after it is burned is not excessive. Pennsylvania supplies most of our anthracite although small deposits are scattered through some of the western states. Anthracite makes an excellent fuel because it burns with much less smoke than bituminous coal does.

10. Coke is a good fuel. Coke is left as a residue from the destructive distillation of bituminous coal. Most of the coke produced is used as a reducing agent in the production of pig iron as well as other metals. A considerable amount is used for making fuel gas. Some coke is consumed as a household fuel. It burns with a clean, smokeless flame and has a high heat content per pound of fuel. Coke leaves little ash.

3. LIQUID FUELS

11. Liquid fuels have advantages. Liquid fuels, such as fuel oil, flow through pipes from storage tanks to burners. Automatic thermostats control the operation of an oil burner. During the spring and fall, when little heat is needed for the home, an oil burner operates only when necessary. By contrast, a coal furnace once started must be kept going, must be stoked, and the ashes must be removed regularly. The heat content of fuel oil is high, usually more than 10,000 calories per gram.

Against these advantages are some disadvantages. Oil burners, like all mechanical devices, sometimes get out of order. They require expert servicing to keep them operating efficiently. Severe storms sometimes interrupt the electricity needed to operate the oil burner. The high costs of installation,

Fig. 41–5. Coal is widely distributed throughout the United States.

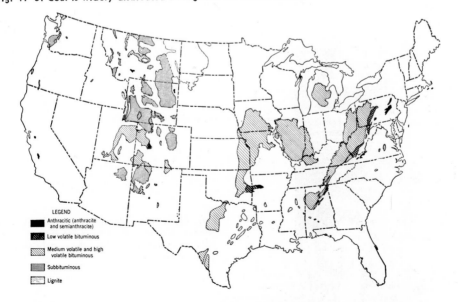

LEGEND

Anthracitic (anthracite and semianthracite)

Low volatile bituminous

Medium volatile and high volatile bituminous

Subbituminous

Lignite

increased electric bills, and the cost of service calls may make the total cost higher than other available fuels. However, the consumer may be willing to pay a slightly higher cost to secure the conveniences possible with liquid fuels.

12. The source of liquid fuels. Petroleum supplies almost all the liquid fuels used in the United States. This valuable natural resource is separated by refining into a variety of fuels and lubricants. The composition and refining of petroleum will be discussed in Chapter 42. Gasoline for operating au-tomobiles is the liquid fuel produced in greatest volume. Kerosene, a liquid fuel with a somewhat higher boiling point than gasoline, is used for oil lamps, for some oil stoves, and as a jet aircraft fuel. Diesel oil, another product resembling kerosene, is being used in Diesel locomotives, as well as in trucks on the highways. New installations of oil burners in homes have increased the consumption of fuel oil greatly in recent years. Heavier grades of fuel oil are used for oil burners in factories and for oil-burning ships.

4. GASEOUS FUELS

13. Combustible gases make convenient fuels. Fuel gases have all the advantages of liquid fuels. They flow through pipes to the gas burner where they are to be used. Gas can be turned on or shut off at a moment's notice, and the flow may be regulated automatically by thermostats. Gas is kindled instantly, leaves no ash, and the flame may be concentrated exactly where it is needed. The heat value of fuel gases per unit of volume is usu-ally high. If the burner is regulated properly, a hot, smokeless flame is produced with complete combustion. The flow of gas to homes and factories is not subject to interruptions due to storms because the gas pipes are buried underground. Gas makes an ideal fuel for cooking and heating homes. It is equally desirable for many industrial uses.

14. Compare the cost of different fuels. The cost of a fuel is an important factor in the choice of a fuel for home or factory heating. Fuels vary tremendously in cost in different communities, depending on nearness to sources such as mines, gas wells, or oil fields. A fuel that is expensive in one section of the country may be the most economical fuel to use in another section because of lower transportation costs. To compare different fuels in cost you should calculate the number of heat units available per dollar.

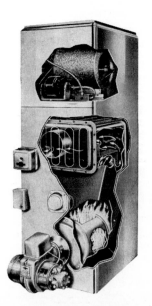

Fig. 41-6. An oil-burning forced warm-air furnace. Liquid fuel flows to the burner, burns only when needed, and produces only gaseous combustion products.

Fig. 41-7. Although many natural gas pipe lines cross rivers, lakes, and beds of streams underwater, some pipe lines, such as this one, cross on specially-built bridges of their own.

15. Natural gas. We have already learned that when vegetable matter decomposes under water, *marsh gas,* or *methane,* CH_4, is formed. This gas may form as much as 90% of the natural gases that are found in tremendous volumes in West Virginia, Texas, Oklahoma, Pennsylvania, California, Kansas, Indiana, Louisiana, and some other states.

Natural gas is an excellent fuel. It furnishes about 1100 Btu per cubic foot, an amount considerably greater than that furnished by other fuel gases. It is one of our most valuable natural resources. Eventually the supply will be exhausted, but it is estimated that the supply will last for decades. In a recent year, more than 9 trillion cubic feet of natural gas was marketed in the United States.

While natural gas has been used for many years in cities near the gas wells, it is only since 1945 that long pipe lines

Fig. 41-8. Coal gas is made by heating bituminous coal in vertical retorts. Tar, ammonia, and sulfur compounds must be removed from the gas before it is piped to the consumers.

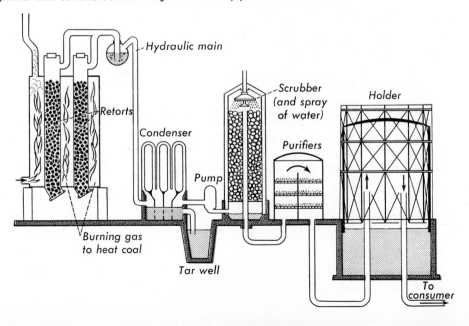

have brought this fuel to cities far distant from the gas wells. Today natural gas is supplied to most of the cities and towns of the country as a household fuel for cooking and heating homes.

16. Coal gas. In the manufacture of coke, coal gas is a valuable by-product. Although natural gas has largely replaced coal gas for household use, coke must be produced for the iron and steel industry. Thus the making of coal gas will continue. Bituminous coal is heated in iron retorts. The heating is continued until most of the volatile matter has been driven off. Besides the combustible gas, the volatile matter consists of ammonia, coal tar, and other impurities. From the retorts, the gas passes through a large iron pipe (the hydraulic main) to the condensers in which it is cooled. As the gas cools, most of the vaporized tar condenses to a liquid and collects in a pool at the bottom of the condenser. A pump then forces the gas through the rest of the purifying apparatus. Ammonia, which is very soluble in water, is the next impurity to be removed from the gas. The gas enters the bottom of a tall tower called a *scrubber*. This tower is loosely filled with large pieces of coke. Water sprays down from the top of the tower. As this water trickles downward over the pieces of coke, it meets the gas moving upward. The ammonia contained in the gas is dissolved in the falling water. The scrubber also removes the last portions of tar from the gas. Besides a small amount of coal tar, the liquid from the bottom of the scrubber contains a considerable amount of ammonia in solution. In large plants, this ammonia is recovered and converted into ammonium sulfate, which is used as a fertilizer.

The gas still contains compounds of sulfur, especially hydrogen sulfide, H_2S, which must be removed before the gas is sent to the consumers. The *purifiers,* which are used to remove the sulfur compounds, are large boxes. Spread out on shelves in the purifying boxes is a mixture of ferric oxide (rusted iron) and wood shavings. The wood shavings make the mass porous, permitting the gas to come in contact with the ferric oxide. Hydrogen sulfide is removed from the gas as it passes through several of these boxes in turn. The equation for this reaction is:

$$Fe_2O_3 + 3\ H_2S \rightarrow Fe_2S_3 + 3\ H_2O$$

The purified gas then goes to the storage holder.

From a ton of high-volatile coal it is possible to obtain from 10,000 to 12,000 cubic feet of gas. The by-products include 1200 to 1400 lb of coke, about 120 lb of coal tar, and a smaller quantity of ammonia.

17. Producer gas. A cheap gas suitable for industrial use can be made by forcing a blast of hot air and steam through a deep bed of coal or coke (see Fig. 41-9). The combustible products are carbon monoxide and hydrogen, but the gas contains a large proportion of incombustible nitrogen derived from the air blast. The nitrogen dilutes the gas and lowers the heat value. No attempt is made to remove the impurities from producer gas, which is consumed right in the factory where it is made.

18. Water gas. If a blast of steam is forced up through a white-hot bed of coke or anthracite, two combustible gases are produced. These gases are hydrogen and carbon monoxide, as shown in the following equation:

$$C + H_2O \rightarrow H_2\uparrow + CO\uparrow$$

Because water in the form of steam is used to make this mixture of gases, it is commonly known as **water gas.** The preceding reaction takes place efficiently only when the coke is very hot. The blast of steam cools the glowing coke after a few minutes to a temperature at which the reaction does not take place efficiently. Consequently, the making of water gas must be interrupted while a blast of air is used to raise the coke to the required temperature. Some of the fuel is consumed in this "warming up" process, according to the following equation:

$$C + O_2 \rightarrow CO_2\uparrow$$

The carbon dioxide is valueless as fuel. During the warming-up process, which is called the "air run," the cover above the *superheater* is raised. The products of combustion pass up the stack into the atmosphere (see Fig. 41-10). When the fuel in the *generator* has again reached the required temperature, the air blast is stopped. The cover above the superheater is lowered, and the steam blast is turned on. The combustible gas which is now produced is directed through a pipe to the purifying apparatus. Thus water gas is

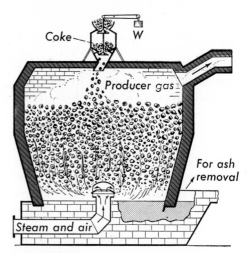

Fig. 41–9. Producer gas for industrial use is made by blowing steam and air through a bed of hot coke or anthracite.

made by an *intermittent* process. The "air run" produces waste gas that is discarded, and the "steam run" yields a mixture of combustible gases that is collected.

Water gas is purified before it is sent to the consumer by a process similar to that used for purifying coal gas. However, water gas contains far less coal tar and other impurities than coal gas. Hence the purification of water gas is less of a problem to the gas company.

Although water gas has been replaced by natural gas as a household fuel in most communities, the manufacture of water gas for industrial purposes is still very important. Carbon

Fig. 41–10. Much water gas is made from coke or anthracite and steam.

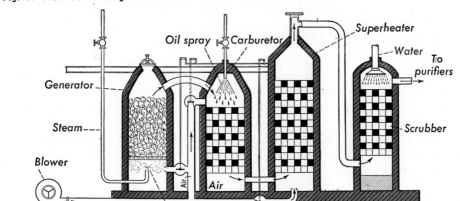

monoxide and hydrogen can be produced at much lower costs by this process than by any other method. These gases are of increasing value in the chemical industry for the synthesis of chemical compounds.

19. Enriched water gas. A mixture of carbon monoxide and hydrogen, when burned, does not yield sufficient heat per cubic foot to comply with most state laws. Hence, the water gas must be enriched to increase its fuel value. Water gas is enriched by two methods.

1. By spraying fuel oil into the carburetor chamber. Fig. 41-10 shows a chamber designated the *carburetor*. The carburetor is filled with loosely-stacked firebricks that form what is called a *checkerwork*. As the hot gases from the generator pass through this chamber, the bricks are heated white-hot. If fuel oil is sprayed down on these hot bricks, the molecules that compose the fuel oil are broken up or "cracked" into simpler molecules. These simpler gaseous molecules have very high fuel value when burned. By including a certain proportion of them with the water gas, the fuel value of the mixed gas is increased. The cracking process occurs in the carburetor and continues in the superheater. All the gases become blended or mixed together in the superheater.

2. By adding propane or butane. A newer method of enriching water gas is to add *propane* or *butane* to it. Propane, C_3H_8, and butane, C_4H_{10}, are combustible gases extracted from natural gas, or produced in the refining of petroleum. They can be converted into liquids with moderate pressure. Liquefied propane and butane, as well as mixtures of the two, are shipped in tank cars from the gas wells or re-

fineries where they are produced. When the valve on a tank of liquefied butane is opened, the liquid evaporates rapidly, forming an excellent fuel gas. Many gas companies today merely add the required amount of propane or butane to the water gas to raise the heat content to comply with state law.

20. Bottled gas is available for rural homes. Bottled gas, delivered in steel cylinders, provides gas of high fuel value at a cost that is reasonable. Bottled gas is liquefied propane, butane, or a mixture of these compounds. The steel cylinders containing the liquefied fuel are stored outside the building (in case of a possible leak). Copper tubing leads the gas through the wall to the stove in the kitchen. A delivery service provides full cylinders to replace the empty ones as needed. A newer method is to have a large tank of liquefied gas on the delivery truck. The smaller cylinders at homes are then filled from the large tank on the delivery truck.

21. The explosive range of a gas. Not all proportions of a combustible gas and air will explode. A mixture that contains too much gasoline vapor to explode when ignited is called *too rich*. Similarly, a mixture of gasoline vapor and air may contain so much air that it is *too lean* to explode. To secure the greatest mileage from a gallon of motor fuel, the mixture should be adjusted to give the most violent explosion.

The explosive range of a gas is a pair of percentages, representing the proportions of a gas mixed with air, between which the mixture of the gas and air will explode if ignited. For example, any mixture that contains *between* 3% and 82% of acetylene, C_2H_2, mixed with air will explode when ignited. The equation for the combustion of acetylene is as follows:

$$2\ C_2H_2 + 5\ O_2 \rightarrow 4\ CO_2\uparrow + 2\ H_2O\uparrow$$

Hence the most violent explosion occurs when two volumes of acetylene are mixed with five volumes of oxygen, or with about twenty-five volumes of air.

Hydrogen has a wide explosive range when mixed with air. Any mixture of hydrogen and air which contains from 10% to 66% of hydrogen will explode if ignited. The explosion is most violent when the mixture contains about 29% of hydrogen. The explosive range of mixtures of gas and air should be kept in mind when gas leaks occur in a closed space. To search for the leak with a lighted match may result in a violent explosion. A soap solution which bubbles at the leak is safer.

Summary

A fuel is any substance which burns and supplies heat. A good fuel should have a high heat content, should yield little ash, should be inexpensive, and should not produce undesirable waste products as it burns. Its heat content may be determined by means of a calorimeter.

The solid fuels include: wood, peat, lignite, bituminous coal, anthracite, and coke. They are all obtained from plants, either directly, or as the fossil remains of plants that lived in past geologic ages.

Practically all of the liquid fuels used in the United States are obtained from petroleum. Liquid fuels have advantages over solid fuels because they leave no solid ashes, and are easily regulated by automatic devices.

Combustible gases make very convenient fuels because, like liquid fuels, they flow through pipes, leave no solid ashes, and can be regulated easily. Natural gas is distributed through pipe lines to communities remote from natural gas wells. It is an excellent fuel that has a very high heat content. Coal gas is made by the destructive distillation of bituminous coal. Ammonia, coal tar, and coke are valuable by-products. Water gas is composed almost entirely of carbon monoxide and hydrogen. It may be enriched by the addition of propane and butane, or by the addition of gases obtained by partially decomposing fuel oil. Bottled gas is used extensively in rural homes for cooking.

The explosive range of a gas is a pair of percentages, representing the proportions of a gas mixed with air, between which the mixture of the gas and air will explode if ignited.

Test yourself on these terms

anthracite	coke	peat
bituminous coal	enriched water gas	producer gas
calorimeter	explosive range of a gas	purifier
carboniferous age	heat content of a fuel	scrubber
carburetor	lignite	superheater
checkerwork	liquid fuels	water gas
coal gas	natural gas	wood

Questions

Group A

1. (*a*) What is a fuel? (*b*) What is the original source of almost all fuels?
2. What are the characteristics of a good fuel?
3. What objections are there to the use of peat as a household fuel?
4. What are the different probable stages in the evolution of anthracite?
5. From what source are most of our liquid fuels obtained?
6. What is the principal component of natural gas?
7. What products are obtained by the destructive distillation of bituminous coal?
8. What impurity is removed from coal gas by application of the countercurrent principle?
9. Why do we say that water gas is made by an intermittent process?
10. How does producer gas differ in composition from water gas?

Group B

11. What explanation is given for the more luxuriant growth of vegetation during the carboniferous age?
12. Why is it possible for many large cities to have natural gas, even though they are far distant from the natural gas fields?
13. How is coal gas purified before it is distributed to the consumers?
14. Describe two ways in which water gas may be enriched.
15. How is the heating value of a solid fuel measured?
16. Compare lignite and bituminous coal as to carbon and heat content.
17. Why are large quantities of coke being produced when gaseous and liquid fuels are becoming more popular for home heating?
18. Write the equation for the reaction between ferric oxide and hydrogen sulfide.
19. What is the cheapest method for producing hydrogen and carbon monoxide for industrial purposes?
20. Explain what is meant by the *explosive range* of hydrogen and air.

Some things for you to do

1. Find out how fuels in your community compare in cost on a Btu basis.
2. Visit your local gas works if manufactured gas is distributed in your community.
3. Determine the percentage of moisture in various powdered coal samples by heating weighed 1-gram portions in crucibles in an oven for one hour at 105° C. The loss in weight during this heating is assumed to be moisture.
4. The dried samples obtained in No. 3 may be slowly heated until the crucibles are at dark red heat and all black particles of carbon have burned off. The material which remains is ash. Calculate the percentage of ash in each sample.

Chapter 42 PETROLEUM

1. The nature of petroleum. Petroleum, sometimes called *crude oil,* is a liquid that is obtained from beneath the surface of the ground. It is a complex mixture of many hydrocarbons. Petroleum varies greatly in composition. Oil from some fields yields *paraffin wax* as one of the end products of distillation. Such oil is called a ***paraffin-base oil.*** Oil from other fields may contain certain ring compounds called *naphthenes.* Such an oil is known as ***naphthene-base oil.*** Some oils are mixtures of both types of crude oil.

Petroleum from different wells shows wide variation in color. The oil from some wells is amber. Other wells produce a brownish oil, and still others yield an oil that is almost black. Sulfur compounds are present as objectionable impurities in some petroleum. These sulfur compounds must be removed in the refining process before such oil can be used as a fuel.

2. The origin of petroleum. Petroleum is believed to be a material resulting from the partial decomposition of animals and plants that lived in the

VOCABULARY

Alkylation. The combining of simple hydrocarbons with unsaturated hydrocarbons under the influence of heat, pressure, and the presence of a catalyst.

Catalytic cracking. The breaking-up of large molecules into smaller ones by using a catalyst together with high temperature and high pressure.

Hydroforming. The forming of ring compounds by heating straight chain hydrocarbons with hydrogen in the presence of a catalyst.

Petroleum. A liquid mixture of hydrocarbons obtained from beneath the surface of the ground.

Polymerization. The combining of simple molecules of the same kind to form a more complex one.

Thermal cracking. The breaking-up of large molecules into smaller ones by the use of high temperature and high pressure.

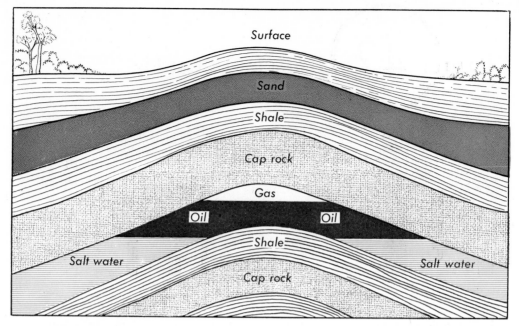

Fig. 42–1. Petroleum, natural gas, and salt water commonly saturate the oil-bearing sands under domes of cap rock in some favored locations.

Fig. 42–2. Cross-section of a rotary drilling rig used in drilling for petroleum.

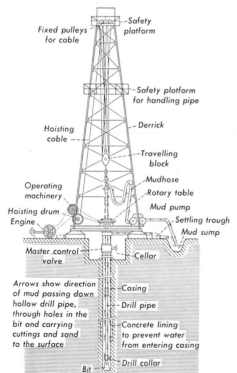

sea. Changes in the earth's crust have buried this material underground, sometimes at great depths.

In certain areas, an upward bulging of impervious rock has produced a dome-like formation. It is under these domes that *natural gas, petroleum,* and *salt water* are frequently found. The natural gas, having the lowest density, rises to the top of the dome. Here it is confined by the impervious rock above, and may collect under great pressure. Below the natural gas, the crude oil will saturate a porous sandstone, called the **oil-bearing sand,** or will be found in dolomite or sandstone formations. Salt water commonly accumulates in a layer below these sands (see Fig. 42-1).

When a drill penetrates the oil-bearing sands, the pressure of the natural gas may force the oil upward. As the pressure of the gas diminishes, the oil is obtained by pumping. It is difficult to tell at the surface of the ground just where these deeply-buried domes are located, or to estimate their extent. However, the seismograph, using the reflections of explosive shock waves from underground rock layers, provides much useful information. Scientific devices such as the *magnetometer* and the *gravity meter* are important tools to the geophysicist locating oil deposits.

3. Where is petroleum found? In the United States, petroleum was first produced at Titusville, Pennsylvania, in 1859. Later, oil fields were opened in Ohio and West Virginia. Texas is now far in the lead in oil production, followed by California, Louisiana, Oklahoma, Kansas, Wyoming, New Mexico, Illinois, Colorado, Mississippi, Arkansas, and Montana. Several other states produce smaller amounts.

Canada, Mexico, and Venezuela also have rich oil deposits. The richest deposits yet found are located in Saudi Arabia, Iran, and other Middle East countries.

4. Pipe lines transport oil long distances. Pipe lines that are buried a few feet underground lead from the oil fields to distant refineries. Pumping stations located at 10 to 60 mile intervals, depending on the terrain, force the crude oil through the pipe lines from as far away as Oklahoma to refineries in New Jersey and Pennsylvania. Other pipe lines deliver oil from Texas to refineries at Whiting, Indiana, and large cities located on the Great Lakes. Branch lines connect different oil fields with the main lines, forming a vast underground transportation system (see Fig. 42-3).

5. The refining of petroleum. The refining of petroleum is the separation of crude oil into fractions with properties

Fig. 42-3. This map shows present and prospective pipe lines for transporting petroleum and petroleum products throughout the United States and Canada. The pipe lines now operating are shown in color while the ones under construction are shown in black.

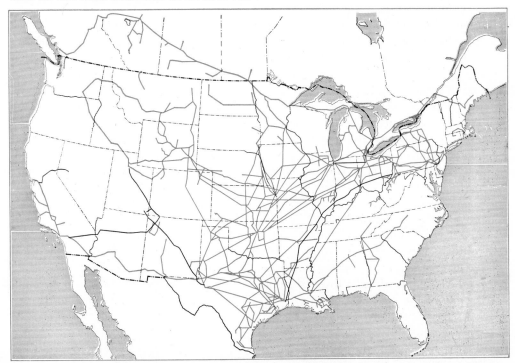

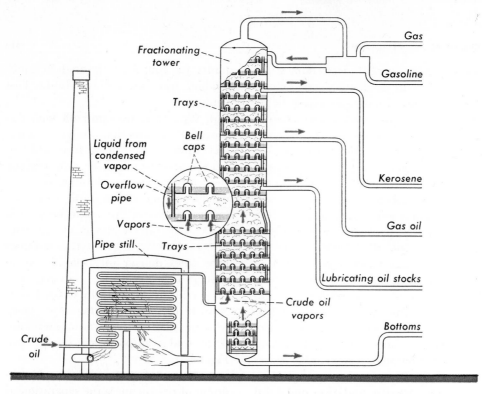

Labels on figure:
Gas
Gasoline
Fractionating tower
Trays
Bell caps
Liquid from condensed vapor
Overflow pipe
Vapors
Pipe still
Trays
Kerosene
Gas oil
Lubricating oil stocks
Crude oil vapors
Bottoms
Crude oil

Fig. 42-4. Cross-section of a pipe still and fractionating tower used in refining petroleum.

that make them suitable for certain uses. It is accomplished by **fractional distillation.** No attempt is made to separate the petroleum into single, individual hydrocarbons. Instead, fractions that distill over between certain temperature ranges are collected in separate receivers. *Gasoline* is mostly a mixture of hexane, C_6H_{14}; heptane, C_7H_{16}; and octane, C_8H_{18}. Other hydrocarbons are also present. *Kerosene* contains hydrocarbons that distill over at higher temperatures. Decane, $C_{10}H_{22}$, and dodecane, $C_{12}H_{26}$, are two of the hydrocarbons found in kerosene. Still higher boiling mixtures are known as *fuel oil* or *gas oil*. *Lubricating oils* have even larger molecules and still higher boiling points. *Greases, petroleum jelly, paraffin wax,* and *petroleum coke* are products obtained near the end or at the end of the heating.

A continuous process employing a *pipe still* and a *fractionating tower* is in general use. These are large affairs that have a capacity for distilling 10,000 barrels of crude oil a day. The fractionating towers are about 100 feet tall. In operation, the crude oil is heated to a temperature of about 700° F in the coiled pipes of the pipe still. The vapors are then discharged into the fractionating tower at a point near its base. Here the portion of the crude oil with the highest boiling point condenses and is drawn off to collecting vessels. Inside the tower are platforms or shallow troughs on which liquids from the condensed vapors collect. Those portions of the crude oil that have the lowest boiling points, and consequently are the most difficult to condense as liquids, pass up through the tower. Pipes that project through the tower at different heights lead off the overflow of condensed liquids from the platforms. Gasoline, together with other more volatile portions of the petroleum, passes over as a gas from the top of the tower. The gasoline fraction, and the more volatile naphtha fraction, are liquefied in separate condensers. The still uncondensed gases may be piped to the polymerizer (see Section 9) or be used as fuel in the refinery. Each of the liquid fractions may be redistilled to effect a better separation. Each fraction is also treated with chemicals to remove impurities.

6. What is a good motor fuel? The motorist is interested in the performance of the gasoline in his automobile, not in its chemical formula. The following are some of the characteristics a good gasoline should have. *1.* It should contain enough volatile matter to make starting of the engine easy. *2.* It should be free of gummy residues that would cause valves to stick and also form carbon within the cylinder head. *3.* It should give good mileage per gallon. *4.* There should be no "knock," particularly on hills.

7. What causes "knocking"? "Knocking" in an automobile engine is caused by too rapid burning of the mixture of gasoline vapor and air within the cylinders. Instead of a smooth, steady push, the top of the piston is given a sudden, hammer-like blow when the fuel burns too rapidly. This causes a loss in power, may be harmful to the engine, and is noticed as a succession of knocking sounds. To get the maximum power from the fuel, the mixture of gasoline vapor and air must be highly compressed. Modern automobile engines compress this mixture to one eighth, or even to one tenth of its normal volume before firing. Such a high compression engine tends to knock badly unless a gasoline with good antiknock properties is used.

Knocking may be prevented in two

Fig. 42-5. Exterior view of a pipe still (right) and fractionating tower (left).

ways: *1.* by using a fuel that has less tendency to knock; and *2.* by adding a catalyst to the gasoline. Gasoline that is made up principally of straight chain hydrocarbons tends to knock badly in automobiles. Such a hydrocarbon is normal heptane, C_7H_{16}, with the following structural formula:

$$
\begin{array}{ccccccc}
\text{H} & \text{H} & \text{H} & \text{H} & \text{H} & \text{H} & \text{H} \\
\text{H:C:C:C:C:C:C:C:H} \\
\text{H} & \text{H} & \text{H} & \text{H} & \text{H} & \text{H} & \text{H}
\end{array}
$$

Hydrocarbons with side chains burn less rapidly and give smoother operation in an automobile engine. Ring compounds, such as benzene, C_6H_6, also have less tendency to knock than straight chain hydrocarbons. To improve the antiknock properties of gasoline, refiners try to produce gasoline that contains a large proportion of side chain hydrocarbons or ring compounds.

Certain compounds, when added to gasoline in small amounts, improve the antiknocking properties. In some unknown way they seem to slow up the combustion and make the gasoline operate more smoothly. The best known of these is *lead tetraethyl,* $Pb(C_2H_5)_4$. Halogen compounds such as 1,2-dibromoethane are used with the lead tetraethyl to prevent the products of combustion from fouling the spark plugs. Gasoline to which lead tetraethyl is added is known as **leaded gasoline.** It should not be used for purposes other than as a motor fuel because of the poisonous nature of this compound.

8. What is the octane rating? The *octane rating* of a gasoline is a number. The higher the number, the less the tendency of the gasoline to knock in a high compression engine. To determine the number, the gasoline being rated is burned in a standard test engine. Its performance in the test engine is compared with a fuel of known octane number. The fuels used as standards are *normal heptane* and 2,2,4-trimethylpentane, which is also called **iso-octane.** The 2,2,4-trimethylpentane has side chains, as shown by the following structural formula:

$$
\begin{array}{ccccccc}
 & & & \text{H} \\
 & \text{H} & \text{H:C:H} & \text{H} & & \text{H} & & \text{H} \\
\text{H} : & \text{C} : & \text{C} : & \text{C} : & \text{C} : & \text{C} : & \text{H} \\
 & \text{H} & \text{H:C:H} & \text{H} & \text{H:C:H} & \text{H} \\
 & & \text{H} & & \text{H}
\end{array}
$$

Iso-octane has excellent antiknock properties and is given an arbitrary rating of 100. Normal heptane knocks very badly and is given a rating of zero. Suppose the gasoline being tested behaves similarly to a mixture of 90% iso-octane and 10% heptane. Then such a gasoline will have an octane rating of 90. Good gasolines have a rating of 90 or higher. Recently chemists have produced gasolines with even better antiknock properties than pure iso-octane. Thus it is possible to have a gasoline with an even higher rating than 100. Aviation gasoline has an octane rating of over 100.

9. How do refiners increase the yield of gasoline? Crude oil contains only a small percentage of gasoline. The yield of gasoline is increased by a number of methods, such as the following.

1. Thermal cracking. When crude oil is heated to a high temperature under high pressure, the bonds of some of the larger molecules are weakened until the molecule is "cracked," or split up into simpler molecules which are more easily vaporized. For example, a molecule of $C_{16}H_{34}$ may be cracked to yield a molecule of C_8H_{18}, octane, and a molecule of C_8H_{16}, octene. This increases the amount of gasoline that is obtained from a barrel of crude oil.

2. Catalytic cracking. This process is similar to thermal cracking in that heat and pressure are used. The catalytic cracking process also employs a catalyst to increase the rate at which cracking occurs and to enable the process to be carried out at a lower temperature than that needed for thermal cracking. Many different substances may be used as catalysts. The choice of which catalyst to use will depend on the products desired. Different catalysts favor the production of different products from the cracking process. Aluminum chloride and zirconium dioxide are two catalysts which have been used. Catalytic cracking is more efficient than thermal cracking. It produces better quality gasoline and greater quantities of home heating oil.

3. Polymerization. Polymerization is the opposite of cracking. In this process, simple molecules such as methane, CH$_4$, ethane, C_2H_6, and others, are polymerized, or "bunched," to make molecules of the proper size for gasoline. This is accomplished by heating the hydrocarbon with a suitable catalyst such as aluminum silicate. An example of a polymerization reaction is that between two molecules of isobutene, C_4H_8, to form an isomer of octene, C_8H_{16}. The octene may then be hydrogenated to form an isomer of octane.

4. Casing-head gasoline. Natural gas consists mostly of methane, but it also contains some other hydrocarbons. If it is cooled and compressed, these other hydrocarbons may be extracted from the natural gas. They form a volatile liquid which is called *"casing-head" gasoline.* It is blended with other gasolines and helps to make the fuel quick-starting.

10. Hydroforming and alkylation improve the quality of gasoline. Both of these processes result in a rearrangement of the molecules to produce more side chain or ring compounds. Thus

Fig. 42–6. A catalytic cracking unit breaks up large molecules found in petroleum and produces more molecules of the size required for gasoline.

Fig. 42–7. Oil is used for lubrication and cooling during metal cutting and grinding operations.

the antiknock properties are increased.

Hydroforming consists of heating gasoline of poor quality with hydrogen in the presence of a catalyst. Ring compounds are formed from straight chain hydrocarbons by causing the ends of the chains to join. Hydroformed gasoline, rich in ring compounds, has excellent antiknock properties.

Alkylation is a process that produces gasoline with extremely high octane numbers. In this process, simpler hydrocarbons are made to unite with unsaturated hydrocarbons such as ethylene, C_2H_4, by heat and pressure in the presence of a catalyst. Aviation gasoline is made by such a process.

11. Synthetic petroleum can be made. A petroleum-like mixture can be made by synthesis from carbon monoxide and hydrogen with the aid of a catalyst by the *Fischer-Tropsch process.* From this mixture gasoline, kerosene,

Diesel fuel, and paraffin wax have been extracted.

Another process for producing synthetic petroleum is the ***Bergius process.*** This process involves hydrogenation of low grade coal at high temperature and high pressure. Gasoline and lubricating oils of high quality have been produced by this method. Both of these processes are at present much more expensive than the refining of natural petroleum. However, they do offer possibilities for the time when our natural petroleum supply dwindles.

12. Petroleum yields many products. More than 25 billion gallons of gasoline are produced each year in the United States. In addition, other products of petroleum are important commodities.

1. Benzine and naphtha are volatile flammable mixtures that have a lower boiling range than gasoline. They are used to some extent as solvents for oil or grease. Painters sometimes use benzine as a substitute for turpentine.

2. Kerosene is used as a fuel for oil stoves, or as an illuminant in oil lamps and lanterns. It is less volatile than gasoline. A kerosene-like fuel is now being used in some types of jet aircraft.

3. Fuel oil is used in tremendous amounts for homes that are heated by oil burners. The lighter grades are used for household oil burners, while the heavier grades are used for the oil burners in factories or aboard ships.

4. Dieselene is the fuel for Diesel engines. It resembles fuel oil in composition. *Normal cetane,* $C_{16}H_{34}$, is used for rating dieselene just as octane is used as a standard for gasoline.

5. Dry cleaning solvent is much less volatile than gasoline and thus is much safer to use for dry cleaning garments.

It is a purified, deodorized product that has a boiling range near that of kerosene.

6. *Lubricating oils* vary in viscosity from thin, mobile fluids for lubricating sewing machines to thick, viscous liquids for heavy trucks. One should always use oil of the viscosity specified by the manufacturer of the machine to secure proper lubrication.

Some automobile lubricating oils now have added detergents which keep carbon particles and dirt in suspension in the oil. This helps to keep the automobile engine clean.

7. *Greases* are solids, or semisolids, at ordinary temperatures. Some greases have added graphite. They are used on bearings that are not easily lubricated by oil.

8. *Petroleum jelly* is a refined petroleum grease that is much used for making medicinal ointments.

9. *Petroleum coke* is a decomposition product obtained in refining petroleum. It is used for making carbon electrodes because it leaves no ash.

10. *Paraffin wax* is used in making candles and as an electrical insulator. It is also used for making waxed paper.

A new field for the petroleum industry is the making of chemicals from petroleum as a raw material. From petroleum a variety of commercially pure hydrocarbons may be prepared. In Chapter 16 we learned how some of these hydrocarbons, such as methane, ethylene, and acetylene, may be used as starting materials for the production of other organic compounds. In the following chapters we shall learn how other chemicals derived from petroleum are used in the production of alcohols, detergents, insecticides, plastics, synthetic rubber, textiles, and many other products.

Fig. 42–8. Asphalt is a product obtained from the fractional distillation of petroleum which is used as a binder in highway surfacing.

Summary

Petroleum, or crude oil, is a complex mixture of many hydrocarbons. Petroleum is believed to be a material resulting from the partial decomposition of marine animal and vegetable organisms. Petroleum is transported long distances from the oil fields to refineries in underground pipe lines.

Petroleum is separated by fractional distillation into fractions that are mixtures of different hydrocarbons. Gasoline, kerosene, fuel oil, lubricating oil, grease, paraffin wax, and petroleum coke are some of the important products obtained from petroleum. Pipe stills and fractionating towers are employed in a continuous process of distilling petroleum.

Too rapid combustion of gasoline in an autombile engine results in knocking. Straight chain hydrocarbons knock badly in an automobile engine, while branch chain and ring hydrocarbons have much better antiknock properties. Catalysts, such as lead tetraethyl, increase the antiknock quality of gasoline. The octane rating is a number that indicates the antiknock quality of gasoline.

The yield of gasoline may be increased by thermal cracking, catalytic cracking, polymerization, and the addition of casing-head gasoline. Hydroforming and alkylation improve the quality of gasoline. Gasoline can be made synthetically but it is too expensive a process to compete with natural gasoline in the United States. Petroleum yields a variety of useful products. Benzine and naphtha are used as solvents. Kerosene is used as a fuel. Dieselene is the fuel for Diesel engines. Dry cleaning solvent is used for cleaning garments. Oils and greases are used as lubricants. Petroleum coke is used for making electrodes. Paraffin wax is used for candles, wax paper, and as an electrical insulator. Petroleum is the source of a variety of commercially pure hydrocarbons used as starting materials for producing other organic compounds.

Test yourself on these terms

alkylation	fractionating tower	naphthene-base oil
benzine	fuel oil	octane rating
Bergius process	gasoline	oil-bearing sand
casing-head gasoline	grease	paraffin-base oil
catalytic cracking	hydroforming	paraffin wax
cetane	kerosene	petroleum
crude oil	"knocking"	petroleum coke
Dieselene	leaded gasoline	petroleum jelly
dry cleaning solvent	lead tetraethyl	pipe still
Fischer-Tropsch process	lubricating oil	polymerization
fractional distillation	naphtha	thermal cracking

Questions

Group A

1. What is the probable origin of petroleum?
2. Name five main products obtained from crude oil.

3. What four characteristics should a good motor fuel possess?

4. Describe two ways in which a fuel which knocks in an automobile engine may be improved.

5. What is the *octane rating* system used in testing gasolines?

6. (*a*) What is meant by *cracking* crude oil? (*b*) In what two ways is this done?

7. Why do we not commercially produce petroleum by synthetic methods?

8. For what types of synthetic products does the petroleum industry provide the raw materials?

9. Why can you not write a formula for petroleum such as you do for sugar, salt, and sulfuric acid?

10. What is used for rating Dieselene?

11. (*a*) What is fractional distillation? (*b*) How is it employed in the petroleum industry?

12. What is the chemical nature of gasoline?

Group B

13. What is the difference in the type of hydrocarbon in a paraffin-base oil and in a naphthene-base oil?

14. Describe the underground formations that yield petroleum.

15. Why are pipe lines used so extensively for transporting petroleum products?

16. Describe the operation of a fractionating tower.

17. What happens in the cylinder of an automobile engine when the engine knocks?

18. (*a*) What is meant by *leaded gasoline?* (*b*) Why must it not be used for any other purpose than as a motor fuel?

19. Draw structural formulas for n-heptane and 2,2,4-trimethylpentane.

20. Give an example of a polymerization reaction used to increase the yield of gasoline from crude oil.

21. How does the addition of casing-head gasoline improve the quality of a fuel?

22. Why do petroleum refiners make use of hydroforming and alkylation?

Some things for you to do

1. Large oil companies distribute literature consisting of charts that describe the different petroleum products which they market. Procure such a chart and study it. Make a short report to the class about the different petroleum products.

2. Find out the octane numbers of the different gasolines sold in your community, as reported by the operators of the filling stations.

3. Note the large storage tanks for petroleum products which are usually found in the outskirts of all large cities. Have the man in charge explain what they store in the tanks, and how the tanks are constructed.

4. Talk with automobile salesmen and filling station operators to learn how the problem of higher compression ratios and adequate fuel for new-model automobiles is being solved.

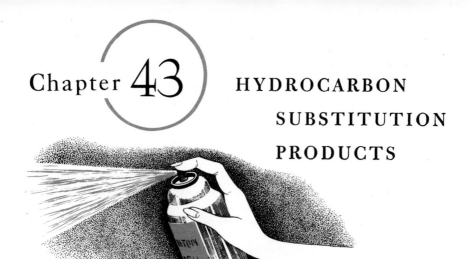

Chapter 43

HYDROCARBON SUBSTITUTION PRODUCTS

1. HYDROCARBON SUBSTITUTION PRODUCTS

1. Halogen substitution products of methane. In Chapter 18, Section 6, we learned that the halogens react with methane to form substitution products. An atom of a halogen may be substituted for an atom of hydrogen in methane. Under certain conditions, we can substitute halogen atoms for each of the four hydrogen atoms in methane. This reaction occurs in four separate steps:

$$CH_4 + Cl_2 \rightarrow CH_3Cl + HCl$$
$$CH_3Cl + Cl_2 \rightarrow CH_2Cl_2 + HCl$$
$$CH_2Cl_2 + Cl_2 \rightarrow CHCl_3 + HCl$$
$$CHCl_3 + Cl_2 \rightarrow CCl_4 + HCl$$

CH_3Cl, chloromethane, or methyl chloride, is a colorless gas that is widely used in preparing other organic compounds.

CH_2Cl_2, dichloromethane, or methylene chloride, is a volatile, colorless liquid which is very stable and unreactive. It is used in one type of paint remover.

$CHCl_3$, trichloromethane, or chloroform, is a sweet-smelling, colorless liquid used as a solvent. It is also used as an anesthetic.

CCl_4, tetrachloromethane, or carbon tetrachloride, is a colorless, volatile liquid. It is an excellent agent for removing grease spots from clothing because it is a good solvent and will not burn

VOCABULARY

Detergent. A substance which removes dirt.

Esterification. The process of producing an ester by reaction of an acid with an alcohol.

Saponification. The process of making a soap by hydrolysis of an ester with an alkali.

Substitution product. A compound in which various atoms or groups have been substituted for one or more atoms.

or explode. Its vapors are toxic, however, and there must be good ventilation whenever carbon tetrachloride is used. Carbon tetrachloride forms dense vapors which can blanket a small fire, shut out the oxygen, and extinguish the fire. Fire extinguishers filled with this liquid are kept in homes and automobiles. They are effective for small fires, but adequate ventilation must be provided because the vapors are poisonous.

2. Commercial preparation of chloroform and carbon tetrachloride. While the direct chlorination of methane does yield chloroform and carbon tetrachloride, this method is not generally used for the commercial preparation of these compounds because of difficulty in controlling the reaction and in separating the products.

Fig. 43–1. A methylene chloride-based paint remover helps in renovating Independence Hall in Philadelphia.

Chloroform is manufactured by reducing carbon tetrachloride with moist iron.

Carbon tetrachloride is prepared commercially by the reaction between carbon disulfide, CS_2, and sulfur monochloride, S_2Cl_2, using iron as a catalyst.

$$CS_2 + 2\ S_2Cl_2 \xrightarrow{Fe} CCl_4 + 6\ S$$

The sulfur produced in this reaction is used to make more sulfur monochloride.

3. Organic groups derived from the alkanes. We have seen that CH_3Cl is sometimes called methyl chloride. CH_3— is the methyl group. It occurs frequently in organic compounds. It consists of a carbon atom which has shared three of its four valence electrons with hydrogen atoms. The fourth

Fig. 43–2. A hand-pump fire extinguisher containing carbon tetrachloride is being used to put out this oily-rag fire.

valence electron is available for covalent bond formation with another atom. In methyl chloride this fourth valence electron is shared with a chlorine atom. One of the valence electrons of the chlorine atom is likewise shared with the carbon atom. The electron-dot formulas below illustrate these structures.

$$\overset{\text{H}}{\underset{\text{H}}{\text{H:C·}}} \qquad \overset{\text{H}}{\underset{\text{H}}{\text{H:C:Cl}}}$$

Methyl group   Methyl chloride

The name of the methyl group is derived from that of the alkane with the same number of carbon atoms, methane, by replacing the suffix -ane with -yl.

Other alkanes form similar groups. For example, C_2H_5— is the ethyl group, and C_3H_7— is the propyl group.

4. Other halogen substitution products. Chloroethane, or ethyl chloride, C_2H_5Cl, is sprayed on the skin before minor operations. It evaporates so rapidly that it cools and anesthetizes the tissues.

1,2-dibromoethane, $BrCH_2CH_2Br$, is used with lead tetraethyl in antiknock fluid for gasoline. During the combustion of the gasoline, lead tetraethyl is decomposed. 1,2-dibromoethane supplies bromine so the lead may be removed from the engine in the exhaust gases as lead bromide. Otherwise, deposits of lead oxide would foul the spark plugs.

Tri-iodomethane, or iodoform, CHI_3, is a yellow solid that is made by treating ethanol (ethyl alcohol) with iodine in the presence of a mild alkali such as potassium carbonate. Iodoform has such a peculiar, persistent odor that this reaction may be used as a test for ethanol.

Dichlorodifluoromethane, CCl_2F_2, commonly called Freon, is used as a refrigerant in mechanical refrigerators and in air conditioners. It is also used as the propellant in spray cans of various kinds. Freon is nontoxic, nonflammable, and noncorrosive. It is prepared from carbon tetrachloride and hydrofluoric acid with antimony compounds used as catalysts.

$$CCl_4 + 2\ HF \xrightarrow{\text{catalyst}} CCl_2F_2 + 2\ HCl$$

2. ALCOHOLS

5. Alcohols contain hydroxyl groups. Alcohols are a class of compounds which have a hydrocarbon group and one or more —OH, hydroxyl, groups. For example, methanol has the formula CH_3OH. It is also called *methyl alcohol* or *wood alcohol*. Ethanol has the formula C_2H_5OH, and is called *ethyl alcohol* or *grain alcohol*. Glycerol, or glycerin, is a nonpoisonous alcohol that has the formula $C_3H_5(OH)_3$. There are many other alcohols in organic chemistry.

While many alcohols are soluble in water, they are not ionized by water. An alcohol exists in water solution in the form of molecules. Since the hydroxyl group of an alcohol *does not produce* hydroxide ions in water solution, alcohols *do not have* the properties of inorganic hydroxides.

6. The simplest alcohol is methanol. Methanol is a colorless liquid with a rather pleasant odor. It has a low density, and boils at 66.7° C. It is very poisonous, even when used externally.

Fig. 43–3. There are many alcohols in chemistry. These three, methanol, ethanol, and ethylene glycol, are used as antifreeze in automobiles.

If taken internally in small quantity it causes blindness by paralyzing the optic nerve. Larger amounts cause death. Methanol is a good fuel, burning with a hot, smokeless flame. Large quantities are used as an automobile radiator antifreeze. It is also used as a vehicle for shellac, a denaturant for ethanol, and as a starting material in the preparation of other organic compounds. Methanol is made from carbon monoxide and hydrogen in the presence of a catalyst.

7. The preparation of ethanol. *1. From ethene (ethylene).* Large quantities of ethylene are produced during the cracking of petroleum. This ethylene may be hydrated, using sulfuric acid as a catalyst, to produce ethanol.

$$C_2H_4 + H_2O \xrightarrow{H_2SO_4} C_2H_5OH$$

2. By fermentation. If yeast is added to a dilute solution of sugar or molasses at room temperature, chemical action

soon begins to occur. Bubbles of carbon dioxide are liberated and ethanol is produced. The equation which summarizes the reaction is:

$$C_6H_{12}O_6 \rightarrow 2\ C_2H_5OH + 2\ CO_2\uparrow$$

The yeast plants secrete an enzyme, *zymase,* which acts as a catalyst in changing the sugar into alcohol and carbon dioxide.

Fig. 43–4. This shows a plant for the manufacture of ethyl alcohol from ethylene.

Both of these processes are widely used today for the commercial production of ethanol. However, the hydration of ethylene is a less expensive method to carry out, and is gradually accounting for a greater proportion of the total production.

8. The properties of ethanol. Ethanol is a colorless liquid which has a peculiar odor and a sharp, biting taste. It boils at 78° C and freezes at −115° C. It burns with a nearly colorless blue flame. Alcohol is a good solvent for many organic compounds which are insoluble in water. Accordingly, it is used for making tinctures, spirits, and fluid extracts for medicinal use. Much alcohol is used as an antifreeze in automobiles. Large amounts are used for making ether and acetaldehyde.

9. What is denatured alcohol? Denatured alcohol is a mixture, composed principally of ethanol, to which poisonous and nauseating materials have been added. These materials are added to make sure that it will not be used for beverage purposes. Pure ethanol is subject to a Federal tax of $16.00 a gallon, but denatured alcohol can be manufactured and sold tax-free for industrial

purposes. *Rubbing alcohol* is a kind of denatured alcohol that is made for external use only. Its chief use is as an antiseptic.

10. The higher alcohols. Alcohols with a greater number of carbon atoms per molecule than ethanol are sometimes called *higher* alcohols. *Propanol,* or propyl alcohol, C_3H_7OH, is used as a solvent. *Butanol,* or butyl alcohol, C_4H_9OH, and *pentanol,* or amyl alcohol, $C_5H_{11}OH$, are used in making lacquers. *Dodecanol,* or lauryl alcohol, $C_{12}H_{25}OH$, is used for manufacturing one type of soapless detergent. Other higher alcohols are known, but they have very limited uses. The higher alcohols used as solvents are made by fermentation, using special biological varieties of yeast.

11. Ethylene glycol and glycerol are alcohols. Ethylene glycol, $C_2H_4(OH)_2$, is an alcohol containing two hydroxyl groups. It is used extensively as a "permanent type" antifreeze in automobile radiators. Its boiling point is so much higher than that of water that it does not readily evaporate or boil away.

Glycerol, or glycerin, $C_3H_5(OH)_3$, is

Fig. 43–5. A view of the bottom of the stills in a plant that produces ethanol by fermentation.

a colorless, odorless, viscous liquid with a sweet taste. It has a low vapor pressure and is hygroscopic. It is used in making synthetic resins for paints, by the tobacco industry to keep cigarettes moist, in the manufacture of cellophane, in making nitroglycerin, and in some toilet soaps. Glycerol is used in some lotions because it keeps the skin from becoming dry and chapped. It is an important pharmaceutical ingredient, and is used, too, in many foods and beverages. Glycerol is a by-product of soap manufacture.

3. ETHERS, ALDEHYDES, KETONES, ORGANIC ACIDS, AND ESTERS

12. Ethers are organic oxides. Ordinary ether, or *ethyl ether*, $(C_2H_5)_2O$, is a volatile liquid of characteristic odor that is very flammable. It is made by heating ethanol and sulfuric acid to 140° C.

$$2 \; C_2H_5OH \xrightarrow{H_2SO_4} C_2H_5OC_2H_5 + H_2O$$

Besides its familiar use as an anesthetic, ether is employed as a solvent for fats and oils.

13. There are other ethers besides ethyl ether. By heating methanol instead of ethanol with sulfuric acid, *methyl ether*, $(CH_3)_2O$, is formed. With propyl alcohol, *propyl ether*, $(C_3H_7)_2O$, can be made by the same process. Since there are many alcohols, it is possible to make many different ethers.

14. What are the aldehydes? An *aldehyde* is a compound which has a hydrocarbon group and one or more $-CHO$ groups. For example, *acetaldehyde* has the formula CH_3CHO, and benzaldehyde has the formula C_6H_5CHO. Both of these aldehydes are important in producing a variety of organic compounds. Aldehydes are made by mild oxidation of an alcohol.

15. Formaldehyde is an important compound. If we pass methanol vapor and a regulated amount of air over heated copper, formaldehyde is produced.

$$2 \; CH_3OH + O_2 \xrightarrow{Cu} 2 \; HCHO + 2 \; H_2O$$

At room temperature, formaldehyde is a gas with a suffocating odor. Dissolved in water, it makes an excellent

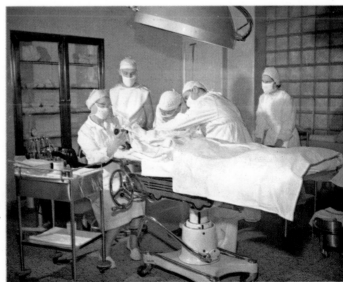

Fig. 43–6. Ether is used as an anesthetic during a surgical operation.

Fig. 43–7. This photograph shows a chemical plant in which isopropyl alcohol is converted to acetone.

disinfectant. It is sometimes used to treat seeds before they are planted to destroy injurious fungi, such as molds or blights. Seed potatoes are treated with formaldehyde solution to prevent scab. It is used for preserving anatomical specimens, and for making the embalming fluid used by undertakers. But by far the largest use for formaldehyde, which reacts with phenol or urea, is in the making of certain types of plastics.

16. Acetone is the simplest ketone. *Ketones* are a class of organic compounds that contain the $\diagup CO$, or *carbonyl* group. They may, like the aldehydes, be prepared by mild oxidation of a certain type of alcohol. Acetone, CH_3COCH_3, is prepared in this manner by oxidation of 2-propanol, $CH_3CHOHCH_3$. Another common method of preparing acetone is by special bacterial fermentation of molasses.

Acetone, a colorless, volatile liquid, is widely used as a solvent in the manufacture of acetate rayon, and in paint and varnish removers. Tanks of acetylene gas contain asbestos saturated with acetone. The acetylene dissolves in the acetone and thus increases the amount of acetylene which may safely be compressed into the tank. Acetone and other ketones are used for cleaning metals, removing stains, and for preparing synthetic organic chemicals.

17. The occurrence of organic acids. Many organic acids and their salts occur naturally in sour milk, in unripe fruits, in rhubarb and sorrel, as well as in other plants. All organic acids contain the —COOH, or *carboxyl* group.

It is the hydrogen atom bonded to an oxygen atom in the carboxyl group which is ionized in water solution and gives these substances their typical acid properties. The hydrogen atoms bonded to carbon atoms in these acids are *never* ionized in water solution.

Some organic acids are made by oxidizing their corresponding alcohols or aldehydes.

18. Formic acid is a fairly strong acid. Formic acid, HCOOH, is prepared from sodium hydroxide and carbon monoxide under pressure. This reaction yields sodium formate, HCOONa.

$$NaOH + CO \rightarrow HCOONa$$

If sodium formate is heated with sulfuric acid, formic acid distills off.

$$HCOONa + H_2SO_4 \rightarrow$$
$$HCOOH\uparrow + NaHSO_4$$

Formic acid is found in nature in stinging nettles, in the sting of bees, wasps, and hornets, and in red ants. Formic acid is used commercially in the dyeing industry.

19. Acetic acid is present in vinegar. Vinegar is made from apple cider which has fermented to form hard cider. The alcohol in hard cider is oxidized slowly to acetic acid. A ferment known as "mother of vinegar" promotes the change. The equation is:

$$C_2H_5OH + O_2 \rightarrow CH_3COOH + H_2O$$

Good vinegar contains from 4% to 6% acetic acid. Malt vinegar and wine vinegar are made by a similar process of fermentation and oxidation.

Some acetic acid is still obtained as a by-product of the destructive distillation of wood. Pure acetic acid is produced by the catalytic oxidation of acetaldehyde. Concentrated acetic acid is a colorless liquid that is a good solvent for some organic chemicals. It is used for making cellulose acetate, one of the synthetic fibers.

20. Oxalic acid is a white solid. This organic acid has the formula $(COOH)_2$. It is an active poison. Oxalic acid is used as a reducing agent, in blueprints, in bleaching flax and straw, in cleaning brass and copper, and in removing ink spots and rust stains.

21. Tartaric acid comes from grapes. This acid has the formula

$$(CHOH)_2(COOH)_2$$

It is obtained from potassium hydrogen tartrate, which collects as a sediment in the bottom of wine barrels. Both tartaric acid and potassium hydrogen tartrate, which is commonly known as *cream of tartar,* are used as the acid substance in some baking powders. The

Fig. 43-8. Vinegar is made by the fermentation and oxidation of natural sugars and starches found in various grains and in apples.

double salt, *sodium potassium tartrate,* $NaKC_4H_4O_6$, is used in medicine under the name of *Rochelle salts.*

22. The occurrence of citric acid. Citric acid is a white, crystalline solid. It occurs in such fruits as raspberries, gooseberries, and currants, and is present also in lemons, limes, and other citrus fruits. The acid is used in soft drinks. A solution of magnesium citrate is used as a laxative in medicine.

23. Salicylic acid is used to make aspirin. Salicylic acid has the following formula:

It is a white, crystalline solid which is made from phenol, C_6H_5OH. If we treat salicylic acid with methanol, in the presence of sulfuric acid, we get *methyl salicylate,* or synthetic oil of wintergreen. Salicylic acid treated with acetic acid yields *acetyl salicylic acid,*

better known as *aspirin.* Aspirin has the following formula:

Aspirin is used for relieving the discomfort of colds, and to help relieve mild pain from headaches and other conditions.

24. What is an ester? An *ester* is produced when an acid reacts with an alcohol. For example, *ethyl acetate* is the ester formed when ethanol and acetic acid react.

$$C_2H_5OH + CH_3COOH \xrightarrow{H_2SO_4} CH_3COOC_2H_5 + H_2O$$

Such reactions, which result in the formation of esters, are **esterification reactions.** Reactions between acids and alcohols are reversible. Consequently, sulfuric acid is used to absorb the water that is produced in these reactions, thereby forcing them in the direction of ester formation.

It is possible, too, to have an ester formed by the union of an alcohol with an inorganic acid. *Glyceryl trinitrate,* commonly known as nitroglycerin, is an example.

Esters give fruits their characteristic flavor and odor. *Amyl acetate* has an odor somewhat resembling bananas. As "banana oil" this ester is used as the vehicle for aluminum paints which are used for coating steam radiators. *Ethyl butyrate* has an odor and flavor that resembles pineapples. Ripe pineapples contain some of this ester, together with smaller amounts of other esters.

Fig. 43–9. Ethyl butyrate is one of the esters that give pineapples their characteristic odor and flavor.

4. SOAPS AND SOAPLESS DETERGENTS

25. Saponification means soap making. *Stearin* is the glyceryl ester of stearic acid. If we treat stearin with an alkali, such as sodium hydroxide, they react to form soap and glycerol as in the following equation:

stearin $\quad$ + sodium hydroxide →

$$C_3H_5(C_{17}H_{35}COO)_3 + 3\,NaOH \quad\longrightarrow$$

soap $\quad$ + $\quad$ glycerol

$$3\,C_{17}H_{35}COONa + C_3H_5(OH)_3$$

Stearin is obtained from beef and mutton tallow. *Palmitin,* an ester found in palm oil, and *olein,* an ester found in lard, olive oil, and cottonseed oil, are also used in making soap. Coconut oil contains a high content of *lauric acid,* $C_{11}H_{23}COOH$, and *myristic acid,* $C_{13}H_{27}COOH$. It is also an important raw material for making soap.

26. The kettle method of making soap. In this method, the fats and oils are added to giant kettles. Sodium hydroxide solution is poured in, and the mixture then boiled. When the reaction is complete, sodium chloride is added to "salt out" the colloidal soap from the glycerol and water. The soap is next transferred to a *crutching machine,* in which it is thoroughly mixed. Now, it is run into molds which may hold about 1200 lb each, where it is permitted to solidify. The large blocks are next cut into slabs by means of steel wires. The strips or slabs are then ready for the final cutting and stamping into cakes of the desired size and shape.

27. The hydrolyzer method of making soap. In this method, fat is pumped into the bottom of the hydrolyzer, which is a stainless steel tube about three feet in diameter and 70 feet high. The fat rises through the superheated water which is pumped into the top of the hydrolyzer. The fat, possibly stearin, undergoes hydrolysis forming an acid, such as stearic acid, and glycerol.

Fig. 43–10. This photograph shows the surface of a kettle of soap that is being heated and agitated by steam which enters through coils at the bottom of the tank.

$$C_3H_5(C_{17}H_{35}COO)_3 + 3\ H_2O \rightarrow$$
$$3\ C_{17}H_{35}COOH + C_3H_5(OH)_3$$

Note that this hydrolysis is the reverse of an esterification reaction. The glycerol is drawn off with the water at the bottom of the hydrolyzer. The stearic acid is drawn off the top. After purification, the stearic acid is reacted with sodium hydroxide to form soap.

$$C_{17}H_{35}COOH + NaOH \rightarrow$$
$$C_{17}H_{35}COONa + H_2O$$

The soap is further processed into cakes as in the kettle method.

The advantage of the hydrolyzer

method is that it can be operated on a continuous production basis, whereas the kettle method is essentially a "batch" process.

28. Toilet soaps differ from laundry soaps. Toilet soaps are made from the best quality fat. This is made to react with just the right amount of sodium hydroxide. Such soaps are made with great care to make sure that there is no excess sodium hydroxide in the finished product. In a toilet soap any excess sodium hydroxide would be very injurious to the skin. All soaps contain some perfume to conceal the unpleasant smell of raw soap, but toilet soaps have more expensive perfumes added to impart a pleasing scent as well.

Laundry soaps are made from cheaper fat. They usually contain an excess of sodium hydroxide, which helps in removing grease from soiled garments. Inexpensive perfumes, such as oil of pine, or oil of sassafras, are used in laundry soaps to cover the raw soap smell. Laundry soaps also have fillers added in the crutching machine. These fillers have some detergent value and are cheaper than soap. A *detergent* is a substance that removes dirt. *Rosin* is such a filler and increases the ability of the soap to form suds. *Sodium silicate* (water glass) is another filler often found in laundry soaps. *Borax* and *sodium carbonate* are frequently added to assist in removing grease by their alkaline reaction in water.

Fig. 43–11. The long vertical steel tube in the center of the photograph is the hydrolyzer used in one method of producing soap.

29. Some other special soaps. *Floating soaps* are made by beating air into the soap while it is in the crutching machine. *Transparent soaps* may contain glycerol. They may also be made by dissolving soap in alcohol, and then evaporating the solvent alcohol. *Medicated soaps* have some substance added to the soap that is said to possess medicinal value. *Deodorant soaps* have a small amount of certain substances that are intended to overcome the odor of perspiration. *Powdered soaps* are made by grinding a hard dry soap to a fine powder. Frequently powdered sodium carbonate is mixed with the powdered soap for laundry purposes. *Scouring soaps* are usually made from mixtures of powdered soap, sodium carbonate, and some gritty substance, such as powdered sand or powdered pumice.

30. Soapless detergents. *Soapless detergents* are products which offer real competition to soap as cleaning agents. These substances are **wetting agents** which lower the surface tension of water. This causes the liquid to spread through the fibers of cloth readily, thus loosening the dirt (see Chap. 33, Section 6). They do not hydrolyze to produce the hydroxide ion, so they can be used for delicate fabrics. They work equally well with hard and soft water, an important advantage where hard water is commonly available.

A number of higher alcohols have been found to be satisfactory for making wetting agents. One of the most common soapless detergents is made by treating lauryl alcohol, $C_{12}H_{25}OH$, with sulfuric acid and sodium hydroxide, to make *sodium lauryl sulfate*. Other long chain alcohols, as well as other types of complex organic compounds, are also used. Soap manufacturers are now making soapless detergents as well as soaps. These soapless detergents are sold for household use under various trade names. Manufacturers of chemicals and refiners of petroleum supply the higher alcohols required for the production of soapless detergents.

Summary

Hydrocarbon substitution products may be made by substituting for one or more of the hydrogen atoms in a hydrocarbon an atom such as chlorine, or a group such as hydroxyl. Trichloromethane, chloroform, is a sweet-smelling, colorless liquid used as a solvent and anesthetic. Tetrachloromethane, carbon tetrachloride, is a colorless, volatile liquid used as a solvent and in fire extinguishers.

CH_3- is the methyl group. Its name is derived from methane by replacing the suffix -ane with -yl. Other groups, similarly named, are C_2H_5-, ethyl group, and C_3H_7-, propyl group.

Alcohols are a class of compounds with an organic group and one or more hydroxyl groups. Methanol and ethanol are important and well-known compounds. Denatured alcohol is principally ethyl alcohol, to which poisonous and nauseating materials have been added to make it unfit for beverage purposes. Some of the higher alcohols are used as solvents. Ethylene glycol, an alcohol with two hydroxyl groups, is used as "permanent type" antifreeze. Glycerol is a nonpoisonous alcohol that has three hydroxyl groups.

Ethers are organic oxides. Ethyl ether is used as a solvent and as an anesthetic. Aldehydes are organic compounds with one or more —CHO groups. Formaldehyde is the best-known aldehyde. Ketones contain the $\diagdown CO$ group. Acetone is a well-known ketone. Organic acids have the —COOH, or carboxyl group. Acetic acid is a common organic acid that is present in vinegar. An ester is produced by the reaction of an acid and an alcohol. Many esters have pleasant fruity odors.

Soap is made by the reaction between fats or oils and sodium hydroxide. Laundry soaps are made from cheap fat and usually have an excess of sodium hydroxide. Toilet soaps are made from better grade fat and do not have an excess of sodium hydroxide.

Soapless detergents are wetting agents which lower the surface tension of water. They produce no hydroxide ions in solution and may be used with delicate fabrics.

 **Test yourself on these terms**

acetic acid	detergent	glycerol
acetone	ester	hydrolyzer method
alcohol	esterification	ketone
aldehyde	ethanol	kettle method
aspirin	ether	methanol
carbon tetrachloride	ethylene glycol	methyl group
carbonyl group	ethyl group	saponification
carboxyl group	formaldehyde	soapless detergents
chloroform	formic acid	stearin
denatured alcohol	Freon	substitution product

Questions

Group A

1. What are the names and formulas for the four chlorine substitution products of methane?
2. (a) What are the uses of carbon tetrachloride? (b) What precaution must be exercised in its use?
3. How are the names of the alkyl groups, such as methyl, ethyl, and propyl, derived?
4. What is an important use for 1,2-dibromoethane?
5. What compound is produced in the test for ethanol?
6. How do alcohols differ from inorganic hydroxides?
7. What is the effect of methanol on the human body?
8. How is ethanol produced by the fermentation of molasses?
9. Why is alcohol denatured?
10. What is meant by the term *higher alcohol?*
11. How are ethers prepared?
12. How is formaldehyde used in a biology laboratory?
13. Give several uses for acetone.

14. Where is formic acid found in nature?

15. What is the function of sulfuric acid in an esterification reaction?

16. Why do you think some esters have the odor of certain fruits?

17. How does laundry soap differ from toilet soap?

18. (a) What are soapless detergents? (b) What advantage do they have over soap?

Group B

19. Write the equation for the commercial production of carbon tetrachloride.

20. What method is used for preparing dichlorodifluoromethane?

21. What is the characteristic group in: (a) an alcohol; (b) an ether; (c) an aldehyde; (d) a ketone; (e) an acid?

22. Write the equation for the preparation of ethanol from ethylene.

23. What alcohol is used as "permanent type" antifreeze?

24. What property does glycerol have which makes it suitable for keeping tobacco moist?

25. By what method is formaldehyde prepared from methanol?

26. In what three ways may acetic acid be prepared?

27. (a) What is the formula for oxalic acid? (b) What are its uses?

28. What is unusual about the formula for salicylic acid?

29. Write an equation showing the formation of the ester, butyl acetate.

30. Write the equation for the production of soap from stearin and sodium hydroxide.

31. What is the principal advantage of the hydrolyzer method for preparing soap?

32. Why is only one hydronium ion produced when a molecule of acetic acid ionizes when there are four hydrogen atoms in the molecule?

Some things for you to do

1. Ask your instructor to show you the supply of organic chemicals in the laboratory stockroom. Look especially for alcohols, ether, formaldehyde, chloroform, carbon tetrachloride, acetone, benzene, toluene, xylene, phenol, acetic acid, citric acid, and salicylic acid.

2. Prepare synthetic oil of wintergreen, the methyl ester of salicylic acid. Add 0.5 g of salicylic acid to a small Erlenmeyer flask. Pour in 5 ml of methanol, and then cautiously add 2 ml of concentrated sulfuric acid. Warm the flask gently, and note the odor of wintergreen. Your instructor may give you directions for preparing other esters.

3. Make up 1% solutions of various synthetic detergents in water. Determine the pH of such solutions using Universal Indicator, or short-range Hydrion test paper.

Chapter 44 TEXTILES AND PAPER

1. NATURAL FIBERS

1. What are textiles? *Textiles* is a collective term for the different fabrics produced by weaving. Threads or yarns are interlaced according to a pattern. The threads or yarns may be derived from: *1.* vegetable; *2.* animal; *3.* mineral; or *4.* synthetic sources. The yarn is made by combing the fibers so that they lie parallel, and then twisting several together to make a continuous strand. The yarn may be dyed before it is woven, or the woven cloth may be colored by immersing it in dye baths. Cotton and linen are frequently bleached with chemicals to produce "white goods." Silk and wool are not so frequently bleached.

2. Cotton is our most important fiber. *Cotton fibers* used in textiles vary in length from $\frac{3}{4}$ inch to $2\frac{1}{2}$ inches. The longer the fibers, the better the quality, and the longer the cloth made from them will wear. Under the microscope, individual cotton fibers appear like flattened, twisted tubes. They are nearly pure cellulose, $(C_6H_{10}O_5)_n$. The exact molecular weight is not known, but it is believed that *"n"* is probably a large number. Cotton absorbs moisture readily and is a poor conductor of heat. When immersed in a concentrated solution of sodium hydroxide, stretched cotton fibers swell, become rounded, more lustrous, and stronger.

VOCABULARY

Chromophor. An atom or group of atoms in a molecule which is believed to be responsible for the color of many organic dyes.

Mercerizing. The treatment of stretched cotton fibers with concentrated sodium hydroxide.

Spinneret. A metal plate with many small holes used in forming a synthetic fiber.

Textile. A fabric produced by weaving.

Weighting. The repeated dipping of raw silk into a solution of tin chloride or iron chloride.

This process is called **mercerizing.** Mercerized cotton is used for making cotton socks. Cotton burns readily, leaving almost no ash. While alkalies do not injure cotton, acids react with it very readily.

3. Linen is the textile of permanence. *Linen fibers* are obtained from the flax plant before the seeds mature. Linen fibers come from the bundles of *bast fibers* that surround the center of the plant stem. Individual fibers are soft, lustrous, and about two feet long. Under the microscope, they appear as transparent tubes, with junctions at intervals. Linen, like cotton, is nearly pure cellulose and has similar chemical properties.

Linen absorbs moisture faster than any other fiber, a property that adapts it for summer garments. The fibers leave no lint on other objects, a property that recommends it for dish towels. Linen fibers are strong, and linen thread is used for sewing when strength is required. Linen lacks *resiliency,* that is, it does not spring back after being folded. This property causes linen garments to wrinkle or crease quite easily.

4. Wool is the fiber for warmth. *Wool* is the curly hair, particularly of sheep, but the term also includes the hair from goats, llamas, alpacas, and camels. Wool tends to mat together, enclosing much "dead air." For this reason wool is a good heat insulator. Wool is a protein and contains carbon, hydrogen, oxygen, nitrogen, and sulfur. It burns poorly, forming a black, charred mass with an unpleasant odor. Under the microscope, wool fibers appear to be made up of tiny, scale-like plates that overlap each other like shingles. Alkalies damage wool. Concentrated solutions of alkalies, especially when hot, will convert wool to soluble materials. Soaps that contain much free alkali injure it. Wool has resiliency and the fibers spring back to their original position after bending or folding. Woolen garments tend to hold their shape better than other natural fibers.

The quality of wool is determined by length of fiber, fineness, luster, and texture. *Virgin wool* is wool that has not previously been woven into cloth.

Fig. 44-1. Cotton fibers as they appear under the microscope.

Fig. 44-2. Linen fibers as they appear under the microscope.

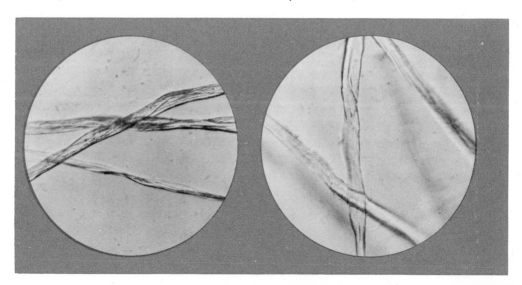

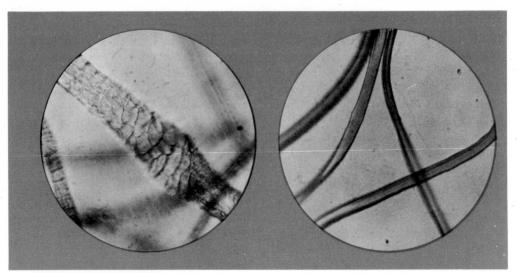

Fig. 44-3. The appearance of wool fibers as viewed through a microscope.

Fig. 44-4. The appearance of silk fibers as viewed through a microscope.

Scraps of unworn woolen cloth are shredded into fibers and form **reprocessed wool.** Old, worn, woolen rags are shredded into fibers to form *shoddy.* The shredding operation breaks some of the fibers, so reprocessed wool does not wear as well as virgin wool.

5. Silk is the luxury fiber. Silk is used to make luxurious fabrics which we admire for their soft, silky luster. Raw silk is obtained by patiently unwinding the cocoons of the silkworm. Raw silk consists of two proteins, *fibroin* and *sericin.* The fibers are very fine, about $\frac{1}{2500}$ inch in diameter, and remarkably strong. They are lustrous, semi-transparent, free of joints or scales, and thus smooth to the touch. Silk is elastic and resilient. It burns poorly, swelling to form a gummy mass. Alkalies destroy silk, and acids also injure this fiber. Silk is more readily affected by chemicals than many other textile fibers. It unites with dyes easily, forming brilliantly colored fabrics with a beautiful **sheen.** Silk unites with the chlorides of tin and iron. Raw silk is dipped re-

peatedly in solutions of these compounds to form **weighted silk.** Such weighted fabrics tend to crack, particularly when the silk is exposed to light and perspiration. **Pure dye silk** has not been weighted.

6. Mineral fibers are fireproof. *Asbestos* is the name given to the fine, silky fibers obtained from *chrysotile,* a hydrated magnesium silicate rock. The peculiar, fibrous nature of this mineral was probably produced by the action of steam on the hot, volcanic rock. It is fireproof, and most acids do not affect it, so it is valuable for making fireproof curtains and pads. It is also used as insulation.

Glass wool, a fluffy mass of very fine fibers of glass, is produced in large quantities. It is made by directing a blast of high pressure steam against molten glass as it issues under pressure from small openings. Glass wool will not burn, does not rot, and is vermin-proof. It makes an excellent heat insulator that is used in the walls of refrigerators. Glass wool can be spun into yarn and woven into cloth. Such a glass cloth is suitable for filtering corrosive solutions that would destroy ordinary cloth or filter paper. Glass cloth is used for other purposes for which it is adapted because of its fireproof nature.

2. SYNTHETIC FIBERS

7. How are synthetic fibers made? Synthetic fibers are made by forcing a suitable liquid through tiny holes in a metal plate. The plates, called *spinnerets,* are about the size of a dime and have from 10 to 150 holes, depending on the desired size of the fiber. This process imitates that of the silkworm which has two silk-spinning glands located just below the mouth. Large synthetic fiber mills have hundreds of spinnerets arranged in long rows. Some synthetic fibers are ejected directly into an acid bath to convert them from a liquid to a solid. Other filaments are hardened as they drop through a tube of warm, dry air.

8. Rayon is regenerated cellulose. Two processes are used for producing rayon in the United States today: *1. viscose process;* and *2. cuprammonium process.* Wood pulp or cotton linters (fibers of cotton too short for spinning) are the raw materials used for making rayons.

1. Viscose process. Sodium hydroxide solution is used to convert wood pulp or cotton linters into a compound called *alkali cellulose.* The alkali cellulose is changed to *cellulose xanthate* by treatment with carbon disulfide. The cellulose xanthate is then dissolved in sodium hydroxide to form *viscose solution.* The viscose solution is carefully filtered and then forced through the spinneret into a bath of dilute sulfuric acid. The sulfuric acid reconverts the viscose solution into a continuous glossy transparent filament of cellulose. Several filaments are twisted to form rayon thread. More than 80% of the rayon used in this country is made by this process now.

2. Cuprammonium process. In the cuprammonium process, cellulose is dissolved in a mixture of cupric sulfate solution and ammonia water. The bluish liquid is forced through a spinneret, first into water, and then into a bath of dilute acid. This process produces

Fig. 44–6. The spinneret for making rayon is made of non-tarnishing metal. The insert shows a white arrow pointing to the spinneret in place on the machine that makes rayon.

Fig. 44–5. Asbestos is a mineral fiber that will not burn.

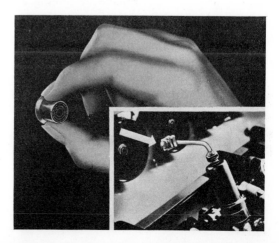

Bemberg rayon. Like viscose, it is a *regenerated cellulose,* that is, cellulose which was converted into a liquid, and then back into a solid again. Viscose and cuprammonium rayon lose considerable strength when wet. Perspiration and light gradually weaken them. They burn readily.

9. Cellulose acetate fiber. This type of fiber, formerly called acetate rayon, is made by treating cellulose with acetic acid, acetic anhydride, and sulfuric acid. When the reaction is complete, the batch is added to water. Cellulose acetate separates as solid, white flakes. The flakes are dissolved in acetone, a volatile organic liquid, to make a spinning liquid. A cellulose acetate filament is formed when the liquid is forced through a spinneret into a tube through which dry air circulates.

Cellulose acetate loses less strength when wet and is not injured by perspiration and light. A hot iron destroys cellulose acetate fabric because of its low decomposition temperature. Since cellulose acetate is also soluble in some organic solvents, certain dry cleaning fluids will dissolve it.

10. Nylon is a versatile synthetic fiber. *Nylon* is made by a series of complex reactions using coal, air, and water as basic raw materials. It is a strong, elastic fiber that is made by forcing a melted solid through a spinneret. From the basic raw materials, two complex compounds, *adipic acid* and *hexamethylene diamine* are produced. Combina-

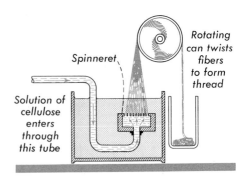

Fig. 44–7. As the cellulose solution flows through the spinneret holes into the dilute acid, it changes to solid threads.

tion of these chemicals forms a solid called *nylon salt.* The molecules of nylon salt polymerize to form giant molecules. The polymerized nylon salt is melted and forced through a spinneret. The filaments are stretched to about four times their original length, thus increasing the strength and elasticity of the finished product. The elasticity of nylon has made it a popular fiber for use in hosiery.

Nylon is lustrous, very strong, wears well, shrinks little, can be washed easily, and is not injured by water or dry cleaning solvents. Mildew and clothes moths do not affect it. The melted nylon salt can be colored before spinning, or the finished yarn can be dyed. Thus nylon can appear in a variety of attractive colors.

11. Other synthetic fibers. Many other synthetic fibers are being used today. Each of them has some special property or use to recommend it. *Acrilan,*

Fig. 44–8. In one process of rayon manufacture, cotton fibers (left) are converted into a syrupy liquid called viscose (center). The viscose solution is converted into threads of rayon (right) by passing it through spinnerets.

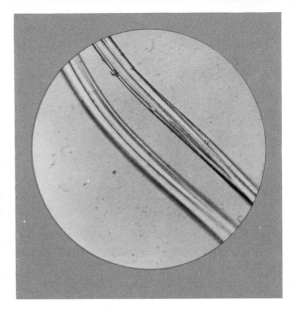

Fig. 44–9. Rayon fibers as they appear under a microscope.

Orlon, and *Dynel* are fibers which are made from acrylonitrile. Acrilan is used to make synthetic furs. Orlon yarn is knitted into fine sweaters. Dynel is good for suits; it withstands rain well. *Dacron* is a polyester fiber used for curtains. Blended with long-fiber Egyptian cotton, it makes a quick-drying fabric for shirts, blouses, and suits, that requires no ironing. *Vinyon* is made by polymerizing vinyl chloride and vinyl acetate. It withstands acids, water, and chemicals. *Velon* is a polymerized vinylidene chloride. It is not affected by

Fig. 44–10. This luxurious coat and pouch bag are made from a furlike fabric of Dynel and Orlon.

sun or perspiration. *Saran* is another vinylidene chloride textile that is strong and wears well. It is used for outdoor furniture. *Vicara* is made from zein, which comes from corn. Vicara is not strong but it is a fiber which can be blended easily.

Recently four new fibers, called *Darlan, Verel, Zefran,* and *Creslan,* entered the field. Further research promises more useful synthetic fibers.

Fig. 44–11. Ropes of Dacron polyester fiber greatly outlast ordinary ropes in towing operations.

3. BLEACHING AND DYEING

12. The common bleaching agents. Natural fibers are commonly bleached when white yarn or white fabrics are desired. Vegetable fibers, such as cotton and linen have long been bleached with sunlight. Sunlight bleaches so slowly that we use chemicals more often today. Chlorine and hydrogen peroxide are used for bleaching vegetable fibers. Sulfur dioxide, hydrogen peroxide, and sodium "perborate," actually sodium peroxyborate, $NaBO_2 \cdot 3 H_2O \cdot H_2O_2$, are used for bleaching animal fibers.

13. The bleaching of cotton. Chlorine bleaches cotton *indirectly,* because it is the oxygen set free from the solution that actually decolorizes the cloth. Several methods for utilizing chlorine for bleaching are in use: *1.* chlorine gas may be dissolved in water; *2.* a solution of sodium hypochlorite, like *Clorox* for example, is prepared by dissolving chlorine in sodium carbonate solution; *3.* H.T.H. (high test hypochlorite), a triple salt of sodium hypochlorite, calcium hypochlorite, and sodium chloride may be used; or *4.* a new heavy-duty dry bleach, *Halane,* may be dissolved in water to produce a solution of sodium hypochlorite. Hydrogen peroxide is being used in increasing amounts for industrial bleaching of cotton, now that a cheaper method of producing hydrogen peroxide by electrolysis is available.

14. The bleaching of wool and silk. Wool and silk are animal fibers that are destroyed by chlorine. Hence other chemicals must be used to bleach them. Sulfur dioxide gas has long been used as the bleaching agent, but it does not give permanent results because the fibers regain their color slowly when exposed to air. Hydrogen peroxide is now favored for bleaching these textiles.

New powdered bleaches containing sodium "perborate" may also be used for bleaching silk and wool, as well as rayon, nylon, and other synthetic fibers. The mild bleaching action of the oxygen released by sodium "perborate" in water whitens the fabric without chemically injuring it.

15. Optical bleaches make cloth appear whiter. Some manufacturers of detergents include an optical bleach in their product. Optical bleaches are also used by those who weave cloth from various synthetic fibers. An ***optical bleach*** is a substance which remains in the cloth after washing or rinsing and replaces the blue light waves which are absorbed by the cloth. Optical bleaches have the property of absorbing ultraviolet light from sunlight and converting it into visible blue light. The restoration of this blue light in the light reflected from white cloth makes it appear whiter, as though it had been more thoroughly bleached.

Fig. 44–12. A commercial method of bleaching cotton goods.

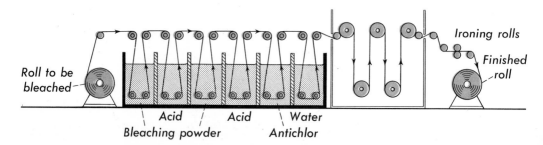

Roll to be bleached

Acid   Acid   Water

Bleaching powder   Antichlor

Ironing rolls

Finished roll

16. Dyes are produced from coal tar. Formerly, dyers used extracts from leaves, roots, berries, and barks for dyeing cloth. A few animal products and some mineral compounds were also used. Good dyes were expensive and the variety of colors limited. The accidental discovery of synthetic *mauve* in 1856 by William H. Perkin (1838–1907) began a new industry, the manufacture of coal tar dyes. *There are no dyes in coal tar.* But when coal tar is fractionally distilled, benzene, naphthalene, and anthracene are separated from the black, sticky liquid. These serve as raw materials for the preparation of more complex materials called **intermediates.** From the intermediates, by a series of complex reactions, still more complex compounds are produced which have brilliant colors. These colored substances are often called **coal tar dyes** because coal tar furnishes the basic raw materials. All of the dyes have a complex structure and a long chemical name. Whether a complex organic compound will be a bright dye or a colorless compound seems to depend on the presence of certain groups called **chromophors.** One of the common chromophors is the *azo group* ($-N=N-$). The molecules of many dyes contain this group. For example, the structural formula of methyl orange, a dye which is often used as an indicator, is given below:

$$Na-O-\overset{\displaystyle O}{\underset{\displaystyle O}{\overset{\|}{\underset{\|}{S}}}}-\underset{}{\bigcirc}-N=N-\underset{}{\bigcirc}-N\overset{\displaystyle CH_3}{\underset{\displaystyle CH_3}{}}$$

Fig. 44–13. A large roll of cotton cloth being printed with a dye.

You will notice the presence of the azo group in the formula above. The chemical name for methyl orange is *sodium dimethylaminoazobenzene sulfonate.* This name and formula are given merely to show the complexity of composition of coal tar dyes and need not be memorized. Other dyes have similarly complex structures.

17. Several classes of dyes are used. There are hundreds of different dyes in common use. Some are adapted for wool and silk, others are used for cotton and linen. Special dyes are used for acetate. In general, the animal fibers are easier to dye than the vegetable fibers. Some of the common classes of dyes are the following.

1. Direct dyes. Direct dyes can be used for all the natural fibers. The fabric is immersed in a solution of the dye and allowed to simmer until the dye has been absorbed.

2. Acid dyes. Acid dyes are the alkaline salts of complex color acids. They give bright, fast colors with wool and

silk but will not cling to cotton and linen. Acid dyes will not fade in light. But fabrics that have been dyed with acid colors must not be washed with alkali because the dye will be removed as the alkali reacts with the color acid.

3. Mordant dyes. Mordant dyes are those which require a preparatory chemical to make the dye cling to cotton and linen. There are different groups of mordant dyes. One such group is the *basic dyes.* Methyl violet, methylene blue, fuchsine, and malachite green are well-known basic dyes.

To dye cotton with one of these dyes, the cloth is first soaked in a solution of aluminum sulfate. Then the cloth is dipped in ammonia water without rinsing. The sticky precipitate of aluminum hydroxide is the **mordant** that fills the flattened tubes of the cotton fibers. The cloth is then immersed in the dye bath. The basic dye unites with the mordant held by the fiber, coloring it with a bright, fast color. Salts of iron, chromium, and tin are used in the same manner as aluminum sulfate. By using different chemical compounds with the same dye, it is often possible to get a variety of shades of color.

4. Vat dyes. Indigo is a good example of a vat dye. In the presence of a reducing agent, indigo white is produced. It is soluble in alkalies. When cotton is saturated with indigo white solution, and then exposed to air, oxidation takes place. The indigo white changes to *insoluble indigo blue,* which is firmly deposited within the fibers. It is a very fast (permanent) dye which is popular for overalls because it is fast to light and washing. It is also used to dye wool yarn for men's suits. Many other vat dyes are in use.

4. PAPER

18. Paper is a fibrous material. Paper is a fibrous material that is made from cellulose. The principal raw materials are wood pulp and the fibers of cotton and linen. To make paper, the individual fibers are separated by chipping, shredding, and beating the raw material. Bleaching is usually necessary when making white paper. The fibers are mixed with a great deal of water to make a thin suspension called "soup" by the papermaker. This soup is forced through a thin slit in the bottom of the stock box onto a moving wire screen. As the water drains through the wire screen, the fibers become tangled together to form a fibrous sheet. The fibrous sheet then passes over rollers that squeeze out the excess water and iron the surface to a smooth finish. Finely-divided materials are added to the paper stock in the beater, a machine that disintegrates the cellulose into fibers. These materials add weight and body to the paper, and prevent ink from running. The surface of some paper is coated with casein or gelatin to add gloss to the sheets.

19. What is mechanical pulp? *Pulp* is the name given to the crude sheets of tangled fibers first produced from logs of poplar, spruce, or certain kinds of pine. Wood contains *lignin,* a nitrogenous compound, in addition to cellulose. If the wood is merely ground to fibers, and formed into sheets, the product is called **mechanical pulp.** Newspapers are printed on bleached mechanical pulp because it is cheap and can be produced in quantity.

20. What is chemical pulp? *Chemical pulp* is also made from wood, but the wood chips are *digested,* or boiled under pressure, with a chemical solution to remove the lignin. Three processes for making chemical pulp are in use at the present time.

1. Sulfite process. The wood chips are digested with a solution of calcium hydrogen sulfite, $Ca(HSO_3)_2$, and sulfur dioxide, SO_2, in large boilers under pressure. After digestion, the fibrous mass is bleached with chlorine to make white stock. Sulfite pulp is of good quality and is the principal component of book paper and the white paper used in schools.

2. Soda process. Poplar logs are commonly converted into pulp by the soda process. The chips are digested with a solution of sodium hydroxide to get rid of the lignin. The digested material is bleached with chlorine, as in the sulfite process.

3. Sulfate process. The sulfate process produces "Kraft" paper from southern pine trees. The chips are digested with sodium sulfate and sodium hydroxide. The resin and lignin are removed by the digesting operation.

21. What is the difference between pulp and paper? *Pulp* is the crude, fibrous material obtained from wood, and formed into sheets. *Paper* is a refined product made by blending different kinds of pulp, adding weighting chemicals, and again forming into sheets. Most paper is also given a surface coating so that it will take ink better.

22. What is rag paper? Cotton and linen rags make paper of the highest quality. The rags are disintegrated into fibers in a *beater.* The beater is an elliptical-shaped tank that is fitted with revolving knives that tear the fibers apart. The rag stock is mixed with a

Fig. 44-14. Poplar, spruce, and certain kinds of pine are the source of most of our ordinary paper.

great deal of water, and circulates around and around through the beater, passing through the knives at each revolution. Finely-divided barium sulfate, calcium carbonate, and other powders are added to the stock in the beater as weighting agents. After the stock has been completely disintegrated in the beater, it is transferred to the stock box, and passes through the papermaking machine. The papermaking, or *Four-drinier* (for-*drin*-ih-ay) , *machine* converts the stock into sheets.

Fig. 44-15. In this beater, wood pulp is separated into individual fibers for papermaking.

Fig. 44–16. This huge paper-making machine produces a sheet of paper 20 feet wide at the rate of 2000 feet per minute.

Paper that contains no other fibers than those from cotton and linen is called 100% rag content. It is the most expensive paper and is used for important documents. Rag paper will stand folding and creasing many times without breaking. It does not become brittle, even after many years. United States paper money is printed on rag paper that has a few colored fibers of silk or nylon scattered through it to prevent counterfeiting. By mixing rag stock with different percentages of wood pulp, many different qualities of paper are made for particular purposes.

23. Cellophane is regenerated cellulose. *Cellophane* is not paper because it is not a sheet of tangled fibers. It is made from cotton linters by a process similar to that for making viscose rayon. The viscose solution, however, instead of being extruded through a spinneret to form fibers, is extruded through a narrow slit in the bottom of the stock box. The viscose is solidified into transparent sheets by passage through an acid bath. It may be waterproofed with transparent lacquer.

Cellulose acetate in sheet form is used for photographic film and for "safety" motion picture film.

Saran is also produced in sheet form for covering foods and other materials with a self-sealing, airtight wrapper.

Still other transparent wrapping materials are described in the next chapter.

Fig. 44–17. Cellophane and other transparent plastic materials are used widely in packaging fresh foods for market.

Summary

Cotton is the most important fiber. It is nearly pure cellulose. Alkalies do not injure cotton, but acids react with it readily. Linen is the fiber of permanence. It is also cellulose and is derived from the flax plant. Linen absorbs moisture faster than other fibers. Wool is the fiber for warmth. It is a protein which has a scaly appearance under the microscope. Alkalies damage wool. Silk is the luxury fiber, composed of two proteins. It forms strong fibers.

Asbestos is a mineral fiber obtained from a silicate rock. It is fireproof. Glass wool makes an excellent, fireproof heat insulator. It is sometimes woven into glass cloth.

Synthetic fibers are made by forcing a suitable liquid through tiny holes in a metal plate called a spinneret. Rayon, regenerated cellulose, is made from cellulose by two different processes in the United States: *1.* viscose process; and *2.* cuprammonium process. Cellulose acetate is made by treating cellulose with acetic acid, acetic anhydride, and sulfuric acid. Nylon is a versatile synthetic fiber. There are many other synthetic fibers being produced today.

Sunlight, chlorine, and hydrogen peroxide are used for bleaching cotton and linen. Sulfur dioxide, hydrogen peroxide, and sodium peroxyborate are used for bleaching animal fibers.

Dyes were formerly derived from plant sources but today they are synthesized as complex organic chemicals. Cotton and linen require dyes that are different from those used to dye wool and silk. Some dyes are made fast to the cloth with the aid of mordants.

Paper is a fibrous material that is made from wood pulp or the fibers of cotton and linen. Mechanical pulp is made from wood, ground to fibers. Chemical pulp is digested with chemicals to remove the lignin from the wood chips. Rag paper is the strongest, most lasting, and the most expensive paper. Cellophane is regenerated cellulose.

Test yourself on these terms

asbestos	dye intermediate	paper
bleaching	glass wool	pulp
cellophane	linen	rayon
cellulose acetate	mechanical pulp	silk
chemical pulp	mercerizing	spinnerets
chromophor	mordant	textile
cotton	nylon	weighting
dye	optical bleach	wool

Questions

Group A

1. What are the four sources of textile fibers?
2. (*a*) How is cotton mercerized? (*b*) How does this improve the cotton?
3. Why is linen the fiber preferred for dish towels?

4. Why are winter suits and overcoats made of wool?
5. What is the difference between *virgin wool, reprocessed wool,* and *shoddy?*
6. How do linen and cotton differ in composition from silk and wool?
7. What are the uses for glass wool?
8. What is the raw material used for making rayon?
9. Why are nylon filaments stretched after being formed?
10. Which synthetic fiber is used for making synthetic furs?
11. Of which synthetic fiber is the seating material of outdoor furniture commonly made?
12. Why do we call certain dyes *coal tar dyes?*
13. What are the main classes of dyes?
14. What is the difference between pulp and paper?
15. How is newsprint made?
16. What is the difference between viscose rayon fiber and cellophane?

Group B

17. What are the physical and chemical properties of cotton?
18. What would be likely to happen if a wool sweater were washed with laundry soap?
19. Why is asbestos fireproof?
20. How are all of the synthetic fibers formed?
21. What chemical is now being used to bleach all the natural fibers?
22. What types of fibers can be successfully bleached with sodium "perborate"?
23. How do "optical bleaches" make white cloth appear whiter?
24. What is the function of a mordant in dyeing?
25. What are the three kinds of chemical pulp?
26. What is the appearance under the microscope of: (*a*) a cotton fiber; (*b*) a linen fiber; (*c*) a wool fiber; (*d*) a silk fiber; (*e*) a rayon fiber?
27. Describe the chemical changes which occur during the viscose process for making rayon.
28. How does cellulose acetate fiber differ from rayon?
29. Why do we say that chlorine bleaches cotton *indirectly?*
30. What is H.T.H.?
31. What is meant by a chromophor in a dye molecule?

Some things for you to do

1. Unravel threads of cotton, linen, silk, wool, rayon, and nylon so that they are separated into individual fibers. Examine each kind separately under a compound microscope. Make a sketch of each fiber.
2. Procure a sample of cloth that is about half wool and half cotton. Gently boil a two-inch square of the cloth for 5 minutes in 5% solution of sodium hydroxide. The wool will dissolve completely, leaving the cotton. Examine the rinsed, dried residue of cotton.
3. Pluck apart the silky fibers from a piece of asbestos rock. Twist some of the fibers into a thread. See if it will burn.
4. Examine the labels of the powdered bleaches on your grocer's shelves to learn the active bleaching ingredient in each.

Chapter 45

RUBBER

AND PLASTICS

1. RUBBER

1. What is rubber? *Rubber* is a plastic hydrocarbon that is obtained from the sap of rubber trees. A milky fluid, called *latex,* drips from V-shaped gashes in the trunks. Latex contains about 35% rubber in colloidal suspension. When acetic acid is added to latex, the rubber *coagulates,* or gathers into a mass. After being washed and dried, it is shipped to market in large sheets.

The simplest formula for rubber is $(C_5H_8)_x$. The C_5H_8 unit is presumed to have this structure:

The "x" is believed to be a large number. Consequently, rubber molecules are giants when compared with many simpler molecules. In this instance, the C_5H_8 is called a *monomer* (single part). When many monomers join, the giant molecule is called a *polymer* (many parts). Rubber is thus a polymer of C_5H_8. The monomers in rubber are joined in a zigzag chain that accounts for its elasticity.

2. The compounding of rubber. Raw rubber is mixed with a number of powdered solids between heavy rollers in a powerful machine called a *mill.* The rubber, sulfur, and other powders forming the batch are squeezed through the rollers over and over again until they are thoroughly mixed. The formula for the batch varies according to the products to be made. Sulfur is

VOCABULARY

Monomer. A simple molecule, or single unit of a polymer.

Plastic. A natural or synthetic material which can be shaped while soft into a required form and then hardened to produce a durable finished article.

Polymer. A compound formed by two or more simpler molecules or radicals.

Vulcanization. The heating of rubber with other materials to improve its properties.

Fig. 45-1. This rubber mill softens rubber compound in preparation for its use in tire manufacture.

smaller in white sidewall tires, the sidewalls are inferior in quality when compared to black tires, even though they are more expensive. Zinc oxide is added to many batches and produces white rubber. Diantimony trisulfide yields a red rubber. Organic catalysts, known as *accelerators,* are added to speed the vulcanization process. *Anti-oxidants* are also organic chemicals that prevent the rubber from becoming hard and brittle. A certain percentage of rubber that has been reclaimed from old automobile tires is usually added to the batch. Very cheap rubber goods may have various fillers, such as whiting or clay, added. After mixing, the product is shaped either in a mold or from thin sheets. The whole mass is then vulcanized. *Vulcanization is the heating of the rubber mixture to a definite temperature for a definite time.* It gives the article a permanent shape, makes it more elastic, and causes it to lose its sticky qualities. The changes which occur during vulcanization are many and complex. It is believed, however, that the sulfur atoms form cross-linkages between adjacent rubber molecules.

always one of the many ingredients used in making rubber. Automobile tires contain considerable amounts of carbon black. This increases the wearing qualities of the tires by forming bonds between the rubber molecules. Because the amount of carbon black is

Foam rubber is used as an upholstery material for cushions and mattresses. One process for making foam rubber is to mix ammonium carbonate with the batch in the mill. The heat of vulcanization forms bubbles of ammonia, carbon dioxide, and water vapor within the rubber. In another process, air is whipped into latex in a mixing ma-

Fig. 45-2. Tires are vulcanized in "watchcase" molds. Here a worker removes a vulcanized tire from its mold.

Fig. 45-3. Foam rubber cushion being removed from its vulcanizing mold.

chine. The enclosed air expands during vulcanization, forming bubbles within the foam rubber.

3. Thiokol, the first commercial synthetic rubber. Thiokol was developed in the late 1920's by J. C. Patrick, who discovered it while experimenting to find a cheaper antifreeze solution. It is made from 1,2-dichloroethane, $ClCH_2CH_2Cl$, and sodium polysulfide, Na_2S_x. It is vulcanized by using zinc oxide. The structural unit of Thiokol is:

$$-S-S-\underset{\underset{\displaystyle H}{|}}{\overset{\overset{\displaystyle H}{|}}{C}}-\underset{\underset{\displaystyle H}{|}}{\overset{\overset{\displaystyle H}{|}}{C}}-S-S-$$

Thiokol does not swell, rot, or change its physical properties when in contact with gasoline, chemicals, or air.

It remains firm and rubbery over a wide temperature range. Thiokol is used for lining fuel and paint spray hose, for printing rollers, and as a sealant in airplane wing fuel tanks. When Thiokol is mixed with an oxidizing agent, it produces a solid fuel which is used in rockets and guided missiles.

4. Neoprene, a hydrocarbon synthetic rubber. Scientists produced hydrocarbon synthetic rubber about 1910 by polymerizing isoprene, C_5H_8. However, the cost was too high to compete with natural rubber from plantations in the East Indies. In 1931 *neoprene,* a

Fig. 45-4. The La Crosse, an Army surface-to-surface guided missile, burns a fuel containing Thiokol.

successful hydrocarbon synthetic rubber, appeared on the market. The research work of Dr. J. A. Nieuwland of the University of Notre Dame made neoprene possible. Acetylene is converted into vinyl acetylene using copper salts as catalysts.

$$H-C\equiv C-H \xrightarrow{\text{catalyst}} \begin{matrix} H & H \\ | & | \\ C=C-C\equiv C-H \\ | \\ H \end{matrix}$$

acetylene   vinyl acetylene

When treated with hydrochloric acid, vinyl acetylene yields chloroprene:

$$\begin{matrix} H & H \\ | & | \\ C=C-C\equiv C-H \\ | \\ H \end{matrix} + HCl \longrightarrow \begin{matrix} H & H & H \\ | & | & | \\ C=C-C=C \\ | & | & | \\ H & Cl & H \end{matrix}$$

vinyl acetylene   chloroprene

The catalytic polymerization of chloroprene yields neoprene. The structural unit of neoprene is:

$$\begin{matrix} H & Cl & H & Cl & H & H \\ | & | & | & | & | & | \\ -C-C-C-C=C-C- \\ | & | & | & | \\ H & | & H & H \\ & C-H \\ & || \\ & H-C-H \end{matrix}$$

Oils and greases, which act on natural rubber, causing it to swell and rot, have little effect on neoprene. Hence this synthetic material is used for gasoline hoses at filling stations.

5. GR–S, the synthetic for tires. *GR–S* (Government Rubber-Styrene), formerly called *Buna S,* is used for making automobile tires. It is made by churning *butadiene* and *styrene* together in soapy water. Butadiene,

$$\begin{matrix} H & H & H & H \\ | & | & | & | \\ C=C-C=C \\ | & & & | \\ H & & & H \end{matrix}$$

is made by cracking petroleum, or it can be made from alcohol. Styrene,

$$\bigcirc\!\!-\!\!\begin{matrix} H & H \\ | & | \\ C=C \\ | \\ H \end{matrix}$$

is made from benzene, or it can also be made from petroleum. Churning in soapy water at 41° F, using cumene hydroperoxide as a catalyst, causes the chemicals to polymerize to form *GR–S* rubber. The addition of an acid causes

Fig. 45–6. This picture diagram shows the relative amounts of the raw materials used to produce GR–S synthetic rubber. The nine ingredients at the left form a milklike latex after about 12 hours in the steel pressure kettle. The finished rubber at the right is produced after the removal of water from the latex by coagulation and drying. GR–S rubber is composed only of butadiene and styrene. The other ingredients serve to regulate and accelerate the chemical changes.

the rubber to separate in curd-like masses, which are washed and dried. The structural unit of *GR–S* is:

$$-C-C-C-C=C-C-C-C-C-C=C-C-$$

GR–S is a good all-purpose synthetic rubber. It can be used in place of natural rubber for most purposes. *GR–S* is excellent for tire treads because it resists wear better than other synthetic rubbers. More than three-quarters of a million tons have been produced in one year in synthetic rubber factories in the United States.

6. Other synthetic rubbers. *GR–I,* or butyl rubber, is made from *isobutylene* and *isoprene.* These materials react at −140° F with aluminum chloride

used as a catalyst. *GR–I* holds air better than natural rubber and is used for inner tubes. It also resists the action of ozone and many other chemicals.

Nitrile rubber is produced from acrylonitrile and butadiene. While produced in much smaller quantities than *GR–S* and *GR–I,* nitrile rubber is important because it does not swell on contact with oils and greases.

Silicone rubber has the remarkable property of being usable over the wide temperature range of −130° F to +500° F. The long-chain molecules of silicone rubber consist of alternate silicon and oxygen atoms, with some carbon groups as side chains. This rubber is colorless and not readily affected by solvents.

Hypalon synthetic rubber is produced by reacting polyethylene with chlorine and sulfur dioxide. Hypalon can be colored in an unlimited range of colors which do not fade. It has high resistance to weather and chemicals.

Just recently a process has been developed for producing a synthetic rubber of the same composition as natural rubber. The process involves polymerization of isoprene at 104° F using finely-divided lithium as a catalyst. Production of this rubber, called *Coral* rubber, is to begin shortly.

2. PLASTICS

7. What are plastics? The term plastics was originally applied to those substances that could be formed or shaped by molding. In its broadest meaning, it includes such diverse materials as glass, steel, rubber, and rosin, as well as the familiar celluloid and Bakelite. A more limited meaning has come into general use, so that we usually understand plastics to be hard, gummy solids. Chemists think of plastics as *synthetic resins,* as distinguished from such natural resins as rosin and shellac. Plastics may be made from the raw materials of nature, or from synthetic chemicals. The number of different plastics that can be produced seems to be limitless, as well as the different useful products which we can make from them.

8. There are two types of synthetic plastics. Synthetic plastics may be divided into two groups, *thermoplastic* and *thermosetting.* Those which are *thermoplastic* may be softened and changed in shape by gentle heating. Plastic eyeglass frames are thermoplastic. By careful heating, the optician adjusts the length of the bows to fit the wearer. The **thermosetting plastics,** once heated, set into a hard mass which cannot be softened. Bakelite is a good example of a thermosetting plastic. Radio cabinets and the outer cases of telephone sets are made from thermosetting plastics and cannot be changed in shape after they are formed.

The nature of the reaction that produces the plastic seems to be the factor that determines whether a plastic will be thermoplastic or thermosetting. Thermoplastic resins are polymerization products. That is, molecules join other similar molecules to form a large cluster. Lucite and Krene are two thermoplastic materials. Thermosetting plastics are produced by condensation reactions. When the two chemicals used to form them unite, water is set free. For example, when phenol and formal-

Fig. 45–7. Protective coatings of Hypalon add long life and sparkling color to wood, metal, rubber, and fabrics.

dehyde solution are heated together, water and Bakelite resin are produced.

9. Properties determine the uses for individual plastics. The uses for a particular plastic depend on its properties. Such properties as resistance to acids, bases, water, oils, and organic solvents have been carefully determined and catalogued for each of the commercial plastics. Combustibility, electrical insulating properties, hardness, resistance to scratching, strength, toughness, ease of machining, and solubility in oils are other important properties.

Phenolic plastics are excellent insulators and are used for making parts of electrical appliances. Polystyrene plastics are not affected by water and are used for bathroom tiles. Urea-formaldehyde plastics are hard and tough. They are used for making the cases of computing scales which must withstand hard knocks. Methyl methacrylate plastics are transparent, adapting them for lenses or full-view airplane nosepieces. Polyethylene is semiflexible and resists the action of water and many other liquids. Consequently, it is used for nonbreakable containers for these liquids. Plastics which are soluble in oils can be used to make enamel paints. A plastic that may be excellent for one purpose may be entirely unfitted for another. Hence the study of the properties of plastics is very important in this industry.

10. What do we make from plastics? Plastics may appear on the market in the form of sheets, rods, or blocks, from which various objects can be fabricated. Thermosetting plastics are sold by the manufacturers in the form of "molding powders." Wood flour or asbestos may be mixed with the plastic material as a filler. A weighed quantity of molding

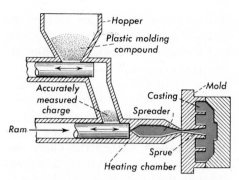

Fig. 45-8. This diagram shows how plastic articles are manufactured by injection molding.

powder is placed between two heated dies in a powerful hydraulic press. Under the influence of heat and pressure, the molding powder is converted into a plastic that takes the shape of the die. After a short time interval that varies according to the thickness of the piece, the press opens and the finished article pops out. Radio cabinets and small kitchen articles are made in this manner. The material that composes the molding powder undergoes polymerization during the heating process.

Thermosetting plastics are used to make many laminated articles. *Laminated* means built up in layers or plates. Sheets of cotton cloth or paper are dipped in Bakelite varnish, and then piled one on top of another until the desired thickness is secured. When the pile is placed in a hydraulic press, and heat and pressure are applied, a hard plastic sheet is the result. Laminated plastics are used for making gears, electric distribution panels, and such articles as airplane propellers.

Plasticizers are sometimes mixed with the plastic substance to make it easier to work, or to increase the hardness of the final product. Camphor and castor oil have long been used as plasticizers. *Lubricants* such as wax or stearic acid are sometimes added to free the plastic from the mold easily. *Accelerators* like calcium oxide, zinc chloride, and oxalic acid are used to speed up the polymerization process. Coloring materials may be added so as to produce any desired shade in the finished product.

11. What are some well-known synthetic plastics? Among the many synthetic plastics, the following are probably familiar to all of us.

1. Cellulose nitrate. Cellulose nitrate is made by the reaction between cotton and nitric acid. Sulfuric acid is mixed with the nitric acid to absorb the water produced in the reaction. The nitrated cotton is dissolved in a mixture of alcohol and ether. When the solvent evaporates, a jelly-like mass is left. *Celluloid* is a cellulose nitrate plastic to which camphor has been added to serve as a plasticizer. First produced in 1869, it is the oldest of the synthetic plastics. Celluloid burns with a flash, a disadvantage that limits its uses.

2. Phenolic plastics. When phenol is boiled with a solution of formaldehyde in the presence of a catalyst, a hard, gummy residue is produced. Bakelite is a thermosetting plastic produced in this manner. Cresol, C_7H_7OH, can be used instead of phenol, and other aldehydes can be used in place of formaldehyde. Thus a group of plastics can be made from these related chemicals. The phenolic plastics are incombustible and resist the action of chemicals and solvents well.

3. Urea-formaldehyde. Synthetic urea, $CO(NH_2)_2$, and formaldehyde heated together with a catalyst produce a plastic notable for its great strength. Articles made from this plastic include "unbreakable" dishes and water tumblers, besides buttons and novelties.

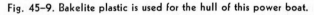

Fig. 45–9. Bakelite plastic is used for the hull of this power boat.

Fig. 45-10. Lucite acrylic resin globes are used in these street lighting fixtures. Notice how well the fluorescent lighting is dispersed to adequately illuminate the street.

4. Vinylite plastics. Krene resins are mixtures of polymers of vinyl chloride and vinyl acetate. Acetylene is the raw material used as the starting point in the manufacture of these plastics. Transparent belts and suspenders are made of this plastic, while the textile known as Vinyon has a similar composition. Vinylite phonograph records are now popular because they are nonbreakable. Therefore they are useful for children's records.

5. Polystyrene. Styrene, C_8H_8, was mentioned when we studied rubber, earlier in this chapter. Styrene is polymerized to form a plastic known as *polystyrene.* This plastic is unaffected by water, a property that adapts it for certain uses.

6. Methacrylates. One of the most popular of the plastics is the group known as the methacrylate resins. Acetylene is the raw material for making this group, just as it was for making Vinylite resins. Methyl methacrylate is the best known of the group. It is marketed under the names Lucite and Plexiglas. It is particularly notable for its clear transparency. It machines well and is strong and shatterproof. Some of the uses for the plastic are: lenses, toilet articles, fancy jewel boxes, costume jewelry, and, when colored pink, imitation gums in which false teeth are mounted to make dentures.

7. Polyethylene. Ethylene may be polymerized at high pressure, with a catalyst, to form a soft, semi-flexible plastic which is molded into bottles or produced in sheet form for making bags. Polyethylene bottles are the familiar "squeeze" bottles in which toiletries are marketed. Polyethylene bags are used by laundries for wrapping clean shirts, dresses, and blankets. These bags may also be used for packing new merchandise, such as shoes or purses.

8. Tetrafluorethylene. Ethylene, with

Fig. 45-11. Tetrafluorethylene plastic can be machined into small parts, such as these for electronic apparatus.

four fluorine atoms substituted for the hydrogen atoms, may also be polymerized to form a useful plastic. It may be produced in the form of fibers for making chemical-resistant fabrics, or as rods from which small parts may be machined. Tetrafluorethylene plastic has a very low coefficient of friction, and is used in applications where heat-resistant, nonlubricated moving parts are needed.

These examples of types of plastics which are being manufactured today are not to be considered as a complete list of all plastic materials available. In fact, it has been possible to give here only a few of the main types of plastics. However, enough have been listed to show that the new field of plastics is a large one and still growing. It is possible to make many types of plastics related to these we have discussed, by simply using slightly different, but related, chemical starting materials.

Summary

Latex is a milky fluid that is obtained from the sap of the rubber tree. When acetic acid is added to latex, the rubber, which is dispersed in the fluid, coagulates into a solid mass. Rubber is a polymer of a hydrocarbon whose simplest formula is C_5H_8. Rubber is compounded in a mill with sulfur and other powders. Carbon black added to the batch makes a rubber that wears well, especially for automobile tires. Zinc oxide is used for making white rubber, and diantimony trisulfide for red rubber. After mixing, the batch of raw rubber is formed into shape, and is then vulcanized by heating it to a definite temperature for a definite time.

Thiokol is the first commercial synthetic rubber. Thiokol is used for lining fuel and paint spray hoses, and as a sealant in airplane wing fuel tanks. Neoprene is a hydrocarbon synthetic rubber. It is used for gasoline hoses at filling stations. GR–S is a synthetic rubber used for tires.

Plastics are substances that can be formed by molding. They may be made from raw materials of nature, or from synthetic chemicals. Synthetic plastics may be divided into two classes, thermoplastic and thermosetting. The uses for individual plastics are determined by the set of properties that pertain to each. There are many different synthetic plastics, including the following: 1. cellulose nitrate; 2. phenolic plastics; 3. urea-formaldehyde; 4. vinylite; 5. polystyrene; 6. the methacrylates; 7. polyethylene; and 8. tetrafluorethylene.

Test yourself on these terms

accelerators	lubricant	polymerization
anti-oxidant	methacrylates	polystyrene
cellulose nitrate	monomer	tetrafluorethylene
coagulate	neoprene	thermoplastic
foam rubber	phenolic plastic	thermosetting
GR–I	plastic	Thiokol
GR–S	plasticizer	urea-formaldehyde
laminated	polyethylene	vinylite
latex	polymer	vulcanization

Questions

Group A

1. What is the difference between a monomer and a polymer?
2. What probably accounts for the elasticity of rubber?
3. How is rubber compounded?
4. What is *vulcanization?*
5. What property of Thiokol makes it useful in airplane wing fuel tanks?
6. What advantage does neoprene have over natural rubber?
7. What does the chemist usually mean by the term *plastics?*
8. What are some of the properties of a plastic that determine whether or not it is suitable for a particular purpose?
9. How are laminated articles made?
10. (*a*) What is celluloid? (*b*) What disadvantage does it have?

Group B

11. How is rubber coagulated from its colloidal suspension in latex?
12. Why are accelerators and anti-oxidants used in making rubber goods?
13. How may foam rubber be made?
14. (*a*) What materials are polymerized to produce *GR–S* rubber? (*b*) What is an important use for *GR–S* rubber? (*c*) Why is it used for this purpose?
15. (*a*) What is an important use for *GR–I* rubber? (*b*) Why is it used for this purpose?
16. What atoms comprise the long-chain molecules of silicone rubber?
17. What substances are included in the broadest meaning of *plastics?*
18. (*a*) What is the difference between a *thermoplastic* and a *thermosetting* plastic? (*b*) Give an example of each.
19. What do the following terms mean in the plastics industry: (*a*) *plasticizers;* (*b*) *accelerators;* (*c*) *lubricants;* (*d*) *pigments?*
20. Give an outstanding characteristic of each of the following plastics: (*a*) urea-formaldehyde; (*b*) phenolic; (*c*) polystyrene; (*d*) methacrylate; (*e*) vinylite; (*f*) polyethylene; (*g*) tetrafluorethylene.

Some things for you to do

1. Procure a blowout repair kit from an automobile supply store. The sheet rubber in the repair kit is unvulcanized stock. Note how sticky it is. Get an old inner tube and apply a patch, following the directions that come with the repair kit. Note how vulcanization of the sheet rubber is accomplished. Is the patch still sticky?
2. Test the difference between thermoplastic and thermosetting plastics under the influence of heat. An old pair of eyeglass frames will serve as a thermoplastic substance. Bakelite objects are thermosetting. Other plastic objects that are no longer useful may be used for the test. Immerse each in hot water in a beaker and observe which ones can be changed in shape by gentle heating.

Check your progress in chemistry

1. What factors should be considered in choosing a fuel?
2. What evidence do we have that coal was once vegetation?
3. What is bottled gas?
4. By what process is petroleum separated into the various useful products?
5. What are the substances used as standards in rating gasoline?
6. For what purpose is petroleum coke used?
7. Draw an electron-dot formula for an ethyl group.
8. By what two processes is ethanol made?
9. Write equations to show the preparation of formic acid from sodium hydroxide and carbon monoxide.
10. What kind of chemical reaction is utilized in the production of soap?
11. Why do linen garments crease and wrinkle easily?
12. For what purposes is glass cloth used?
13. What property of Dacron-cotton fabrics makes them useful for shirts and suits?
14. What fabrics may be dyed with acid dyes?
15. What is the empirical formula for the structural unit in natural rubber?
16. What is an important property of Hypalon synthetic rubber?
17. Of what type of plastic is Lucite or Plexiglas an example?

Challenging your knowledge

1. Why is it impossible to separate completely a mixture of methanol and ethanol by ordinary distillation?
2. Why are all the solutions from which synthetic fibers are prepared filtered so carefully?
3. How does the paper used for printing dollar bills differ from newspaper?

GLOSSARY

Absorption. A soaking up of one substance through the entire mass of another.

Accelerator. A substance that speeds up a chemical reaction by acting as a positive catalyst.

Acid. A substance containing hydrogen which yields hydrogen ions as the only positive ions in water solution; in the general sense, a proton donor.

Acid anhydride. (1) An oxide of a nonmetal which unites with water to form a solution which contains an acid. (2) A compound derived from an acid by the removal of water from the acid.

Activated. (1) Rendered more reactive. (2) Pertaining to an adsorbent, the surface of which has been freed of adsorbed gases.

Activation energy. See *energy, activation.*

Activity series. A table of metals or nonmetals arranged in order of descending activity.

Adsorbate. A material adsorbed on the surface of another.

Adsorbent. A material upon whose surface adsorption occurs.

Adsorption. The concentration of a gas, liquid, or solid on the surface of a solid or liquid.

Aeration. The process of mixing a substance, usually a liquid, with air or some other gas, so that the substance may dissolve or combine with it.

Aerosol. A suspensoid in which a gas is the dispersing medium.

Air conditioning. The system for regulating the temperature, humidity, and circulation of air, and for filtering out dust particles from the air.

Alcohol. A compound containing a hydrocarbon group and one or more —OH, hydroxyl, groups.

Aldehyde. A compound which has a hydrocarbon group and one or more —CHO groups.

Alkadiene. A straight or branched chain hydrocarbon with two double bonds between carbon atoms.

Alkane. A straight or branched chain hydrocarbon in which the carbon atoms are connected by only single covalent bonds; a member of the paraffin series.

Alkene. A straight or branched chain hydrocarbon in which two carbon atoms are connected by a double covalent bond; a member of the olefin series.

Alkylation. The combining of simple hydrocarbons with unsaturated hydrocarbons under the influence of heat, pressure, and catalysts.

Alkyne. A straight or branched chain hydrocarbon in which two carbon atoms are connected by a triple covalent bond; a member of the acetylene series.

Allotrope. One of the two or more different forms of an element.

Alloy. A material composed of two or more metals.

Alloy, anti-friction. An alloy which reduces friction.

Alloy, fusible. An alloy which has a low melting temperature.

Alluvial. Pertaining to soil, sand, or gravel deposited by running water.

Alnico. A strongly ferromagnetic alloy of iron, nickel, aluminum, and cobalt.

Alpha particle. Particle identical with a helium nucleus emitted from the nucleus of a radioactive element.

Alum. A double salt that is a sulfate of a monovalent and a trivalent metal.

Aluminothermy. A thermite or similar reaction.

Amalgam. An alloy of mercury with another metal or metals.

Amorphous. Without definite shape.

Amphiprotic. Capable of acting either as an acid or as a base.

Amphoteric. See *amphiprotic.*

Analysis. The separation of a material into its component parts to determine the composition.

Angstrom. A unit of linear measure; 1×10^{-8} cm.

Anhydrous. Without water of hydration.

Annealing. The process of heating a material to above a certain temperature and then slowly cooling it in order to decrease its hardness and brittleness.

Anode. A positively-charged electrode.

Antichlor. A substance used to remove traces of chlorine left in bleached goods.

Anti-friction alloy. See *alloy, anti-friction.*

Anti-oxidant. A substance which retards oxidation.

Aqua regia. A mixture of concentrated nitric and hydrochloric acids capable of reacting with gold.

Arc-type furnace. A furnace in which the heat is produced by an electric arc between carbon electrodes.

Aromatic hydrocarbon. See *hydrocarbon, aromatic.*

Atmosphere. The layer of gases which surrounds the earth.

Atom. The smallest particle of an element that can enter into combination with other elements.

Atomic bomb. An explosive device whose source of energy is a fission reaction.

Atomic mass. See *mass, atomic.*

Atomic number. The number of protons in the nucleus of an atom.

Atomic theory. See *theory, atomic.*

Atomic weight. See *weight, atomic.*

Avogadro number. The number of atoms in 1 gram-atom of an element; the number of molecules in 1 mole of a molecular substance; 6.0238×10^{23}.

Baking soda. Sodium hydrogen carbonate, $NaHCO_3$.

Barometer. An apparatus for measuring atmospheric pressure.

Base. A substance that combines with hydrogen ions; a proton acceptor.

Basic anhydride. An oxide of a metal which unites with water to form a solution which contains the basic hydroxide ions.

Beneficiation. Any process, physical or chemical, which renders an ore more suitable for reduction.

Bessemer converter. An egg-shaped furnace in which iron is converted into steel by burning out impurities with a blast of air.

Beta particle. Particle identical with an electron emitted from the nucleus of a radioactive element.

Betatron. A device for accelerating electrons.

Binary. Pertaining to compounds made up of two elements.

Binary compound. See *compound, binary.*

Binding energy. See *energy, binding.*

Biocolloid. A lyophilic colloidal system existing within plant and animal organisms.

Blast furnace. A tall cylindrical chamber in which iron oxide is reduced using coke, limestone, and a blast of hot air.

Bleaching. The operation by which color is partially or wholly removed from a colored material.

Blister copper. Crude copper as produced in a reverberatory furnace.

Block tin. Solid tin, as distinguished from tin plate.

Borazon. A crystalline form of boron nitride, equal in hardness to a diamond.

Brass. An alloy of copper and zinc.

Breeder reactor. A nuclear reactor used for making fissionable material.

British thermal unit. The amount of heat needed to raise the temperature of one pound of water one Fahrenheit degree.

Bronze. An alloy of copper and tin.

Brownian movement. The haphazard motion of colloidally dispersed particles as a result of collisions with the molecules of the dispersing medium.

Buffer. A substance which, when added to a solution, causes a resistance to any change in pH.

Buffered solution. See *solution, buffered.*

Calcine. A partially roasted copper ore.

Calorie. The amount of heat needed to raise the temperature of one gram of water one Centigrade degree.

Calorimeter. An apparatus for measuring quantities of heat.

Carboloy. An extremely hard alloy of cobalt and tungsten carbide.

Carboniferous Age. A geological period in which plants grew luxuriantly.

Carbonyl group. The $\text{\textgreater}CO$ group.

Carboxyl group. The $-COOH$ group.

Carburetor. The second or middle chamber of a water gas apparatus in which the gas is often enriched by spraying in oil or by adding propane.

Carrier. A substance used to transfer an element or radical from one material to another.

Carrier catalyst. See *catalyst, carrier.*

Casing-head gasoline. A volatile liquid, containing hydrocarbons other than methane, formed when natural gas is cooled and compressed.

Catalyst. An agent which influences the rate of a chemical action without itself being permanently altered.

Catalyst, carrier. A catalytic agent which influences the speed of a reaction by forming an intermediate compound with one of the reactants.

Catalyst, contact. A catalytic agent which influences the speed of a reaction by altering the contact efficiency between the molecules of the reactants.

Catalyst, negative. A catalyst which decreases the rate of a chemical reaction.

Catalyst, positive. A catalyst which increases the rate of a chemical reaction.

Catalytic agent. See *catalyst.*

Catalytic cracking. See *cracking, catalytic.*

Catalytic poison. A specific material which when preferentially adsorbed on the surface of a contact catalyst retards or stops the catalytic action.

Cathode. A negatively charged electrode.

Caustic. (*1*) Capable of converting some types of animal and vegetable matter into soluble materials by chemical action. (*2*) A substance with such properties.

Celsius scale. The Centigrade thermometer scale.

Cement. A mixture made from limestone and clay which, after mixing with water, sets to a hard mass.

Centi-. Metric prefix meaning 0.01.

Centigrade temperature. Temperature on the Centigrade scale which has the two fixed points as 0° and 100°.

Chain reaction. A reaction in which the material or energy which initiates the reaction is also one of the products.

Chamber process. A process for making sulfuric acid in large lead chambers, using oxides of nitrogen to promote the necessary reactions.

Checkerwork. Loosely stacked firebricks in a chamber, providing a circuitous passage for fuel gas or air.

Chemical bond. The linkage between atoms produced by transfer or sharing of electrons.

Chemical change. A change in which new substances with new properties are formed.

Chemical equation. An expression which shows, by the use of symbols and formulas, the changes in arrangement of the atoms which occur during a chemical reaction.

Chemical equilibrium. See *equilibrium, chemical*.

Chemical formula. See *formula, chemical*.

Chemical properties. Those properties which pertain to the behavior of a material in changes in which its identity is altered.

Chemical symbol. Either a single capital letter, or a capital letter and a small letter used together, as an abbreviation for (*1*) an element; (*2*) an atom of an element; (*3*) a gram-atom of an element.

Chemistry. The science dealing with the composition of substances and the changes in composition which these substances undergo.

Chemistry, organic. The study of carbon compounds.

Chlorination. The addition of chlorine to a material.

Chromophor. An atom or group of atoms in a molecule which is believed to be responsible for the color of many organic dyes.

Coagulate. To form into a compact mass.

Coal gas. A fuel gas obtained by the destructive distillation of bituminous coal.

Coke. The residue from the destructive distillation of bituminous coal.

Colloidal state. A state of subdivision of matter ranging between the dimensions of ordinary molecules and microscopic particles.

Colloidal suspension. A two-phase system having dispersed particles suspended in a dispersing medium.

Combustion. Any chemical action which occurs so rapidly that both noticeable heat and light are produced.

Combustion, spontaneous. A combustion started by the accumulation of heat from slow oxidation.

Common-ion effect. The shift in equilibrium which occurs when a substance is added to a solution of a second substance with which it has a common ion, the volume being kept constant.

Composition reaction. A chemical reaction in which two or more substances combine to form a more complex substance.

Compound. A substance which may be decomposed into two or more simpler substances by ordinary chemical means.

Compound, binary. A compound consisting of only two elements.

Compound, stable. A compound that does not decompose easily.

Compound, unstable. A compound that decomposes easily.

Concentrated. Containing a relatively large amount of solute.

Condensation. (*1*) Changing a material such as a vapor to a liquid. (*2*) Increasing the size of very small particles up to colloidal size. (*3*) A reaction between raw materials in the making of a plastic that results in the formation of water as one of the products.

Constant. A magnitude that does not change in value.

Constant, equilibrium. The product of the concentrations of the substances produced at equilibrium divided by the product of the concentrations of reactants, each concentration raised to that power which is the coefficient of the substance in the chemical equation.

Constant, ionization. The equilibrium constant of a reversible reaction by which ions are produced from molecules.

Constant, velocity. The speed of a reaction, at a fixed temperature, in which the concentration of each reactant is 1 mole per liter.

Contact agent. See *catalyst, contact*.

Contact catalyst. See *catalyst, contact*.

Contact process. A process for making sulfuric acid in which the sulfur dioxide and oxygen come in contact with a catalyst.

Control rod. A rod of neutron-absorbing material used in regulating the reaction in a nuclear reactor.

Converter reactor. A reactor in which one type of fissionable material is used to produce another type of fissionable material.

Corrode. To gnaw or eat away by chemical action, especially the action of an acid on a metal.

Countercurrents. Movement of a gas and liquid in opposition to one another.

Covalence. Covalent bonding.

Covalent bonding. Bonding in which atoms share a pair of electrons.

C.P. Abbreviation for "chemically pure."

Cracking. A process of breaking down

complex organic molecules by the action of heat, or a catalyst, or both.

Cracking, catalytic. The breaking-up of large molecules into smaller ones by using a catalyst together with high temperature and high pressure.

Cracking, thermal. The breaking-up of large molecules into smaller ones by the use of high temperature and high pressure.

Critical pressure. See *pressure, critical.*

Critical size. The amount of radioactive material required to sustain a chain reaction.

Critical temperature. The highest temperature at which it is possible to liquefy a gas with any amount of pressure.

Critical volume. The volume occupied by one mole of a gas at its critical temperature and critical pressure.

Crystal. A solid with a definite shape or structure.

Crystal, ionic. A crystal consisting of ions arranged in a systematic order.

Crystal, macromolecular. A crystal consisting of molecular groups or aggregates of these groups arranged in a systematic order.

Crystal, molecular. A crystal consisting of molecules arranged in a systematic order.

Crystalline. Consisting or made of crystals.

Cullet. Old, broken, glass.

Cupel. A porous crucible or dish of bone ash.

Cyclotron. An electromagnetic device for accelerating protons or deuterons in a spiral path.

Data. A group of facts or statistics.

Decomposition reaction. A chemical reaction in which a complex substance breaks down to form two or more simpler substances.

Decrepitation. The loss of mechanically held water when certain crystals are heated.

Dehydrating agent. A substance which removes water from a material.

Deliquescence. The property of certain substances to take up water from the air to form a solution.

Density. The weight per unit volume.

Destructive distillation. See *distillation, destructive.*

Detergent. A substance which removes dirt.

Detonator. A sensitive explosive used to start the main explosion.

Deuterium. The isotope of hydrogen having one proton and one neutron in the nucleus.

Developing. A process in photography in which the reduction of the silver compound, started by light, is promoted by the action of an alkaline, organic reducing agent.

Diatomic. Consisting of two atoms.

Diffusion. The process of spreading out spon-

taneously to fill a space uniformly; the intermingling of the particles of substances.

Diluent. A diluting agent.

Dilute. Containing a relatively small amount of solute.

Dipole. A polar molecule, one region of which is positive and another region is negative.

Diprotic. Referring to an acid with two replaceable hydrogen atoms.

Dispersion. A scattering, or state of being scattered.

Dissociation. The separation of the ions of an electrovalent substance during the solution process.

Distillation. The process of evaporation followed by condensation of the vapors in a separate vessel.

Distillation, destructive. The process of decomposing materials by heating them in a closed vessel without access to air or oxygen.

Distillation, fractional. The separation of the components of a mixture which have slightly different boiling points by carefully controlled vaporization.

Domain. Small magnetized regions formed by groups of properly aligned atoms of ferromagnetic substances.

Double replacement reaction. A chemical reaction in which the component substances exchange places.

Drier. A catalyst, such as an oxide of lead or manganese, added to paint to promote the drying of the paint.

Dross. A powdery scum that floats on top of molten metals.

Duralumin. An alloy of aluminum, copper, manganese, and magnesium.

Dust explosion. An explosion resulting from the ignition of dust suspended in the air, particularly within a confined space.

Dutch process. A process for making white lead using lead buckles, acetic acid, and decomposing tanbark or manure.

Dye. A substance used for coloring textiles.

Dynamite. An explosive made by absorbing nitroglycerin in wood flour mixed with sodium nitrate.

Effervescence. The rapid escape of a gas from a liquid in which it was dissolved.

Efflorescence. The property of hydrated crystals to lose water of hydration when exposed to the air.

Electrochemical. Pertaining to spontaneous oxidation-reduction reactions used as a source of electrical energy.

Electrode. A conductor by which the current either enters or leaves an electrolyte.

Electrolysis. Separation of a compound into simpler substances by electricity.

Electrolyte. A substance whose water solution conducts the electric current.

Electrolytic. Pertaining to forced oxidation-reduction reactions which utilize electrical energy from an external source.

Electron. A negatively charged particle found in an atom. It has $\frac{1}{1837}$ of the mass of a hydrogen atom.

Electron pair. Two electrons which occupy the same orbital.

Electron, valence. One of the electrons in an incomplete outer shell of an atom.

Electron-volt. The energy required to move an electron across a potential difference of one volt.

Electronegative element. See *element, electronegative.*

Electronegativity. The property, relative to other atoms, of a given atom or radical group to attract and hold valence electrons.

Electroplating. Deposition of a metal on a surface by means of an electric current.

Electropositive element. See *element, electropositive.*

Electroscope. A device for determining the presence of electric charge.

Electrovalence. Ionic bonding.

Element. A substance which may not be further decomposed by ordinary chemical means.

Element, electronegative. An element having a relatively strong attraction for valence electrons.

Element, electropositive. An element having a relatively weak attraction for valence electrons.

Element, parent. The heaviest, most complex, naturally-occurring element in a disintegration series of radioactive elements.

Element, rare earth. An element which differs in electronic configuration from that of next lower or higher atomic number only in the number of electrons in the second-from-outside shell.

Element, transition. An element which differs in electronic configuration from that of next lower or higher atomic number only in the number of electrons in the next-to-the-outside shell.

Element, transuranium. An element with a higher atomic number than uranium, atomic number 92.

Empirical formula. See *formula, empirical.*

Emulsion. See *emulsoid.*

Emulsoid. A colloidal system in which there is a strong attraction between the dispersed substance and the dispersing liquid.

Endothermic. Pertaining to a chemical change in which heat energy is absorbed.

End point. That point reached in titration in which the quantities of acid and hydroxide present are chemically equivalent.

End reaction. Reactions between certain ions which run to completion due to the removal of the ions from solution.

Energy. The capacity for doing work.

Energy, activation. Energy required initially to start a reaction.

Energy, binding. The energy which holds the protons and neutrons together in the nucleus of an atom.

Energy, free. The energy of a reaction which can be converted to useful work outside the reaction.

Energy, kinetic. Energy of motion.

Energy level. A region about the nucleus of an atom in which electrons move. A shell.

Energy, potential. Energy of position.

Enzyme. A catalyst produced by living cells.

Equilibrium. A dynamic state in which two opposing processes take place at the same time and at the same rate.

Equilibrium, chemical. The state of balance attained in a reversible chemical action in which the speeds of the opposing reactions are exactly equal.

Equilibrium constant. See *constant, equilibrium.*

Equilibrium, ionic. The state of balance attained in a reversible ionization action between un-ionized molecules in solution and their hydrated ions.

Equilibrium, solution. The physical state attained in which the opposing processes of dissolving and crystallizing of a solute occur at equal rates.

Equivalent weight. See *weight, equivalent.*

Ester. A compound formed by the reaction between an acid and an alcohol.

Esterification. The process of producing an ester by reaction of an acid with an alcohol.

Ether. An organic oxide.

Eudiometer. A gas-measuring tube.

Evaporation. The escape of molecules from the surface of liquids and solids.

Exothermic. Pertaining to a chemical change in which heat energy is released.

Explosive. A compound or mixture which decomposes suddenly with the production of a large volume of gas.

Explosive range of a gas. A pair of percentages, representing the proportions of a gas mixed with air, between which the mixture of the gas and air will explode if ignited.

External phase. The dispersing medium of a colloidal suspension.

Feldspar. A complex silicate, usually aluminum silicate with either sodium or potassium silicate.

Fermentation. A chemical change produced by the action of an enzyme.

Ferrosilicon. An alloy of iron and silicon.

Filtration. The process of removing suspended material from a liquid by allowing the liquid to pass through a material such as filter paper or a layer of sand.

Fission. The break-up of a nucleus into two medium-weight parts.

Fixing. In photography, the operation of removing unchanged silver salts after the picture has been developed, thereby fixing the image on the film or plate.

Flame. A burning gas.

Flame, oxidizing. The outer cone of a burner flame.

Flame, reducing. The inner cone of a burner flame.

Flame test. A test to determine the identity of an element in a compound by the color which the compound imparts to a flame.

Flammable. Capable of burning readily.

Flotation. A process by which low-grade ores are separated from gangue as a result of preferential wetting action.

Fluid. A material which flows; a liquid or gas.

Flux. (1) A material used to promote the fusion of minerals. (2) A substance used to remove the oxide coating from a metallic surface prior to soldering or welding.

Formality. The concentration of a solution expressed in gram-formula weights per liter of solution.

Formal solution. See *solution, formal.*

Formula. A shorthand method of representing the composition of substances using chemical symbols and numerical subscripts.

Formula, chemical. A shorthand notation using chemical symbols and numerical subscripts to represent the composition of a substance.

Formula, empirical. A chemical formula denoting the constituent elements of a substance and the relative number of atoms of each.

Formula equation. A concise symbolized picture of a chemical change.

Formula, molecular. A chemical formula denoting the constituent elements of a molecular substance and the number of atoms of each composing one molecule.

Formula, simplest. See *formula, empirical.*

Formula, structural. A formula which indicates kind, number, arrangement, and valence bonds of the atoms in a molecule.

Formula weight. See *weight, formula.*

Fractional distillation. See *distillation, fractional.*

Free energy. See *energy, free.*

Fuel. A material which is burned to provide heat.

Fuller's earth. An aluminum silicate used as an adsorbent.

Fungicide. A chemical material that kills non-green, microscopic plants known as fungi.

Fusible alloy. See *alloy, fusible.*

Fusion. The combination of two lightweight nuclei to form a heavier, more stable nucleus.

Galvanize. To coat iron or steel with zinc.

Gamma ray. High energy X ray emitted from the nucleus of a radioactive element.

Gangue. Worthless rock or vein matter in which valuable minerals occur.

Gas. The state of matter characterized by neither a definite volume nor a definite shape.

Gas, ideal. The perfect gas; one which conforms exactly to the Gas Laws.

Geiger counter. A device for determining the presence of radiation from radioactive materials.

Gel. A jelly-like mass consisting of a colloidal suspension of a liquid in a solid.

Generator. In chemistry, the vessel in which a reaction occurs to produce a desired gaseous product.

German silver. An alloy of copper, zinc, and nickel.

Glass. An amorphous material, usually transparent, consisting ordinarily of a mixture of silicates.

Gram. The metric unit of mass (weight).

Gram-atom. One gram-atomic weight of an element.

Gram-atomic weight. See *weight, gram-atomic.*

Gram-equivalent weight. See *weight, gram-equivalent.*

Gram-formula weight. See *weight, gram-formula.*

Gram-molecular volume. The volume, in liters, of 1 gram-molecular weight of a gas at S.T.P.; commonly referred to as the molar volume.

Gram-molecular weight. See *weight, gram-molecular.*

Gram-molecule. One gram-molecular weight of a molecular substance.

Group. A vertical column of elements in the Periodic Table.

Half-life. The length of time required for the disintegration of one-half of the present number of atoms of a radioactive element.

Halogen. The name given to the family of elements having seven valence electrons.

Hard water. Water containing ions such as calcium and magnesium which form precipitates with soap.

Heat of formation. The quantity of heat energy liberated or consumed when a compound is formed from its constituent elements.

Heavy water. Water containing deuterium atoms in place of ordinary hydrogen atoms.

Heterogeneous. Having parts with different properties.

Homogeneous. Having similar properties throughout.

Homogeneous reactor. A reactor in which the fuel, a uranium salt, is dissolved in the moderator, water.

Homologous series. A series of similar compounds which conform to a general formula.

Hydrate. A crystallized substance that contains water of hydration.

Hydrated ion. See *ion, hydrated.*

Hydration. The attachment of water molecules to particles of the solute.

Hydraulic mining. The use of a stream of water to wash away dirt and rock particles, exposing valuable ore.

Hydrocarbon. A compound containing hydrogen and carbon.

Hydrocarbon, aromatic. A hydrocarbon with alternating single and double covalent bonds in six-membered carbon rings.

Hydroforming. The forming of ring compounds by heating straight chain hydrocarbons with hydrogen in the presence of a catalyst.

Hydrogenation. The addition of hydrogen to a material.

Hydrogen bomb. An explosive device whose source of energy is a fusion reaction.

Hydrogen bond. A weak chemical bond between a hydrogen atom in one polar molecule and the negative atom in a second polar molecule of the same substance.

Hydrolysis. The reaction of a salt with water to form a solution which is acidic or basic.

Hydronium ion. A hydrated proton; the H_3O^+ ion.

Hydrosol. A suspensoid in which water is the dispersing medium.

Hydrous oxide. See *oxide, hydrous.*

Hygroscopic. Absorbing and retaining moisture from the atmosphere.

Hypothesis. A possible or tentative explanation.

Ice point. 0° C; 32° F.

Ideal gas. See *gas, ideal.*

Immiscible. Not capable of being mixed.

Indicator. A substance which changes in color on the passage from acidity to alkalinity, or the reverse.

Inertia. A resistance to change of position or motion; a property of matter.

Ingot. A molded block of steel.

Inhibitor. A negative catalyst.

Inorganic. Pertaining to materials which are not hydrocarbons or their derivatives.

Insecticide. A chemical substance which kills insects.

Insoluble. Not soluble, or soluble to only a very small extent.

Internal phase. The dispersed particles of a colloidal suspension.

Ion. An atom or group of atoms with an unbalanced electrostatic charge.

Ion exchange resin. A resin which can exchange hydrogen ions for positive ions; or one which can exchange hydroxide ions for negative ions.

Ion, hydrated. An ion of a solute to which molecules of water are attached.

Ionic bonding. Bonding in which one or more electrons are transferred from one atom to another.

Ionic crystal. See *crystal, ionic.*

Ionic equilibrium. See *equilibrium, ionic.*

Ionization. The formation of ions from polar solute molecules by the action of the solvent.

Ionization constant. See *constant, ionization.*

Isomer. One of two or more compounds having the same composition but different structure.

Isotope. One of two or more forms of atoms with the same atomic number but with different atomic weight.

Kaolin. A fine white clay composed of hydrated aluminum silicate.

Kelvin temperature. Temperature on the Kelvin scale, which is numerically 273° higher than that on the Centigrade scale.

Kernel. The portion of an atom, excluding the valence electrons.

Ketone. An organic compound that contains the $\diagdown$CO, carbonyl, group.

Kiln. A type of furnace used for producing quicklime, making glass, baking pottery, etc.

Kilo-. Metric prefix meaning 1000.

Kindling temperature. The lowest temperature at which a substance takes fire and continues to burn.

Kinetic energy. See *energy, kinetic.*

Kinetic theory. See *theory, kinetic.*

Knocking. A pounding sound produced in automobile engines by too-rapid combustion of the mixture of gasoline vapor and air.

Lake. A pigment made by precipitating a dye with aluminum hydroxide.

Laminated. Built up in layers or plates.

Law. In science, a statement of how phenomena in nature are related, as demonstrated by laboratory experiment.

Law of octaves. A statement made by Newlands that the properties of any element are repeated in the eighth element beyond when the elements are arranged according to atomic weight.

Law, periodic. The chemical properties of elements are periodic functions of their atomic numbers.

Leavening agent. A substance which releases carbon dioxide in a dough or batter.

Lehr. A cooling oven for annealing glass.

Lifting power. The difference between the weight of a given volume of air and that of the same volume of a gas less dense than air.

Lignite. A partially mineralized peat.

Lime. Calcium oxide, CaO.

Linear accelerator. A particle accelerator in which the particles travel in a straight line through many stages of relatively small potential difference.

Liquefaction. The process of converting a gas or solid to a liquid.

Liquid. The state of matter characterized by a definite volume, but an indefinite shape.

Liter. The metric unit of volume (capacity).

Lithopone. A white paint base composed of barium sulfate and zinc sulfide.

Litmus. A dye, extracted from lichens, which is used as an indicator.

Lunar caustic. Silver nitrate.

Lye. A term used for either sodium hydroxide or potassium hydroxide.

Lyophilic. Pertaining to a colloidal system of the emulsoid type.

Lyophobic. Pertaining to a colloidal system of the suspensoid type.

Macromolecular crystal. See *crystal, macromolecular.*

Mass. The quantity of matter which a body possesses; a measure of inertia.

Mass, atomic. The mass of an atom expressed in atomic mass units of 1.660×10^{-24} g.

Mass number. The whole number value closest to the exact atomic mass of an atom.

Matte. A crude mixture of sulfides produced in a partially refined ore.

Matter. Anything which occupies space and has weight.

Mercerizing. The treatment of stretched cotton fibers with concentrated sodium hydroxide.

Metal. One of a class of elements which show a luster, are good conductors of heat and electricity, and are electropositive.

Metalloid. An element having certain properties characteristic of a metal, but which is generally classed as a nonmetal.

Metamorphic. A term applied to rocks that have undergone a change in form due to heat or pressure.

Meter. The metric unit of length.

Metric system. A decimal system of weights and measures.

Milli-. Metric prefix meaning 0.001.

Miscible. Capable of being mixed.

Mixture. A material consisting of two or more kinds of matter each of which retains its own characteristic properties.

Moderator. A material which slows down neutrons.

Molality. The concentration of a solution expressed in moles of solute per 1000 grams of solvent.

Molal solution. See *solution, molal.*

Molarity. The concentration of a solution expressed in moles of solute per liter of solution.

Molar solution. See *solution, molar.*

Molar volume. The volume, in liters, of 1 mole of a gas at S.T.P.; taken at 22.4 liters for ordinary gases.

Mole. The gram-molecular weight of a molecular substance. Generally extended to include the gram-formula weight of a nonmolecular substance and the gram-atomic weight of an element represented as monatomic.

Molecular crystal. See *crystal, molecular.*

Molecular formula. See *formula, molecular.*

Molecular weight. See *weight, molecular.*

Molecule. The smallest particle of an element or compound that can exist free and still exhibit all of the properties of the substance.

Molecule, polar. A molecule in which there is a separation of charge caused by a nonuniform electron distribution.

Monatomic. Consisting of one atom.

Monel metal. A nickel-copper alloy.

Monoclinic. Referring to those crystals having one oblique intersection of the axes.

Monomer. A simple molecule, or single unit of a polymer.

Mordant. A substance which, by combining with a dye, produces a fast color in a textile fiber.

Mortar. A mixture of lime, sand, and water.

Mother liquor. The saturated solution remaining after crystals have separated from a solution.

Muriatic acid. Technical grade hydrochloric acid.

Natural gas. A combustible gas formed in nature by the decomposition of vegetable matter.

Negative catalyst. See *catalyst, negative.*

Neutralization. The reaction between hydrogen ions and hydroxide ions to form water.

Neutron. A neutral particle found in the nucleus of an atom. It has about the same mass as a proton.

N.F. The abbreviation for *National Formulary,* a book containing a list of medicinal substances and formulas.

Nichrome. An alloy of nickel, chromium, iron, and manganese.

Nitralloy. An alloy steel that has been treated with ammonia.

Nitride. A compound of nitrogen and a more positive element.

Nitrocellulose. A powerful explosive made by treating cellulose with nitric and sulfuric acids.

Nitrogation. The direct addition of nitrogen compounds to the soil.

Nitrogen cycle. A cycle of changes through which nitrogen passes. Starting as nitrate in the soil it becomes, in turn, plant protein, animal protein, dead matter, ammonia, nitrite, nitrate.

Nitrogen fixation. The process of converting elementary nitrogen into nitrogen compounds.

Nitroglycerin. Glyceryl trinitrate, a powerful and sensitive explosive.

Nodule. A knob-like swelling on the roots of plants of the bean and pea family in which nitrogen-fixing bacteria grow.

Nonelectrolyte. A substance whose water solution does not conduct the electric current appreciably.

Nonflammable. Not capable of being burned.

Nonmetal. One of a class of elements which are usually poor conductors of heat and electricity and are electronegative.

Nonpolar bond. A covalent bond between atoms with negligible difference in electronegativity.

Normality. The concentration of a solution expressed in equivalent weights of solute per liter of solution.

Normal solution. See *solution, normal*.

Nuclear change. A change which involves changes in the identity of the atoms themselves.

Nuclear disintegration. The emission of a proton or neutron from a nucleus as a result of bombarding the nucleus with alpha particles, protons, deuterons, or neutrons.

Nuclear equation. An equation representing changes in the nuclei of atoms.

Nuclear reactor. A device in which the controlled fission of radioactive material produces new radioactive substances and energy.

Nucleus. The positively-charged, dense central part of an atom.

Occlusion. The adsorption of a gas on a solid.

Octane rating. A number indicating how a gasoline behaves with regard to knocking when compared with a test fuel given an arbitrary rating of 100.

Octet. An outer shell of an atom containing four electron pairs.

Oil of vitriol. Concentrated sulfuric acid.

Open-hearth. A large furnace in which steel is made in a shallow pool.

Optical bleach. A substance which remains in cloth after washing or rinsing and replaces the blue light waves absorbed by the cloth.

Orbital. A possible electron orbit in a shell or energy level.

Ore. A mineral containing an element that can be extracted profitably.

Organic. Pertaining to carbon compounds, particularly hydrocarbons and their derivatives.

Organic chemistry. See *chemistry, organic*.

Organosol. A suspensoid in which an organic liquid is the dispersing medium.

Oxidation. (*1*) The process by which oxygen unites with some other substance. (*2*) A reaction in which an atom, a group of atoms, or an ion loses electrons.

Oxidation number. A special valence number assigned to each element to indicate the number of electrons gained, lost, or shared unequally.

Oxidation state. See *oxidation number*.

Oxide. A compound consisting of oxygen and usually one other element.

Oxide, hydrous. A hydrated metallic oxide.

Oxidizing agent. (*1*) A compound, rich in oxygen, which gives up oxygen readily. (2) A substance which takes up electrons during a chemical reaction.

Oxidizing flame. See *flame, oxidizing*.

Oxygen-carbon dioxide cycle. The cycle of events whereby plants take in carbon dioxide and give off oxygen in photosynthesis, and animals take in oxygen and give off carbon dioxide in respiration.

Ozone. An allotropic form of oxygen containing three atoms per molecule.

Parent element. See *element, parent*.

Peat. Moss, sedge, or other form of vegetation which has undergone partial decomposition under water.

Peptization. The process of preparing colloidal suspensions by the addition of a substance which acts upon the suspended particles reducing them to colloidal dimensions.

Peptizing agent. A substance which when added to a suspension causes peptization.

Period. A horizontal row of elements in the Periodic Table.

Periodic law. See *law, periodic*.

Periodic Table. A tabular arrangement of the chemical elements based on their atomic structure.

Permalloy. A high nickel alloy steel that is easily magnetized.

Permanent hardness. Hardness, caused by the sulfates of calcium and magnesium, which can be removed by adding chemical softeners.

Peroxide group. The $^-$:Ö:Ö:$^-$ group.

Petroleum. A liquid mixture of hydrocarbons obtained from beneath the surface of the ground.

pH. Hydrogen ion index; the common

logarithm of the reciprocal of hydrogen-ion concentration.

Phenolphthalein. An indicator which is colorless in the presence of excess H+ ions and red in the presence of excess OH− ions.

Phenomenon. An observed condition or situation in nature of unique significance.

Phlogiston theory. See *theory, phlogiston.*

Photosynthesis. The process by which plants build carbohydrate foods with the aid of sunlight, using carbon dioxide and water as the raw materials, and chlorophyll as the catalyst.

Physical change. A change in which the identifying properties of a substance remain unchanged.

Physical properties. Those properties which can be determined without causing a change in the identity of a material.

Pickling. Removing the surface impurities from a metal by dipping it into an acid bath.

Pigment. A coloring agent.

Pigment color. Color due to the absorption by pigments of some portions of white light.

Plastic. A natural or synthetic material which can be shaped while soft into a required form and then hardened to produce a durable finished article.

Plasticizer. A substance which makes plastics easier to work.

Polar bond. A chemical bond, essentially covalent, resulting from the unequal sharing of a valence electron between atoms of intermediate difference in electronegativity.

Polar molecule. See *molecule, polar.*

Poling. The use of green wood to prevent oxidation in the production of crude copper.

Polymer. A compound formed by two or more simpler molecules or radicals.

Polymerization. The combining of simple molecules of the same kind to form a more complex one.

Porcelain. A product made from pure white clay mixed with powdered feldspar and usually fired twice in a kiln.

Positive catalyst. See *catalyst, positive.*

Potential energy. See *energy, potential.*

Precipitate. (*1*) An insoluble product formed by chemical action between the solutions of two soluble substances. (*2*) To produce such an insoluble product.

Pressure. Force per unit area.

Pressure, critical. The pressure required to liquefy a gas at its critical temperature.

Pressure, standard. The pressure exerted by a column of mercury 760 mm high at 0° C.

Pressure, vapor. Pressure due to the vapor of confined liquids and solids.

Producer gas. A cheap fuel gas for industrial purposes made by blowing a blast of steam and air through red-hot coke.

Product. An element or compound resulting from chemical action.

Proportion. The relation of one portion to another; the equality between ratios.

Protective agent. A colloidal substance which when adsorbed on suspended particles stabilizes the system.

Protein. A complex organic compound necessary for the growth of living things or the repair of worn-out tissue.

Proton. A positively charged particle found in the nucleus of an atom. It has $\frac{1836}{1837}$ of the mass of a hydrogen atom.

Proton acceptor. A base according to the Brönsted concept.

Proton donor. An acid according to the Brönsted concept.

Pulp. Crude sheets of tangled fibers produced from poplar, spruce, or pine logs.

Radical. A group of atoms which usually behaves as if it were a single atom.

Radioactive. Having the property of radioactivity.

Radioactive decomposition. A radioactive change in which a nucleus emits a particle and rays, forming a lighter, more stable nucleus.

Radioactive fall-out. The showering down of radioactive particles which were originally carried high into the air by a nuclear explosion.

Radioactive tracer. A radioactive element introduced in small quantities to determine the behavior of chemically similar nonradioactive atoms in various physical or chemical changes.

Radioactivity. The spontaneous, uncontrollable disintegration of the nucleus of an atom with the emission of particles and rays.

Rare earth element. See *element, rare earth.*

Reactant. An element or compound entering into a chemical action.

Redox. Pertaining to oxidation-reduction reactions.

Reducing agent. (*1*) A substance which takes oxygen from another compound. (*2*) A substance which supplies electrons during a chemical reaction.

Reducing flame. See *flame, reducing.*

Reduction. (*1*) The removal of oxygen from a compound. (*2*) A reaction in which an atom, a group of atoms, or an ion gains electrons.

Refractory. (*1*) Not readily melted. (*2*) A substance which is not readily melted.

Relative humidity. The amount of moisture present in the air as vapor compared with the amount in saturated air at that temperature.

Replacement reaction. A chemical reaction in which one substance is displaced from its compound by another substance.

Resistance furnace. A furnace in which the

heat is produced by the electrical resistance of loose pieces of coke.

Resonance. The property of an atom or molecule of shifting its electronic structure between two or more different patterns.

Resonance hybrid. A molecule whose properties show that its structure resonates among several possible covalent bonding arrangements.

Respiration. The process by which a plant or animal absorbs oxygen and gives off products of oxidation in the tissues, especially carbon dioxide.

Reversible reaction. A chemical reaction in which the products may re-form the original reactants under suitable conditions.

Rhombic. Referring to those crystals having three unequal axes at right angles to one another.

Riffle. A strip laid crosswise in a sluice for retaining gold particles.

Roasting. Heating in the presence of air.

Sacrificial metal. The metallic electrode of an electrochemical cell that is oxidized.

Salt. A compound formed by a positive ion, other than hydrogen, and a negative ion, other than hydroxide.

Salting out. The precipitation of a colloidal dispersion by the addition of a soluble salt.

Saponification. The process of making a soap by hydrolysis of an ester with an alkali.

Saturated. (*1*) Pertaining to a solution in which the concentration of solute is the maximum possible under existing conditions. (*2*) Pertaining to an organic compound which has only single covalent bonds between carbon atoms.

Scattering. The deflection of rays of light sidewise by particles of suspended matter.

Science. A body of systematized knowledge.

Scientific notation. A system of writing large and small numbers using the form $M \times 10^n$, where M is a number between 1 and 10 and n is a positive or negative integer.

Sedimentary. A term applied to rocks formed from sediment that has been deposited in layers.

Sedimentation. The process of removing suspended matter from water by the addition of chemicals and subsequent settling.

Self-protective metal. A metal which forms a nonporous, nonscaling coat of tarnish.

Shell. A region about the nucleus of an atom in which electrons move.

Shell-filler. An explosive that requires a severe shock to set it off.

Sherardize. To galvanize by the condensation of zinc vapor on a ferrous metal surface.

Significant figure. A digit in an observed quantity which is known to be accurate.

Silicone. One of a group of compounds containing a chain of alternate silicon and oxygen atoms, with hydrocarbon groups attached to the silicon atoms.

Simplest formula. See *formula, empirical.*

Slag. An easily melted product of the reaction between the flux and the impurities of an ore.

Slaking. The addition of water to quicklime, CaO, to produce hydrated lime, $Ca(OH)_2$.

Sluice. A trough for washing out gold from gold-bearing gravel.

Slurry. A watery mixture.

Smokeless powder. A nitrocellulose explosive.

Solid. The state of matter characterized by a definite shape.

Solubility. The amount of a solute that can be dissolved in a given amount of solvent, under specified conditions.

Soluble. Capable of being dissolved.

Solute. The dissolved substance in a solution.

Solution. A homogeneous mixture of two or more substances, the composition of which may be varied up to a definite limit.

Solution, buffered. A solution containing a relatively high concentration of a buffer salt which tends to maintain a constant pH.

Solution equilibrium. See *equilibrium, solution.*

Solution, formal. A solution containing 1 gram-formula weight of solute per liter of solution.

Solution, molal. A solution containing 1 mole of solute per 1000 grams of solvent.

Solution, molar. A solution containing 1 mole of solute per liter of solution.

Solution, normal. A solution containing 1 gram-equivalent weight of solute per liter of solution.

Solution, standard. A solution that contains a definite concentration of solute which is known precisely.

Solvation. The adsorption of molecules of the dispersing liquid by dispersal particles.

Solvent. The dissolving medium in a solution.

Specific gravity. The ratio of the density of a substance to the density of a standard of reference. Solids and liquids are referred to water; gases are commonly referred to air.

Specific surface. The ratio of surface area to volume.

Spectroscope. An optical instrument consisting of a collimator tube, a glass prism, and a telescope, used for producing and viewing spectra.

Spectrum. The pattern of colors formed by passing light through a prism.

Spelter. Commercial zinc.

Spiegeleisen. Ferromanganese alloy added to iron in the steel-making process.

Spinneret. A metal plate with many small holes used in forming a synthetic fiber.

Spontaneous combustion. See *combustion, spontaneous.*

Stable compound. See *compound, stable.*

Stalactite. An icicle-like mass of calcium carbonate hanging from the roof of a limestone cave.

Stalagmite. A mass of calcium carbonate rising from the floor of a limestone cave, formed by the dripping of calcium bicarbonate solution from the cave roof.

Standard pressure. See *pressure, standard.*

Standard solution. See *solution, standard.*

Standard temperature. 0° Centigrade.

Steam point. 100° C; 212° F.

Stellite. A hard alloy of cobalt and chromium.

Sterling. Pertaining to silver which contains 7.5% copper.

Stibnite. A sulfide ore of antimony.

S.T.P. The abbreviation for "standard temperature and pressure."

Structural color. Color due to the scattering of white light by colloidally suspended particles.

Structural formula. See *formula, structural.*

Sublime. To pass from the solid to the gaseous state without liquefying.

Subscript. A number written below and to the side of a symbol. If at the left, it represents the atomic number; if at the right, it represents the number of atoms of the element.

Substance. A homogeneous material consisting of one particular kind of matter.

Substitution product. A compound in which various atoms or groups have been substituted for one or more atoms.

Superheated water. Water heated under pressure to a temperature above its normal boiling point.

Superheater. A chamber of a water gas apparatus.

Supersaturated. Pertaining to a solution which contains an amount of solute in excess of that normally possible under existing conditions.

Superscript. A number written above and to the side of a symbol. If at the right, it represents the approximate atomic weight of the atom represented by the symbol.

Suspension. See *suspensoid.*

Suspensoid. A colloidal suspension in which there is little attraction between the dispersed substance and the dispersing liquid.

Synchrotron. A particle accelerator in which particles move in a circular path due to the varying of the oscillating voltage and the magnetic field.

Synthesis. A combining of simple substances to make a more complex substance.

Synthetic. Man-made. Artificial.

Tartar emetic. Potassium antimonyl tartrate.

Tempering. The regulation of the iron carbide, and thus the hardness of steel by a process of heating and sudden cooling.

Temporary hardness. Hardness, caused by the bicarbonates of calcium and magnesium, which can be removed by boiling the water.

Ternary. Composed of three elements.

Textile. A fabric produced by weaving.

Theory. An explanation of scientific phenomena supported by abundant evidence, but not capable of laboratory demonstration.

Theory, atomic. A theory which explains the definite composition of substances and the proportions in which substances react with one another in terms of the atoms of which substances are composed.

Theory, kinetic. A theory pertaining to the motion of the ultimate particles of substances, and, in particular, of the molecules of gases.

Theory, phlogiston. An obsolete theory which explained combustion as being due to the loss of a substance called phlogiston.

Thermal cracking. See *cracking, thermal.*

Thermite reaction. The reaction by which a metal is prepared from its oxide by reduction with aluminum.

Thermoplastic. Refers to a plastic that can be softened by heat.

Thermosetting. Refers to a plastic that cannot be softened by heat.

Titanium sponge. Powdered titanium.

Titration. Determination of the concentration of a solution by comparing it with a standard solution, usually employing burettes for the operation.

Total valence. See *valence, total.*

Toxic. Poisonous.

Transition element. See *element, transition.*

Transmutation reaction. A reaction in which the nucleus of an atom undergoes a change in its positive charge, and consequently in its identity.

Transuranium element. See *element, transuranium.*

Triad. A group of three elements, the middle one of which has an atomic weight which is approximately the same as the average of the atomic weights of the other two elements.

Triprotic. Referring to an acid with three replaceable hydrogen atoms.

Tritium. The isotope of hydrogen having one proton and two neutrons in the nucleus.

Trunnion. One of a pair of opposite protruding pivots that provide a means of turning a heavy vessel.

Tuyère. A blowpipe in the base of a blast furnace.

Tyndall effect. The diffusion of light by colloidal particles.

Type metal. An alloy of antimony, tin, and lead.

Ultramicroscope. A microscope in which the object is illuminated at right angles to the optical axis of the microscope.

Unsaturated. An organic compound with a double or triple bond between two carbon atoms.

Unstable compound. See *compound, unstable.*

U.S.P. The abbreviation for *United States Pharmacopoeia,* an official guide in compounding medicines.

Valence. The number of electrons gained, lost, or shared by an atom in bonding with one or more atoms.

Valence electron. See *electron, valence.*

Valence, total. The product of the valence of an element or radical by the number of atoms of the element or the number of radicals taken.

Vapor. The gaseous state of substances which normally exist as liquids or solids.

Vapor pressure. See *pressure, vapor.*

Velocity constant. See *constant, velocity.*

Volatile. Easily vaporized.

Vulcanization. The heating of rubber with other materials to improve its properties.

Water gas. A fuel gas made by blowing a blast of steam through a bed of red-hot coke.

Water glass. A water solution of sodium silicate.

Water of hydration. Water that has united with some chemicals as they form crystals called hydrates.

Water softener. A chemical substance which removes hardness from water.

Weight. The measure of the earth's gravitational attraction for a body.

Weight, atomic. The average relative weight of the atoms of the naturally-occurring mixture of isotopes of an element based on the weight of the atoms of the naturally-occurring mixture of oxygen isotopes as 16.0000.

Weight, equivalent. A term used to connote equal combining power.

Weight, formula. The sum of the atomic weights of all the atoms present in the chemical formula.

Weight, gram-atomic. The weight of an element in grams equal to its atomic weight.

Weight, gram-equivalent. The weight of a substance, in grams, which will combine with or replace one gram of hydrogen.

Weight, gram-formula. The weight of a substance in grams equal to its formula weight.

Weight, gram-molecular. The weight of a molecular substance in grams equal to its molecular weight.

Weight, molecular. The formula weight of a molecular substance.

Weighted silk. Silk that has been dipped in solutions of certain tin salts.

Weighting. The repeated dipping of raw silk into a solution of tin chloride or iron chloride.

White lead. A paint base composed of basic lead carbonate.

Word equation. A brief statement which identifies the reactants entering into chemical action and the products formed.

X rays. Radiations similar to light or radio waves but which have a high frequency and a short wave length.

Zeolite. A sodium silico-aluminate used to soften water.

APPENDIX

TABLE 1.—METRIC–ENGLISH EQUIVALENTS

1 inch = 2.54 centimeters.	1 meter = 39.37 inches.
1 quart (U. S. liquid) = 0.946 liter.	1 liter = 1.06 quarts (U. S. liquid).
1 ounce = 28.35 grams.	1 gram = 0.035 ounce.
1 pound = 453.6 grams.	1 kilogram = 2.2 pounds.
1 ton = 0.907 metric ton.	1 metric ton = 1.10 tons.

TABLE 2.—TEMPERATURE CONVERSION FORMULAS

$$C = \tfrac{5}{9}(F - 32) \qquad F = \tfrac{9}{5}C + 32 \qquad K = C + 273$$

In these formulas C is Centigrade temperature, F is Fahrenheit temperature, and K is Kelvin temperature.

TABLE 3.—INTRODUCTION TO NOMENCLATURE OF CERTAIN TYPES OF INORGANIC COMPOUNDS
(by the System of the International Union of Chemistry)

The system of inorganic nomenclature proposed by the International Union of Chemistry attempts to provide a method of naming *any* inorganic compound in such a way that its composition and structure may be derived from its name. Since there are many very complex inorganic compounds, the complete system of nomenclature is beyond the scope of high school work. However, you are given below the rules for naming, and some examples of formulas and names, for the types of inorganic compounds encountered in high school chemistry.

1. Binary Compounds. These are named by giving the name of the more electropositive element, then the root of the name of the second element, and finally the suffix –ide. If it is necessary to indicate the relative proportions of the elements in the compound, there are two ways of doing this. *1.* By the use of a Roman numeral to designate the oxidation number of the more electropositive element. This method is usually employed with salts. *2.* By the use of Greek numerical prefixes as described in Chapter 6, Section 14.

Examples:

$NaBr$	Sodium bromide
$FeCl_2$	Iron(II) chloride
$FeCl_3$	Iron(III) chloride
CO	Carbon monoxide
Pb_3O_4	Trilead tetroxide

2. Ternary Compounds. If these contain anions with well-known names, they, too, may be named using a Roman numeral to designate the oxidation number of the electropositive element.

Examples:

$Fe_3(PO_4)_2$	Iron(II) phosphate
$Hg(NO_3)_2$	Mercury(II) nitrate
Cu_2SO_4	Copper(I) sulfate

3. Acids. These are named according to the systems described in Chapter 21, Section 6.
4. Mixed Salts. If a salt has two cations, the more electropositive cation is named first.

Example: $KCaPO_4$ Potassium calcium phosphate

The hydrogen in an acid salt is named just before the anion.

Example: $NaHCO_3$ Sodium hydrogen carbonate

TABLE 4.—ELECTRONIC ARRANGEMENT OF THE ELEMENTS

	SHELL					SHELL						
	K	L	M	N	O		K	L	M	N	O	P	Q
Hydrogen	1					Tellurium	2	8	18	18	6		
Helium	2					Iodine	2	8	18	18	7		
Lithium	2	1				Xenon	2	8	18	18	8		
Beryllium	2	2				Cesium	2	8	18	18	8	1	
Boron	2	3				Barium	2	8	18	18	8	2	
Carbon	2	4				Lanthanum	2	8	18	18	9	2	
Nitrogen	2	5				Cerium	2	8	18	20	8	2	
Oxygen	2	6				Praseodymium	2	8	18	21	8	2	
Fluorine	2	7				Neodymium	2	8	18	22	8	2	
Neon	2	8				Promethium	2	8	18	23	8	2	
Sodium	2	8	1			Samarium	2	8	18	24	8	2	
Magnesium	2	8	2			Europium	2	8	18	25	8	2	
Aluminum	2	8	3			Gadolinium	2	8	18	25	9	2	
Silicon	2	8	4			Terbium	2	8	18	27	8	2	
Phosphorus	2	8	5			Dysprosium	2	8	18	28	8	2	
Sulfur	2	8	6			Holmium	2	8	18	29	8	2	
Chlorine	2	8	7			Erbium	2	8	18	30	8	2	
Argon	2	8	8			Thulium	2	8	18	31	8	2	
Potassium	2	8	8	1		Ytterbium	2	8	18	32	8	2	
Calcium	2	8	8	2		Lutetium	2	8	18	32	9	2	
Scandium	2	8	9	2		Hafnium	2	8	18	32	10	2	
Titanium	2	8	10	2		Tantalum	2	8	18	32	11	2	
Vanadium	2	8	11	2		Tungsten	2	8	18	32	12	2	
Chromium	2	8	13	1		Rhenium	2	8	18	32	13	2	
Manganese	2	8	13	2		Osmium	2	8	18	32	14	2	
Iron	2	8	14	2		Iridium	2	8	18	32	17	0	
Cobalt	2	8	15	2		Platinum	2	8	18	32	17	1	
Nickel	2	8	16	2		Gold	2	8	18	32	18	1	
Copper	2	8	18	1		Mercury	2	8	18	32	18	2	
Zinc	2	8	18	2		Thallium	2	8	18	32	18	3	
Gallium	2	8	18	3		Lead	2	8	18	32	18	4	
Germanium	2	8	18	4		Bismuth	2	8	18	32	18	5	
Arsenic	2	8	18	5		Polonium	2	8	18	32	18	6	
Selenium	2	8	18	6		Astatine	2	8	18	32	18	7	
Bromine	2	8	18	7		Radon	2	8	18	32	18	8	
Krypton	2	8	18	8		Francium	2	8	18	32	18	8	1
Rubidium	2	8	18	8	1	Radium	2	8	18	32	18	8	2
Strontium	2	8	18	8	2	Actinium	2	8	18	32	18	9	2
Yttrium	2	8	18	9	2	Thorium	2	8	18	32	18	10	2
Zirconium	2	8	18	10	2	Protactinium	2	8	18	32	20	9	2
Niobium	2	8	18	12	1	Uranium	2	8	18	32	21	9	2
Molybdenum	2	8	18	13	1	Neptunium	2	8	18	32	23	8	2
Technetium	2	8	18	14	1	Plutonium	2	8	18	32	24	8	2
Ruthenium	2	8	18	15	1	Americium	2	8	18	32	25	8	2
Rhodium	2	8	18	16	1	Curium	2	8	18	32	25	9	2
Palladium	2	8	18	18	0	Berkelium	2	8	18	32	27	8	2
Silver	2	8	18	18	1	Californium	2	8	18	32	28	8	2
Cadmium	2	8	18	18	2	Einsteinium	2	8	18	32	29	8	2
Indium	2	8	18	18	3	Fermium	2	8	18	32	30	8	2
Tin	2	8	18	18	4	Mendelevium	2	8	18	32	31	8	2
Antimony	2	8	18	18	5	Nobelium	2	8	18	32	32	8	2

TABLE 5.—PRESSURE OF WATER VAPOR IN MILLIMETERS OF MERCURY

°C	mm	°C	mm	°C	mm
0	4.6	21	18.7	30	31.8
5	6.5	22	19.8	35	42.2
10	9.2	23	21.1	40	55.3
15	12.8	24	22.4	50	92.5
16	13.6	25	23.8	60	149.4
17	14.5	26	25.2	70	233.7
18	15.5	27	26.7	80	355.1
19	16.5	28	28.3	90	525.8
20	17.5	29	30.0	100	760.0

TABLE 6.—HEAT OF FORMATION OF COMPOUNDS

NAME OF COMPOUND	HEAT OF FORMATION K-cal/mole	NAME OF COMPOUND	HEAT OF FORMATION K-cal/mole
Acetylene	−54.9	Lead sulfide	22.2
Aluminum oxide	389.5	Magnesium chloride	153.2
Ammonia	10.9	Magnesium oxide	145.8
Barium sulfate	345.3	Mercuric chloride	53.4
Calcium chloride	190.7	Mercuric fulminate	−64.5
Calcium hydroxide	236.1	Mercuric oxide	21.7
Calcium oxide	151.7	Nitric oxide	−17.0
Carbon dioxide	94.4	Nitrous oxide	−21.5
Carbon disulfide	−22.0	Nitrogen dioxide	−7.4
Carbon monoxide	26.4	Potassium bromide	94.0
Carbon tetrachloride	33.2	Potassium chloride	104.3
Cupric oxide	34.9	Potassium hydroxide	102.0
Cupric sulfate	178.7	Potassium nitrate	118.8
Dinitrogen pentoxide	14.6	Potassium sulfate	338.6
Dinitrogen tetroxide	−1.9	Silver chloride	30.6
Diphosphorus pentoxide	365.8	Silver nitrate	30.1
Ferric oxide	190.7	Silver sulfide	5.0
Ferric oxide (magnetic)	266.9	Sodium chloride	98.4
Hydrogen bromide	8.6	Sodium hydroxide	101.9
Hydrogen chloride	22.0	Sodium nitrate	112.5
Hydrogen fluoride	64.0	Sodium sulfate	326.3
Hydrogen iodide	−5.9	Stannic chloride	127.4
Hydrogen oxide (water)	68.4	Sulfur dioxide	69.3
Hydrogen peroxide	44.5	Sulfur trioxide	103.2
Hydrogen sulfide	5.3	Zinc oxide	84.4
Lead monoxide	52.5	Zinc sulfide	45.9

TABLE 7.—TABLE OF SOLUBILITIES

S, soluble in water. A, soluble in acids, insoluble in water. P, partially soluble in water, soluble in dilute acids. I, insoluble in dilute acids and in water. a, slightly soluble in acids, insoluble in water. d, decomposes in water.

	ACETATE	BROMIDE	CARBONATE	CHLORATE	CHLORIDE	CHROMATE	HYDROXIDE	IODIDE	NITRATE	OXIDE	PHOSPHATE	SILICATE	SULFATE	SULFIDE
Aluminum	S	S		S	S		A	S	S	a	A	I	S	d
Ammonium	S	S	S	S	S	S		S	S		S		S	S
Barium	S	S	P	S	S	A	S	S	S	S	A	S	a	d
Calcium	S	S	P	S	S	S	S	S	S	P	P	P	P	P
Cupric	S	S		S	S		A		S	A	A	A	S	A
Ferrous	S	S	P	S	S		A	S	S	A	A		S	A
Ferric	S	S		S	S	A	A	S	S	A	P		P	d
Lead	S	S	A	S	S	A	P	P	S	P	A	A	P	A
Magnesium	S	S	P	S	S	S	A	S	S	A	P	A	S	d
Manganese	S	S	P	S	S		A	S	S	A	P	I	S	A
Mercurous	P	A	A	S	a	P		A	S	A	A		P	I
Mercuric	S	S		S	S	P	A	P	S	P	A		d	I
Potassium	S	S	S	S	S	S	S	S	S	S	S	S	S	S
Silver	P	a	A	S	a	P		I	S	P	A		P	A
Sodium	S	S	S	S	S	S	S	S	S	S	S	S	S	S
Stannous	d	S		S	S	A	A	S	d	A	A		S	A
Stannic	S	S			S	S	P	d		A			S	A
Strontium	S	S	P	S	S	P	S	S	S	S	A	A	P	S
Zinc	S	S	P	S	S	P	A	S	S	P	A	A	S	A

TABLE 8.—SOLUBILITY OF COMPOUNDS

The numbers give the number of grams of anhydrous compound that can be dissolved in 100 grams of water at the given temperatures.

COMPOUND	0° C	20° C	60° C	100° C
Calcium hydroxide	0.19	0.17	0.12	0.08
Calcium sulfate (gypsum)	0.18	0.19	0.20	0.16
Cerium sulfate	17.35	9.16	3.73	
Cupric sulfate	14.3	20.7	40.0	75.4
Mercuric chloride	3.6	6.5	16.3	61.3
Potassium bromide	53.5	65.2	85.5	104.0
Potassium chlorate	3.3	7.4	24.5	57.0
Potassium chloride	27.6	34.0	45.5	56.7
Potassium nitrate	13.3	31.6	110.0	246.0
Potassium sulfate	7.4	11.1	18.2	24.1
Sodium chloride	35.7	36.0	37.3	39.8
Sodium nitrate	73.0	88.0	124.0	180.0

TABLE 9.—SOLUBILITY RULES

1. Common sodium, potassium, and ammonium compounds are *soluble* in water.
2. Common nitrates, acetates, and chlorates are *soluble*.
3. Common chlorides are *soluble* except silver, mercurous, and lead. (Lead chloride is soluble in hot water.)
4. Common sulfates are *soluble* except calcium, barium, strontium, and lead.
5. Common carbonates, phosphates, and silicates are *insoluble* except sodium, potassium, and ammonium.
6. Common sulfides are *insoluble* except calcium, barium, strontium, magnesium, sodium, potassium, and ammonium.

TABLE 10.—DENSITY AND SPECIFIC GRAVITY OF GASES

Gas	Density Grams Per Liter S.T.P.	Specific Gravity Air Standard	Gas	Density Grams Per Liter S.T.P.	Specific Gravity Air Standard
Acetylene	1.173	0.907	Hydrogen sulfide	1.539	1.190
Ammonia	0.771	0.596	Methane	0.717	0.554
Carbon dioxide	1.977	1.529	Nitric oxide	1.340	1.037
Carbon monoxide	1.250	0.967	Nitrogen	1.251	0.967
Chlorine	3.214	2.486	Nitrous oxide	1.978	1.530
Hydrogen	0.0899	0.0695	Oxygen	1.429	1.105
Hydrogen chloride	1.639	1.268	Sulfur dioxide	2.927	2.264

TABLE 11.—SOLUBILITY OF GASES IN WATER

Volume of gas (reduced to S.T.P.) that can be dissolved in 1 volume of water.

Gas	0° C	10° C	20° C
Air	0.0292	0.0228	0.0187
Ammonia	1298.9	910.4	710.6
Carbon dioxide	1.713	1.194	0.878
Chlorine	4.54	3.148	2.299
Hydrogen	0.0215	0.0196	0.0182
Hydrogen chloride	506.7	473.9	442.0
Hydrogen sulfide	4.670	3.399	2.582
Nitrogen	0.0235	0.0186	0.0155
Oxygen	0.0489	0.0380	0.0310
Sulfur dioxide	79.79	56.65	39.37

TABLE 12.—PHYSICAL CONSTANTS OF IMPORTANT ELEMENTS

| Name | Specific Gravity | | Melting Point ° C | Boiling Point ° C |
	Water Std.	Air Std.		
Aluminum	2.70		660	1800
Antimony	6.68		630.5	1380
Arsenic	5.73		814 (36 atm)	615 (sublimes)
Barium	3.6		850	1540
Bismuth	9.75		271.3	1450
Boron	3.33		2300	2500 (sublimes)
Bromine	3.12		−7.2	58.8
Calcium	1.55		810	1240
Carbon	1.7–3.5		(sublimes above 3500° C)	4200
Chlorine		2.486	−101.6	−34.6
Chromium	7.1		1615	2200
Cobalt	8.90		1495	2900
Copper	8.9		1083	2336
Fluorine		1.312	−223	−187
Gold	19.3		1063	2600
Hydrogen		0.0695	−259	−253
Iodine	4.93		113.5	184.4
Iron	7.86		1535	3000
Lead	11.34		327.4	1620
Magnesium	1.74		650	1100
Manganese	7.2		1260	1900
Mercury	13.55		−38.9	356.6
Nickel	8.90		1455	2900
Nitrogen		0.967	−209.9	−195.8
Oxygen		1.105	−218	−183
Phosphorus	1.8–2.3		44.1	280
Platinum	21.37		1773.5	4300
Potassium	0.86		62.3	760
Radium	5		960	1140
Silicon	2.42		1420	2600
Silver	10.5		960.8	1950
Sodium	0.97		97.5	880
Strontium	2.6		800	1350
Sulfur	2.0		114.5	444.6
Tin	7.28		231.9	2270
Titanium	4.5		1800	(Over 3000)
Tungsten	19.3		3370	5900
Zinc	7.14		419.5	907

ACKNOWLEDGMENTS

The authors gratefully acknowledge the courtesy and cooperation of the following individuals and organizations who have been kind enough to supply the photographs used in this book. The authors are particularly grateful to Miss Frances L. Orkin who obtained most of these photographs.

Air Reduction Co.: Figs. 29-4, 30-18

Allied Chemical and Dye Corp.: Figs. 26-1, 28-7

Aluminum Company of America: Figs. 34-5, 34-6

American Cyanamid Co.: Fig. 19-2

American Gas Assoc.: Figs. 18-2, 41-7

American Museum of Natural History: Figs. 19-8, 41-4

American Petroleum Inst.: Fig. 42-2

American Smelting & Refining Co.: Figs. 36-5, 36-9

American Viscose Corp.: Figs. 44-6, 44-8

Anaconda Copper Mining Co.: Fig. 37-1

Atomic Energy Commission: Fig. 39-12

Baker Chemical Works: Fig. 21-7

Bausch-Lomb Co.: Fig. 33-2

Beryllium Corp: Fig. 34-1

Bethlehem Steel Co.: Figs. 35-3, 35-8, 35-14

Bettmann Archive: Figs. 7-1, 9-11, 14-2

Brookhaven National Lab.: Figs. 39-5, 39-9

Brown Brothers: Figs. 4-1, 5-2, 29-5

Cal-Pictures: Fig. 37-2

Cape Cod Chamber of Commerce: Fig. 10-1

Carborundum Co.: Figs. 40-4, 40-6

Chase Manhattan Bank: Fig. 39-18

Cities Service Co.: Figs. 42-6, 42-8

Coors Porcelain Co.: Fig. 34-16

Copper and Brass Research Assoc.: Figs. 36-2, 36-7

Corning Glass Works: Fig. 40-8

Crown Zellerbach Corp.: Fig. 44-16

Crucible Steel Company of Amer.: Fig. 35-18

Culver Service: Fig. 38-1

Curtis Bay Towing Co.: Fig. 44-11

Cushing, Charles Phelps: Figs. 10-12, 26-7

Deberry, S. E.: Figs. 10-5, 10-10, 28-8, 34-13, 34-14, 43-3, 44-1, 44-2, 44-3, 44-4, 44-9

Delco Appliance Division: Fig. 41-6

Denver Equipment Co.: Fig. 33-9

Diamond Match Co.: Fig. 31-4

Dole Photo: Fig. 43-9

Dow Chemical Co.: Figs. 26-10, 29-6, 34-4

Dow Corning Corp.: Fig. 1-2

Du Pont de Nemours, E. I. & Co.: Figs. 30-6, 33-1, 37-12, 43-1, 45-5, 45-7, 45-10, 45-11

Dynel: Fig. 44-10

Eastman Kodak Co.: Figs. 36-10, 36-11

Electro Metallurgical Co.: Figs. 29-7, 35-16

Exide Automotive Division: Fig. 37-9

Food Machinery & Chemical Corp.: Figs. 10-15, 37-3

Free Lance Photographers Guild: Fig. 44-17

Freeport Sulphur Co.: Fig. 27-2

Fyr-Fyter Co.: Fig. 43-2

Galloway, Ewing: Figs. 33-3, 35-19, 37-6

Gendreau, Philip: Frontispiece, Fig. 25-2

General Electric Co.: Figs. 8-10, 16-3, 16-4, 18-4, 40-3

Goodyear Tire & Rubber Co.: Fig. 3-1

Graphite Bronze Co.: Fig. 31-7

Grimaldi, Matt: Fig. 38-2

Grinnell Corp.: Fig. 31-8

Gulf Oil Corp.: Fig. 42-1

Hartmann, Eric: Fig. 40-10

Heinz, H. J. & Co.: Fig. 43-8

Homestake Mining Co.: Fig. 36-13

Indiana Limestone Co.: Fig. 25-1

Inglefield, C. L.: Fig. 10-9

International Minerals & Chemical Corp.: Fig. 31-1

International News Photos: Fig. 39-11

International Paper Co.: Figs. 44-14, 44-15

Johns-Manville: Figs. 34-2, 44-5

Johnson . . . Richland, Washington: Fig. 39-15

Jones & Laughlin Steel Corp.: Fig. 26-8

Kaiser Graphic Arts: Fig. 25-9

Kidde, Walter & Co.: Fig. 17-8

Libbey-Owens Ford Glass Co:. Figs. 40-7, 40-12

Life Magazine: Figs. 2-4, 36-4, 36-6, 36-8, 36-12

Linde Air Products Co.: Fig. 7-7

Lithium Corporation of Amer.: Fig. 24-1

Mallincrodt Chemical Works: Figs. 19-1, 19-9

Martin, Glenn & Co.: Fig. 12-2

Mergenthaler Linotype Co.: Fig. 31-6

Metal & Thermit Corp.: Fig. 34-9

Micro Essential Laboratory: Fig. 21-5

Monkmeyer Press Photo: Fig. 34-15

Morton Salt Co.: Fig. 24-5

National Board of Fire Underwriters: Fig. 7-10

National Cylinder Gas Co.: Figs. 7-6 (left), 17-5

National Fire Protection Assoc.: Fig. 7-14

National Lead Co.: Fig. 34-18

National Portland Cement Co.: Fig. 25-11

National Safety Council: Fig. 7-17

N. Y. Public Library: Figs. 9-9, 14-1, 24-3

Norton Co.: Fig. 34-12

Nuclear Instrument and Chemical Corp.: Fig. 38-5

Ohaus Scale Corp.: Fig. 13-1

Olin Mathieson Chemical Corp.: Fig. 21-2

Owens-Illinois Glass Co.: Fig. 1-1, Unit 4 Preview

Owens-Illinois Daylight Research House: Fig. 40-11

Pennsylvania Salt Manufacturing Co.: Fig. 31-5

Permutit Co.: Figs. 25-4, 25-5, 25-6

Phelps Dodge Copper Products Corp.: Fig. 36-3

Philadelphia Quartz Co.: Fig. 33-10

Polytechnic Institute of Brooklyn: Fig. 3-6

Potash Company of Amer.: Fig. 24-8

Premier Mill Corp.: Fig. 33-6

Presto Products: Fig. 10-2

Procter & Gamble Co.: Figs. 43-10, 43-11

Reynolds Metal Co.: Fig. 34-8

Rittase, William M.: Unit 1 Preview

Robinson-Hannagan Assoc.: Fig. 40-1

Santa Fe Railway: Fig. 25-3

Schupack, Mark: Figs. 27-9, 38-3

Science Service: Figs. 5-1, 20-2

Shell Chemical Corp.: Fig. 43-4

Shell Oil Co.: Figs. 30-10, 30-17

Shostal: Figs. 35-6, 44-13

Smithsonian Institution: Fig. 36-1

Society of American Bacteriologists: Fig. 3-2

Solvay Process Division: Fig. 19-12

Squibb, E. R. & Sons: Fig. 43-6

Standard Oil Company of

New Jersey: Figs. 18-1, 42-5, 42-7

Stanford University, Photographic Dept.: Fig. 35-2

Steelways: Figs. 35-5, 35-7, 35-10, 35-11, 37-8

Sugar Information: Fig. 10-3

Symes & Olds Co.: Fig. 37-11

Torkel Korling, Hedrich-Blessing: Fig. 40-9

Underwood & Underwood: Fig. 22-3

Union Carbide and Carbon: Figs. 33-11, 45-9

U. S. Air Force: Figs. 1-5, 39-14

U. S. Army: Fig. 45-4

U. S. Dept. of Agriculture, Soil Conservation Service: Fig. 30-3

U. S. Geological Survey: Fig. 37-4

U. S. Industrial Chemicals: Figs. 17-1, 43-5

U. S. Dept. of Interior: Fig. 41-5

U. S. Navy: Fig. 3-7

U. S. Rubber Co.: Figs. 12-1, 21-1, 45-1, 45-2, 45-3, 45-6

U. S. Steel Corp.: Figs. 35-13, 35-15

U. S. Weather Bureau: Fig. 1-3

Univ. of California: Fig. 2-3 Radiation Lab.: Fig. 39-10

Weissner Studio: Fig. 16-11

Westinghouse: Fig. 34-17

Westvaco Chlorine Products Corp.: Fig. 26-4

Wettlin: Fig. 30-19

Wide World Photos: Figs. 7-5, 7-6 (right), 39-1

Wright, Hamilton: Fig. 35-4

INDEX

Page references for illustrations are printed in *italics*.

THE ELEMENTS, THEIR SYMBOLS, ATOMIC NUMBERS, AND ATOMIC WEIGHTS

The more important elements are printed in red type.

Name of element	Symbol	Atomic number	Atomic weight	Name of element	Symbol	Atomic number	Atomic weight
Actinium.......	Ac	89	227	Mercury.......	Hg	80	200.61
Aluminum......	Al	13	26.98	Molybdenum...	Mo	42	95.95
Americium.....	Am	95	[243]	Neodymium....	Nd	60	144.27
Antimony......	Sb	51	121.76	Neon..........	Ne	10	20.183
Argon..........	A	18	39.944	Neptunium.....	Np	93	[237]
Arsenic........	As	33	74.91	Nickel........	Ni	28	58.71
Astatine........	At	85	[211]	Niobium.......	Nb	41	92.91
Barium........	Ba	56	137.36	Nitrogen.......	N	7	14.008
Berkelium......	Bk	97	[245]	Nobelium......	No	102	
Beryllium......	Be	4	9.013	Osmium........	Os	76	190.2
Bismuth........	Bi	83	209.00	Oxygen........	O	8	16
Boron..........	B	5	10.82	Palladium......	Pd	46	106.7
Bromine.......	Br	35	79.916	Phosphorus....	P	15	30.975
Cadmium......	Cd	48	112.41	Platinum......	Pt	78	195.09
Calcium........	Ca	20	40.08	Plutonium......	Pu	94	[242]
Californium.....	Cf	98	[248]	Polonium.......	Po	84	210
Carbon........	C	6	12.011	Potassium......	K	19	39.100
Cerium........	Ce	58	140.13	Praseodymium..	Pr	59	140.92
Cesium.........	Cs	55	132.91	Promethium....	Pm	61	[145]
Chlorine.......	Cl	17	35.457	Protactinium ...	Pa	91	231
Chromium......	Cr	24	52.01	Radium.......	Ra	88	226.05
Cobalt.........	Co	27	58.94	Radon.........	Rn	86	222
Copper.........	Cu	29	63.54	Rhenium.......	Re	75	186.22
Curium........	Cm	96	[245]	Rhodium.......	Rh	45	102.91
Dysprosium	Dy	66	162.51	Rubidium......	Rb	37	85.48
Einsteinium....	E	99	[255]	Ruthenium.....	Ru	44	101.1
Erbium........	Er	68	167.27	Samarium.....	Sm	62	150.35
Europium......	Eu	63	152.0	Scandium......	Sc	21	44.96
Fermium.......	Fm	100	[252]	Selenium.......	Se	34	78.96
Fluorine........	F	9	19.00	Silicon.........	Si	14	28.09
Francium.......	Fr	87	[223]	Silver.........	Ag	47	107.880
Gadolinium.....	Gd	64	157.26	Sodium........	Na	11	22.991
Gallium........	Ga	31	69.72	Strontium......	Sr	38	87.63
Germanium.....	Ge	32	72.60	Sulfur.........	S	16	32.066
Gold..........	Au	79	197.0	Tantalum......	Ta	73	180.95
Hafnium.......	Hf	72	178.58	Technetium.....	Tc	43	[99]
Helium.........	He	2	4.003	Tellurium......	Te	52	127.61
Holmium......	Ho	67	164.94	Terbium.......	Tb	65	158.93
Hydrogen......	H	1	1.0080	Thallium........	Tl	81	204.39
Indium.........	In	49	114.82	Thorium.......	Th	90	232.05
Iodine.........	I	53	126.91	Thulium.......	Tm	69	168.94
Iridium........	Ir	77	192.2	Tin............	Sn	50	118.70
Iron...........	Fe	26	55.85	Titanium.......	Ti	22	47.90
Krypton.......	Kr	36	83.8	Tungsten.......	W	74	183.86
Lanthanum.....	La	57	138.92	Uranium.......	U	92	238.07
Lead..........	Pb	82	207.21	Vanadium......	V	23	50.95
Lithium........	Li	3	6.940	Xenon.........	Xe	54	131.30
Lutetium.......	Lu	71	174.99	Ytterbium.....	Yb	70	173.04
Magnesium.....	Mg	12	24.32	Yttrium........	Y	39	88.92
Manganese.....	Mn	25	54.94	Zinc...........	Zn	30	65.38
Mendelevium ...	Mv	101	[256]	Zirconium......	Zr	40	91.22

A value given in brackets denotes the mass number of the isotope of longest known half-life.
Because of natural variations in the relative abundance of the isotopes of sulfur the atomic weight of this element has a range of ± 0.003.